This catalogue is dedicated to the memory of Charles A Oakley CBE, LLD, a founder of the Scottish Film Council whose foresight in rescuing historical film inspired the Scottish Film Archive.

SCOTTISH FILM ARCHIVE CATALOGUE

1st Edition

74 Victoria Crescent Road, Glasgow G12 9JN

ISBN 0 9525857 0 7

Printed for HMSO Scotland by CCN^os 73210; 65765 and (3808) 7/95

CONTENTS

INTRODUCTION

It is the purpose of the Scottish Film Archive to locate and preserve archival film reflecting all aspects of Scottish life in the 20th Century. Since its inception in 1976 the Archive has acquired material at a faster rate than can be viewed and catalogued. This volume, our first printed catalogue, represents only a portion of the total holdings of the Archive - that portion which has been shotlisted and catalogued in full. There remains much more to be viewed.

In publishing this volume we fulfill the aim to make this information more accessible to researchers and historians. By summarising the content we can indicate the range of material, the nature of the collection and its provenance.

Of course not every film can be viewed. Some titles may exist solely as original negative or preservation master material, some stock may be too fragile or shrunk to withstand even the gentle demands of our Steenbeck tables. However the Archive has an ongoing programme of repair and duplication, and is increasingly utilising videotape technology to increase access to the collection. For those whose principles require film to be seen on film this will be of little comfort. It is a fact of life, however, that the scale of the preservation requirements of our collection necessarily precludes our ability to offer immediate access to every title in the Archive.

A publication of this nature represents untold hours of viewing, shotlisting and cataloguing. We would record our gratitude to former colleagues and project staff who have contributed to the creation of this data: Alan Crossan, Derek Morison, Catriona Stewart, Ann Barefoot, David Sams, Roy Muller, Michael Chromy, Malcolm McCarthur and Claudine Rodger.

Anne Docherty has contributed immensely to this work since 1976, both in terms of assembling the information, and latterly in proofreading the text.

Jo Sherington joined the Archive as librarian in 1990 and with her professional skill has brought the Archive into the computer age. The long awaited realisation of this publication is due in the largest part to the time and energy she has devoted to the project. I would like to extend an appreciation and thanks for the patient, good natured attention she has brought to bear on this laborious task.

I am delighted to offer you, the researcher, the fruits of our labours in locating and saving Scotland's history on film.

Janet McBain

Curator

ARRANGEMENT OF THE CATALOGUE

MAIN ENTRIES

The films are arranged numerically by the Archive's reference number. There are some gaps in the number sequence, due to films having been withdrawn from the catalogue.

Each entry includes the reference number, title of the film, date, guage, colour, sound and footage, and whether or not the Archive has a viewing copy available. Production credits are included, where known, and each entry has a synopsis.

Title

Where the title to a film is known, but does not appear on the film, it is enclosed in square brackets. Where the title to a film is not known, a descriptive title has been given, and is enclosed in parentheses.

Date

An † after the date indicates production date.

An * after the date indicates that the date has been taken directly from the film stock.

Films may have more than one date, e.g.:

 1936-'38   (1936 to 1938)
 1936/'38   (1936 and 1938)

Films that are not dated are indicated with the abbreviation: n.d.

Guage

The different guages are:

 35mm
 16mm
 9.5mm
 std. 8mm   (standard 8mm)
 super 8mm (super 8mm)

Colour

If a film is black and white and/or colour it is indicated with:

 b/w
 col
 b/w & col
 tinted

Silent or Sound

Silent films are indicated with:

 silent
 mute   (picture only from a sound film
            without the soundtrack)

Sound films are indicated by the soundtrack used:

 comopt   (combined optical soundtrack)
 commag   (combined magnetic soundtrack)
 sep opt   (separate optical soundtrack)
 sep mag   (separate magnetic soundtrack)

Footage

The length of the film is indicated by the footage given, eg.

 16mm of 400ft = 10 mins
 35mm of 1000ft = 10 mins.

Reference or Viewing

As the Archive's priority has to be the preservation of the film collection, those titles for which we only have the original cannot be viewed until a duplicate copy has been printed.

In this instance the film will have *REF* marked beside the entry.

If there is a viewing copy the film will have *VIEW* marked beside the entry.

Production credits

Where the production credits are known, but not shown on the film the credits are shown in square brackets. Italicized abbreviations are used for the production credits which are as follows:

sp.	Sponsor or Sponsoring Agency
p.c.	Production Company
d.	Director
p.	Producer
cam.	Camerawork
ph.	Photographer
w.	Writer
filmed by	Made by an amateur film-maker
filmed as a local topical	Made by an amateur film-maker as a local newsreel

TITLE INDEX

The title index is arranged alphabetically with the film's reference number in the right hand column.

SUBJECT INDEX

The subject headings are arranged alphabetically, with each entry within the subject category arranged by reference number. The subject index is not comprehensive, but is designed to give the researcher a good indication of what relevant films there are.

If a particular subject term is not used in our index, then the correct term to search under will be indicated, e.g.

ABBEYS
See MONASTIC BUILDINGS

Cross-references to other terms in the subject index are indicated, e.g.

CLOTHING (FASHION ETC.)
See also COSTUME/ TEXTILE INDUSTRY

It is not possible to include in this catalogue every subject and personality reference to the Archive's holdings, and for extensive research we would recommend users to make an appointment to visit the Archive for additional information.

Jo Sherington
Librarian

ACRONYMS AND ABBREVIATIONS

ARP	Air Raid Precautions
ATC	Army Training Corps
AEU	Amalgamated Engineering Union
BFI	British Film Institute
CAC	Caledonian Associated Cinemas
CEA	Cinema Exhibitors' Association
CND	Campaign for Nuclear Disarmament
COI	Central Office of Information
CWS	Co-operative Wholesale Society
EFS	Educational Films of Scotland
GB Instructional	Gaumont British Instructional
GPO	General Post Office
GSA	Glasgow School of Art
HIDB	Highlands & Islands Development Board
IAC	Institute of Incorporated Amateur Cinematographers
IFA	International Film Associates
JPC	Joint Production Committee
KOSB	King's Own Scottish Borderers
LMS	London Midland Scottish
LSCC	Ladies' Scottish Climbing Club
MOI	Ministry of Information
MT	Motor Transport
MTV	Motor Transport Vessel
MV	Motor Vessel
NCB	National Coal Board
NCRC	National Cash Register Company
NCPS	National Cycling Proficiency Scheme
NFS	National Fire Service
NI	Northern Ireland
NUS	National Union of Students
NUWSS	National Union of Women's Suffrage Societies
OEEC	Organisation for European Economic Co-operation
OTC	Officers' Training Corps
Pathe BIF	Pathe British Instructional Films
PE	Physical Education
PS	Paddle Steamer
PE	Physical Education
RAF	Royal Air Force
RSA	Royal Scottish Academy
SAAC	Scottish Assocation of Amateur Cinematographers
SAFF	Scottish Amateur Film Festival
SCWS	Scottish Co-operative Wholesale Society
SED	Scottish Education Department
SEFA	Scottish Educational Films Association
SFC	Scottish Film Council
SPCA	Society for the Prevention of Cruelty to Animals
SSEB	South of Scotland Electricity Board
SSPMH	Scottish Society for the Parents of the Mentally Handicapped
STUC	Scottish Trades Union Council
SYHA	Scottish Youth Hostels Association
TA	Territorial Army
TB	Tuberculosis
ULRO	Urquhart Lindsay and Robertson Orchar's Club
UNICA	International Union of Amateur Cinematographers
YMCA	Young Men's Christian Association

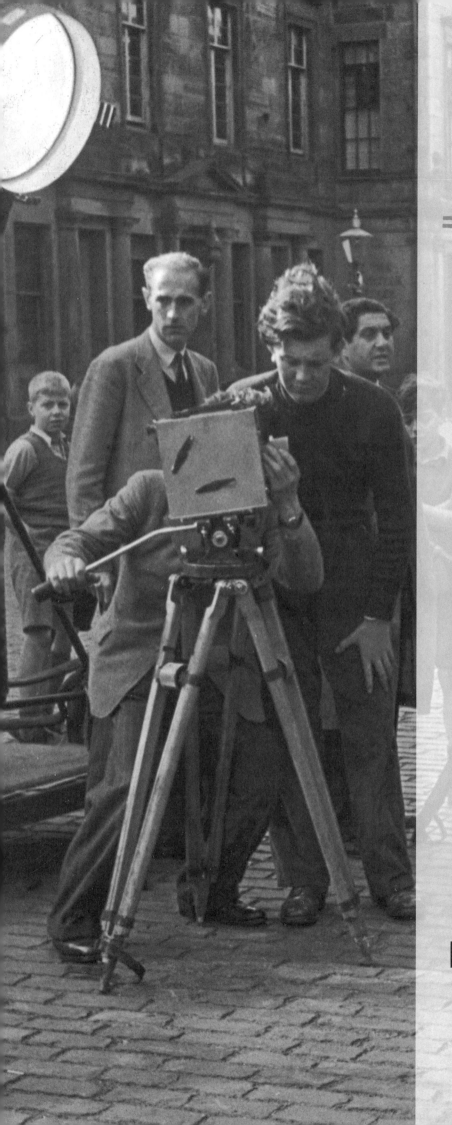

SCOTTISH FILM ARCHIVE

1ST EDITION

CATALOGUE

0001 (GLASGOW TRAMS AND BOTANIC GARDENS)

1950*

| 35mm | col | mute | 190ft | VIEW |

[filmed by Stanley L. Russell, Thames and Clyde]

The Botanic Gardens, Glasgow with shots of the tulip beds, and the Kibble Palace. A tram and bus pass each other on Great Western Road.

0002 (TRAMS IN GLASGOW)

1962

| 16mm | col | silent | 850ft | REF |

[filmed by SAAC]

Views of trams in Glasgow.

0004 INTO THE MISTS

1956

| 16mm | col | silent | 350ft | REF |

[filmed by W.S. Dobson]

The story of the last Edinburgh tram. Shots of horse-drawn omnibus.

0005 PASSING OF THE TRAMCAR, THE

1894-'62

| 16mm | col | silent | 2290ft | REF |

sp. Greater Glasgow Passenger Transport Executive

The last tram to run in Glasgow.

0007 SCOTS OF TOMORROW

1950s,c

| 35mm | b/w | sep opt | 1130ft | VIEW |

sp. Joint Production Committee (SEFA/SFC)
p.c. Campbell Harper Films Ltd.

Scottish school pupils studying scientific and historical projects.

0008 GLASGOW UNIVERSITY CELEBRATES

1951

| 35mm | b/w | comopt | 948ft | VIEW |

p.c. Movietone News

Glasgow University celebrates its Fifth Centenary with various events including a torchlight procession, and a reception attended by Lord Provost Hetherington and J. M. McCormack.

0009 FIFTH CENTENARY OF THE UNIVERSITY OF GLASGOW

1951

| 16mm | b/w | mute | 468ft | VIEW |

compiled by SFC

Celebrations in Glasgow attended by students from around the world including a torchlight procession and bonfire.

James S. Nairn , manager of the Playhouse, Inverness, painting foyer as a Christmas fairyland.

3

0010 ABERDEEN UNIVERSITY QUATER CENTENARY CELEBRATIONS

1906

| 35mm | b/w | silent | 279ft | REF |

sp. Aberdeen City Corporation
p.c. Scottish Film Council

Procession of dignitaries in horse-drawn carriages to Aberdeen University Quater Centenary ceremony. [See also ref 0042.]

0011 HARRY LAUDER LEAVES FOR AMERICA

1913

| 35mm | b/w | silent | 155ft | VIEW |

p.c. Gaumont News

Harry Lauder leaves for Liverpool from London's Euston Station. He boards the liner the "Lusitania".

0012 GLASGOW'S YESTERDAYS

1910-'22

| 35mm | b/w | silent | 730ft | VIEW |

sp. Scottish Film Council
p. James Hart

A selection of amateur films made in the early years of the 20th century looking at life in Glasgow including holidaymakers at Wemyss Bay, a picnic at Rouken Glen, a recruiting march in 1914 and pedestrians strolling along Great Western Road in 1922.

0013   GOVAN FAIR 1947
1947

35mm	b/w	silent	624ft	VIEW

sp. Vogue Cinema, Govan
filmed by Elder Dalrymple Productions

Coronation of the Fair Queen, with the procession and motorcade in Govan, Glasgow.

0014   (EDINBURGH SAYS FAREWELL TO THE TRAMS)
1956

16mm	b/w&col	silent	1065ft	REF

sp. Edinburgh Corporation Transport

Shots of the last tram leaving Tollcross, Edinburgh, ending up in the scrapyard at Coatbridge.

0015   STUDENTS' CHARITIES DAY GLASGOW
1926

35mm	b/w	silent	450ft	VIEW

p.c. Grosvenor Topical

McAlister's Rag Time Band plays in Glasgow's streets, while students parade through Glasgow for charity.

0016   ORPHEUS CHOIR
1951

35mm	b/w	comopt	1170ft	REF

p.c. Connoisseur Films

Sir Hugh Roberton conducts the Orpheus choir as they sing various Scottish songs.

0017   DAY IN THE HOME, A
1951

35mm	b/w	comopt	1255ft	VIEW

sp. SEFA/SFC
p.c. Campbell Harper Films Ltd.

The every day chores and family life in a Scottish home.

0018   LANIMER DAY, LANARK
1951

35mm	b/w	silent	550ft	REF

The 811th Lanimer Day festival in Lanark, with the coronation of the Lanimer Queen and procession.

0019   GREAT WESTERN ROAD 1914
1914

35mm	b/w	silent	630ft	VIEW

[filmed by James Hart]

Sunday morning church-goers promenade along Great Western Road, Glasgow.

0020   JAMES WATT
1959

35mm	b/w	comopt	1440ft	VIEW

sp. Educational Films of Scotland
p.c. Thames and Clyde
d. Stanley L. Russell

The life and work of the inventor of steam engines, James Watt.

0021   LORD LOTHIAN PRESENTS HIS CREDENTIALS AT THE WHITE HOUSE
1939

35mm	b/w	comopt	50ft	VIEW

p.c. Movietone News

Lord Lothian arrives at the White House as the new British envoy to the United States. He is met by the President. [Incomplete]

0022   MIDNIGHT MATINEE FOR THE REFUGEES
1939

35mm	b/w	comopt	85ft	VIEW

p.c. Gaumont British News

Fund raising event in the Alhambra Theatre, Glasgow. Lord Provost Dollan, Mr. and Mrs. Green, Sir Cecil Weir and Lord Inverclyde attend. January 1939.

0023A   ROYAL TOUR OF SCOTLAND
1944

16mm	b/w	comopt	108ft	VIEW

p.c. Movietone News

The Queen opens the Aberdeen Sailors' Home.

0023B   GLASGOW ARMY EXHIBITION
1944

16mm	b/w	comopt	54ft	VIEW

p.c. Movietone News

The opening of the Glasgow Army Exhibition at Queen's Park Recreation Ground in the presence of Sir Alexander King of the Ministry of Information.

0023C   HAMPDEN PARK INTERNATIONAL: ENGLAND V SCOTLAND
1944

16mm	b/w	comopt	60ft	VIEW

p.c. Movietone News

England v Scotland football match at Hampden Park, attended by General Montgomery.

0023D ROYAL TOUR OF SCOTLAND

1944

16mm	b/w	comopt	30ft	VIEW

p.c. Gaumont British News

Queen Elizabeth visits a nursery school in Aberdeen, and opens the Sailors' Home.

0023E GREATEST BATTLESHIP LAUNCH

1944

16mm	b/w	comopt	30ft	VIEW

p.c. Gaumont British News

Princess Elizabeth launches the battleship HMS "Vanguard" at John Brown's yard in Clydebank.

0024 CHRISTMAS 1937

1937

16mm	b/w	silent	468ft	REF

filmed by Frank Marshall

Family Christmas at Kilallan.

0025 (HISTORY OF THE TAILOR AND GARMENT WORKERS UNION)

1945-'51c

16mm	b/w	comopt	720ft	REF

sp. National Union of Tailor and Garment Workers
p.c. Data Film Unit
[d. Francis Gysin]

Footage of Union conference attended and addressed by the Prime Minister, C.R. Attlee and Ernest Bevin.

0026 WHO'S THERE

1966

16mm	col	comopt	575ft	REF

sp. Labour Party

Instructions on how to canvass and determine the voting behaviour of the public.

0027 SKYE

1969

16mm	col	comopt	324ft	REF

d. Iain Dunnachie

Life on the island of Skye with footage of peat cutting and fishing.

0028 WESTERN ISLES

1943

16mm	col	comopt	550ft	VIEW

p.c. Merton Park Productions
d. Terence Egan Bishop

Life on Harris in the Western Isles during World War II. A local family await news of their son after the sinking of the "Atlantic Queen".

0029 HARNESSING THE HILLS

1949

35mm	b/w	comopt	1345ft	VIEW

sp. Scottish Office
p.c. Merlin Films
d. Michael Hankinson and A.H. Luff

The opening of Lochalsh hydro-electric station in 1948 when power lines were connected to villages in the Highlands for the first time. Don Mundy, Australia's sheep shearing champion is featured in the film.

5

0030   IT BEGAN ON THE CLYDE
1946

16mm	b/w	comopt	540ft	VIEW

sp. MOI for the Dept. of Health for Scotland
p.c. Greenpark Productions
d. Ken Annakin

A look at stress and work fatigue amongst Clydeside workers during the war, and how Ballochmyle hospital helped to overcome this.

0031   ARP SCHOOLS
1940*

16mm	b/w	silent	435ft	VIEW

d. Stanley L. Russell

Children are shown how to use a respirator during an air raid. Filmed in Knightswood Primary School, Glasgow.

0032   SCOTLAND'S WATER SUPPLY
1950

35mm	b/w	comopt	800ft	VIEW

sp. Dept. of Health for Scotland
p.c. Editorial Productions

A look at the improvements to the water supply in rural areas brought about by the construction of the Lammermuir reservoir.

0033   HIGHLAND DOCTOR
1943

16mm	b/w	comopt	756ft	VIEW

sp. MOI for the Dept. of Health for Scotland
p.c. Paul Rotha Productions
d. Kay Mander

How medical facilities improved after the 1912 Dewar Committee. In particular, how the 'air ambulance' increased health care in the Western Isles.

0034   FACE OF SCOTLAND
1938

16mm	b/w	comopt	480ft	VIEW

sp. Films of Scotland
p.c. Realist Film Unit
d. Basil Wright

Made for the 1938 Empire Exhibition under the supervision of John Grierson, the film looks at the history of Scotland, its religion, agriculture, and industry.

0035   SCOTTISH WOMEN'S HOSPITALS
1917

16mm	b/w	silent	180ft	VIEW

sp. National Union of Women's Suffrage Societies

Daily life in one of the fourteen field hospitals in France set up by the NUWSS during WWI, staffed entirely by women. Much of the work was done by Dr Elsie Inglis.

0036   ATROCITIES, THE
1945

16mm	b/w	comopt	252ft	VIEW

p.c. Movietone News

British MPs tour Germany in 1945, to look at Buchenwald and Belsen Concentration Camps.

0037   QUEEN'S OWN HIGHLANDERS
1964

16mm	col	silent	432ft	REF

filmed by William S. Dobson

Prince Philip attends a military ceremony at Holyrood House, Edinburgh, to present colours to the amalgamated 1st Battn., Queen's Own Highlanders.

0038   FRASERS' RETURN
1959

16mm	col	comopt	612ft	REF

p.c. SSEB

A Scots family return from Canada and observe changes which have taken place in Scotland. They see innovations in the home, due to the Scottish Electric Grid.

0039   UPSTREAM
1932

16mm	b/w	comopt	645ft	VIEW

p.c. Empire Marketing Board
d. Arthur Elton

Produced by John Grierson, the film shows the different methods of salmon fishing in Scotland.

0040   NEW LEASE OF LIFE
1960c

16mm	b/w	comopt	864ft	REF

sp. COI in co-operation with the OEEC
p.c. Editorial Films
d. Guy Blanchard

How a group of people are helped to return to work after illness and long absence, by attending the Industrial Rehabilitation Unit at Wadden in London.

0041   LAUNCHING OF THE 'QUEEN MARY'
1934

16mm	b/w	silent	288ft	VIEW

The launch of the liner "Queen Mary" at John Brown's shipyard, Clydebank, by King George V and Queen Mary.

6

0042	**ABERDEEN 1906**				
1906					
35mm	*b/w*	*comopt*	*900ft*		*VIEW*

sp. Aberdeen City Corporation
p.c. Scottish Film Council

King Edward and Queen Alexandra open the new extension to Marischal College, during Aberdeen University's 4th centenary celebrations. Lord Provost Lyon is knighted. Sound version made in 1956. [See also ref 0010.]

0043	**(LARGS SUMMER SEASON 1936)**				
1936					
16mm	*b/w*	*silent*	*300ft*		*REF*

A Concert at Barrfield Pavilion, Largs. Concert party includes variety artists George West and Jack E. Raymond.

0044	**GLASGOW AND THE CLYDE COAST**				
1910					
35mm	*b/w*	*silent*	*690ft*		*VIEW*

sp. London and North Western Railway
p.c. Glasgow Film Society

Holidaymakers setting out from Glasgow, and travelling by train and steamer down the coast to Rothesay and Ettrick Bay.

0045	**EMPIRE EXHIBITION**				
1938					
35mm	*b/w*	*comopt*	*900ft*		*VIEW*

p.c. British Movietone News

King George V1 and Queen Elizabeth at Ibrox Stadium Glasgow, to open the Empire Exhibition. Walter Elliot and Sir James Lithgow are present.

0046	**LANIMER DAY, LANARK**				
1952-'60					
35mm	*b/w*	*comopt*	*900ft*		*REF*

p.c. Thames and Clyde Film Productions

Lanark's Lanimer Day glimpsed through the years. Shots of a procession through the streets with some of the people carrying the 'birks' (twigs and branches). The Lanimer Queen is chosen.

0048	**PORT OF GLASGOW**				
1936c					
16mm	*b/w*	*silent*	*360ft*		*VIEW*

p.c. Scottish Educational Film Association

View of the banks of the River Clyde, Glasgow. The dock area is seen filled with cargo vessels, ferries, and shipyards.

0049A	**ARMISTICE SERVICE VICTORIA PARK WHITEINCH**				
1928					
35mm	*b/w*	*silent*	*50ft*		*VIEW*

p.c. Grosvenor Topical News

Service held in Victoria Park, Whiteinch, Glasgow. Veterans attend the service beside the war memorial.

0049B	**(SCHOOL SPORTS DAY)**				
1928c					
35mm	*b/w*	*silent*	*50ft*		*VIEW*

p.c. Grosvenor Topical News

School sports day in Glasgow.

0050	**LAUNCHING OF THE "QUEEN MARY"**				
1934					
16mm	*b/w*	*silent*	*92ft*		*REF*

sp. Lizars, Edinburgh

"Queen Mary" is launched by King George V and Queen Mary, at John Brown's shipyard, Clydebank. 26th September, 1934.

0051	**QUEEN IN SCOTLAND, THE**				
1953					
35mm	*b/w*	*comopt*	*1100ft*		*REF*

p.c. Universal News

Queen Elizabeth on a Coronation visit to Scotland. Provost Sir James Millar presents the Queen with the Keys to Edinburgh, the Queen also visits Holyrood House, St Giles' Cathedral and the city of Glasgow.

0052	**SYHA CONFERENCE**				
1958					
35mm	*col*	*comopt*	*367ft*		*REF*

An SYHA Conference and display of national dancing.

0053	**GOVAN FAIR 1952**				
1952					
35mm	*b/w*	*silent*	*640ft*		*VIEW*

sp. Vogue Cinema, Govan
p.c. Elder Film Productions

Official ceremonial opening of Old Govan Fair, Glasgow. Coronation of the Fair Queen by Mrs Singleton, wife of the director of the Vogue Cinema.

0054	**ROYAL VISIT OF GEORGE VI**				
1937					
16mm	*b/w*	*comopt*	*216ft*		*VIEW*

p.c. Gaumont British News

The King and Queen are received in Edinburgh by Walter Elliot, the Secretary of State. Shots of the Ceremony of the Keys at Edinburgh Castle. [Incomplete.] [See also ref 0819.]

7

0055   GLASGOW TRAMS, 21 MAY 1960

1960

std.8mm	col	silent	200ft	REF

filmed by Revd. John Walsh

Views of trams in Glasgow.

0056   TRAM ROUTES IN GLASGOW AND STEAM RAILWAYS

1960-'62

std.8mm	col	silent	900ft	REF

filmed by I.C. MacDougall

Various tram routes in Glasgow, and steam railways in Britain.

0057   OUR TRANSPORT SERVICES

1949

16mm	b/w	silent	400ft	VIEW

sp. Glasgow Corporation Education Committee
p.c.Campbell Harper Films Ltd.
[d. Willie J. McLean]

The story of Glasgow Municipal Transport System from hansom cabs to trams and buses.

0058   ONE HUNDRED YEARS OF FAMILY BUSINESS

1966

16mm	b/w	comopt	100ft	REF

p.c. Thames and Clyde

Made to commemorate 100 years of the Firhill Iron Works, founded by James Shaw.

0059   SCOTTISH INDUSTRY, A

1930c

35mm	b/w	silent	800ft	REF

sp. A. & G. Paterson Limited

Trees are felled, logs are loaded onto motorised wagons and taken to a sawmill, to be made into fencing.

0060   NEWS PARADE 1939

1939

16mm	b/w	silent	324ft	REF

A news compilation featuring Franco's victory, the sinking of the submarine USS "Squalus", floods in China, a 'Love Parade' in Canada, the German invasion of Poland and France's declaration of war.

0061   YACHTING ON THE "PANTHER"

1935c

16mm	b/w	silent	400ft	REF

A family on board their yacht with other sailing vessels seen in the distance.

0062   GLASGOW - OUR CITY

1949

16mm	b/w	silent	552ft	VIEW

sp. Glasgow Corporation Education Committee
p.c. Campbell Harper Films Ltd.
d. Stanley L. Russell

Glasgow old and new, with shots of contemporary street life and local industries. The film is interspersed with photographs of 17th and 18th century Glasgow.

0063   CLYDE FITTINGS

1957

16mm	col	sep opt	330ft	VIEW

p.c. Clyde Tube Forgings with assistance from the Industrial Panel of the Scottish Film Council

The welding process and manufacture of pipe fittings are shown in the Clyde Tube Forgings on Hillington Industrial Estate. [See also Ref. 2019.]

0064   QUEEN ELIZABETH RECEIVES THE HONOURS OF SCOTLAND

1953

16mm	b/w	silent	285ft	REF

The Queen receives the Honours of Scotland at St. Giles' Cathedral, Edinburgh.

0065   EMPIRE EXHIBITION

1938

16mm	col	silent	450ft	REF

[filmed by James Blair]

Rare colour footage of the Empire Exhibition, Bellahouston Park, Glasgow and of the first major dancing water displays ever built.

0066   DALGUISE BOYS' CAMP

1952

16mm	col	silent	144ft	REF

The 'clans' compete for the 'Cock' standard by racing, tug of war and general competitions at the Dalguise boys' camp.

0067   SAMSON STRIPPER

1952

35mm	b/w	comopt	1260ft	VIEW

sp. Mavor and Coulson Limited
p.c. W. M. Larkins Studio (in association with the Film Producers Guild)
d. William Larkins

A demonstration of the Samson Stripper working at the coalface.

GRAMPIAN TELEVISION

KEEPING NORTH SCOTLAND IN THE PICTURE

| Queen's Cross,
Aberdeen
Tel: (0224) 646464
Fax: (0224) 635127 | Albany House,
Dundee
Tel: (0382) 739363
Fax: (0382) 480230 | 23 Huntly Street,
Inverness
Tel: (0463) 242624
Fax: (0463) 223637 | Seaforth House,
Stornoway
Tel: (0851) 704433
Fax: (0851) 706406 |

9

| 0068 | HOW PLANT BREEDING CAN HELP THE FARMER |

1948

| 16mm | col | comopt | 650ft | | REF |

sp. Dept. of Agriculture for Scotland
p.c. Films of Great Britain Limited

A Government sponsored film to show how new techniques of plant breeding could produce healthier crops.

| 0069 | WORK SIMPLIFICATION APPLIED TO CLERICAL OPERATIONS |

1946

| 16mm | b/w | comopt | 600ft | | REF |

sp. Central Office of Information
p.c. Kinocrat Productions

How a series of clerical operations in an office were simplified and speeded up, by eliminating strain and inefficiency.

| 0070 | LOGGING IN THE SUNDARABANS. EAST PAKISTAN |

1946

| 16mm | b/w | mute | 1000ft | | REF |

sp. Pakistan Industrial Development Corporation
d. Elizabeth Balneaves and Stewart Johnston

The story of the transport of logs from the forest areas of East Pakistan to the Khulna Newsprint Mill eighty miles upriver.

| 0071 | HESSIAN LOOM AND COP LOADER |

1950c

| 16mm | b/w | silent | 300ft | | REF |

sp. Urquhart, Lindsay, Robertson Orchar Limited

Jute manufacture, Dundee. A hessian loom in operation.

0072   VISIT TO MAVOR AND COULSON, A

1950c

| 35mm | b/w | comopt | 1800ft | VIEW |

sp. Mavor and Coulson Limited
p.c. Thames and Clyde
d. Stanley L. Russell

A tour of the Mavor and Coulson Bridgeton works, Glasgow.

0073   MULTI-JIB CUTTING AND LOADING IN THIN COKING COALS

1955c

| 16mm | b/w | comopt | 540ft | REF |

sp. Mavor and Coulson Limited

Demonstration of Mavor and Coulson coal cutting and loading machine.

0074   MODERN MECHANICAL LOADING OF COAL

1942c

| 16mm | b/w | silent | 350ft | REF |

p.c. Atlas Films

Demonstration of a Duckbill loader at the coalface, the film also includes statistics on coal production. [Part Two only.]

0075   GROWTH OF AN INDUSTRY

1953c

| 16mm | b/w&col sep opt | 364ft | VIEW |

sp. National Cash Register Company, Dundee

A demonstration of the production and testing of new cash registers at the NCR factory at Camperdown, Dundee.

0076   NATIONAL CASH REGISTER COMPANY, DUNDEE

1953c

| 16mm | col | comopt | 108ft | REF |

p.c. NCRC in assoc. with Industrial Panel of SFC

Publicity film for the National Cash Register Company in Dundee. [Section only.]

0077   REPORT ON INDUSTRIAL SCOTLAND

1948

| 16mm | b/w | comopt | 285ft | VIEW |

sp. Central Office of Information
p.c. Crown Film Unit

A view of the industrial central belt of Scotland, including shipyards, factories and industrial estates.

0078   BELTS RUN ON IDLER ROLLERS

1955

| 16mm | b/w | comopt | 720ft | REF |

sp. Mavor and Coulson Limited

Publicity film for Mavor and Coulson's quarry machinery shown at work at their Portland Cement Works, Tilberry and chalk quarries of the south-east.

0079   CANALS IN SCOTLAND

1946c

| 16mm | b/w | silent | 250ft | VIEW |

filmed by SEFA (Glasgow Group)

Scotland's three canals, the Crinan, Caledonian, and Forth and Clyde are shown in operation.

0080   ROYAL NORTHERN YACHT CLUB REGATTAS

1935-'38

| 16mm | b/w | silent | 145ft | REF |

filmed by E.F.L. Mucklow

Shots of the schooner "Lelanta", and yachts "Mafalda" and "Margaret".

0081   HIGHLAND GAMES

1952

| 16mm | b/w | silent | 230ft | REF |

The Glasgow Highland Gathering at Ibrox Stadium, Glasgow.

0082   MODERN MECHANICAL MINING IN A SOUTH AFRICAN COAL MINE

1955c

| 16mm | b/w | silent | 400ft | REF |

p.c. Mavor and Coulson Limited

A promotional film demonstrating Mavor and Coulson's mining machinery in a South African coal mine.

0083   ROYAL NATIONAL YACHT CLUB REGATTA, ROTHESAY

1938

| 16mm | b/w | silent | 324ft | REF |

filmed by E.F.L. Mucklow

Yachts are lined up at Hunter's Quay, Argyllshire, ready for racing.

0084   SWEDISH OLYMPIC GYMNASTS

1938

| 16mm | b/w | silent | 400ft | VIEW |

filmed by J. McRoberts

Display of gymnastics by the men and women's Swedish Olympic Gymnasts Team in the Kelvin Hall, Glasgow.

0085	ROOTES GROUP, THE				
1963					
16mm	col	comopt	696ft		VIEW

p.c. Glasgow Films

Footage of the Rootes Car factory at Linwood which produced the Hillman Imp. The opening ceremony is attended by the Duke of Edinburgh.

0087	LANARK'S 813TH LANIMER DAY				
1953					
35mm	b/w	silent	855ft		REF

Lanimer Day celebrations in Lanark including a procession of floats, coronation of the Lanimer Queen, and the Cornet's Flag carried by Town Councillor Macpherson.

0088	LANIMER DAY, LANARK				
1954					
35mm	b/w&col	silent	510ft		REF

[filmed by Stanley Russell]

The procession of floats through Lanark, and the coronation of the Lanimer Queen.

0089	LANARK LANIMER DAY				
1955					
35mm	b/w	silent	1140ft		REF

Procession of floats through Lanark, coronation of the Lanimer Queen, and the Cornet Flag is carried by Lord Cornet Andrew Inglis.

0090	CHARLES RENNIE MACKINTOSH				
1965					
16mm	col	comopt	765ft		VIEW

filmed by SEFA

A look at Mackintosh's work, including his own house in Glasgow's Southpark Avenue; Scotland Street School; Cranston's Tea Rooms, and Glasgow's School of Art.

0093	HUGH SMITH MACHINE TOOLS TECHNICAL FILM				
1940s					
16mm	b/w	silent	288ft		REF

A demonstration of how a ship's frame cold bending machine operates. Filmed in Alexander Stephen's Yard, Linthouse, Glasgow.

0096	HER MAJESTY OPENS SCOTTISH INDUSTRIES EXHIBITION				
1949					
16mm	b/w	comopt	72ft		VIEW

p.c. Movietone News

Queen Elizabeth and Princess Margaret open the Scottish Industries Exhibition at the Kelvin Hall, Glasgow, accompanied by Sir Steven Bilsland.

0097	BLACK AND DECKER LIMITED				
1948c					
16mm	b/w	comopt	144ft		REF

p.c. Thames and Clyde

Manufacture of components for Black and Decker tools.

0098	LIEDER DER VOLKER (SONGS OF THE PEOPLE)				
1960s					
16mm	col	comopt	936ft		REF

sp. WWF Koln
p.c. Horst Film Productions
d. Hans Herro Krause

Scottish folk music from Jeannie Robertson, Jimmy McMeath and the Royal Scottish Country Dance Society. Filmed in Blair Castle. [German narrative.]

0099	SUBSIDENCE				
1965					
16mm	b/w	silent	396ft		REF

sp. Cementation Company Limited
p.c. Thames and Clyde

A look at various types of subsidence, and how to overcome the problem, using St. Andrews' Episcopal Church in Wishaw as an example.

0100	SCOTLAND'S FOREST FACTORIES				
1950c					
16mm	b/w	silent	1080ft		VIEW

sp. A. & G. Paterson Limited
p.c. Topical Press Agency
d. John Oliver

A look at how a tree is felled, and then processed at a timber yard.

0105	AMATEUR CINEMATOGRAPHY				
1948					
16mm	b/w	comopt	100ft		VIEW

p.c. Thames and Clyde
[d. Stanley Russell]

Demonstration on how to make a film, made as a trailer for the 10th Scottish Amateur Film Festival held in the Cosmo Cinema, Glasgow.

0106	GLASGOW'S POLICE				
1934					
35mm	b/w	mute	630ft		VIEW

p.c. Meteor Film Producing Society
filmed by Stanley L. Russell

Captain Sillitoe speaks about the Glasgow Police as part of an effort to "de-mystify" the police in the public's eye. Scenes include police at work in Glasgow, sports day at Hampden Park, and a police parade. [Entered for the 1934 Scottish Amateur Film Festival under the title POLICE.]

11

0107   FREEDOM OF ABERFELDY

1943

| 35mm | b/w | comopt | 765ft | VIEW |

sp. Ministry of Information
p.c. Campbell Harper Films Ltd.
d. Alan Harper

A look at the village of Aberfeldy during wartime when the women provided a 'home' for Dominion troops on leave.

0108   GRAND UNION CANAL

1938

| 16mm | b/w | silent | 280ft | REF |

p.c. Elder Dalrymple Productions
d. John Elder

Map of canal routes from London to Birmingham and the industrial north. The film shows canal barges loading and unloading at docks.

0109   LION AND THE LAMB, THE

1950c

| 16mm | b/w | comopt | 612ft | REF |

sp. Glasgow and West of Scotland SPCA
p.c. Thames and Clyde
d. Stanley L. Russell

SPCA inspects farm and transport points, and shows how to care for working animals, including pit ponies.

0111   WORLD OF STEEL

1938

| 35mm | b/w | comopt | 480ft | VIEW |

sp. Colvilles Limited
p.c. Scottish Film Productions

Made for screening at the Empire Exhibition Glasgow, the film gives an illustration of steel rolling mill production for girders for the Empire Exhibition Tower.

0112   CROFTER BOY

1955

| 35mm | b/w | comopt | 1710ft | VIEW |

sp. Joint Production Committee of SEFA and SFC
p.c. Thames and Clyde
d. Stanley L. Russell

A dramatised documentary of life in a crofting community.

0113   HOSPITAL TEAM

1945

| 16mm | b/w | comopt | 960ft | VIEW |

sp. Dept. of Health
p.c. Verity Films Limited

Dramatised recruiting film presenting the various opportunities in hospital work, including the work of the radiographer, physiotherapist and dietician.

0114   WAVERLEY STEPS

1948

| 35mm | b/w | comopt | 2852ft | VIEW |

sp. COI for the Scottish Home Department
p.c. Greenpark Productions in assoc. with the Film Producers' Guild
d. John Eldridge

Dramatised documentary about the inhabitants of Edinburgh during the course of a single day. [Shown at the Edinburgh Film Festival in 1948.]

0115   LORD PROVOST P. J. DOLLAN VISITS GOVAN SCHOOLS

1938-'41c

| 35mm | b/w | comopt | 90ft | VIEW |

p.c. Gaumont British News

Provost and Lady Dollan visit three schools in Govan, Glasgow. They meet pupils and parents.

0116   PRINCESS MARY PRESENTS NEW COLOURS TO ROYAL SCOTS

1926

| 35mm | b/w | silent | 405ft | VIEW |

[filmed by James Hart for Grosvenor Topical News]

Princess Mary, Colonel in Chief of the Royal Scots, presents the new Colours to the 1st Battalion at Maryhill barracks, Glasgow. [Incomplete.]

0117   CHURCH PARADE OF GLASGOW LOWLAND SIGNAL UNITS

1926

| 35mm | b/w | silent | 54ft | VIEW |

[filmed by James Hart for Grosvenor Topical News]

Troops in church parade marshalling for inspection in Glasgow. [Incomplete.]

0118   (BOY SCOUTS PARADE IN GEORGE SQUARE)

1926c

| 35mm | b/w | silent | 54ft | VIEW |

[attributed to James Hart for Grosvenor Topical News]

Boy Scouts parade in Glasgow's George Square.

0119   DAY OF REMEMBRANCE MEMORIAL AT THE GLASGOW CENOTAPH

1927

| 35mm | b/w | silent | 362ft | VIEW |

[filmed by James Hart for Grosvenor Topical News]

Parade into George Square of war veterans. General Sir Ian Hamilton meets some of the men and makes his speech at the Cenotaph.

0120	CROFTERS, THE				
1944					
16mm	*b/w*	*comopt*	*810ft*		*VIEW*

sp. MOI with the Ministry of Agriculture
p.c. Greenpark Productions

A look at everyday life in the crofting community of Achriesgill in Sutherland.

0122	VICTORY PARADE				
1946					
16mm	*col*	*comopt*	*755ft*		*VIEW*

p.c. Castleton Knight Production

Scenes in London when peace was declared on 8th May 1945. Shots of the motorcade led by Winston Churchill. The film concludes with footage of the celebrations one year later on the first anniversary of VE Day.

0123	CITY SIDELIGHTS NO. 2				
1951/'52					
35mm	*b/w*	*comopt*	*1380ft*		*VIEW*

p.c. Elder Film Productions

A look at some of Glasgow's interesting and historical sites, in particular Kelvingrove Art Gallery and Museum. The film also includes scenes of the Scottish Flyweight boxing Championship at Paisley on 17th January, 1951.

0124	MAKING OF THE HOLY BIBLE				
1950c					
16mm	*b/w*	*comopt*	*180ft*		*REF*

sp. Collins Limited
p.c. Elder Film Productions

Printing the pages of a Bible on India paper and the handwork involved in folding, gilding and binding.

0126	(GLASGOW TRAMS - TRIMS)				
1955c					
16mm	*b/w*	*silent*	*130ft*		*REF*

[filmed by Louise Annand]

Glasgow trams being repaired. [Trims only.]

0127	PACIFIC PANORAMA				
1956					
16mm	*col*	*silent*	*810ft*		*REF*

filmed by Nat and Nettie McGavin

Hollywood by night; sheep farming and harvesting in New Zealand; Sydney bridge and harbour; rice fields in Indonesia; a Chinese wedding and a Fijian home.

0128	KING'S VISIT TO CANADA, THE				
1939					
16mm	*b/w*	*silent*	*310ft*		*VIEW*

p.c. British Movietone News

King George VI and Queen Elizabeth tour Canada, and then visit the World's Fair in New York.

0129	HOLIDAY AT DORNOCH, A				
1937					
16mm	*b/w*	*silent*	*216ft*		*REF*

filmed by Nat and Nettie McGavin

A holiday in Dornoch in the Highlands, including a visit to Carnaig Cottage and Loch Maree.

0130	NEW YORK AND WORLD'S FAIR				
1939					
16mm	*col*	*silent*	*324ft*		*REF*

filmed by Nat and Nettie McGavin

A holiday in New York with shots of Wall Street, Fifth Avenue, Rockerfeller Centre, George Washington Statue, the World's Fair, and Broadway at midnight.

0131	CROSSING NORTHERN LATITUDES				
1936					
16mm	*b/w*	*silent*	*324ft*		*REF*

filmed by Nat and Nettie McGavin

Holiday scenes in Iceland, Spitzbergen and Norway.

0132	CANADIAN CAMEOS				
1939					
16mm	*col*	*silent*	*324ft*		*REF*

filmed by Nat and Nettie McGavin

A holiday in Canada, with scenes of Quebec, Montreal, Toronto, Niagara Falls, and the Rideau Canal.

0133	MAJORCAN MEDLEY				
1953c					
16mm	*col*	*silent*	*468ft*		*VIEW*

filmed by Nettie McGavin

Scenes of local life in Majorca including shots of local fishing and the Fiesta in Valldemosa. The film also looks at the Moorish influence on the island's buildings.

0134	HIMALAYAN HOLIDAY				
1951c					
16mm	*col*	*silent*	*500ft*		*VIEW*

filmed by Nettie McGavin

A sunrise in Darjeeling, shots of Mount Everest, rice threshing and a visit to Dr. Graham's Childrens Home in Kashmir.

13

0135	GLASGOW TAKES CARE OF ITS OLD FOLK				
1949c					
35mm	b/w	comopt	898ft		VIEW

sp. Glasgow Corporation Welfare Department
p.c. Thames and Clyde
d. Stanley L. Russell

How Glasgow takes care of its old people through the provision of Old Folks' Homes, including Forest Hall, Crookston Home, and Woodburn Home.

0136	HOLIDAYING IN HARRIS			
1938				
16mm	b/w	silent	460ft	VIEW

[filmed by Nat and Nettie McGavin]

A look at life in Harris including its fishing industry and the making of Harris tweed.

0140	IDLING IN INDIA			
1930s				
16mm	col	silent	975ft	REF

filmed by Nettie McGavin

A holiday taken in India, with a tour to Delhi, the Mohammedan Mosque, the Taj Mahal, the Punjab, Calcutta and Madras.

0141	CONSTRUCTION OF THE KING GEORGE V BRIDGE, GLASGOW			
1924-'27				
16mm	b/w	silent	936ft	VIEW

filmed by Mr. Dundas

A record of the construction of George V Bridge in Glasgow by Melville, Dundas & Whitson Ltd.

0142	ROYAL VISIT TO SCOTLAND			
1953				
35mm	b/w	comopt	1100ft	VIEW

p.c. Gaumont British News

A royal visit to Edinburgh with attendance at the General Assembly and the garden party at Holyrood House. The royal party then moves on to Glasgow where the Queen and the Duke of Edinburgh watch a youth rally at Hampden Park.

0143	JERASH AND BAALBEK			
1930s				
16mm	col	silent	320ft	REF

[attributed to Nat and Nettie McGavin]

Ruins at Jerash and Baalbek.

0144	CANADIAN CAMEOS NO. 2			
1939				
16mm	col	silent	396ft	REF

filmed by Nettie McGavin

A visit to Calgary during the Stampede celebrations, with calf roping and steer riding contests, a visit to the Rockies, and the Athabasca Falls.

0145	TREETOPS			
1951c				
16mm	b/w&col	comopt	260ft	VIEW

filmed by Nat and Nettie McGavin

A holiday at "Treetops", Kenya, where elephants and other animals are seen gathering after dusk.

0146	CEYLON CALLING			
1930s				
16mm	col	silent	340ft	VIEW

filmed by Nettie McGavin

A holiday in Ceylon, with visits to Colombo, and Kandy.

0147	AFRICAN ANIMALS			
1951c				
16mm	col	silent	485ft	REF

filmed by Nettie McGavin

Shots of African animals in Kruger National Park and Nairobi Game Reserve.

0148	SARDINIA			
1958c				
16mm	col	silent	500ft	VIEW

[attributed to Nettie McGavin]

A holiday in Sardinia with scenes at the port of Alghero.

0149	ITALIAN INTERLUDE			
1952c				
16mm	col	silent	568ft	VIEW

filmed by Nettie McGavin

The Mediterranean Coast, Lake Como, Milan and the Italian Alps. [Prizewinning film at the 1952 Scottish Amateur Film Festival.]

0150	ROYAL SOUTH AFRICAN TOUR			
1951c				
16mm	b/w	silent	575ft	REF

p.c. British Movietone News

King George and Queen Elizabeth on tour in South Africa where the King opens the Ninth Union Parliament, visits Kruger Park and meets Zulu warriors.

0151	SWITZERLAND 1947			
1947				
16mm	*col*	*silent*	*288ft*	*REF*

filmed by Nettie McGavin

A holiday in Switzerland, with visits to Montreux, Interlaken, and Lucerne.

0152	AFRICAN ANECDOTES			
1954				
16mm	*col*	*silent*	*612ft*	*REF*

Views of Port Elizabeth, Cape Town, Pretoria and Southern Rhodesia. The film also features a visit to an ostrich farm, a look at a Boer farmhouse and a trip to Victoria Falls.

0153	KENYA TO DURBAN			
1954				
16mm	*col*	*silent*	*900ft*	*REF*

filmed by Nat and Nettie McGavin

A holiday in Africa including footage of the Kenya Tea Gardens, a coffee plantation, women of the Kikuyu tribe and street scenes in Nairobi.

0154	STEEL AND ENGINEERING			
1935c				
16mm	*col*	*comopt*	*360ft*	*REF*

filmed by Wm. Beardmore and Co. Ltd. /SFC Industrial Panel

Shots of the "Empress of Britain" leaving Greenock for Canada and of the interior of the Parkhead steel works.

0155	WEST OF INVERNESS			
1946c				
16mm	*b/w*	*comopt*	*325ft*	*VIEW*

d. Stephen Durell

The role of the steam train in the West Highlands of Scotland with shots of goods, livestock and parcels being loaded and unloaded. Crofters are seen ploughing fields and cutting peat.

0156	CIVIL DEFENCE IN GLASGOW			
1942				
16mm	*b/w&col silent*		*1565ft*	*REF*

[filmed by B.J. Humble]

Made to demonstrate civil defence procedures and the organisations involved.

0157	(ANTI-GAS PRECAUTIONS IN GLASGOW)			
1942c				
16mm	*b/w*	*silent*	*360ft*	*REF*

[filmed by B. J. Humble]

Emergency services are seen in action as the alarm is raised for a gas attack.

0158	CIVIL DEFENCE			
1942c				
16mm	*b/w*	*silent*	*685ft*	*REF*

[attributed to Ben H. Humble]

A demonstration by the Civil Defence Corps, showing a basic rescue operation involving fire-fighting and searching for survivors beneath the rubble.

0159	SCOTTISH CUP TIE			
1937				
16mm	*b/w*	*comopt*	*70ft*	*VIEW*

filmed as a local topical for Regal Picture House, Dumfries

The Scottish Cup Tie with shots of the crowd, the teams coming out and highlights of the football match.

0160	JUTE MANUFACTURE			
1963				
std.8mm col		*silent*	*320ft*	*REF*

filmed by Giddings and Lewis-Fraser Ltd.

The processes of jute manufacture at Giddings and Lewis-Fraser Ltd. Filmed in the company's Wellgate Mill, Arbroath.

0161	DOMINION MONARCH			
1948c				
16mm	*b/w&col silent*		*360ft*	*REF*

filmed by Mr. Clark

Life on an ocean-going liner including shots of the wireless office and the wheelhouse, the crew and passengers. The 'Crossing the Line' ceremony is also featured.

0162	VIEWS OF THE CLYDE AND AROUND			
1950c				
16mm	*b/w*	*silent*	*216ft*	*REF*

filmed by Mr. Clark

Various shots of ships on slipways and dock scenes.

0163	EAST OF SUEZ			
1953c				
16mm	*b/w&col silent*		*540ft*	*REF*

filmed by Mr. Clark

Panoramic views of the Suez Canal, Durban, British East Africa, and Basrah.

0164	ABERDEEN			
1950s				
16mm	*b/w&col silent*		*1370ft*	*REF*

filmed by Mr. Clark

Everyday life, the industries and farming in and around Aberdeen.

15

Staff of the Playhouse Cinema, Aberdeen, pre-war.

0165   SECTIONS FROM "CURRENT ACCOUNT" WAVERLEY PROGRAMME

1976

16mm	col	mute	470ft		REF

p.c. BBC Television

Shots on board the Clyde steamer the "Waverley", on deck and in the engine room.

0166   THIS FILM IS DANGEROUS

1948

16mm	b/w	comopt	715ft		REF

sp. The Admiralty
p.c. British Documentary Films Limited
d. Ronald Haines

A naval instructional film showing how to care for nitrate film stock and what to do in the event of fire.

0167   PARAFFIN YOUNG

1937

9.5mm	b/w	silent	700ft		VIEW

sp. Scottish Oils Limited
p.c. Realist Film Unit
d. Ralph Bond

Made for display at the Scottish Oils and Shell Mex Pavilion at the Empire Exhibition of 1938, the film looks at the life and work of James Young, the pioneer of coal distillation for the production of oil.

0168   DUMFRIES 1932 - GUID NYCHBURRIS DAY

1932

35mm	b/w	silent	920ft		VIEW

filmed as a local topical for ABC Cinema, Dumfries

The Riding of the Marches and coronation of Queen of the South.

0169	DUMFRIES 1933 - GUID NYCHBURRIS DAY

1933

35mm	b/w	silent	900ft	VIEW

filmed as a local topical for ABC Cinema, Dumfries

The Riding of the Marches, the pageant and coronation of the Queen of the South.

0170	DUMFRIES GUID NYCHBURRIS DAY

1934

35mm	b/w	silent	760ft	VIEW

filmed as a local topical for ABC Cinema, Dumfries

Guid Nychburris Day festival including the procession and coronation ceremony. The film also shows football matches between Queen of the South and Hibernian and Queen of the South and Rangers at Palmerston Park.

0171	(DUMFRIES 1935)

1935

35mm	b/w	silent	870ft	VIEW

filmed as a local topical for ABC Cinema, Dumfries

The Duke of Gloucester visits Dumfries and opens its New Muncipal Buildings. Shots of Guid Nychburris Week Celebrations with the coronation of the Queen of the South and the street procession.

0172	DUMFRIES 1936 - GUID NYCHBURRIS DAY

1936

35mm	b/w	silent	630ft	VIEW

filmed as a local topical for ABC Cinema, Dumfries

The Installation ceremony of the Cornet, the Investiture of Queen of the South, Midsteeple Ceremony and Fancy Dress competition at the annual Dumfries festival.

0173	DUMFRIES 1937

1937

35mm	b/w	silent	630ft	VIEW

filmed as a local topical for ABC Cinema, Dumfries

The Lord Provost, Cornet and members of the Town Council attend Divine Service in St. Michael's Church. Shots of the Installation of the Cornet and Investiture of the Queen of the South.

0174	(SS "BERENGARIA")

1923

35mm	tinted	silent	990ft	REF

[filmed by Jackie Johnston, newsreel cameraman]

Voyage of the liner "Berengaria" from New York to London in May 1923, as seen through the eyes of passenger John Harrod. [Incomplete.]

0175	DUMFRIES 1959 - GUID NYCHBURRIS CELEBRATIONS

1959

35mm	b/w	silent	810ft	VIEW

filmed as a local topical for the Lyceum Cinema, Dumfries

Procession of the town council, installation of the Cornet, coronation of the Queen, and pageant.

0176	DUMFRIES, GUID NYCHBURRIS DAY

1956

35mm	b/w	silent	720ft	VIEW

filmed as a local topical for the Lyceum Cinema, Dumfries

The pageant and coronation of the Festival Queen.

0177	SCOTTISH CUP TIE THIRD ROUND

1950c

35mm	b/w	silent	540ft	VIEW

sp. Lyceum Cinema, Dumfries
filmed by Elder Film Productions

Shots of the football teams coming onto the pitch at Palmerston Park, the captains toss and shots of the match from the sidelines.

0178	DUMFRIES 1949 GUID NYCHBURRIS DAY

1949

16mm	b/w	silent	270ft	REF

filmed as a local topical for the Lyceum Cinema, Dumfries

Investiture of the Cornet, shots of the crowds, the horse race and procession of horsemen through the "city gates".

0179	DUMFRIES 1950 GUID NYCHBURRIS FESTIVAL

1950

35mm	b/w	silent	720ft	VIEW

filmed as a local topical for the Lyceum Cinema, Dumfries

Kirkin' of the Cornet at St. Michael's Church; Installation of the Cornet and Queen of the South; Riding of the Marches; Cornet's Ball and Children's Fancy Dress Parade. [Incomplete.]

0180	DUMFRIES 1953 GUID NYCHBURRIS FESTIVAL

1953

35mm	b/w	silent	990ft	REF

filmed as a local topical for the Lyceum Cinema, Dumfries

King's Own Scottish Borderers Freedom Ceremony and march past by troops and veterans.

17

0181   DUMFRIES 1955 GUID NYCHBURRIS FESTIVAL

1955

35mm	b/w	silent	630ft	VIEW

[filmed as a local topical for the Lyceum Cinema, Dumfries]

Shots of the projection room of the Lyceum Cinema and scenes from Festival celebrations including the Riding of the Marches through Townhead and Kirkgate Ports. [Incomplete.]

0182   EDINBURGH

1966

35mm	col	comopt	1680ft	VIEW

sp. Educational Films of Scotland
p.c. Campbell Harper Films Ltd.

Everyday life in Edinburgh with a look at the city's heritage.

0183   QUEEN OF THE SOUTH V MORTON

1949*

35mm	b/w	silent	270ft	VIEW

[filmed as a local topical for the Lyceum Cinema, Dumfries]

Queen of the South v Morton at Palmerston Park, Dumfries.

0184   (LYCEUM CINEMA TRAILERS AND ADVERTISEMENTS)

1956c

35mm	b/w	comopt	525ft	REF

[filmed as a local topical for the Lyceum Cinema, Dumfries]

Compilation of Lyceum cinema trailers and advertisements, with special emphasis on Christmas 1955 and New Year.

0185   DUNDEE JUTE

1948

16mm	b/w	silent	396ft	VIEW

filmed by J. R. L. Halley

A demonstration of how jute is manufactured in the Halley and Sons Wallace Craigie Works in Dundee. [An amateur prize-winner in 1949.]

0186   ROYAL VISIT TO SCOTLAND

1953

35mm	b/w	comopt	835ft	VIEW

p.c. Gaumont British News

Queen Elizabeth presents new colours to the First Batallion Argyll and Sutherland Highlanders. The Duke of Edinburgh is admitted into the Order of the Thistle at St Giles' Cathedral, Edinburgh.

0188   ROYAL OCCASIONS OF SCOTLAND

1897-'37

35mm	b/w	silent	1350ft	VIEW

made by Film Society of Glasgow

A compilation of royal events including King Edward VII opening the new building at Marischall College, Aberdeen 1906, the Prince of Wales at the launching ceremony of a ship at John Brown's yard in 1921 and a visit by the Royal Family to Edinburgh in 1937.

0189   BLOOD TRANSFUSION IN BATHGATE

1951

16mm	col	silent	360ft	REF

filmed by Bathgate and District Photo. and Cine Soc.

A demonstration of a blood transfusion with an appeal for donors.

0190   YOUR GLASS OF SHERRY

1960

16mm	b/w	comopt	600ft	VIEW

sp. John Harvey and Sons Limited
p.c. Thames and Clyde
d. & ph. Stanley Russell

Shot in Jerez and Seville the film illustrates how sherry is made.

0191   STORY OF CULROSS, THE

1938

35mm	b/w	comopt	870ft	VIEW

p.c. Scottish Film Productions
p. Stanley L. Russell

A look at the historic town of Culross in Fife with views of the ruined Abbey, houses and Town Cross.

0192   DAVID LIVINGSTONE

1956c

16mm	b/w	comopt	576ft	VIEW

GB Instructional
p Frank Wells, d David Middlemas, ap D B Mayne

A dramatised version of the life of David Livingstone. [Silent and sound versions.]

0193   THINGS THAT HAPPEN NO. 3

1937

16mm	b/w	comopt	322ft	REF

p.c. Scottish Film Productions (1928) Ltd.
[d. Stanley L. Russell]

St. Andrews and North Berwick swimming pools, a display of gymnastics, police on traffic duty and a dramatised bank robbery are all featured in this cinemagazine.

0194A MINISTRY OF FOOD FLASHES				
1940s				
16mm	b/w	comopt	125ft	REF

sp. Ministry of Food

Series of wartime shorts illustrating the best use of food and the economies to be made.

0194B CHRISTMAS 1943				
1943				
16mm	b/w	comopt	50ft	REF

filmed as a local topical for the Lyceum Cinema, Dumfries

A wartime Father Christmas passes on Christmas greetings on behalf of the cinema's management.

0195A MERRY CHRISTMAS AND A HAPPY NEW YEAR				
1951				
16mm	b/w	comopt	108ft	REF

[filmed as a local topical for the Lyceum Cinema, Dumfries]

Various trailers wishing cinema patrons a Merry Christmas and a Happy New Year.

0195B GUID NYCHBURRIS DAY				
1951				
16mm	b/w	silent	150ft	REF

[filmed as a local topical for the Lyceum Cinema, Dumfries]

The festival celebrating Guid Nychburris Day, Dumfries.

0196 ROAD THROUGH THE SUNSET ISLES				
1937				
35mm	b/w	silent	1440ft	VIEW

sp. David McBraynes Limited
p.c. J. C. Elder
d. J.C. Elder

A hiking holiday through the Hebrides, exploring Lewis, Harris, the Uists, Benbecula and Barra. [Issued with "Honeymoon Cruise No 1 and 2" as a musical travelogue entitled "Bonnie Scotland Calls You" (1938). [See refs. 0415 and 0260.]

0197 GLENHAR FACTORY, HILLINGTON				
1953				
16mm	b/w&col silent		720ft	VIEW

[filmed by Jack Harris]

Interior shots of Glenhar factory (decorated to celebrate the coronation) with shots of the cutting and sewing of ladies' fashions. Models give a fashion show of men's and women's wear produced by the factory.

0198 CHINA				
1930c				
16mm	b/w	silent	300ft	VIEW

[filmed by David Keith]

Workers in the paddy fields; threshing and ploughing; street scenes and men at work in the shipyards in China.

0199 WINDSOR				
1933c				
16mm	b/w&col silent		440ft	REF

[filmed by David Keith]

Shots of Windsor and its environs, the film also contains footage of the Edinburgh Floral Clock and Botanic Gardens.

0201 HIGHLAND HORSE SHOW, ALLOA				
1932c				
16mm	col	silent	36ft	REF

[filmed by David Keith]

The Highland Horse Show in Alloa, with a display of military horse-riding.

0202 FRIENDS OF UNCLE DAVID				
1933c				
16mm	b/w	silent	105ft	REF

[filmed by David Keith]

Shots of a family group.

0231 SCOTLAND FOR FITNESS				
1937				
35mm	b/w	comopt	396ft	VIEW

sp. Films of Scotland
p.c. GB Instructional
d. Brian Salt

Made for the 1938 Empire Exhibition under the supervision of John Grierson, the film was part of a campaign to improve the fitness of the Scots.

0232 "QUEEN MARY" GOES DOWN TO THE SEA				
1936				
35mm	b/w	comopt	150ft	VIEW

p.c. Gaumont British News

The liner the "Queen Mary" in the fitting out basin at Clydebank and shots of the vessel pulling out to sea.

0233 GATHERING OF BRAEMAR ROYAL HIGHLAND SOCIETY				
1949				
16mm	col	silent	510ft	REF

Gathering of the Braemar Royal Highland Society attended by King George V.

19

20

0234 GORDON HIGHLANDERS' PRESENTATION OF THE FREEDOM OF THE CITY OF ABERDEEN
1949

16mm	col	silent	504ft		REF

sp. Corporation of the City of Aberdeen

The Duke of Gloucester, Colonol-in-Chief of the Regiment accepts the casket and scroll and freedom of the City. Crowds watch the parade along Union Street.

0235 PRESENTATION OF NEW COLOURS TO GORDON HIGHLANDERS
1961c

16mm	col	comopt	625ft		REF

The Queen presents new colours to the Gordon Highlanders, at Balmoral Castle.

0236 PORTHLETHEN CHURCH
1935c

35mm	b/w	silent	180ft		REF

[filmed by Ernest Bromberg News for Newscine, Aberdeen]

Church parade and service by members of the Grant Lodge of the Loyal Order of Ancient Shepherds to mark the retiral of Reverend A. R. Grant.

0237 FLICKS OF ABERDEEN'S TERRITORIAL WEEK
1940c

35mm	b/w	silent	300ft		VIEW

[filmed by Ernest Bromberg for Newscine, Aberdeen]

Lord Provost Mitchell and Major Lyon (Chairman of Territorial Association) visit the Field Company and watch a military display.

0238 (ABERDEEN'S "BLACK FRIDAY")
1940

35mm	b/w	silent	495ft		VIEW

[filmed by Ernest Bromberg for Newscine, Aberdeen]

Footage of the impact of the first daylight air-raid on Aberdeen, known locally as "Black Friday".

0239 ABERDEEN CELEBRATES THE CORONATION
1937

35mm	b/w	silent	410ft		VIEW

[filmed by Ernest Bromberg for Cosmo Cinema, Aberdeen]

Aberdeen celebrates the Coronation with a service, parade and a coronation ball at the Palais de Danse.

0241 (CINEMA NEWS, ABERDEEN)
1937

35mm	b/w	silent	720ft		VIEW

[filmed by Ernest Bromberg]

Local news of Aberdeen, including footage of a Scotland and Ireland rugby match, a circus, a TA parade with land girls and Women's Army Corps.

0242 THEIR MAJESTIES ATTEND DIVINE SERVICE
1938c

35mm	b/w	silent	360ft		VIEW

[filmed by Ernest Bromberg for Newscine, Aberdeen]

King George attends Divine Service at Crathie Church, Aberdeenshire.

0244 NEWSREEL
1940c

35mm	b/w	silent	380ft		VIEW

[filmed by Ernest Bromberg for Newscine, Aberdeen]

Aberdeen's Armistice Day Service and a cycling rally at Echt.

0245A BRITISH MEDICAL ASSOCIATION CONFERENCE IN ABERDEEN
1939*

35mm	b/w	silent	265ft		REF

[filmed by Ernest Bromberg]

British Medical Association Conference in Aberdeen.

0245B SCHOOL SPORTS
1939

35mm	b/w	silent	180ft		REF

[filmed by Ernest Bromberg]

Footage of Aberdeen's High School for Girls' primary sports day.

0246A ARP
1939

35mm	b/w	silent	95ft		VIEW

[filmed by Ernest Bromberg for Newscine, Aberdeen]

An ARP exercise for dealing with a gas attack.

0246B QUEEN ELIZABETH (QUEEN MOTHER)
1939

35mm	b/w	silent	270ft		VIEW

[filmed by Ernest Bromberg for Newscine, Aberdeen]

The Queen Mother opens Aberdeen's new Sports Stadium at Linksfield.

0247	LAYING FOUNDATION STONE OF THE BISHOP SEABURY MEMORIAL				
1938c					
35mm	b/w	silent	175ft		VIEW

[filmed by Ernest Bromberg for Newscine, Aberdeen]

Joseph P. Kennedy, American Ambassador to Britain, lays the foundation stone for the Bishop Seabury Memorial at St. Andrews Cathedral, Aberdeen.

0248	MEMBERS OF BOTH TEAMS LEAVE HOTEL FOR GAME				
1938*					
16mm	b/w	silent	60ft		REF

[filmed by Ernest Bromberg for Newscine, Aberdeen]

Football players seen leaving a hotel for a game.

0249	(MILITARY PARADE IN ABERDEEN)				
1941c					
35mm	b/w	silent	1080ft		VIEW

[filmed by Ernest Bromberg for Newscine, Aberdeen]

Military parade through Aberdeen and the laying of a wreath at the War Memorial. The film includes footage of the opening ceremony of the Robert Gordon College Pavilion.

0250	NEVILLE BUTLER'S TEST SPEECHES				
1941					
16mm	b/w	comopt	192ft		REF

Sir Neville Montague Butler, Minister of Foreign Affairs to the US, comments on US involvement in the second World War.

0251	INTRODUCING SCOTLAND				
1958					
35mm	col	comopt	1800ft		VIEW

sp. Educational Films of Scotland
p.c. Thames and Clyde
d. Stanley L. Russell

A discussion of the social, economic and geographical infrastructure of Scotland, including scenes of Glasgow, Aberdeen and Edinburgh.

0252	GAELIC MOD				
1956c					
35mm	b/w	mute	385ft		VIEW

[sp. BBC Television]
[p.c. Thames & Clyde Ltd.]
[d. Stanley Russell]

Gaelic songs performed at the Mod.

0253	TAM TRAUCHLE'S TROUBLES				
1934					
16mm	b/w	comopt	1400ft		VIEW

sp. Glasgow Corporation Education Department
p.c. Pathe Pictures Limited

One of a series of films produced for the Glasgow Necessitous Children's Holiday Camp Fund, it promotes the benefits of the Holiday Camp to children and parents alike.

0255A	CAMPING WE WILL GO, A				
1956					
16mm	col	silent	720ft		REF

filmed by L.A. Russell

A record of how Dalguise Sports Camp provides holidays for children who come from deprived areas.

0255B	LETTER FROM JOHNNY				
1958c					
16mm	col	silent	828ft		REF

filmed by L.A. Russell

A young boy writes home to his parents about the various activities he has taken part in at the Dalguise Camp including hiking, playing hockey and a tug of war.

0255C	CAMPING IS FUN				
1957c					
16mm	col	silent	580ft		REF

filmed by L. A. Russell

Some of the activities available at Dalguise Camp including rambling, various sports and the Grand Concert.

0256	EILEAN AN FHRAOICH [ISLE OF LEWIS]				
1937					
16mm	b/w	silent	1095ft		VIEW

sp. Lewis Hospital, Stornoway
filmed by Dr. Peter John MacLeod

Scenes of life in the Outer Hebrides showing herring fishing, crofting, cutting peat, and roof thatching. The Lewis Hospital Carnival is also featured with a pipe band, floats and a display of Highland dancing.

0257	FESTIVAL OF FELLOWSHIP				
1937					
35mm	b/w	comopt	675ft		VIEW

sp. Glasgow Corporation Education Department
[p.c. Scottish Film Productions]

School children on a day trip by steamer to Ardgoil, as part of Glasgow's celebrations for coronation year.

21

0258   VISIT OF HRH DUCHESS OF KENT TO WEST OF SCOTLAND

1944

16mm	b/w	comopt	100ft		REF

filmed by Russell Productions

The Duchess of Kent arrives at the opening of the British Sailors' Centre, Greenock, is met by Lord Inverclyde and cheered by onlooking crowds.

0259   ARRIVAL OF THE MAIL STEAMER IN LERWICK

1920c

16mm	b/w	silent	54ft		REF

Mail steamer arrives in Lerwick in the Shetland Isles.

0260   HONEYMOON CRUISE NO. 2

1936c

16mm	b/w	silent	445ft		VIEW

sp. David MacBraynes Limited
p.c. Elder Film Productions
d. J.C. Elder

Film highlights the scenic beauty of the Highlands on the Oban to Inverness steamer route. [Issued with refs. 0196 and 0415 as a musical travelogue entitled "Bonnie Scotland Calls You" in 1938.]

0262   ROAD SAFETY

n.d.

16mm	b/w	silent	22ft		REF

sp. Lanarkshire Road Safety Committee

A description of safety procedure for boarding or leaving a bus.

0264   QUEEN OF THE MILKY WAY

1944

16mm	b/w	comopt	360ft		REF

p.c. Russell Productions Ltd.
d. Stanley L. Russell

Dairy farming in Ayrshire.

0265A   RUGBY, SCOTLAND'S TRIUMPH

1951

35mm	b/w	comopt	265ft		VIEW

p.c. Movietone News

A rugby match between Scotland and Wales at Murrayfield, Edinburgh.

0265B   RUGBY, SCOTLAND V IRELAND

1951

35mm	b/w	comopt	225ft		VIEW

p.c. Movietone News

Rugby match between Scotland and Ireland at Murrayfield, Edinburgh.

0265C   RUGBY, SCOTLAND V IRELAND

1951

35mm	b/w	comopt	228ft		VIEW

p.c. Gaumont British News

Rugby match between Scotland and Ireland at Murrayfield, Edinburgh.

0266   CROWNING OF THE MERCHANT NAVY QUEEN, THE

1944c

16mm	b/w	comopt	357ft		REF

sp. Merchant Navy Comforts Service
p.c. Russell Productions Limited
d. Stanley L. Russell

Appeal on behalf of the Merchant Navy Comforts Service Week in Burnley, including footage of a parade and coronation of the Merchant Navy Queen.

0268   PROGRESS REPORT

1946

35mm	b/w	comopt	930ft		VIEW

sp. Glasgow Corporation Housing Department
p.c. Thames and Clyde

A survey of Municipal Housing Activity in Glasgow. New council housing at Knightswood, Cranhill, Pollock and Tollcross.

0269   AMERICANS WALK OFF WITH THE WALKER CUP

1947

35mm	b/w	comopt	245ft		VIEW

p.c. Movietone News

Filmed at the Royal and Ancient golf course, St Andrews. The American captain is presented with the Walker Cup. Will Fyffe and Sir Alexander B. King are spectators.

0270   FROM FOREST TO FACTORY

1959

16mm	b/w	silent	650ft		VIEW

sp. A. & G. Paterson Limited
p.c. Commercial and Educational Films
d. John Oliver

A demonstration of how timber is felled and some of its products being assembled in the factory including trellis fencing and boxes.

0271   GOOD HEALTH TO SCOTLAND

1943

16mm	b/w	comopt	680ft		VIEW

sp. MOI for Dept. of Health for Scotland
p.c. Scottish Films Ltd.
d. Stanley Russell

Made during the war, the film promotes various health measures e.g. ante-natal clinics, school milk, holiday camps for children and inoculation.

22

0272	BIRTHDAY			
1946				
16mm	b/w	comopt	770ft	REF

sp. MOI for Dept. of Health for Scotland
p.c. Data Film Unit
w. & d. Budge Cooper p. Donald Alexander

Illustration on how to fully utilise an ante-natal clinic, to ensure the health of an unborn baby.

0273	YOUR CHILDREN'S TEETH			
1945				
16mm	b/w	comopt	500ft	VIEW

sp. MOI for Dept. of Health
p.c. Realist Film Unit
d. Jane Massy

Advice on how to ensure that a baby will grow up to have healthy teeth.

0274	HIGHLAND LADDIE			
1952				
16mm	b/w	comopt	870ft	VIEW

p.c. Campbell Harper Films Ltd.

A look at the life, crafts and industries of the Highlands including crofting, fishing, forestry work and tweed-making. [Filmed to try to dissuade people from the Highlands emigrating south.]

0275	SCOTLAND'S GARDENS AND ALLOTMENTS			
1945				
16mm	col	silent	440ft	REF

Shots of Craigbank Gardens, Edinburgh and Portree Horticultural Show.

0276	SEINE NET			
1952c				
16mm	b/w	comopt	680ft	VIEW

sp. Scottish Home Department
p.c. Campbell Harper Films Ltd.
d. Henry Cooper

A demonstration on how to use a Seine net for trawling.

0277	ABERDEEN ANGUS			
1947				
16mm	b/w	comopt	270ft	REF

sp. COI for Dept. of Agriculture for Scotland
p.c. Campbell Harper Films Ltd.

A look at the history of the Aberdeen Angus breed, its distinctive qualities and characteristics.

0278	AYRSHIRE CATTLE			
1947				
16mm	b/w	comopt	370ft	VIEW

sp. COI for Dept. of Agriculture for Scotland
p.c. Campbell Harper Films Ltd.

The particular qualities of the Ayrshire breed of cattle are highlighted.

0279	POWER FOR THE HIGHLANDS			
1943				
16mm	b/w	comopt	540ft	VIEW

sp. MOI for the Scottish Office
p.c. Paul Rotha Productions

A look at the possibilities of Hydro-Electric power for the Highlands.

0280	HILL SHEEP FARM			
1948				
16mm	b/w	comopt	670ft	VIEW

sp. COI for Dept. of Agriculture for Scotland
p.c. Campbell Harper Films Ltd.

An account of the life and work of a Scottish hill sheep farm.

0281	NORTH EAST CORNER			
1946*				
16mm	b/w	comopt	800ft	VIEW

sp. COI for the Scottish Office
p.c. Greenpark Productions
d. John Eldridge

The industries, scenery and history of the North East of Scotland.

0282	CITY SIDELIGHTS - SECTIONS			
1956-'58				
16mm	b/w	comopt	570ft	REF

p.c. Elder Film Productions

Different aspects of Glasgow life; hairdressing at Lewis's store, an exhibition of armour at Kelvingrove Museum, art students at the School of Art and trams and trolley buses at Glasgow Cross.

0283	MARCH			
1971				
16mm	col	comopt	470ft	REF

sp. TUC
p.c. Freeprop Films Group

Record of the TUC March from Hyde Park to Trafalgar Square, in protest against the Industrial Relations Bill.

23

0284   CRAIGMOUNT SCHOOL FILMS
1949-'59

16mm	b/w&col	silent	3950ft		REF

Craigmount School activities; school plays and trips to Athens and Venice.

0285   (ROADSIDE DRAMA)
1950s

16mm	col	silent	110ft		REF

A humorous story involving a car breakdown.

0286A   LAUNCHING A SHIP
1937

16mm	b/w	silent	120ft		VIEW

sp. Glasgow Education Authority

Dignitaries view the launching of the "Salacia" at Harland and Wolffe shipyard, Govan.

0286B   LIGHTERS
1936c

16mm	b/w	silent	125ft		REF

p.c. Elder Dalrymple Productions

Shots of a 'Lighter' being loaded with a cargo of barrels and their transfer to another ship.

0288   CALLY HOUSE
1942

16mm	b/w	comopt	370ft		VIEW

sp. MOI for the Scottish Education Department
p.c. Scottish Film Productions
d. Stanley L. Russell

A look at Cally House, a wartime evacuation school in Gatehouse-of-Fleet. It was Britain's first local authority co-educational boarding school for senior pupils.

0291   CHILDREN OF THE CITY
1944

16mm	b/w	comopt	1050ft		VIEW

sp. MOI for the Scottish Education Department
p.c. Paul Rotha Productions
d. Budge Cooper

A dramatised study of child delinquency in Scotland, filmed in Dundee.

0292   LIFE OF BURNS, THE
1933

16mm	b/w	silent	375ft		REF

filmed by J. French Gegg

The homes and haunts of Robert Burns; his birthplace, Poosie Nansie's Inn, Gavin Hamilton's house where the poet was married, and the Tam O'Shanter Inn.

0294   START IN LIFE, A
1944*

16mm	b/w	commag	790ft		REF

sp. MOI with the Ministry of Health
p.c. Realist Film Unit
d. Brian Smith

A picture of the health services for children in Britain; pre-natal advice, maternity care, children's clinics, day nurseries, school children being given school milk and taking part in outdoor activities and games.

0295   SEA SCOUTS PART II
1947*

16mm	b/w	silent	400ft		REF

Sea Scouts taking part in the RSMYC race and on a summer cruise on the west coast of Scotland.

0296   SCOTLAND AND THE NEW WORLD
1953*

35mm	b/w	comopt	1728ft		VIEW

sp. Central Office of Information
p.c. Anglo Scottish Pictures
d. Charles Heath

A look at the social and economic changes in Scotland during the 1950s, from the restoration of Iona Abbey to the development of new industries.

0297   NEW MINE, THE
1944

16mm	b/w	comopt	610ft		VIEW

sp. British Council
p.c. GB Instructional
d. Donald Carter

Mining practices used at Comrie Colliery.

0298   THIS IS THE LIFE
1957

16mm	col	silent	780ft		REF

sp. Scottish Industrial Sports Association
p. L. A. Russell

Workers are seen leaving a shipyard and a boy reads the Dalguise Camp 1957 pamphlet; the film goes on to show the same boy enjoying a holiday at Dalguise Camp.

0299   LUDHIANA MADE THE DIFFERENCE
1958*

16mm	col	comopt	990ft		REF

sp. Ludhiana Christian Medical College
p.c. Burt Martin and Associates
d. Charles Davis

Located in Ludhiana (the Punjab), this film highlights the importance of medicine in helping a pregnant woman.

0300   OUR PUBLIC PARKS
1949

| 16mm | b/w | silent | 483ft | VIEW |

sp. Glasgow Corporation Education Committee
p.c. Thames and Clyde

How Glasgow's public parks bring the countryside to industrial Glasgow, providing city workers with fresh air and exercise.

0301   LAND OF INVENTION
1940

| 16mm | b/w | comopt | 376ft | VIEW |

sp. British Council
p.c. British Films
d. Andrew Buchanan

The macadamised road, the first locomotive engine, gas lighting, the steam-hammer, electric telephone and chloroform are among the Scottish inventions shown in this film.

0302   LAND O'CLANS
1938

| 16mm | b/w | comopt | 620ft | VIEW |

filmed by Widgey Newman

The Highlands, its landscape, fishing, sheepfarming and local crafts.

0303   FUTURE OF SCOTLAND
1948

| 16mm | b/w | comopt | 739ft | VIEW |

sp. J. Arthur Rank Organisation
p.c. Sergei Nolbander

A look at Scotland's idustries, education and culture. Tom Johnston, the former Secretary of State, talks about devolution for Scotland.

0304   [AUTOMATIC POTATO HARVESTER]
1963

| 16mm | col | mute | 122ft | REF |

[p.c. Ministry of Agriculture, Fisheries and Food]

Made for the 1963 Royal Highland Show, the film illustrates an automatic potato harvester in operation.

0305   [GASKIN REPORT, THE]
1969

| 16mm | col | comopt | 435ft | VIEW |

sp. Central Office of Information

Professor Gaskin of Aberdeen University outlines his report on NE Scotland and the results of a two year programme of bringing more industry and people into the area.

0306   HAPPY WEEKEND
1951

| 16mm | b/w&col silent | 570ft | VIEW |

[p.c. Norton Park Group]
[filmed by T. Ritchie, Nigel McIsaac, Raymond Townsend]

Story of an experiment in mural painting at Norton Park Junior School, Edinburgh.

0307   NEW DAY
1959

| 35mm | col | comopt | 1820ft | VIEW |

sp. Films of Scotland Committee
p.c. Templar Film Studios

Life in Glenrothes New Town as seen through the eyes of a miner and his family.

0308   [BOWING PRINCIPLES FOR STRING PLAYERS]
1975

| 16mm | b/w | comopt | 546ft | REF |

sp. EFS/Scottish Arts Council
p.c. Pelicula Films
d. Michael Alexander

Joan Dickson, a cellist, demonstrates bowing principles for string players.

0309   [OPENING OF COSMOS YOUTH CENTRE, ST. ANDREWS]
1971

| 16mm | b/w | mute | 99ft | REF |

p.c. Pelicula Films

Princess Anne opens the Cosmos Youth Centre in St. Andrews. 1st July, 1971. [Incomplete.]

0310   [RAF LEUCHARS RECEIVE FREEDOM OF THE CITY OF ST. ANDREWS]
1968

| 16mm | b/w | mute | 80ft | REF |

RAF Leuchars receive the freedom of the City of St. Andrews.

0311   [BOBBY JONES RECEIVES FREEDOM OF ST. ANDREWS]
1958

| 16mm | b/w | comopt | 254ft | REF |

Provost Leonard presents American golfer Bobby Jones Jnr. with the Freedom of St Andrews.

25

0312   SIR PATRICK SPENS
1956*

16mm	b/w	comopt	252ft	VIEW

sp. Educational Films of Scotland
p.c. Campbell Harper Films Ltd.
d. W.J. Maclean

The ballad of Sir Patrick Spens, illustrated with drawings.

0313   RAKES OF GLASGOW
1950*

16mm	b/w	comopt	315ft	VIEW

sp. JPC of SEFA and SFC
p.c. Thames and Clyde
p. Stanley L. Russell

Demonstration of the dance "Rakes of Glasgow" by members of the Scottish Country Dancing Society.

0314   SPORT IN SCOTLAND
1938*

35mm	b/w	comopt	945ft	VIEW

sp. Films of Scotland
p.c. Scottish Film Productions
[d. Stanley L. Russell]

An illustration of various sports particular to Scotland including events at a highland games, angling, yachting, golf, shinty and football. Made for the Empire Exhibition of 1938.

0315   HOW OUR CITY IS GOVERNED
1949

16mm	b/w	silent	420ft	VIEW

sp. Glasgow Corporation Education Committee
p.c. Campbell Harper Films Ltd.
[d. Willie J. McLean]

Local Government election procedure and Glasgow Corporation committees in session.

0316   OUR SCHOOLS
1948

16mm	b/w	silent	350ft	VIEW

sp. Glasgow Corporation Education Committee
p.c. Thames and Clyde

The education provided by the schools and colleges of Glasgow.

0317   OUR HOMES
1949

16mm	b/w	silent	370ft	VIEW

sp. Glasgow Corporation Education Committee
p.c. Thames and Clyde Film Company

The progress of corporation housing in Glasgow from tenement homes to metal-framed buildings and the models for high-rise flats.

0318   RADIO SCOTLAND. PIRATE RADIO SHIP
1974

super 8mm	col	silent	100ft	REF

filmed by Charles Fletcher

Footage of a Pirate Radio Ship and footage of the opening of the motorway at Charing Cross in Glasgow.

0319   UNVEILING CEREMONY OF THE CAMERONIANS "SCOTTISH RIFLES"
1927

35mm	b/w	silent	367ft	VIEW

Unveiling ceremony of the Cameronians "Scottish Rifles" Regimental Memorial by Field Marshall Earl Haig, in the grounds of the Kelvin Hall, Glasgow.

0320   STORY OF HILLINGTON, THE
1947*

16mm	b/w	silent	850ft	REF

sp. Glen-Har Limited
p.c. Jay's Film Service

A look at 'Glen-Har' fashions including the various stages in the making of garments, to an exhibition of the final models. Factory workers are seen enjoying a Christmas party and a visit to Patrick Thomson's store in Edinburgh.

0322   (HILLINGTON INDUSTRIAL ESTATE EXHIBITION)
1946*

16mm	b/w	silent	65ft	REF

filmed by Jack Harris

Some of the exhibitors' stands at the industrial exhibition including those of Cardonald Margarine, Shaw Petrie Limited, Rolls Royce and Scottish Precision Castings Limited .

0323   TWO SISTERS
1937*

16mm	b/w	comopt	195ft	REF

filmed by Stanley L. Russell

The wedding of Christina Maxwell Russell and James Chalmers Macknight at Bridge of Earn. 12th June, 1928.

0324   MONEY TO BURN
1965

16mm	col	comopt	250ft	VIEW

sp. Bank of Scotland
p.c. Grange Film Productions
d. Ian Brock

Old money is rendered useless and is burned at the Bank of Scotland, Edinburgh.

Queue outside the Regal Cinema, Stirling, 1930s.

0325	**(DUMFRIES)**				
1941*					
35mm	b/w	silent	400ft		REF

Scenes of Guid Nychburris Day Festival including a football match at Palmerston Park and a fancy dress parade.

0326	**KOSB - PRESENTATION OF COLOURS**				
1955					
35mm	b/w	silent	160ft		REF

HRH the Duchess of Gloucester presents new colours to the 5th Battalion of the King's Own Scottish Borderers.

0327	**(FOOTBALL MATCH - DUMFRIES)**				
1949*					
16mm	b/w	silent	80ft		VIEW

Queen of the South play football at Palmerston Park in the Borders town of Dumfries.

0328	**CITY SIDELIGHTS NO. 3**				
1956-'58					
35mm	b/w	comopt	1120ft		VIEW

sp. Cosmo Cinema, Glasgow
p.c. Elder Film Productions

One of a series of five magazine films of Glasgow, featuring the Glasgow School of Art with scenes of art students at work.

0329	**(X-RAY UNIT IN DUMFRIES)**				
1957					
35mm	b/w	silent	330ft		VIEW

filmed by the Lyceum Cinema, Dumfries

The mobile x-ray unit at Dumfries in the Borders.

| 0330 | CITY SIDELIGHTS NO. 4 |

1956-'58

| 35mm | b/w | comopt | 1100ft | VIEW |

sp. Cosmo Cinema, Glasgow
p.c. Elder Film Productions

One of a series of five magazine films of Glasgow, includes footage of macaroni and semolina being made in a Glasgow factory, students at the Scottish Hotel School and trams around Trongate.

| 0331 | OUR HEALTH SERVICES |

1949

| 16mm | b/w | silent | 420ft | VIEW |

sp. Glasgow Corporation Education Committee
p.c. Campbell Harper Films Ltd.
[d. Willie J. McLean]

A description of the main requirements for a healthy city through its hospital care and public health.

| 0332 | [ENSIGN EWART] |

1963*

| 16mm | col | silent | 180ft | VIEW |

A military brass band marches from Edinburgh Castle to the Ensign Ewart pub in the Royal Mile where an army officer gives a speech.

| 0333 | DIABOLICAL LIBERTY, A |

1967*

| 16mm | col | comopt | 700ft | REF |

sp. Royal Bank of Scotland
p.c. Park Film Studios
d. Douglas Gray

The material benefits that can be gained if wages are paid through the bank.

| 0334 | RARE TEAR, A |

1969*

| 16mm | col | comopt | 600ft | REF |

sp. Royal Bank of Scotland
p.c. Park Film Studios
d. Douglas Gray

A promotional film for the 'Royal Bank Saving stamps'.

| 0335A | BO'NESS UNITED VERSUS FORTH RANGERS |

1949

| 35mm | b/w | silent | 640ft | REF |

[sp. Hippodrome Cinema]
[filmed by Dickson's Pictures]

Bo'ness United play Forth Rangers for the Evening News Trophy.

| 0335B | SCOTTISH JUNIOR CUP FINAL |

1949

| 35mm | b/w | comopt | 200ft | VIEW |

p.c. Scottish Movietone News

Scottish Junior Cup Final between Shawfield Juniors and Bo'ness United at Hampden Stadium, Glasgow.

| 0336 | BO'NESS CHILDREN'S FAIR FESTIVAL |

1950

| 16mm | b/w | silent | 485ft | VIEW |

[filmed by Louis Dickson for Hippodrome Cinema, Bo'ness]

Bo'ness Children's Fair Festival, including the procession and coronation of the Fair Queen.

| 0337 | BO'NESS CHILDREN'S FAIR FESTIVAL |

1951

| 16mm | b/w | silent | 680ft | VIEW |

[filmed by Louis Dickson for Hippodrome Cinema, Bo'ness]

The procession and coronation of the gala Queen.

| 0338 | BO'NESS CHILDREN'S FAIR FESTIVAL |

1953

| 35mm | b/w | silent | 1455ft | REF |

[filmed by Louis Dickson for Hippodrome Cinema, Bo'ness]

The procession and coronation of the gala Queen. [Incomplete.]

| 0339 | BO'NESS CHILDREN'S FAIR FESTIVAL |

1954

| 35mm | b/w | silent | 1515ft | REF |

[filmed by Louis Dickson for Hippodrome Cinema, Bo'ness]

The procession, fancy dress parade and coronation of the gala Queen.

| 0340 | BO'NESS CHILDREN'S FAIR FESTIVAL |

1955

| 35mm | b/w | silent | 1500ft | REF |

[filmed by Louis Dickson for Caledonian Associated Cinemas]

The procession, coronation of the gala Queen and procession.

| 0341 | BO'NESS CHILDREN'S FAIR FESTIVAL |

1956

| 35mm | b/w | silent | 1390ft | REF |

[filmed by Louis Dickson for Hippodrome Cinema, Bo'ness]

The procession and coronation of the gala Queen.

| 0342 | BO'NESS CHILDREN'S FAIR FESTIVAL |

1958

| 35mm | b/w | silent | 1480ft | REF |

[filmed by Louis Dickson for Caledonian Associated Cinemas]

The procession and coronation of the gala Queen.

0343	BO'NESS CHILDREN'S FAIR FESTIVAL				
1959					
35mm	b/w	silent		1540ft	REF

[filmed by Louis Dickson for Caledonian Associated Cinemas]

The procession, coronation of the gala Queen and fancy dress parade.

0344	BO'NESS CHILDREN'S FAIR FESTIVAL				
1960					
35mm	b/w	silent		1530ft	REF

[filmed by Louis Dickson for Hippodrome Cinema, Bo'ness]

The procession and the coronation of the gala Queen.

0345	BUSMAN'S HOLIDAY				
1959					
35mm	col	comopt		1905ft	VIEW

sp. Films of Scotland
p.c. Anglo Scottish Pictures
d. Jim Goding, Eddie Earp

A coach tour from the Borders to the Scottish Highlands.

0346	(SEA OF GALILEE MISSION HOSPITAL. TIBERIAS)				
1936*					
16mm	b/w	silent		410ft	REF

[filmed by Dr. Herbert Watt Torrance]

The work of the Scottish Mission Hospital in Palestine.

0347	(SEA OF GALILEE MISSION HOSPITAL. TIBERIAS)				
1936					
16mm	b/w	silent		385ft	REF

[filmed by Dr. Herbert Watt Torrance]

The work of the Scottish Mission Hospital in Palestine, as it cares for the sick, young and old. Also footage of Dr. Torrance at home with his family.

0348	WILD FLOWERS OF PALESTINE				
1949*					
16mm	col	silent		255ft	VIEW

filmed by Dr. Herbert Watt Torrance

Films taken by Dr. Herbert Watt Torrance of the Scottish Mission Hospital, Tiberias, and family life during the years 1930-1950. [Commended entry at SAFF 1952.]

0349	JERUSALEM				
1934*					
16mm	b/w	silent		200ft	REF

p.c. Kodak Cinegraph

Scenes of Jerusalem, including the Mosque of Omar, the Wailing Wall, the Well of David, and the Sepulchre of Rachel.

0350	[LAKE GALILEE AND HOLY LAND]				
1953*					
16mm	col	silent		420ft	REF

[filmed by Dr. Herbert Watt Torrance]

Jerusalem, Tiberias Hill and Dr. Harte House, YMCA, at Reniel, Galilee.

0351	[ISRAEL AND JORDAN]				
1962					
16mm	col	silent		665ft	REF

[filmed by Dr. Herbert Watt Torrance]

General views of Israel and Jordan, with shots of farmers ploughing with ox and donkey, street scenes and tourists enjoying the countryside.

0352	FLORAL BEAUTY OF THE HOLY LAND				
1930s					
16mm	col	silent		950ft	REF

[filmed by Dr. Herbert Watt Torrance]

Indigenous flowers and trees of the Holy Land.

0353	SYRIA - INTRODUCING THE DRUZES				
1945*					
16mm	col	silent		375ft	REF

filmed by Dr. Herbert Watt Torrance

Daily life of the Druzes in Syria.

0354	(CONTINENTAL HOLIDAYS)				
1957-'59					
16mm	col	silent		410ft	REF

[filmed by Dr. Herbert Watt Torrance]

Travelogue of holidays in Copenhagen, the Highlands of Scotland, France and Morocco.

0355	[TIBERIAS 1935]				
1935					
16mm	col	silent		240ft	VIEW

[filmed by Dr. Herbert Watt Torrance]

Scenes of Tiberias - fishermen using a dragnet to catch fish, the Mosque of Omar, Damascus Gate, Sea of Galilee and Mount Hermon. [Incomplete.]

0356	(VARIOUS - NO. 1)				
1952*					
16mm	col	silent		230ft	REF

[filmed by Dr. Herbert Watt Torrance]

General views of scenery, lakes and mountains in Israel.

29

0357   [ARAB CUSTOMS]

1935*

| 16mm | b/w | silent | 390ft | | REF |

[filmed by Dr. Herbert Watt Torrance]

Threshing corn, ploughing, fishing and traditional Arab customs of coffee-making and dancing.

0358   (VARIOUS - NO. 2)

1951*

| 16mm | col | silent | 220ft | | REF |

[filmed by Dr. Herbert Watt Torrance]

Various shots of farming and fishing in Israel.

0359   (VARIOUS - NO. 3)

1936*

| 16mm | b/w | silent | 410ft | | REF |

[filmed by Dr. Herbert Watt Torrance]

Arab life showing an Arab encampment, women threshing corn and baking bread, a camel train and a sheep market.

0360   HOMEWARD BOUND 1939

1939

| 16mm | b/w&col | silent | 280ft | | REF |

[filmed by Dr. Herbert Watt Torrance]

Holidaying in Athens, Rome, Pisa and the Italian Riviera.

0361   JULIA AND LYDIA

1934

| 16mm | b/w&col | silent | 543ft | | REF |

[filmed by Dr. Herbert Watt Torrance]

Dr. Torrance of the Scottish Mission Hospital, Tiberias, and his two daughters at home in Palestine and on holiday in Scotland and the USA.

0362   HIGHLAND HOSPITALITY

1939

| 35mm | b/w | comopt | 1995ft | | VIEW |

sp. Allied Hotels
p.c. Scottish Film Productions
[d. Malcolm M. Irvine]

Promotional film for Allied Hotels. We follow a coach tour round the Highlands and Islands of Scotland taking in Oban, Iona, Inverness, Aberdeen and Glencoe.

0363   OVER THE SEA TO SKYE

1961

| 16mm | col | comopt | 640ft | | VIEW |

sp. Films of Scotland
p.c. Anvil Films

The history, legend and landscape of the island of Skye.

0364   PERTHSHIRE PANORAMA

1959

| 16mm | col | comopt | 770ft | | VIEW |

sp. Films of Scotland
p.c. Anglo Scottish Pictures

An introduction to Perthshire highlighting its places of interest, countryside and leisure opportunities.

0365   BLOOD CAN WORK MIRACLES

1961*

| 35mm | col | comopt | 980ft | | REF |

sp. Ministry of Health
p.c. Basic Films
d. Sam Napier Bell

A promotional film to encourage people to become blood donors by emphasising how it saves lives.

0366   STEP AHEAD, A

1966*

| 16mm | col | comopt | 720ft | | REF |

sp. Royal Bank of Scotland
p.c. Park Film Studios
d. Douglas Gray

Made to promote the effectiveness of the Royal Bank of Scotland's computers - branches in Leven, Grantown-on-Spey and at Abbotsinch airport are shown in operation.

0367   BANK AHEAD

1964

| 16mm | col | comopt | 920ft | | REF |

sp. National Commercial Bank of Scotland
p.c. Spectator Films
w.&d. Theo Richmond

Made to mark the merger of the National Commercial Bank of Scotland and the Royal Bank, to form the Royal Bank of Scotland Ltd. [Includes footage of the floating bank in the Orkney Isles.]

0368   (OBAN CELTIC V INVERNESS)

1951*

| 16mm | b/w | silent | 240ft | | REF |

Shinty match between Oban Celtic and Inverness.

0373   THINGS THAT HAPPEN NO. 1

1936

| 16mm | b/w | comopt | 385ft | | VIEW |

p.c. Scottish Film Productions

First in a series of monthly film reviews of Scotland, it reconstructs a bank robbery, looks at the Borzoi dog, shoe manufacture, the making of an evening "coiffure" and the "first sighting" of the Loch Ness Monster!

0374 HAIR
1933

| 16mm | b/w | silent | 384ft | VIEW |

filmed by Meteor Film Producing Society, Glasgow

An amateur film shot in and around Glasgow.

0376A WHERE EVERYBODY GOES
1918

| 35mm | b/w | silent | 22ft | VIEW |

[p.c. Scottish Moving Picture News]

Queue for the Cinema, Coatbridge, showing the film "The Long Trail".

0376B ROUTE MARCH 1ST BATTALION LANARKSHIRE VOLUNTEER REGIMENT
1918

| 35mm | b/w | silent | 70ft | VIEW |

p.c. Scottish Moving Pictures News

1st Battalion Lanarkshire Volunteer Regiment march through Coatbridge.

0376C [LANARKSHIRE REGIMENT]
1918

| 35mm | b/w | silent | 240ft | VIEW |

p.c. Scottish Moving Picture News

Lanarkshire Regiment march through Coatbridge.

0376D OPENING OF DRUMPELLIER MOSS
1919

| 35mm | b/w | silent | 720ft | VIEW |

[p.c. British Moving Picture News]

Opening of Drumpellier Moss Park, gifted to Coatbridge by Mr W. R. Carrick-Buchanan. [Incomplete]

0377 RIVER CLYDE - A SURVEY OF SCOTLAND'S GREATEST RIVER
1939

| 16mm | b/w | comopt | 720ft | VIEW |

sp. Clyde Navigation Trust
p.c. Scottish Film Productions
d. Stanley L. Russell

The River Clyde is traced from its source down to the Firth of Clyde, with a review of its industrial life from Glasgow to Dumbarton.

0379 CITY SIDELIGHTS NO. 1
1956-'58

| 16mm | b/w | comopt | 512ft | VIEW |

p.c. Elder Film Productions

One of a series of five magazine films of Glasgow, including street scenes, contemporary fashion, sweet making, a game of football, and Christmas Eve festivities.

0380 [SHOTS OF EDINBURGH]
1952*

| 16mm | col | silent | 730ft | REF |

Portobello Gala Day; Granton harbour at dusk; Edinburgh Castle; St. Giles' Cathedral; Holyrood Palace; Princes Street Gardens and Bertram Mills circus are all featured in this amateur film of Edinburgh. [Incomplete]

0381 [ROYAL TOUR OF SCOTLAND]
1954*

| 16mm | col | silent | 430ft | REF |

The Queen and Duke of Edinburgh arrive at Turnhouse airport and attend a youth display at Murrayfield and a tree-planting ceremony at Coronation Walk. [Incomplete.]

0382 LAUNCH OF" QUEEN MARY" AT CLYDEBANK
1934

| 16mm | b/w | silent | 95ft | REF |

The "Queen Mary" is launched from John Brown's yard and tugs pull her into berth.

0383 TRUCK TO KEELSON
1956c

| 16mm | b/w | comopt | 290ft | REF |

sp. Gourock Ropework Company Limited
p.c. Templar Film Studios

How ropes are manufactured at Gourock Ropeworks in Port Glasgow for the "Mayflower II".

0384 [ISLE OF BARRA]
1961*

| 16mm | col | silent | 460ft | REF |

[attributed to W. B. Thom]

General views of Barra in the Western Isles and the life of the islanders with shots of a plane landing at Cockleshell Bay, Kisimul's Castle, and the shell processing factory in Sir Compton Mackenzie's former house.

0385 SCOTTISH UNIVERSITIES
1948

| 35mm | b/w | comopt | 2024ft | VIEW |

sp. COI with the Scottish Home Department
p.c. Data Film Unit
d. Francis Gysin

The story of the foundation and growth of the four Scottish universities; St. Andrews, Glasgow, Aberdeen and Edinburgh.

31

0386   MONEY PROGRAMME, THE
1969

16mm	b/w	comopt	820ft	REF

p.c. BBC Television

An excerpt from a BBC documentary on Glasgow's Housing Policy and the controversy surrounding it.

0387   BIG MILL, THE
1963

35mm	col	comopt	2200ft	VIEW

sp. Films of Scotland Committee
p.c. Templar Film Studios
d. Laurence Henson

Filmed mainly at the Ravenscraig and Gartcosh Works of Colvilles Ltd., Lanarkshire, the documentary follows the production of steel sheets and highlights different steel products.

0388   CALLER HERRIN
1947

16mm	b/w	comopt	650ft	VIEW

sp. COI for the Scottish Home Department
p.c. Campbell Harper Films Ltd.
d. Alan Harper

Herring fishing off the north-east coast of Scotland; the film follows the fishing boats from the time they put out to sea to the unloading of the catch at the fish market.

0389   O'ER HILL AND DALE
1932

16mm	b/w	silent	560ft	VIEW

p. Empire Marketing Board Film
d. Basil Wright

Produced by John Grierson, this film shows sheep farming in the Cheviot Hills.

0390   RADAR
1945*

16mm	b/w	comopt	265ft	REF

p.c. Universal News

The basic principles of radar are explained and its importance during World War II.

0391   [HAPPY IN THE MORNING]
1940*

16mm	b/w	comopt	400ft	VIEW

[sp. Ascot Gas Water Heaters Limited]

Advert for Ascot gas water heaters, featuring Henry Hall and his orchestra.

0392   LIFE ON THE FAROE ISLANDS
1948*

16mm	b/w	silent	440ft	REF

sp. Ministry of Education
p.c. Nordisk Film Committee

English version of a Danish film on everyday life on the Faroe Islands with scenes of spinning, sheep shearing and fishing.

0393   OPENING OF SLATEFORD RECREATION GROUND
1924

35mm	b/w	silent	270ft	VIEW

sp. Edinburgh Education Authority

Opening ceremony for Slateford Recreation Ground attended by his Grace the Lord High Commissioner, Mr. Brown.

0394   COOPERAGE
1936

16mm	b/w	silent	390ft	VIEW

[filmed by John Gray]

The craft of cask making at Canonmills Cooperage, Edinburgh.

0395   SCOTTISH SHIPBUILDING
1954c

16mm	col	silent	305ft	VIEW

filmed by SEFA (Dunbartonshire Group)

Shipbuilding in John Brown's yard at Clydebank, from the initial design stages to the final launch.

0396   OUR WATER SUPPLY
1949

16mm	b/w	silent	295ft	VIEW

sp. Glasgow Corporation Education Committee
p.c. Thames and Clyde

The story of Glasgow's water supply from the reservoir at Loch Arklet to the work of the Water Department of Glasgow.

0397   OUR ART GALLERIES
1949

16mm	b/w	silent	400ft	VIEW

sp. Glasgow Corporation Education Committee
p.c. Campbell Harper Films Ltd.
[d. Willie J. McLean]

A tour through various exhibitions in the Kelvingrove Art Gallery and Museum.

0398 RIVER CLYDE, THE
1937*

| 16mm | b/w | silent | 430ft | VIEW |

p.c. Elder Dalrymple Productions

Film follows the River Clyde from its upper reaches down to the Firth.

0399 PROSPEROUS PATH
1959*

| 16mm | col | comopt | 1134ft | VIEW |

sp. Clydesdale and North of Scotland Bank Ltd.
p.c. Glasgow Films
d. Clifford Hanley

A promotional film for the Clydesdale and North of Scotland Bank illustrating how a young couple can utilise banking facilities.

0400 BO'NESS PUBLIC SCHOOL: QUEEN MARY SMITH
1936

| 35mm | b/w | silent | 270ft | VIEW |

[filmed by Louis Dickson for Hippodrome Cinema, Bo'ness]

Bo'ness Children's Fair Festival, with the coronation of "Queen" Mary Smith and accompanying procession through Bo'ness.

0401A BORROWSTOUN SCHOOL: QUEEN JOAN CAMPBELL
1919

| 35mm | b/w | silent | 170ft | VIEW |

[filmed by Louis Dickson for Hippodrome Cinema, Bo'ness]

Bo'ness Children's Fair Festival. The Fair Queen meets children in fancy dress.

0401B KINNEIL SCHOOL: QUEEN ELIZABETH SNEDDON
1920

| 35mm | b/w | silent | 150ft | VIEW |

[filmed by Louis Dickson for Hippodrome Cinema, Bo'ness]

Bo'ness Children's Fair Festival. The Fair Festival Queen greets children in fancy dress parade.

0402A GRANGE SCHOOL: QUEEN ANNE CURRIE
1922

| 35mm | b/w | silent | 180ft | VIEW |

[filmed by Louis Dickson for Hippodrome Cinema, Bo'ness]

Bo'ness Children's Fair Festival Queen, Anne Currie, and her retinue arrive for the coronation ceremony.

0402B BO'NESS PUBLIC SCHOOL: QUEEN ANNE PETRIE
1923

| 35mm | b/w | silent | 60ft | REF |

[filmed by Louis Dickson for Hippodrome Cinema, Bo'ness]

The Bo'ness Festival Queen arrives for her coronation ceremony, watched by crowds.

0402C ST. MARY'S RC SCHOOL: QUEEN HELEN SHAW
1924

| 16mm | b/w | silent | 90ft | REF |

[filmed by Louis Dickson for Hippodrome Cinema, Bo'ness]

The Bo'ness Festival Queen, Helen Shaw arrives for the coronation ceremony and the fancy dress parade.

0403 KINNEIL SCHOOL: QUEEN JOAN PATERSON
1939

| 35mm | b/w | silent | 140ft | VIEW |

[filmed by Louis Dickson for Hippodrome Cinema, Bo'ness]

Bo'ness Children's Fair Festival. Coronation of Queen Joan Paterson and the fancy dress parade.

0404A BO'NESS PUBLIC SCHOOL: QUEEN KATHLEEN JAMIESON
1930

| 16mm | b/w | silent | 95ft | REF |

[filmed by Louis Dickson Hippodrome Cinema, Bo'ness]

Bo'ness Children's Fair Festival with the crowning of the Festival Queen and a fancy dress procession.

0404B ST. MARY'S RC SCHOOL: QUEEN MARY MARKIE
1931

| 16mm | b/w | silent | 85ft | REF |

[filmed by Louis Dickson Hippodrome Cinema, Bo'ness]

The coronation ceremony of Queen Mary Markie and the fancy dress parade at Bo'ness Children's Fair.

0404C BO'NESS ACADEMY 1932: QUEEN HELEN BURNETT
1932

| 35mm | b/w | silent | 200ft | VIEW |

[filmed by Louis Dickson Hippodrome Cinema, Bo'ness]

Bo'ness Children's Fair Festival, coronation of Queen Helen Burnett and fancy dress parade.

33

Queue for the Mickey Mouse Club, Scotland's first, at the New Tivoli, Edinburgh 1936.

34

0404D	BORROWSTOUN SCHOOL 1933: QUEEN MARGARET MCMAHON

1933

16mm	b/w	silent	85ft	REF

[filmed by Louis Dickson for Hippodrome Cinema, Bo'ness]

Bo'ness Children's Fair Festival. Gala queen arrives for her coronation followed by the fancy dress parade.

0404E	KINNEIL PUBLIC SCHOOL: QUEEN HELEN YOUNG

1934

35mm	b/w	silent	140ft	VIEW

[filmed by Louis Dickson for Hippodrome Cinema, Bo'ness]

Bo'ness Children's Fair Festival. Coronation of Queen Helen Young and fancy dress parade.

0405	BORROWSTOUN SCHOOL 1927: QUEEN RUBY HYSLOP

1927

16mm	b/w	silent	56ft	REF

[filmed by Louis Dickson for Hippodrome Cinema, Bo'ness]

Bo'ness Children's Fair Festival. Coronation of Queen Ruby Hyslop and the fancy dress parade.

0406	BO'NESS ACADEMY 1925: QUEEN CATHERINE SNEDDON

1925

16mm	b/w	silent	92ft	REF

[filmed by Louis Dickson for Hippodrome Cinema, Bo'ness]

Bo'ness Children's Fair Festival. Coronation of Cathie Sneddon, the Fair Queen. Also includes footage of the fancy dress parade.

0407A	KINNEIL SCHOOL 1928: QUEEN ELIZABETH KAY

1928

16mm	b/w	silent	70ft	REF

[filmed by Louis Dickson for Hippodrome Cinema, Bo'ness]

Bo'ness Children's Fair Festival with the coronation of the Festival Queen and fancy dress parade.

0407B	GRANGE SCHOOL 1929: QUEEN MARION KILPATRICK

1929

16mm	b/w	silent	80ft	REF

[filmed by Louis Dickson for Hippodrome Cinema, Bo'ness]

Bo'ness Children's Fair Festival. Coronation of Queen Marion Kilpatrick and fancy dress parade.

0408	ST. MARY'S SCHOOL 1937: QUEEN ANNE				
1937					
16mm	b/w	silent	175ft		REF

[filmed by Louis Dickson for Hippodrome Cinema, Bo'ness]

Bo'ness Children's Fair Festival. Coronation of Queen Anne and fancy dress parade.

0409	JUBILEE YEAR 1947: QUEEN MARY SNEDDON				
1947					
35mm	b/w	silent	305ft		VIEW

[filmed by Louis Dickson for Hippodrome Cinema, Bo'ness]

Bo'ness Children's Fair Festival. Coronation of Queen Mary Sneddon followed by the fancy dress parade.

0410	QUEEN JEANETTE MCGUIRE. ST. MARY'S SCHOOL 1948				
1948					
16mm	b/w	silent	78ft		REF

[filmed by Louis Dickson for Hippodrome Cinema, Bo'ness]

Bo'ness Children's Fair Festival. Coronation of Queen Jeanette McGuire before the procession through Bo'ness.

0411	BO'NESS CHILDREN'S FESTIVAL				
1949					
16mm	b/w	silent	396ft		REF

[filmed by Louis Dickson for Hippodrome Cinema, Bo'ness]

Bo'ness Children's Fair Festival. Coronation of Queen Margaret, with pageantry and floats.

0412A	[BO'NESS FAIR]				
1946					
35mm	b/w	silent	280ft		REF

[filmed by Louis Dickson for Hippodrome Cinema, Bo'ness]

Bo'ness Children's Fair Festival and coronation ceremony of the fair queen.

0412B	[BO'NESS FAIR]				
1913c					
35mm	b/w	silent	20ft		REF

[filmed by Louis Dickson for Hippodrome Cinema, Bo'ness]

Bo'ness Children's Fair Festival with dancers at the maypole .

0412C	GRANGE PUBLIC SCHOOL: QUEEN ANDREA WALKER				
1935					
35mm	b/w	silent	210ft		REF

[filmed by Louis Dickson for Hippodrome Cinema, Bo'ness]

Coronation of Bo'ness Children's Fair Festival Queen Andrea Walker and fancy dress parade.

0413	BO'NESS FAIR FESTIVAL 1952				
1952					
35mm	b/w	silent	820ft		REF

[filmed by Louis Dickson for Hippodrome Cinema, Bo'ness]

Coronation of gala Queen at Bo'ness Children's Fair Festival, with footage of the fancy dress parade.

0414	[BO'NESS FAIR c1911-1913]				
1911-'13c					
35mm	b/w	silent	185ft		REF

[filmed by Louis Dickson for Hippodrome Cinema, Bo'ness]

Scenes of Bo'ness Children's Fair Festivals between 1911 and 1913. Coronation of Fair Queen. Maypole dancing.

0415	HONEYMOON CRUISE NO. 1				
1936/'38					
35mm	b/w	silent	1005ft		VIEW

sp. David MacBrayne Limited
p.c. Elder Film Productions
d. J.C. Elder

Issued with "Honeymoon Cruise No 2" and "Road Through the Sunset Isles" as a musical travelogue by the Associated British Picture Corporation entitled "Bonnie Scotland Calls You" (1938), it features a cruise from Oban to Staffa, Iona and Mull. [See also refs. 0196 and 0260.]

35

0416	LEARNING FOR LIVING				
1956*					
35mm	b/w	comopt	3590ft		VIEW

sp. Scottish Education Department
p.c. Campbell Harper Films Ltd.
d. W. J. Maclean

A survey of educational facilities at a junior secondary school in Scotland.

0417	MEN AND WOMEN OF TOMORROW				
1925*					
35mm	b/w	silent	3670ft		VIEW

sp. Edinburgh Education Authority

Made for screening at the 1925 World Educational Congress Edinburgh, the film gives a survey of the educational opportunities offered in Edinburgh from infants up to senior pupils.

0418	ST. KILDA - BRITAIN'S LONELIEST ISLE				
1923					
35mm	b/w	silent	1080ft		VIEW

sp. John McCallum and Company
p.c. Topical Productions, Glasgow
d. Paul Robello and Bobbie Mann

A voyage from Glasgow to St Kilda, containing scenes of the Western Isles and island life of the crofters on St. Kilda.

0419   SAILING 1000 MILES UP THE AMAZON

1936c

16mm	b/w	silent	420ft		REF

sp. Glasgow Education Authority
[p.c. Elder-Dalrymple Film Productions]

A study of Northern Brazil and the course of the Amazon river.

0420   KEEPING OUR CITY CLEAN

1949

16mm	b/w	silent	415ft		VIEW

sp. Glasgow Corporation Education Committee
p.c. Campbell Harper Films Ltd.
[d. Willie J. McLean]

The work of the Cleansing Department in Glasgow.

0421   GLASGOW SUBWAY

1974

16mm	col	silent	1980ft		VIEW

p.c. A-V Service, Glasgow and Strathclyde University
d. John Macpherson

A look at the Glasgow Subway prior to its closure for re-development.

0422   [BENNIE RAIL PLANE]

1931c

16mm	b/w	silent	50ft		VIEW

[filmed by James Anderson]

An illustration of the 4-bladed propellor model of the Bennie Rail Plane in motion on the test stretch at Milngavie, Glasgow. [For the earlier 2-bladed design see ref. 1341.]

0423   STORY OF A SHABBY SUIT, THE

1931

16mm	b/w	silent	350ft		REF

sp. Castlebank Dye Works, Glasgow
d. Ronald L. Jay

How a suit can be revitalised by using the Franco Barbe method of laundering in Glasgow's Castlebank Laundry.

0424   [NEW FRANCO BARBE HAT SHAPES]

1931

16mm	b/w	silent	385ft		VIEW

[sp. Castlebank Dye Works, Glasgow]
[d. Ronald L. Jay]

How to remove stains and clean hats by the Franco Barbe method. [Filmed in Glasgow's Castlebank Laundry.]

0425   HOW SCWS CIGARETTES AND TOBACCO ARE MADE

1938

16mm	b/w	comopt	340ft		VIEW

sp. SCWS
p.c. Jay's Film Service

The manufacture of SCWS cigarettes and tobacco at the Co-op's Shieldhall factory, Glasgow.

0426   [YEAR OF DESTINY]

1936

16mm	b/w	mute	312ft		REF

p.c. British Movietone News

Compilation of events of 1937, including the funeral procession of George V, rumours of war and footage of Mussolini, Hitler and troops.

0427   MARCH OF PROGRESS, THE

1938*

16mm	b/w	comopt	390ft		REF

[sp. SCWS]
p.c. Jay's Film Service

The story of Shieldhall furniture; the production methods at the Co-op's Glasgow factory.

0428   LAND O' BURNS BAKERIES

1931

16mm	b/w	silent	714ft		REF

[sp. James Gilchrist and Sons Limited]
p.c. Jay's Screen Service

The production and distribution of Gilchrist's bread and cakes.

0429   LAND O'BURNS BAKERIES - INTRODUCTION

1931

16mm	b/w	silent	90ft		REF

[sp. James Gilchrist and Sons Limited]
[p.c. Jay's Screen Service]

Footage of the Land o' Burns Bakeries and the Tea Rooms at Boswell Park, Ayr. [Originally intended as an introduction to "Land o' Burns Bakeries" ref. 428]

0430   CASTLEBANK FOR COLLARS

1932*

16mm	b/w	silent	185ft		VIEW

[sp. Castlebank Dye Works, Glasgow]
p.c. Jay's Film Service

Commercial for Castlebank Dyeworks showing the laundering of collars.

36

0431   CRUISE TO ST. KILDA AND THE WESTERN ISLES

1925

| 16mm | b/w | silent | 750ft | VIEW |

p.c. Jay's Screen Service

Record of a voyage from Glasgow to St. Kilda by way of the Western Isles.

0432   MOTION PICTURES THE "KODAK" WAY

1928c

| 16mm | b/w | silent | 250ft | REF |

[Kodak Demonstration Film]

A demonstration of how to make motion pictures the "Kodak" way.

0433   SOLDIER COMES HOME, A

1945*

| 16mm | b/w | comopt | 445ft | REF |

sp. Ministry of Information
p.c. A Gryphon Production for the Film Producer's Guild
d. John Eldridge

Dramatised account of a soldier on leave from Burma who witnesses the horror of bomb damage in London.

0434   (IS WASHDAY WORTHWHILE)

1930c

| 35mm | b/w | silent | 720ft | VIEW |

sp. Castlebank Laundry, Glasgow
p.c. Jay's Film Service
d. Ronald L. Jay

An advert for Castlebank Laundry offering not only a cheap service but a 'job well done' with the popular 'Cost-U-Less' service.

0435   MESSAGE OF THE DRUM, THE

1955c

| 16mm | b/w | comopt | 200ft | REF |

sp. Cadbury's of Bourneville
p.c. Publicity Films
d. Walter R. Creighton

How Cocoa is produced in West African plantations for Cadbury's.

0436   (DOUGLAS FRASER JUTE MACHINERY)

1932*

| 16mm | b/w | silent | 400ft | REF |

sp. Douglas Fraser and Sons Limited
p.c. Jay's Screen Service

How the Fraser "Silver Roll Former" improves the production of jute. Installation in the Hillbank jute works, Dundee.

0437   SEEING IS BELIEVING

1931*

| 16mm | b/w | silent | 115ft | VIEW |

[sp. George Guthrie and Son, Butchers, Glasgow]
d. Ronald L. Jay

An advertising film showing how Guthrie's sausages are made.

0438   BRUNTON'S WIRE AND ROPE WORKS, MUSSELBURGH

1930*

| 35mm | b/w | silent | 3060ft | VIEW |

sp. Brunton's (Musselburgh) Limited
p.c. Jay's Screen Service

The processes involved in the manufacturing of wire rope at Brunton's Wire and Rope Works, Musselburgh.

0439   SCOTLAND'S BRIGHTEST INDUSTRY

1932*

| 16mm | b/w | silent | 170ft | REF |

[sp. Aurora Lamps Limited]
p.c. Jay's Screen Service

The manufacture of Clyde-built Aurora Lamps at Old Kilpatrick.

0440   PIGS IN CLOVER

1931*

| 16mm | b/w | silent | 105ft | VIEW |

[sp. George Guthrie and Son, Butchers, Glasgow]
[d. Ronald L. Jay]

Commercial for Guthrie's pork, shows how pigs are well cared for before reaching the butcher's knife.

0441   KING, GOD BLESS HIM, THE

1935

| 16mm | b/w | silent | 465ft | REF |

p.c. Movietone News

Commemorative film for Royal Jubilee which details episodes from George V's life, including footage of his coronation, his illness in 1928 and the wedding of Prince George and Princess Marina.

0442   BRIEF BEEF BIOGRAPHY, A

1931

| 16mm | b/w | silent | 150ft | VIEW |

[sp. George Guthrie and Son, Butchers, Glasgow]
[p.c. Jay's Screen Service]

An advertising film promoting the quality of George Guthrie's beef cattle.

0443 OVER THE HILLS AND FAR AWAY

1931				
16mm	b/w	silent	150ft	VIEW

[sp. George Guthrie and Son, Butchers, Glasgow]
p.c. Jay's Screen Service

An advert for Guthrie's mutton showing that only the best sheep are selected.

0444 RIVALLING THE RAINBOW

1929				
16mm	col	silent	275ft	REF

filmed by Jay's Screen Service

The Battle of Flowers on Jersey. [Filmed on Kodacolour film stock.]

0445 JERSEY WATER LILIES

1928				
16mm	col	silent	415ft	REF

filmed by Ronald L. Jay

Swimming and diving displays on the island of Jersey. [Filmed on Kodacolour film stock.]

0446 DIVERS WAYS

1929				
16mm	col	silent	216ft	REF

filmed by Ronald L. Jay

Pete Desjardins gives a diving display at the Havre-despas pool , Jersey. [Filmed on Kodacolour film stock.]

0448 (SCENES AT BALMORAL)

1896				
35mm	b/w	silent	67ft	VIEW

filmed by Mr. Downie

Scenes of Queen Victoria at Balmoral with guests and attendants including the Tzar and Tzarina of Russia, Princesses Beatrice and Ena and the Duke of Connaught.

0449 GORDON HIGHLANDERS LEAVE FOR THE BOER WAR

1899				
35mm	b/w	silent	60ft	VIEW

[attributed to Paul Robello and William Walker]

Kilted pipe band leads a contingent of the Gordon Highlanders in Aberdeen's Union Terrace before they embark for the Boer War.

0450 AROUND WICK HARBOUR

1936				
16mm	col	silent	240ft	VIEW

[filmed by Alec Johnston of the Wick Society]

The fishing fleet in Wick Harbour. Steam vessels leaving and returning with a catch of herring to be gutted and packed.

0451 THOUSAND HAPPY DAYS, A

1935c				
35mm	b/w	comopt	585ft	REF

sp. Fereneze Laundry Company Limited, Barrhead
p.c. British Propaganda Films

On the doctor's advice mother is told to give up 'washday' and to take her washing to the laundry to make life easier.

0452 [YARMOUTH FISH QUAY]

1902				
16mm	b/w	silent	64ft	VIEW

The herring fleet at Yarmouth fish quay. Fishergirls (possibly Scots) gut and pack herring.

0453 SCOTS FISHER GIRLS AT YARMOUTH

1930				
16mm	b/w	silent	75ft	REF

The herring fleet in harbour. Scots fishergirls gut herring at Yarmouth.

0454A QUEENSHILL CUP AT CASTLE DOUGLAS, THE

1952*				
35mm	b/w	mute	275ft	REF

filmed by Templar Film Studios

Shots of an open air curling match on a frozen loch in Dumfriesshire.

0454B (DUMFRIES - GUID NYCHBURRIS DAY)

1951*				
35mm	b/w	mute	135ft	REF

filmed as a local topical for the Lyceum Cinema, Dumfries

Coverage of the Guid Nychburris Day celebrations in Dumfries.

0455 SERVICE NOT SELF

1946				
35mm	b/w	comopt	900ft	REF

p.c. Thames and Clyde Film Company
p. Stanley L. Russell

Ceremonies to mark the 25th anniversary of the British Legion (Scotland) attended by the Royal Family, in Edinburgh.

0456 FIGHTING FIELDS

1941				
35mm	b/w	comopt	1048ft	VIEW

sp. MOI & Scottish Dept. of Agriculture
p.c. Scottish Film Productions & GB Instructional
d. Stanley L. Russell

A promotional film on how to fully utilise land during the war; ploughing and harvesting, laying of pipes, and the Women's Land Army at work.

0457	CAMPBELL TURNBULL WEDDING

1949

16mm	b/w	comopt	485ft		REF

p.c. Thames and Clyde Film Production

Coverage of the wedding of Elizabeth Turnbull to Thomas Campbell.

0458	TAM O'SHANTER

1958

35mm	b/w	comopt	1190ft		VIEW

sp. JPC of the SEFA and SFC
p.c. Campbell Harper Films Ltd.

Adapted from the BBC TV production, Robert Burns' poem, "Tam O' Shanter", is recited by Harold Wightman and illustrated with drawings by Edward and Elizabeth Odling.

0459	EDINBURGH FESTIVAL, THE

1965

35mm	col	comopt	2520ft		REF

sp. Films of Scotland
p.c. Campbell Harper Films, Edinburgh

Documentary on the Edinburgh Festival including excerpts from plays, opera, ballet and the military tattoo.

0460	SONG OF THE CLYDE

1941

16mm	b/w	comopt	396ft		VIEW

[sp. British Council]
p.c. Merton Park Productions
d. Jimmy Rogers

A look at the industries on the river Clyde and the streets, traffic and theatres of Glasgow.

0462	NEWS SPOTLIGHT

1944*

16mm	b/w	commag	270ft		REF

p.c. Pathe Gazette

News compilation including footage of the Allied War Crimes Commission, the trial of Vigmund Quisling, Japanese suicide bombers attacking the US Navy and Dutch children receiving food at the British Aid Post.

0463	GATEWAY OF THE EAST,THE

1937

16mm	b/w	silent	270ft		VIEW

p.c. GB Instructional
d. J. C. Elder

Ships on the river Forth and cargo vessels unloading at the docks of Leith.

0464	[BIRTH OF A SHIP]

1951

16mm	b/w	silent	720ft		VIEW

Construction and launch of the "Tofua" at Denny's Yard, Dumbarton.

0465	ENGLAND BEAT SCOTLAND - BUT ONLY JUST

1955c

16mm	b/w	comopt	90ft		REF

p.c. Pathe Gazette

Record of football match between England and Scotland at Hampden Park, Glasgow. [England wins one goal to nil.]

0466	(KING VIDOR AT EDINBURGH FILM FESTIVAL)

1965

16mm	b/w	silent	40ft		REF

[p.c. BBC Television]

King Vidor at luncheon after receiving the Golden Thistle Award at the Edinburgh Film Festival.

0467	PORT OF LEITH

1944c

16mm	b/w	silent	470ft		VIEW

[sp. SEFA]

Cargo being loaded and unloaded at Leith docks including coal, timber, fruit and vegetables.

0468	KING OF GOLF

1951*

16mm	b/w	comopt	360ft		REF

sp. Dunlop Limited
p.c. Faro Films
d. Douglas Rankin

Bobby Locke winning the 1949 and 1950 British Open Golf Championships. Locke demonstrates various golf shots, [based on Bobby Locke's Saturday lessons in the Daily Mail.]

0469	(OPENING OF INDUSTRIAL POWER EXHIBITION)

1951*

16mm	b/w&col	silent	160ft		REF

Princess Elizabeth opens the Industrial Power Exhibition at the Kelvin Hall, Glasgow. [One of the events staged during the Festival of Britain 1951.]

0470 SCOTTISH INDUSTRIES EXHIBITION. GLASGOW
1954

16mm	b/w&col	silent	540ft	REF

Coverage of the Scottish Industries Exhibition, opened by HM the Queen Mother in the Kelvin Hall, Glasgow.

0471 RIGHT CHOICE, THE
1949

16mm	b/w	comopt	715ft	VIEW

[sp. North British Locomotive Company Limited]
p.c. Edward Cook Production
d. John S. Abott, Jnr.

A promotional film for apprentice engineers showing the training offered by the North British Locomotive Co. in Springburn and the sport and leisure facilities available with the apprentices' club.

0472 SPIRIT OF THE GAMES, THE
1958

16mm	b/w	comopt	1520ft	REF

p.c. Special Features Division of the Rank Organisation
Coverage of the Commonwealth Games at Cardiff with footage of the opening ceremony.

0473 SERMON IN STONE, A
1966

16mm	b/w&col	comopt	1200ft	VIEW

The story of the work on restoring Iona Abbey and the origins of the Iona Community in Glasgow in the l930's.

0474 GATEWAY OF THE WEST, THE
1937

16mm	b/w	silent	360ft	VIEW

p.c. GB Instructional
d. John C. Elder

Loading and unloading of goods at the docks in Glasgow; oil tanks on the lower reaches of the Clyde and the liner "City of Dieppe" being towed down river.

0476 CINE CAMERA IN INDUSTRY, THE

16mm	b/w	mute	245ft	REF

p.c. Industrial Panel of the SFC
How the cine camera is used in industry, for example in advertising, and in time and motion studies.

0477 PLAY CENTRES
1949c

16mm	b/w	silent	200ft	VIEW

sp. Glasgow Corporation Education Committee Youth Service
Recreational pursuits enjoyed by children at youth centres and summer camps for secondary school children.

0478 YOUTH CENTRES
1949c

16mm	b/w	silent	430ft	VIEW

sp. Glasgow Corporation Education Committee
filmed by SEFA (Glasgow Group)
The various activities on offer in Glasgow youth centres such as woodwork, sewing, acting and gymnastics.

0479 PLAYS FOR THE PEOPLE
1946c

35mm	b/w	comopt	2175ft	VIEW

p.c. Thames and Clyde
p. Stanley L. Russell
The Citizens Theatre, Glasgow. A young actor is shown around behind the scenes after a successful audition.

0480 DUNDEE
1959*

16mm	col	silent	390ft	VIEW

sp. Educational Films of Scotland
filmed by SEFA (Dundee Branch)
The Industry and life in Dundee with footage of the city; jam making, jute mills at work, tenements and new housing.

0481 DOWN TO THE SEA
1948

16mm	b/w	comopt	792ft	REF

sp. COI for the Board of Trade
p.c. Greenpark Productions
d. Humphrey Swingler

The designing and building, in British yards, of ocean-going merchant ships and liners with footage of ships and liners at anchor in the harbour of Rio de Janeiro.

0482 BORDER WEAVE
1941

16mm	b/w	comopt	540ft	VIEW

sp. COI
p.c. Turner Film Productions
d. John Lewis Curthoys

How tweed is produced in the Scottish Borders showing the different stages involved, from the dying of the wool, spinning and weaving, to the finished product.

0483 GOOD NEIGHBOURS
1946

16mm	b/w	comopt	578ft	VIEW

sp. COI for the Scottish Office
p.c. Greenpark Productions
d. Humphrey Swingler

How members of a local community co-operated to establish a Community Centre for all sorts of recreational activities.

40

0484	OESOPHAGEAL SPEECH				
1950					
16mm	b/w	comopt	396ft		VIEW

sp. COI for the Department of Health for Scotland
p.c. Campbell Harper Films Ltd.

A description of the method of providing a laryngectomised person with a substitute for normal speech.

0486	GLEN IS OURS, THE				
1946*					
16mm	b/w	comopt	1144ft		VIEW

sp. COI
p.c. Verity Films Limited

A drama documentary of how the election of a recently de-mobbed soldier onto the council prevents a glen from being sold.

0487	AN EYE TO THE FUTURE				
1978*					
16mm	col	comopt	795ft		REF

sp. Faculty of Engineering of the University of Glasgow
The contribution of engineering to technology.

0490	FARM IS RECLAIMED, A				
1945					
16mm	b/w	comopt	558ft		VIEW

sp. MOI for the Dept. of Agriculture
p.c. Campbell Harper Films Ltd.
d. Alan Harper

How, with government help and his own good farming sense, a Scottish farmer puts a derelict farm into good heart in one year.

0491	(WILL FYFFE)				
1929					
16mm	b/w	comopt	188ft		VIEW

p.c. Pathe

Produced by Pathe as an early sound test film, it features Will Fyffe delivering a comic monologue and singing "Twelve and a Tanner a Bottle".

0492	STAN AND OLLIE				
1932					
16mm	b/w	silent	235ft		VIEW

[sp. Edinburgh Playhouse]
filmed by Alan J. Harper for the Playhouse Cinema, Edinburgh

Stan Laurel and Oliver Hardy sightseeing in Edinburgh where they visit the castle and make an appearance on stage at the Playhouse Cinema.

0493	QUEEN OF THE BORDER				
1948					
16mm	col	mute	330ft		VIEW

sp. COI for the Board of Trade
p.c. Crown Film Unit
d. Martin Wilson

Scenes at the annual Hawick Festival and footage of Hawick hosiery workers knitting sweaters, and washing, drying and ironing the finished products.

0494	COUNTRY POLICEMAN				
1946					
16mm	b/w	comopt	626ft		VIEW

sp. COI for the Scottish Home Department
p.c. Merlin Films
d. Gilbert Gunn

The work of a country policeman, from trying to catch poachers to checking the safety of an explosives store at a quarry.

0495	SEEDS OF PROSPERITY				
1946					
16mm	b/w	comopt	672ft		VIEW

sp. MOI for the Dept of Agriculture
p.c. Campbell Harper Films Ltd.
d. Alan Harper

A survey of the condition of potato crops and measures taken to combat their disease.

0496	SCOTTISH COALMINING				
1956*					
16mm	col	silent	310ft		VIEW

sp. JPC
filmed by SEFA (Dunbartonshire Branch)
The work of a Scottish coalminer.

0497	DUMFRIES - A MARKET TOWN				
1959*					
16mm	col	silent	330ft		VIEW

filmed by SEFA (Dumfriesshire Production Group)

Flooding in Dumfries, sheep farms, timber yards, ploughing, harvesting and market day in the town.

0498	MAKING CHOCOLATES				
1956*					
16mm	col	silent	390ft		VIEW

filmed by SEFA (Glasgow Group)

How "Milady Chocolates" are made at Birrell's factory, Glasgow.

Aberdeen 1906. Ref.0042

42

0499	SCOTTISH COASTS				
1936					
16mm	*b/w*	*silent*	*380ft*		*VIEW*

p.c. GB Instructional Ltd.
d. J.C. Elder

Life along Scotland's coastlines, visiting the Solway Firth, Aberdeen Harbour, the river Clyde and Kyles of Bute.

0500	HEAVY INDUSTRIES				
1936					
16mm	*b/w*	*silent*	*230ft*		*VIEW*

p.c. GB Instructional Ltd.
d. J.C. Elder

Steelmaking and shipbuilding on the Clyde, Glasgow.

0501	ROUTES AND CENTRES				
1936					
16mm	*b/w*	*silent*	*390ft*		*VIEW*

p.c. GB Instructional Ltd.
d. J.C. Elder

A tour of the principal centres in Scotland for road and rail networks - Stirling, Perth, Dundee, Aberdeen and Inverness.

0502	RAW MATERIALS				
1937					
16mm	*b/w*	*silent*	*300ft*		*VIEW*

p.c. GB Instructional Ltd.
d. J.C. Elder

A look at coal mining and iron works in Scotland, as suppliers to power stations and Clydeside factories.

0503	BILLINGSGATE-THIS ART IS FISHY				
1950c					
16mm	*b/w*	*comopt*	*40ft*		*REF*

Scenes at Billingsgate fish market.

0504 TAY VALLEY
1956*

16mm	col	silent	450ft		VIEW

sp. Educational Films of Scotland
filmed by SEFA (Dundee Branch)

The towns, landscape, farming and industries of the Tay valley.

0505 COUNTY OF DUNBARTON
1947*

16mm	b/w	mute	435ft		VIEW

filmed by SEFA (Dunbartonshire Branch)

A survey of the principal industries in the county of Dunbarton, including shipbuilding on Clydebank, the production of sewing machines at Singer, the construction of pre-fabricated housing in Dumbarton and calico printing in the Vale of Leven.

0506 ABERDEEN AND ITS INDUSTRIES
1961

16mm	col	mute	400ft		VIEW

p.c. Educational Films of Scotland
d. Ralph G. Guiliani, John M. Wright

A survey of Aberdeen's industries, including shipbuilding, granite quarrying, fishing, papermaking, textiles and light engineering.

0507 NORTH OF THE GREAT GLEN
1956

16mm	col	mute	385ft		VIEW

p.c. Educational Films of Scotland
d. Wallace Hall

Crofting in the north of Scotland; the scenery of the Isle of Skye; forestry work and hydro-electric power provided from the lochs and rivers in the Highlands.

0508 SCOTTISH TRADE MISSION TO CANADA
1932

9.5mm	b/w	silent	200ft		REF

[filmed by D.G. Russell]

The Scottish Trade Mission sail on the "Letitia" to Canada, to meet a delegation from the Quebec Board of Trade. They visit Quebec and Montreal.

0509 FICKLE FORTUNE
1930

9.5mm	b/w	mute	325ft		REF

filmed by the Bearsden Film Club

Dramatised film of the life of Rob Roy MacGregor, set in the Trossachs.

0510 BEAUTIFUL DRIMA
1975*

16mm	col	comopt	450ft		VIEW

sp. Coats The Thread Makers
p.c. Rayant Pictures
p. John Durst

The manufacture of "Drima" thread.

0511 SCHOONER "CAPTAIN SCOTT"
1972c

16mm	col	comopt	830ft		VIEW

sp. "Captain Scott" Schooner Committee
p.c. Industrial Communication Limited

The schooner "Captain Scott" offers boys an opportunity to learn seamanship.

0512 STIRLING: GATEWAY TO THE HIGHLANDS
1938c

16mm	b/w	silent	740ft		VIEW

sp. Stirling Town Council
d. James S. Nairn

Historical Stirling and its environs, including Stirling Bridge and Castle, Bannockburn, Beaton's Mill and the Trossachs.

0513 [PADDLE STEAMER IN FIRTH OF FORTH]
1939*

16mm	b/w	silent	45ft		REF

[filmed by Mr. Fleming]

The paddle steamer "Fair Maid" crosses the Firth of Forth.

0514 PRINCE WITH HIS FUSILIERS, THE
1919

35mm	b/w	silent	330ft		VIEW

p.c. Pathe Gazette

HRH the Prince of Wales visits the 1st Royal Scots Fusiliers of which he is Colonel-in-Chief. He inspects the troops and presents medals.

0515A CRICKET MATCH. CARLTON CLUB GROUND
1922

35mm	b/w	silent	60ft		VIEW

A cricket match at the Carlton Club ground, Stockbridge, Edinburgh.

43

0515B   INTERNATIONAL PAGEANT

1922

35mm	b/w	silent	80ft	VIEW

Rotary club pageant and procession along Princes Street, Edinburgh.

0515C   TRIP DOWN THE CLYDE, A

1922

35mm	b/w	silent	40ft	VIEW

Harry Lauder entertains passengers on the deck of a Clyde steamer.

0516   (UNIVERSITY NEWS)

1919-'30

35mm	b/w	silent	680ft	VIEW

p.c. Russell Productions, Pathe Gazette, British Moving Pictures

Compilation of local topical and news stories of Glasgow University life, including a rugby match against Edinburgh University, the rectorial elections, and student charity day.

0517A   BIGGAR AND DISTRICT JUNIOR IMPERIALIST UNION FETE

1928

35mm	b/w	silent	724ft	VIEW

[filmed as a local topical for Daybell's Cinema, Biggar]

Scenes at a local fete attended by prospective and sitting Unionist MPs. A baby contest, rifle shooting and fortune telling are amongst the amusements on offer.

0517B   FOURTH ROUND SCOTTISH CUP. EXCLUSIVE PICTURES...

1928

35mm	b/w	silent	225ft	VIEW

[filmed as a local topical for Daybell's Cinema, Biggar]

Greenock Morton FC versus Third Lanark FC at CappieLow Park, Greenock.

0518   DOLLAN AND THE DOOS

1935*

35mm	b/w	silent	135ft	VIEW

Treasurer Dollan finds relaxation from his civic duties by feeding the pigeons every morning in Queen's Park, Glasgow.

0519   (BAND CONCERT. KELVINGROVE PARK, 1928)

1928

35mm	b/w	silent	188ft	VIEW

[filmed by Grosvenor Topical]

People queueing to enjoy a concert at the bandstand, Kelvingrove Park, Glasgow.

0520   [DR. MACINTYRE'S X-RAY FILM]

1896/1909c

35mm	b/w	silent	60ft	VIEW

The first X-ray cinematograph film ever taken, shown by Dr. Macintyre at the London Royal Society. [See also ref. 0838, 2714.]

0521   STIRLING CHARITIES DAY

1939

35mm	b/w	silent	480ft	VIEW

[filmed by James S. Nairn for the Regal Cinema, Stirling]

Floats at the charities day on behalf of Stirling Royal Infirmary. Fancy dress procession and charity queen.

0522   SAY IT WITH FLOWERS

1928

35mm	b/w	silent	270ft	VIEW

Children's Annual Flower Procession in aid of the Royal Infirmary, Glasgow.

0523   HER MAJESTY THE QUEEN PAYS INFORMAL VISIT TO ABERDEEN

1939c

35mm	b/w	silent	125ft	VIEW

[filmed by Ernest Bromberg for the Newscine, Aberdeen]

The Queen pays an informal visit to Aberdeen where she visits the Royal Infirmary and the Town House.

0524   (HOME GUARD ON MANOEUVRES)

1942c

35mm	b/w	silent	300ft	VIEW

[filmed by Ernest Bromberg for the Newscine, Aberdeen]

Home Guard on parade in barracks yard and then on manoeuvres.

0525   (VISIT OF DUCHESS OF GLOUCESTER)

1939c

35mm	b/w	silent	390ft	VIEW

filmed by Ernest Bromberg for the Newscine, Aberdeen

Duchess of Gloucester visits Aberdeen and inspects the veterans' guard of honour.

0526   OUR CITY - TODAY AND TOMORROW

1949

16mm	b/w	silent	390ft	VIEW

sp. Glasgow Corporation Education Committee
p.c. Thames and Clyde

The city of Glasgow in the 1940s - its buildings, parks, museum, university and housing, showing the plans for major re-development of the city.

0527 JOHN NEWLAND'S DAY. 1950. BATHGATE

1950				
35mm	b/w	silent	800ft	REF

p.c. Thames and Clyde

Festival Day in Bathgate to celebrate John Newland; wreaths are laid at his plaque by the Festival Queen.

0528 ALL ON A SUMMER'S DAY

1933				
16mm	b/w	silent	360ft	VIEW

[filmed by Ian Ross]

Various activities enjoyed on a summer's day by a young couple including swimming, golfing and a picnic.

0529A BRITISH LEGION CONFERENCE IN ABERDEEN

1939c				
35mm	b/w	silent	140ft	VIEW

[filmed by Ernest Bromberg for the Newscine, Aberdeen]

General Sir Ian Hamilton with the Earl of Airlie lay wreaths at war memorial during the British Legion conference.

0529B (OPENING OF NEW BRIDGE OVER DEE BY KING GEORGE AND QUEEN ELIZABETH)

1941				
35mm	b/w	silent	188ft	VIEW

[filmed by Ernest Bromberg for Newscine, Aberdeen]

King George and Queen Elizabeth cut the ribbon to open the new bridge watched by local crowds.

0529C (DAMAGED HOTEL)

1941				
35mm	b/w	silent	30ft	VIEW

[filmed by Ernest Bromberg for Newscine, Aberdeen]

Shots of an Aberdeen hotel damaged by fire or possibly an air raid.

0529D (OPENING OF NEW BATHS. ABERDEEN)

1940				
35mm	b/w	silent	200ft	VIEW

[filmed by Ernest Bromberg for Newscine, Aberdeen]

New swimming baths opened in Aberdeen, with shots of the pool, spectators and swimmers.

0530 SCOTTISH SHALE INDUSTRY

1930				
35mm	b/w	silent	2023ft	VIEW

sp. Scottish Oil Agency Limited
p.c. Topical Press Agency

Technical record of shale mining in West Lothian and the manufacture of by-products.

0531 (GUILD OF AID WORK IN THE GORBALS)

1933-'39				
std.8mm	b/w	silent	380ft	VIEW

[filmed by Marald Grant]

Various aspects of 'Guild of Aid work' in the Gorbals, Glasgow, including a trip to Dunoon, nursery provision, sewing and dancing classes.

0532 CORONATION NEWSREEL

1953				
16mm	b/w	mute	160ft	REF

filmed by personnel of RAF West Freugh

Procession by various armed forces through the streets of Stranraer to celebrate the coronation.

0533 CEREMONIAL PARADE AT RAF WEST FREUGH

1953*				
35mm	b/w	mute	337ft	REF

Ceremonial parade at RAF West Freugh, celebrating the RAF's adoption by the Royal and Ancient Burgh of Sranraer.

0534 KOSB FREEDOM OF ENTRY INTO THE BURGH

1953				
35mm	b/w	mute	920ft	REF

filmed by RAF West Freugh

HRH the Duchess of Gloucester and men of the King's Own Scottish Borderers visit Stranraer to receive the Freedom of Entry into the Burgh.

0535 BISCUIT MAKING IN 1928

1928				
16mm	b/w	comopt	265ft	VIEW

[filmed by Jack MacFarlane]

The production of Macfarlane Lang's rich tea and cream cracker biscuits at the company's Tollcross factory.

45

0536 (NEIL ARMSTRONG IN LANGHOLM)

1972

16mm	b/w	comopt	110ft		REF

p.c. Border Television

Neil Armstrong swears the oath of allegiance and is granted the freedom of the burgh of Langholm.

0537 SHOSTAKOVITCH AND HUGH MACDIARMID

n.d.

16mm	b/w	mute	37ft		VIEW

Shots of Shostakovitch and Hugh MacDiarmid talking, and press and photographers looking on as a musical score is handed to Shostakovitch.

0538 (BOMBING OF THE CLYDE)

1941

35mm	b/w	silent	210ft		VIEW

[*p.c. Pathe*]

Unused news material shot by Pathe in Clydebank showing the aftermath of the Clydebank Blitz 13th -15th March 1941.

0539A RED CROSS WORK AT SALONIKA

1916

35mm	b/w	silent	70ft		REF

p.c. Topical Film Company

An ambulance column moving over a mountain road to the Balkan Front. Shots of the column on the march and of wagons at the rear. [Probably shot by the American cameraman Ariel Varges.] [Film incomplete.]

0539B STRIKE IN DUNDEE, THE

1911

35mm	b/w	silent	125ft		VIEW

p.c. Pathe Feres Cinema Limited

Probably filmed during the Dundee carters' strike 9-24th December 1911, the film contains scenes of strikers persuading blacklegs to join their ranks.

0540 [CHALLENGE TO FASCISM]

1938

16mm	b/w	silent	120ft		VIEW

sp. Glasgow Trades Council and Burgh Labour Party
p.c. Glasgow Kino Film Group
[d. Helen Biggar]

Glasgow May Day Parade and procession of floats in support of "Arms for Spain" and an end to "non-intervention" policy. [Film incomplete.]

0541 [PERTH AND KINROSS BYE-ELECTION]

1964

16mm	b/w	sep mag	106ft		REF

Prospective parliamentary candidates Sir Alec Douglas-Home and Christopher Murray Grieve address voters in the run up to the bye-election.

0542 [LANGHOLM COMMON RIDING]

1965c

16mm	b/w	mute	432ft		VIEW

Scenes from Langholm Common Riding in the Borders, with a procession and dancing in the streets.

0543 [COMMON RALLY]

1955c

16mm	b/w	silent	78ft		REF

Open air Socialist rally, Christopher Murray Grieve attends. [Film incomplete.]

0544 [FROM WOOL TO WEARER]

1913

16mm	b/w	silent	610ft		VIEW

Workers leaving a factory and models displaying fashions from the Hawick mill of Peter Scott and Company.

0545 ATLANTIC TRAWLER

1944

16mm	b/w	comopt	750ft		VIEW

sp. Ministry of Information
p.c. Realist Film Unit
d. Frank Sainsbury

Trawlers at work; the crew on board and landing a catch. The fishing crew are seen with their families on shore shopping and enjoying themselves in the pub.

0546 GLASGOW

1950c

16mm	col	silent	100ft		VIEW

filmed by Frank M. Marshall

Various scenes of Glasgow including Glasgow University, the Cathedral, Sauchiehall Street, Singer's factory, John Brown's shipyard and Hampden Park football stadium.

0547 BURNS MEMORIAL

1936c

35mm	b/w	comopt	375ft		VIEW

p.c. Gaumont British News

Ramsay MacDonald unveils commemorative memorial to the poet Robert Burns in the Borders town of Dumfries.

46

0548	HARRIS				
1950c					
16mm	*col*	*silent*	*99ft*		*VIEW*

[filmed by Frank M. Marshall]

Sheep dipping, island landscape, and the blackhouses on Harris in the Western Isles.

0549	ISLE OF LEWIS				
1950c					
16mm	*col*	*silent*	*72ft*		*VIEW*

filmed by Frank M. Marshall

Life on Lewis in the Western Isles; herring fishing, peat cutting and crofting.

0550	STORNOWAY				
1950c					
16mm	*col*	*silent*	*92ft*		*VIEW*

filmed by Frank M. Marshall

The town and harbour of Stornoway with shots of trawlers at work, new houses being built and of the standing stones at Callanish.

0551	FUNERAL OF PROVOST YOUNG. STRANRAER				
1914					
35mm	*b/w*	*mute*	*485ft*		*VIEW*

p.c. Gaumont News

Horse - drawn funeral procession for Provost Young, Stranraer.

0552	QUEEN MOTHER IN SCOTLAND, THE				
1954					
16mm	*b/w*	*comopt*	*127ft*		*REF*

p.c. Movietone News

The Queen Mother opens the Scottish Industries Exhibition at the Kelvin Hall, Glasgow, and unveils the memorial window in Glasgow Cathedral.

0553	FUNERAL OF MISS JEAN ARMOUR BURNS BROWN				
1937					
35mm	*b/w*	*silent*	*205ft*		*VIEW*

The funeral of Miss Jean Armour Burns Brown, great grand-daughter of Robert Burns, at St. Michael's church in the Borders town of Dumfries.

0554	(SUMMER SEASON IN ABERDEENSHIRE)				
1935*					
16mm	*b/w*	*silent*	*397ft*		*REF*

George West and company on stage and at leisure during the summer revues in Aberdeen.

0555	(PANTOMIME IN SUMMER)				
1934*					
16mm	*b/w*	*silent*	*248ft*		*REF*

Music hall entertainer, George West's stage show with shots of him relaxing with fellow entertainers. Jack E. Raymond, George West's "foil" for many years, is also seen in the film.

0556	(SCENES FROM A PANTOMIME)				
1939*					
16mm	*col*	*silent*	*210ft*		*REF*

Scenes from a pantomime featuring sketches with Jack E. Raymond and George West. [Possibly the Princess Pantomime, Perth.]

0557	MARCH OF THE MOVIES, THE				
1936					
16mm	*b/w*	*comopt*	*720ft*		*VIEW*

sp. Time Life Fortune

The Museum of Modern Art's Film Library with extracts from feature films including "The Great Train Robbery" and the first talkie, "The Jazz Singer".

0558	PATHE PICTORIAL NO. 2				
1953c					
16mm	*col*	*comopt*	*300ft*		*REF*

p.c. Pathe

The crafts of sword-making, flag making and the design of jockeys' horse-racing colours.

0559	PATHE REVIEW OF THE YEAR				
1948					
16mm	*b/w*	*comopt*	*330ft*		*REF*

p.c. Pathe News

News compilation with footage of Ceylon's Independence Day, Marshall Tito, Soviet leaders and Red Army parade, the Berlin Air Lift, athletes at the Olympic Games and the Royal family with the newly born Prince of Wales.

0560	(ARDROSSAN SHIPYARD)				
1919					
35mm	*b/w*	*silent*	*875ft*		*VIEW*

p.c. British Moving Picture News/ Green's Film Service

The construction of the vessel "Cromarty Firth" from the drawing board to the launch at the Ardrossan shipyard.

47

0561A　EXCLUSIVE PICTURES OF ROYAL VISIT TO PAISLEY

1938

| 35mm | b/w | silent | 15ft | VIEW |

[filmed as a local topical]

Shots of crowds lining the street for the royal visit to Paisley.

0561B　SCOTTISH CUP FINAL 1926 ST. MIRREN V CELTIC

1926

| 35mm | b/w | silent | 40ft |

1926 Scottish Cup Final between St. Mirren and Celtic.

0561C　WOMEN'S GUILD OF EMPIRE LEAVE FOR TOUR OF CANADA

1927

| 35mm | b/w | silent | 200ft | VIEW |

[filmed as a local topical]

Women's Guild of Empire Paisley branch wave farewell from Paisley Gilmour Street Station and later, as they board the liner to take them to Canada.

0561D　IT HAPPENED IN PAISLEY

1935c

| 35mm | b/w | silent | 305ft | VIEW |

[filmed as a local topical]

A brief history of the La Scala Cinema, Paisley in its first 14 years, introducing the management and staff.

0561E　EXCLUSIVE TO LA SCALA ... FUNERAL OF FIREMASTER ALEX GIRDWOOD

1937

| 35mm | b/w | silent | 420ft | VIEW |

[filmed as a local topical for La Scala and Kelburne Cinemas]

Funeral of Firemaster Alex Girdwood, at Hawkhead Cemetery, Paisley.

0561F　REVIEW OF PAISLEY'S CIVIL DEFENCE

1941*

| 35mm | b/w | silent | 300ft | VIEW |

The Rt. Hon. Tom Johnston, MP visits the Warden post, and inspects the civil defence parade.

0562　ARDROSSAN SPORTS GALA

1925*

| 35mm | b/w | silent | 190ft | VIEW |

[filmed by H. J. Kemp for La Scala Cinema]

Coverage of Ardrossan Sports Gala with footage of a boxing match between Elkey Clark and Duke Swan.

0563　COUNCIL'S ENTERPRISE

1922*

| 35mm | b/w | silent | 170ft | VIEW |

p.c. Green's Film Service, London and Glasgow

The building of the seawall at Saltcoats, Ayrshire.

0564　SCOTTISH JUNIOR CUP

1924*

| 35mm | b/w | silent | 180ft | VIEW |

[filmed by Harry Kemp for La Scala Cinema]

Coverage of the 1924 Scottish Junior Cup football match. The teams come out from the club hut and the captains toss. Shots of the game in progress.

0565　FUNERAL OF THE EARL OF EGLINTON AND WINTON

1919

| 35mm | b/w | silent | 185ft | VIEW |

[filmed by Harry Kemp for La Scala Cinema]

Funeral of the Earl of Eglinton and Winton, 14 August 1919.

0566　ARDEER SPORTS 1929

1929

| 35mm | b/w | silent | 400ft | VIEW |

[filmed by Harry Kemp for La Scala Cinema]

Sports day at the Nobel Explosives Factory, Ardeer, Ayrshire; tug-of-war, sack race, pillow fight, and 'lancing the bucket' competition.

0567　HARRY KEMP'S "SCOTCH BROTH" ENTERTAINERS

1925*

| 35mm | b/w | silent | 270ft | VIEW |

[filmed by Harry Kemp for La Scala Cinema]

A putting competition, children in the sea bathing and a charabanc carrying the local "entertainers".

0568　NOBEL'S TRIP TO ROTHESAY

1925

| 35mm | b/w | silent | 270ft | VIEW |

[filmed by Harry Kemp for La Scala Cinema]

A workers' outing from the Nobel Explosives Factory at Ardeer - a day trip to Rothesay on board the paddle steamer "King Edward".

0569　SALTCOATS FLOODED

1919

| 35mm | b/w | silent | 720ft | VIEW |

[p.c. Scottish Moving Picture News No.111]

The sea front and streets of Saltcoats flooded by high seas.

0570   GREAT WESTERN ROAD 1922
1922

35mm	b/w	silent	720ft	VIEW

[filmed by James Hart]

Shot as a promotional film for the Grosvenor Cinema, Byres Road, Glasgow, it shows Sunday afternoon promenaders on Glasgow's Great Western Road.

0571   PURE NEW WOOL - AND SCOTTISH
1924*

35mm	b/w	silent	540ft	VIEW

[p.c. Scottish Woollen Trade Mark Association]

Wool being spun and woven into cloth in Scottish tweed mills.

0572   (INVERBERVIE PAGEANT)
1946

16mm	b/w	silent	252ft	REF

Inverbervie Pageant with the re-enactment of the granting of a royal charter by King David II, after he was shipwrecked and saved by the local people in 1341.

0573   GREEN OF GLASGOW, THE
1962

16mm	col	comopt	585ft	VIEW

sp. Schools Museum Service
filmed by SEFA (Glasgow Group)

A history of Glasgow Green, and the benefits it provides - an open space for meetings and sports, the carnival during the Glasgow Fair and the People's Palace museum.

0574   ARDROSSAN AND SALTCOATS PLAYERS - WELCOME HOME
1928

35mm	b/w	silent	355ft	VIEW

filmed by Topical Budget for La Scala Cinema, Saltcoats

Ardrossan and Saltcoats amateur players are welcomed home by cheering crowds. Shot of the Balasco Cup won by the players.

0575   ARDROSSAN SHIPYARD SPORTS
1921*

35mm	b/w	silent	90ft	VIEW

[filmed by Harry Kemp for La Scala Cinema, Saltcoats]

Open air sports for the shipyard workers.

0576   (SCOTTISH GRAND NATIONAL)
1919*

35mm	b/w	silent	230ft	VIEW

p.c. Scottish Moving Picture News

Footage of the Scottish Grand National at Bogside, Ayrshire, won by the "The Turk".

0577   JUNIOR CUP FINAL
1925

35mm	b/w	silent	510ft	VIEW

[filmed by Harry Kemp for La Scala Cinema, Saltcoats]

Coverage of theScottish Junior Cup Final at Love Street stadium, Paisley, between Saltcoats Victoria and St. Anthony's, 30th May 1925, and of the replay at Firhill.

0578   CASHMERE IS SCOTTISH
1973c

16mm	col	comopt	594ft	REF

p.c. Martin Kane Production
d. Abel Goddman

Cashmere wool obtained from Mongolia is spun and knitted at Scottish mills into cashmere knitwear for Pringle, Ballantyne, Braemar and Glenmac.

0579   WORLD OF CASHMERE
1966c

16mm	col	comopt	936ft	REF

sp. Pringle of Scotland
p.c. Associated British Pathe Production
d. Frederick Goode

Cashmere imported from Mongolia is spun and knitted into fine wool at the Pringle's factory in the Borders town of Hawick for Pringle garments.

49

0580   RIVER CLYDE
1954c

16mm	b/w	silent	756ft	VIEW

sp. SEFA and SFC
p.c. Thames and Clyde Film Co.

The Clyde river from source to sea; farming and fruit growing in the Lanarkshire countryside and the river's traditions of heavy industry and shipbuilding.

0581   VARIETY MOMENTS
1935-'40c

35mm	b/w	mute	662ft	VIEW

Alloa Cinema adverts for local businesses.

0584   [SCOTTISH FLYING CLUB PAGEANT. RENFREW]
1933

16mm	b/w	silent	490ft	VIEW

[filmed by Ronald L. Jay]

Aerobatic displays, parachute jumps and presentation of mementos to pilots of 'Comper 2, Atalanta' in commemoration of their flight over Everest.

0585 [BEATLES COME TO TOWN, THE]
1963

16mm	b/w	comopt	196ft		REF

[p.c. Pathe]

The Beatles arrive at the theatre and are mobbed by screaming fans. Paul McCartney backstage in his dressing-room. On stage, the group play "She Loves You" and "Twist and Shout".

0586 DEE VALLEY
1959*

16mm	b/w	silent	467ft		VIEW

sp. JPC
filmed by SEFA (Aberdeen Branch)

An introduction to the industries and attractions of the Dee Valley, including paper making, sheep farming, salmon fishing, rock climbing, its castles and countryside.

0587 CENTRAL SCOTLAND
1962

16mm	col	silent	372ft		VIEW

sp. Educational Films of Scotland
p.c. Park Film Studios

The industries of Central Scotland; dairy and arable farming, steel making, engineering, textiles, coal mining and shipbuilding.

0588 SCOTTISH PLOUGHMAN
1955*

16mm	col	silent	385ft		VIEW

sp. JPC
filmed by SEFA (Edinburgh Branch)

Everyday life and work of a Scottish ploughman, shot at Smeaton Farm, Dalkeith.

0589 NEIL GUNN - LIGHT IN THE NORTH
1971c

16mm	b/w	comopt	416ft		VIEW

sp. Films of Scotland
p.c. Pelicula Films
d. Mike Alexander

Neil Gunn, the Scottish novelist, talks to George Bruce about his life and work.

0590 (CHRISTMAS STREET DECORATIONS IN GLASGOW)
1959*

16mm	col	silent	318ft		REF

Street illuminations in Glasgow by night.

0591 LOOKING BACK
1928

9.5mm	b/w	silent	1260ft		REF

[filmed by James Anderson]

Compilation of activities in the Mearns (Glasgow) between 1928 - 1934: the first Air Pageant at Renfrew, first dirt track meeting, the liner the "Empress of Britain" leaving the Clyde, the opening of Mearns Bowling Club and curling on a frozen loch.

0592 WISHAW CO-OPERATIVE SOCIETY OUTING
1939

16mm	col	silent	347ft		REF

A children's parade and picnic.

0593 VILLAGE BLACKSMITH
1957*

16mm	col	silent	204ft		VIEW

sp. JPC
filmed by SEFA (Lanarkshire Group)

The blacksmith forges and shapes a horseshoe to fit a farm horse.

0594 RURAL SCHOOL
1933

16mm	b/w	silent	387ft		VIEW

p.c. GB Instructional Ltd.
d. Miller Jones

Demonstration of exercises such as jumping, running and skipping, to be undertaken during a PE class, based on the Board of Education Syllabus of Physical Training for Schools.

0595 AT INVERNESS TERRITORIAL ARMY JUBILEE
1957*

35mm	b/w	silent	405ft		REF

[filmed by James S. Nairn for the Playhouse, Inverness]

The Territorial Army parade through the streets of Inverness to celebrate their Jubilee.

0596 PRESENTATION OF FREEDOM OF BURGH OF DINGWALL
1951

35mm	b/w	silent	750ft		REF

[filmed by James S. Nairn]

Provost Grigor presents the Freedom of the Burgh of Dingwall to Rt. Hon. Thomas Johnston PC and to Major John Stirling, MBE, of Fairburn.

0597A (ARCHAEOLOGICAL FIND)
1953*

35mm	b/w	silent	380ft		REF

[filmed by James S. Nairn for the Playhouse , Inverness]

People working at an archaeological dig, possibly of a burial site.

0597B SIR DAVID ROBERTSON. MP. OPENS NEW BRICK WORKS
1953*

35mm	b/w	silent	360ft		REF

[filmed by James S. Nairn for the Playhouse, Inverness]

The ceremony of the lighting of the new kiln at Brora brick works.

0598 [YOUTH SERVICES PARADE]
1958*

35mm	b/w	silent	900ft		REF

[filmed by James S. Nairn for the Playhouse, Inverness]

A parade by the Boys' Brigade, a girls' pipe band, Girl Guides and the Salvation Army. Provost Wotherspoon takes the salute at the Town House, Inverness.

0599 HIGHLAND GATHERING
1959*

35mm	b/w	silent	640ft		VIEW

[filmed by James S. Nairn and James Atterson]

Highland Games with highland dancing, military pipebands and presentation of trophies at the Northern Meeting Park, Inverness.

0600 [REMEMBRANCE DAY 1956]
1956

35mm	b/w	silent	365ft		VIEW

[filmed by James S. Nairn]

Footage of Boys' Brigade march and address by the Lord Provost to commemorate Remembrance Day in Inverness. A wreath is laid at the War Memorial.

0601 (GREEN FAMILY IN INDIA, THE)
1928

16mm	b/w	silent	140ft		REF

[filmed by A. Wood]

The Green family at home in India beside their paper mill at Titaphur.

0603 (HUGH MCLEAN & SONS LTD. BOATBUILDERS)
1931*

16mm	b/w	silent	50ft		REF

Hugh McLean and friends playing golf and shots of the Hugh McLean boatyard at Langlands Road in Govan, Glasgow.

0604 FREEDOM FOR THE RT. HON. THOMAS JOHNSTON
1955*

35mm	b/w	comopt	135ft		REF

[sp. Playhouse Cinema, Inverness]
p.c. Gaumont British News

The Rt. Hon. Thomas Johnston receives the Freedom of Inverness at the Playhouse Cinema.

0605 LESSONS THROUGH THE LETTERBOX
1958c

super 8mm col		mute	320ft		REF

p.c. Postal Courses Dept of the National Council of Labour Colleges

A promotional film to encourage people to enrol for the postal courses run by the National Council of Labour Colleges. [Part I only.]

0606 COUNTER COURTESY
1947

16mm	b/w	comopt	880ft		VIEW

[sp. Co-operative Wholesale Soc. Ltd.]
p.c. Orion Productions
d. Gordon O'Connell, G. Burger

A training film for employees of the Co-op - how to present themselves, how to deal with different types of customer and how to learn as much as possible about the trade.

0607 GET IT AT THE CO-OP
1950

16mm	b/w	comopt	880ft		VIEW

[sp. SCWS]
p.c. Gate Film Productions
d. Gordon O'Connell

An outline of the various activities of the SCWS including the local Co-operative Society meeting, fish curing in Aberdeen, the manufacture of furniture, their hosiery factory at Shieldhall and dairy farm at Monktonhall.

0608 ACHIEVEMENT
1948

16mm	b/w	comopt	810ft		VIEW

[sp. SCWS]
p.c. Orion Productions
d. G. Burger, in assoc. with Gordon O'Connell

Compilation film of Scottish inventors and their products, including John Dunlop's tyres, James Naismith's steam hammer and Kirkpatrick McMillan, inventor of one of the first bicycles.

0609 PRODUCTIVE GROCERY DEPARTMENT - SHIELDHALL FACTORY PRODUCTS

1959				
16mm	col	comopt	320ft	VIEW

[sp. SCWS]
p.c. Gate Film Productions

How jams, sauces, sweets and coffee are manufactured in the Co-op's Shieldhall factory.

0610 HELPING HAND - SCWS BRUSH MAKING, A

1957c				
16mm	b/w	comopt	345ft	VIEW

[sp. SCWS]
p.c. SCWS Film Unit Production
d. Nigel Byass

The processes involved in the manufacture of brushes in the SCWS factory in Glasgow.

0611 BLACK OR WHITE - SHIELDHALL COFFEE ESSENCE

1959				
16mm	col	comopt	115ft	VIEW

[sp. SCWS]
p.c. Gate Film Productions

Coffee beans are ground and percolated to make Co-op coffee essence, at the SCWS Shieldhall factory.

0612 YOUR SILENT SALESMAN

1947				
16mm	b/w	comopt	350ft	VIEW

[sp. SCWS]
p.c. Orion Productions
d. G. O'Connor, G. Burger

A training film for employees of the Co-op, explaining the importance of advertising and how an advertising campaign is mounted.

0613 KNOW YOUR BUSINESS

1947				
16mm	b/w	comopt	375ft	VIEW

[sp. SCWS]
p.c. Orion Productions
d. G. O'Connor, G. Burger

A training film for Co-op branch managers and senior staff on how to to train their own staff and run their shops more efficiently.

0614 EASTERN ROSE

1942				
16mm	b/w	comopt	190ft	VIEW

[sp. SCWS]

Tea plantations in Ceylon, and how Co-op tea is produced for Scottish markets.

0615 BLADNOCH CREAMERY

1959*				
16mm	col	comopt	320ft	VIEW

sp. SCWS
p.c. Gate Film Productions

Film of SCWS Bladnoch Creamery where 'Bluebell' and 'Snowdrop' margarine and 'Whitecrest' cooking fats are produced and packaged.

0616 CHEMICAL SUNDRIES DEPARTMENT

1959*				
16mm	col	comopt	380ft	VIEW

[sp. SCWS]
p.c. Gate Film Productions

Inside the SCWS Chemical Sundries factory, Shieldhall, Glasgow. Here jelly is tested, oats are weighed and wax is melted down for polish.

0617 TOMORROW IS YOURS

1961*				
16mm	col	comopt	480ft	VIEW

[sp. SCWS]

A promotional film to highlight the different types of Co-op retail outlets, including their self service shops and mobile shopping vans. The film also looks at Co-op factories and their products.

0618 REACH FOR A ROCKY

1959*				
16mm	col	comopt	610ft	VIEW

[sp. SCWS]
p.c. Gate Film Productions

Tobacco is harvested in Rocky Mount, North Carolina, then processed in the Co-op's Shieldhall factory Glasgow, as Rocky Mount cigarettes.

0619 BEYOND THE SUNSET

1944				
16mm	b/w	comopt	1210ft	VIEW

sp. Canadian Wheat Board
p.c. Associated Screen News, Montreal

Grain is produced and harvested in Canada, then transported by ship to Liverpool where it is refined into flour.

0620 [BITS O' STICKS]

1951*				
16mm	b/w	comopt	1210ft	VIEW

sp. SCWS
p.c. Gate Film Productions
d. Gordon O'Connell

Made in the SCWS furniture factories at Shieldhall and Beith, the film shows machinery at work and the production of a three-piece suite.

52

Out for Value 1931. Trying on a new purchase in the hat department of Issac Benzie's store, Aberdeen. Ref 2152

0621   PIECE OF CAKE, A
1950c

16mm	col	comopt	1125ft	VIEW

sp. SCWS
p.c. Shaw Films Productions
d. Ernest Morris

The production of semolina and flour at an SCWS mill. The flour is tested for protein, gluten and calcium. Bakers in the mill are seen experimenting with different recipes and give a demonstration on how to make a florence cake and a swiss roll.

0622   PRIDE AND PROGRESS
1949*

16mm	col	commag	1062ft	VIEW

sp. SCWS
p.c. Orion Productions
d. G. Burger

Aerial views of historical and industrial landmarks of Scotland. The role of the Co-op is discussed, and includes shots inside an SCWS factory producing coffee essence and jelly.

0623   MEN OF ROCHDALE
1944

16mm	b/w	comopt	1410ft	VIEW

sp. SCWS
p.c. Verity Films Limited
d. Compton Bennet

The history of the Co-operative movement in Britain. How the Co-op was first set up in Rochdale in 1844, in spite of opposition from the local business community.

0624   ROSE OF THE ORIENT
1938

16mm	b/w	comopt	1705ft	VIEW

sp. SCWS

The history of tea cultivation and the East Indian Tea Company.

0625   WISHAW CO-OP GALA DAY
1909

16mm	b/w	silent	109ft	VIEW

Wishaw Co-operative Society Gala Day including the children's procession to the railway station for their day's outing.

0626   ROYAL ACADEMY SPORTS
1952

35mm	b/w	silent	765ft	REF

[filmed by James S. Nairn for the Playhouse, Inverness]
The Royal Academy's sports day, with the sack race, three legged race and high jump.

0627   DEDICATION OF QUEEN'S PARK
1959*

35mm	b/w	silent	632ft	REF

[filmed by James S. Nairn for the Playhouse, Inverness]
The ceremony and parade to mark the Dedication of Queen's Park, Inverness. Provost J.M.Grigor takes the salute.

0628   HOW TALKIES TALK
1940c

16mm	b/w	comopt	414ft	REF

p.c. GB Instructional
d. Donald Carter

An account of how film sound track is recorded, processed and projected.

0629   INVOCATION
1951

16mm	col	mute	200ft	REF

filmed by Enrico Cocozza
A poetic study of the countryside in film, word and music.

0630   SOUTHERN UPLANDS
1940*

16mm	b/w	silent	342ft	VIEW

p.c. GB Instructional

Introduction to the Southern Uplands of Scotland with footage of sheep farming, agriculture, fishing and textiles.

53

0631   NORTHERN SCOTLAND
1959*

| 16mm | col | silent | 390ft | VIEW |

sp. Educational Films of Scotland
p.c. Thames and Clyde

Industry and farming in the Scottish Highlands and Western Isles, including shots of fishing, forestry work, crofting and city scenes of Aberdeen, Inverness and Stornoway.

0632   ANTARCTIC WHALE HUNT
1947*

| 16mm | b/w | comopt | 665ft | VIEW |

p.c. This Modern Age Ltd.
Whaling in the Antarctic.

0633   STORY OF ALFRED NOBEL, THE
1949*

| 16mm | b/w | comopt | 375ft | REF |

sp. Metro-Goldwyn-Mayer

The story of Alfred Nobel, who discovered dynamite but horrified by its consequences, set up the Nobel peace prize.

0634   (CWS CONGRESS IN GLASGOW)
1940

| 16mm | b/w | mute | 400ft | REF |

sp. Scottish Co-operative Wholesale Society

Shots of the CWS Congress in session in the St. Andrews Halls in Glasgow and delegates on a day trip.

0635   ADVENTURES OF WEE ROB ROY, THE
1936*

| 35mm | b/w | silent | 230ft | VIEW |

An animated film of the adventures of Wee Rob Roy.

0636   BACK TO BACK
1959*

| 16mm | col | comopt | 645ft | REF |

sp. Co-operative Wholesale Society Ltd.
p.c. Anglo-Scottish Pictures Ltd.

The carding, weaving and knitting of merino wool at Co-operative mills.

0637   ANIMAL HUSBANDRY
1949*

| 16mm | b/w | silent | 396ft | VIEW |

p.c. GB Instructional Ltd.
sd. John C. Elder

A look at livestock farming in Scotland.

0638   GLENFINNAN AND THE '45
1945

| 35mm | b/w | comopt | 1510ft | VIEW |

sp. Caledonian Associated Cinemas
p.c. Pathe Pictures Limited

The Gathering at Glenfinnan in the Highlands to mark the 200th anniversary of raising the standard of James VIII of Scotland and III of England.

0639A   TROOPING THE COLOUR
1935*

| 35mm | b/w | silent | 504ft | VIEW |

[filmed as a local topical for the Playhouse, Inverness]

Trooping the colour by the 1st Battalion KOSB at Fort George, Inverness-shire. Brigadier General D.A. MacFarlane takes the salute.

0639B   FERGUSLIE MILLS IN INVERNESS
1936

| 35mm | b/w | silent | 592ft | VIEW |

Ferguslie Mills staff outing to Inverness on "Sma' Shot Day". They visit Culloden and the Ness Islands.

0640   FUNERAL OF THE LATE MAJOR GENERAL LORD LOVAT
1933

| 35mm | b/w | silent | 210ft | VIEW |

[filmed by James S. Nairn for the Playhouse, Inverness]

Coverage of Lord Lovat's funeral, Inverness-shire. February 1933.

0641   GLIMPSE OF THE LIFEBOAT SERVICE
1930

| 35mm | b/w | silent | 765ft | VIEW |

The daily duties of the men working on the lifeboat at Montrose and the hazards they face.

0642   VOTE FOR HARRY KEMP
1922

| 35mm | b/w | silent | 90ft | VIEW |

[filmed by Harry Kemp for La Scala Cinema, Saltcoats]

"Party political broadcast" by Harry Kemp, a candidate for office on Saltcoats Burgh Council, and shown in his cinema in the run up to the election.

0643   SALTCOATS PILGRIMAGE TO LOURDES
1925c

| 35mm | b/w | silent | 50ft | VIEW |

[filmed as a local topical for La Scala Cinema, Saltcoats]

Procession through the streets of Saltcoats with children dressed in white.

0644 SALTCOATS QUATER CENTENARY CELEBRATIONS
1928

| 35mm | b/w | silent | 691ft | VIEW |

[filmed as a local topical for La Scala Cinema, Saltcoats]

Saltcoats Quater Centenary celebrations with the gala procession through the streets.

0645 FROM TUNGSTEN ORE TO LUNA FILAMENT
1947*

| 16mm | b/w | comopt | 792ft | REF |

p.c. Forberg-Film, Stockholm
d. Bengt Jarrel

Introduction to the chemist Scheele's scientific discovery of Tungsten ore for refinement into a luna filament for lights.

0646A INAUGURATION OF INVERNESS AIRPORT
1933

| 35mm | b/w | silent | 315ft | VIEW |

[filmed as a local topical for the Playhouse, Inverness]

The opening of Inverness Airport, by the Duke of Sutherland with demonstrations of parachuting and shots of aircraft taking off and landing.

0646B INAUGURATION OF FIRST HIGHLAND AIR SERVICE
1933

| 35mm | b/w | silent | 585ft | VIEW |

[filmed as a local topical for the Playhouse, Inverness]

The Inverness-Orkney plane is christened by Mrs. Donald McDonald of Scorguie. Passengers board the plane, speeches are made and the plane takes off.

0647 TREASURE ISLAND
1935

| 35mm | b/w | silent | 225ft | VIEW |

[filmed as a local topical for the Playhouse, Inverness]

Children queuing for a special performance of "Treasure Island" at the Playhouse Cinema, Inverness.

0648 DUKE AND DUCHESS OF YORK AND ROYAL ACADEMY SPORTS
1934/1950

| 35mm | b/w | silent | 270ft | VIEW |

[filmed as a local topical for the Playhouse, Inverness]

The Duke and Duchess of York leaving Inverness railway station for Skye,1934 and the Royal Academy sports day 1950.

0649 GRASS
1925

| 16mm | b/w | silent | 1273ft | REF |

d. Merian Cooper and Ernest Schoedsack

A record of Persian nomadic migration.

0650 STARS AND STRIPES
1943

| 16mm | col | comopt | 102ft | VIEW |

sp. National Film Board of Canada
d. Norman McLaren

An experimental film, made without camera, by drawing directly on 35mm film with ordinary pen and ink.

0651 LITTLE PHANTASY, A
1946

| 16mm | col | comopt | 126ft | VIEW |

sp. National Film Board of Canada
d. Norman McLaren

Animated film of an island in a painting which is subject to the forces of nature and the supernatural. [Original painting by Arnold Boecklin.]

0652 HARVESTS OF THE SOIL
1933*

| 16mm | b/w | silent | 360ft | VIEW |

p.c. GB Instructional
d. John C. Elder

A look at the harvesting of different crops, including early potatoes, tomatoes and other fruits.

0653A [BOYS' BRIGADE]
1934*

| 35mm | b/w | silent | 375ft | VIEW |

[filmed as a local topical for the Playhouse, Inverness]

Boys Brigade sports day, Inverness with a relay race, cycle race and procession through the streets.

0653B [AIR SHOW]
1932*

| 35mm | b/w | silent | 210ft | VIEW |

[filmed as a local topical for the Playhouse, Inverness]

Sir Allan Cobham's air display at the aerodrome in Inverness.

0653C [ANNA NEAGLE]
1937*

| 35mm | b/w | silent | 300ft | VIEW |

[filmed as a local topical for the Playhouse, Inverness]

The film star Anna Neagle and her husband Herbert Wilcox visit Inverness for the screening of her film "Victoria the Great", in the Playhouse Cinema.

55

0654A   FUNERAL OF MACKINTOSH OF MACKINTOSH
1938

35mm	b/w	silent	315ft		VIEW

[filmed as a local topical for the Playhouse, Inverness]

The funeral procession of Mackintosh of Mackintosh at Fetty Churchyard, Inverness, 14th November 1938.

0654B   BOYS' BRIGADE (INVERNESS BATTN.) INSPECTION AND PRESENTATION OF COLOURS
1935c

16mm	b/w	silent	90ft		VIEW

[filmed as a local topical for the Playhouse, Inverness]

The Inverness Battalion of the Boys' Brigade inspected and presented with colours by Officer Colonel D.W. Cameron of Lochiel.

0655   [HENDRY'S DOUBLE TOP AMERICAN COLA]
1961*

35mm	b/w	comopt	22ft		REF

sp. SCWS

An advert for Hendry's Double Top American Cola, featuring a song and dance act.

0656   [LOFTY PEAK CAKE MIXES]
1959*

35mm	b/w	comopt	60ft		REF

p.c. Shaw Film Productions

An advert for the Co-operative's Lofty Peak cake mixes.

0657   [COME CO-OPERATIVE SHOPPING]
1963*

35mm	b/w	comopt	45ft		REF

An advert featuring a selection of Co-op offers.

0658   [COME CO-OPERATIVE SHOPPING]
1964*

35mm	b/w	comopt	20ft		REF

An advert for the co-op's Bartlett pear halves and Wheatsheaf dairy cream.

0659   [SAVE IN 1969]
1969*

35mm	b/w	comopt	45ft		REF

An advert showing a selection of Co-op offers.

0660   COME CO-OPERATIVE SHOPPING
1966*

35mm	b/w	comopt	45ft		REF

A selection of Co-op offers.

0661   MUTTON
1946*

16mm	col	silent	292ft		VIEW

sp. BFI and SFC
p.c. GB Instructional

From sheep farm to butcher's shop. How mutton is produced and then sold at the market.

0662   TEXTILES
1946*

16mm	b/w	silent	324ft		VIEW

p.c. GB Instructional
d. John C. Elder

A survey of the textile industry in Scotland featuring the Border woollen mills, linen towns, and jute and cotton mills.

0663   PERU
1939

16mm	b/w	silent	384ft		VIEW

p.c. Eastman Classroom Films

The different faces of Peru from the Inca ruins to its railway system, seaports, mining industry, and its people.

0664   (BOWLS IN HONG KONG)
1926-'35*

16mm	b/w&col	silent	304ft		REF

[filmed by David Keith]

Ex-patriot Britons playing bowls in Hong Kong.

0665   (HOLIDAY IN LONDON)
1931

16mm	b/w	silent	430ft		REF

[filmed by David Keith]

Various landmarks in London, including Buckingham Palace, Marble Arch and the Tower of London. The film also includes brief excerpts from various cartoons.

0666   MISCELLANEOUS SEA-GOING VESSELS
1926*

16mm	b/w	silent	189ft		REF

[filmed by David Keith]

Steamers and paddle steamers on the river Clyde. Shots of the "Mauretania" pulling out of Manhattan harbour. Reel two contains newsreel footage of the launching of the "Queen Mary" at John Brown's shipyard.

0667   (SHEEP DIPPING)
1947*

16mm	col	silent	20ft		REF

[filmed by David Keith]

Sheep are herded into a pen before going through a sheep dip.

0668   (IVORY CARVING)
1932*

16mm	b/w	silent	100ft		REF

[filmed by David Keith]

Ivory carvers at work inside a Chinese workshop.

0669   (SCENES IN THE MIDDLE EAST)
1951*

16mm	col	silent	92ft		REF

[filmed by David Keith]

Scenes at a busy sea port in China.

0670   (SCENES ON THE CLYDE AND EDINBURGH ZOO)
1931

16mm	b/w	silent	129ft		REF

[filmed by David Keith]

Boat trip 'down the Clyde' and film of a visit to Edinburgh Zoo.

0672   OUT OF THE BOX
1942*

16mm	b/w	comopt	395ft		VIEW

sp. SCWS
p.c. Merton Park Productions
d. Terrance Egan Bishop

Account of the birth of the Co-operative movement in Scotland from mid-eighteenth century to the present.

0673   SCOTLAND WELCOMES THEIR MAJESTIES
1941

35mm	b/w	comopt	620ft		VIEW

p.c. Scottish Movietone News

King George VI and Queen Elizabeth visit Scotland. The royal tour includes Clydebank and Paisley, the National Fire Service Training School and Miners Welfare Centre at Blantyre.

0674   (SCWS LOFTY PEAK XMAS CAKE ADVERTISEMENT)
1963*

35mm	b/w	comopt	82ft		REF

p.c. Shaw Film Productions

A television commercial recommending the use of Lofty Peak flour during the festive season.

0675   (SCWS LEMON CURD ADVERTISEMENT)
1965c

35mm	b/w	comopt	44ft		REF

p.c. Shaw Film Productions

Advert for Co-operative lemon curd.

0676   (SCWS CREAMERY BUTTER ADVERTISEMENT)
1964*

35mm	b/w	comopt	20ft		VIEW

Advert for Co-op Creamery butter.

0677   (SCWS PEAR HALVES AND CREAM ADVERTISEMENT)
1964*

35mm	b/w	comopt	20ft		VIEW

Advert for Co-op Bartlett pear halves and Wheatsheaf dairy cream.

0678   (SCWS MARMALADE ADVERTISEMENT)
1963*

35mm	b/w	comopt	45ft		REF

Advert for 3d saving on Co-op Golden Ball marmalade.

0679   (SCWS LOFTY PEAK FLOUR ADVERTISEMENT)
1966*

35mm	b/w	comopt	62ft		REF

A cake is "un-made" to produce a bag of Co-op Lofty Peak flour.

0680   (SCWS COFFEE ESSENCE ADVERTISEMENT)
1960c

35mm	b/w	comopt	40ft		REF

Animated advert for Co-op Shieldhall essence of coffee and chicory.

0681   (SCWS MARGARINE ADVERTISEMENT)
1965c

35mm	b/w	comopt	37ft		REF

Advert for Co-op Orchid margarine.

57

0682 (SCWS MARGARINE ADVERTISEMENT)

1965*

35mm	b/w	comopt	41ft		REF

Advert for Co-op wrapped Bluebell margarine.

0683 (SCWS SPECIAL OFFERS)

1969

35mm	b/w	comopt	60ft		REF

Dramatised scene in the kitchen with mother and daughter returned from the Co-op where they have saved money on pineapples, soup, cream crackers and marmalade.

0684 (SCWS MARMALADE ADVERTISEMENT)

1962c

35mm	b/w	comopt	20ft		REF

p.c. Shaw Film Productions

A television commercial for savings on Co-op Golden Ball marmalade.

0685 (SCWS COFFEE ESSENCE ADVERTISEMENT)

1963*

35mm	b/w	comopt	20ft		REF

Advert for Co-op Shieldhall coffee essence.

0686 (SCWS MARGARINE ADVERTISEMENT)

1961*

35mm	b/w	comopt	37ft		REF

Animated advert for Co-op Bluebell margarine.

0687 (COGENT CIGARETTES ADVERTISEMENT)

1957*

35mm	b/w	comopt	121ft		VIEW

How Co-op Cogent cigarettes are manufactured, and an advert for Cogent cigarettes "Relax with Cogent".

0688 (CO-OP ROCKY MOUNT CIGARETTES ADVERT)

1959*

35mm	col	comopt	23ft		VIEW

An advert for Rocky Mount filter tipped cigarettes, featuring cowboys and a song.

0689 (MONTRIL ORANGE DRINK)

1961*

35mm	b/w	comopt	20ft		VIEW

Advert for the Co-operative's Montril orange drink featuring a children's party.

0690 [1968 CO-OP PRESENTATION FILM]

1968*

16mm	col	comopt	566ft		REF

An outline of the Co-op's aims and objectives.

0691 MUSIC IN AMERICA

1950*

16mm	b/w	comopt	610ft		VIEW

sp. March of Time Forum Edition

Music styles from classical and jazz to swing.

0692 BENEATH THE NORTH SEA

1976c

16mm	col	comopt	790ft		REF

sp. Mobil
p.c. Michael Forlong Productions
d. Michael Forlong

The construction and workings of oil rigs in the Beryl oil field, off the Norwegian coast.

0693 BERYL'S SAGA: THE FIRST CHAPTER

1975

16mm	col	comopt	600ft		REF

sp. Mobil

The construction of 'Beryl A' oil rig platform at Arundel, Norway, and its installation in the North Sea.

0694 WELLS OF MONTROSE, THE

1977

16mm	col	commag	972ft		REF

sp. Amoco
p.c. Charles Barker Films
d. Ferdinand Fairfax

A tribute to the late 'Mitch' Watt who was responsible for many oil and gas operations in the North Sea from 1965-1977.

0695 "QUEEN MARY" GOES DOWN TO THE SEA/WINS BLUE RIBAND

1936

16mm	b/w	comopt	120ft		VIEW

p.c. Gaumont British News

The liner "Queen Mary" is launched at John Brown's shipyard, Clydebank with shots of the liner as she sets off on her maiden transatlantic voyage from Southampton to New York.

0698	**RADIO ADDRESS BY NEIL BEATON, A**				
1943					
16mm	*b/w*	*comopt*	*248ft*		*REF*

sp. International Co-operation
p.c. Tomlins

A radio address by Neil Beaton, President of the SCWS and past chairman of STUC. He discusses the future and past of the co-operative movement and its international role.

0699	**4 AND 20 FIT GIRLS**				
1942*					
16mm	*b/w*	*comopt*	*399ft*		*REF*

p.c. GB Instructional
d. Mary Field

Women exercising during a keep-fit class.

0701	**(SCWS MARGARINE ADVERTISEMENT)**				
1958*					
35mm	*b/w*	*comopt*	*39ft*		*REF*

An advert for the Co-operative's Bluebell margarine.

0702	**EDINBURGH SAYS FAREWELL TO ITS TRAMS**				
1956					
16mm	*col*	*silent*	*98ft*		*REF*

filmed by Brian P. Winpenny

Shots of the last few days of the Edinburgh tram service.

0703	**CLYDE, THE**				
1947					
16mm	*col*	*silent*	*84ft*		*VIEW*

[filmed by Frank M. Marshall]

Steamers, paddle steamers and naval vessels on the river and some of the Clyde shipyards including John Brown's and Fairfields.

0704	**HANDBA' AT KIRKWALL, ORKNEY**				
1940					
16mm	*b/w*	*silent*	*180ft*		*VIEW*

p.c. Craft Studio Production
filmed by W. Kirkness

Scenes from the Handba' festival on New Year's Day in Kirkwall. This was the last festival to be held until the end of the war. [Won best Scottish film award at the SAFF.]

0705	**SADNESS AND GLADNESS**				
1928					
35mm	*b/w*	*silent*	*1220ft*		*REF*

sp. Necessitous Children's Holiday Camp Fund

One of a series of fund-raising films produced in aid of the Necessitous Children's Holiday Camp Fund.

0707	**SCOTLAND**				
n.d.					
9.5mm	*b/w*	*silent*	*300ft*		*REF*

Amateur footage of scenes around Scotland, including Edinburgh's Princes Street and Castle, the Forth Rail Bridge, Burns' cottage and Melrose Abbey.

0711	**(NEWTONMORE V UNIDENTIFIED AT SHINTY)**				
1954*					
16mm	*col*	*silent*	*70ft*		*REF*

Amateur footage of a shinty match.

0712	**[SAUCHIEHALL STREET ROOF TOPS]**				
1956*					
16mm	*b/w*	*silent*	*138ft*		*REF*

[filmed by Louise Annand]

Shots of the exteriors of Glasgow buildings including the Glasgow School of Art, McLellan Galleries, Treron's department store and the La Scala Cinema in Sauchiehall Street.

0713	**REVIEW OF THE YEAR 1940**				
1940					
9.5mm	*b/w*	*silent*	*300ft*		*REF*

p.c. Pathescope

Compilation newsreel footage of events of 1940 including shots of Hitler's defeated ships in Narvik Fjord, men embarking at Dunkirk, the election of Roosevelt as President of the USA, evacuees and bomb damage in Coventry.

0715	**CORONATION OF KING GEORGE V1 AND QUEEN ELIZABETH**				
1937					
9.5mm	*b/w*	*silent*	*300ft*		*REF*

p.c. Pathescope

The Coronation of King George V1 and Queen Elizabeth at Westminster Abbey.

0716	**(PATHESCOPE GAZETTE/NEW EMPIRE NEWS)**				
1940					
9.5mm	*b/w*	*silent*	*400ft*		*REF*

Compilation newsreel footage including Queen Mary on a visit to the Tower of London, Girl Guides at Windsor, police sports at Hendon and the homecoming of the naval battleships the "Ajax" and "Exeter" welcomed by Winston Churchill.

59

0717   PRIME MINISTER AND PRESIDENT
1941c

9.5mm	b/w	silent	100ft	REF

Winston Churchill and Roosevelt sign the Atlantic Charter.

0718   (HOLIDAY FILM)
n.d.

9.5mm	b/w	silent	100ft	REF

A holiday film showing a resort on the north-west coast of France.

0719   BUYING A HORSE
1922c

16mm	b/w	silent	54ft	REF

p.c. Green's Film Service

An extract from a cinemagazine featuring the music hall comedians Power and Bendon.

0720   [HIGHLAND SHOW, DUNDEE]
1949

16mm	col	silent	435ft	REF

[filmed by T.H. Thoms]

The Royal Highland Show in Dundee, attended by the Queen. There is a livestock display, highland dancing and games.

0722   BILLY GRAHAM IN GLASGOW
1955

16mm	b/w	silent	971ft	VIEW

filmed by Revd. Merricks Arnott

Glasgow welcomes Billy Graham, the American evangelist. He addresses crowds at the Kelvin Hall in Glasgow, Clydebank and Hampden Park.

0723   [CO-OP ADVERTISEMENTS STRATHCLYDE SCHOOLWEAR]
1972c

16mm	col	comopt	110ft	REF

Adverts for "Strathclyde" schoolwear: "top ten" shopping buys at the Co-op.

0724   HM THE QUEEN VISITS CENTENARY HOUSE
1968

16mm	col	silent	207ft	REF

sp. SCWS

SCWS centenary year, HM the Queen visits Centenary House, Glasgow, 5th July 1968.

0727   GALLONS OF GOODNESS
1957*

16mm	col	comopt	360ft	VIEW

sp. Co-operative Wholesale Society Limited
p.c. Anglo Scottish Pictures Limited

Dairy production at the Co-op creamery.

0728   [KINGS IN EXILE]
1940*

16mm	b/w	comopt	396ft	REF

p.c. GB Instructional
d. Mary Field

The king penguins at Edinburgh Zoo with an explanation of their life-cycle, illustrated with the use of underwater shots and slow-motion sequences.

0735   [FACTS AND FIGURES NO. 4]
1960c

16mm	b/w	comopt	24ft	VIEW

Various facts and figures relating to Co-op products displayed in stores.

0736   (CO-OP ADVERTISEMENT)
1955c

16mm	b/w	comopt	24ft	VIEW

An advert for the Co-op, featuring a song and shots of people arriving at a Co-op in various forms of transport, including a helicopter, a penny farthing, and on horseback.

0737   (CO-OP ADVERTS)
1969

35mm	b/w&col	comopt	114ft	REF

Five Co-op adverts featuring the "Save in 69" slogan detailing all the latest offers.

0738   EATING AT WORK
1942*

16mm	b/w	comopt	444ft	REF

sp. Gas Industry
p.c. Strand Film Productions
d. Ralph Bond

The need for canteen provision at work and the problems involved.

0739   WHEN DAY IS DONE - GLIMPSES OF MINERS WELFARE
1938*

16mm	b/w	comopt	470ft	VIEW

sp. Coal Industry Publications
d. David Clayton

A look at some of the facilities created by the Miners Welfare Fund, including parks for children, rest homes, and the Miners' Institute.

61

0742   SHIELDHALL FURNITURE - MARCH OF PROGRESS

1938*

16mm	b/w	comopt	384ft		REF

sp. SCWS
p.c. Jay's Film Service

The manufacturing of Shieldhall furniture.

0743   NEW YORK, THE WONDERFUL CITY

1930c

16mm	b/w	silent	320ft		REF

Scenes of New York, including Broadway, the Lower East Side, Wall Street, the Brooklyn Bridge and Central Park.

0744   BIOLOGICAL EXPEDITION. ISLAND OF RAASAY

1934

16mm	b/w	silent	285ft		REF

Dundee University staff on a biological expedition to Raasay in the Western Isles, where they find a unique carved stone in the ruined chapel of St. Malvog.

0745   (BIOLOGICAL EXPEDITION, RONA)

1934c

16mm	b/w	silent	194ft		REF

Dundee University staff on a biological expedition to the island of Rona in the Western Isles. Colin Gibson, an artist, paints scenes from the expedition.

0746   MARINE BIOLOGY

1934

16mm	b/w	silent	330ft		REF

Dundee University staff on a biological and marine expedition to the island of Rona in the Western Isles, to research cliff fauna and marine life.

0747   (EXPEDITION TO RONA)

1933c

16mm	b/w	silent	375ft		REF

Scientific expedition to Rona in the Western Isles by members of Dundee University.

0748   SOUTH RONA EXPEDITION: THE DESCENT TO THE CAVE

1933

16mm	b/w	silent	380ft		REF

Scientific expedition to South Rona in the Western Isles by members of Dundee University.

0749   (LOCAL FILM FROM KIRKINTILLOCH AREA)

1935

9.5mm	b/w	silent	725ft		REF

[filmed by Mr Fletcher while Provost of Kirkintilloch]

An amateur film of scenes in the Kirkintilloch area including Ettrick Bay fun fair, steamers on the Clyde and paddle steamers on the Forth and Clyde canal.

0750   ROMANCE OF ENGINEERING, A

1938

16mm	b/w	comopt	1069ft		VIEW

sp. William Beardmore and Co.
p.c. Scottish Films (1928) Limited
[d. Stanley Russell]

Production of steel components at Parkhead Forge, Glasgow. Made for the 1938 Empire Exhibition.

0751   (BORDER COUNTRY)

1936*

16mm	b/w	silent	750ft		REF

A look at the Borders country, with its abbeys, castles, and countryside.

0752   CRIEFF - OUR TOWN

1953c

16mm	col	silent	452ft		VIEW

filmed by SAAC

A tourist guide to the town of Crieff and surrounding countryside.

0753   [CRIEFF MASTER]

1960c

16mm	col	silent	99ft		REF

filmed by Frank M. Marshall

Various scenes of a riding school in Crieff and surrounding countryside.

0754   MUSIC FROM THE MOVIES

1943*

16mm	b/w	comopt	416ft		VIEW

p.c. Educational Film Corporation of America

Compilation of music, song and dance from some famous artists including Yehudi Menuhin, Harry James, Judy Garland,Bing Crosby, Nelson Eddy and Jeannette McDonald.

0755   VICTORY OVER PAIN

1956*

35mm	b/w	comopt	1725ft		VIEW

sp. Educational Films of Scotland
p.c. Campbell Harper Films Ltd.
d. Henry Cooper

The dramatised story of James Y. Simpson's discovery of the anaesthetic effects of chloroform.

0756	PIONEERS THEN AND NOW				
1964					
16mm	b/w	comopt	1260ft		VIEW

sp. National Union of General and Municipal Workers
p.c. Keith Z. Ord Limited

Filmed during the 49th Congress of National Union of General and Municipal Workers to commemorate the 75th Anniversary of the Union.

0757	TO SAVE A LIFE				
1957*					
35mm	b/w	comopt	285ft		VIEW

sp. Scottish National Blood Transfusion Service

Made as an appeal for more blood donors, the film gives a dramatised account of a boy who receives a blood transfusion.

0758	BLOOD IS LIFE				
1957					
35mm	b/w	comopt	1547ft		VIEW

sp. Scottish National Blood Transfusion Service
p.c. Basic Films
d. Anthony Simmons

A promotional film to show how a Blood Transfusion Centre operates providing a constant supply of well tested blood.

0759	(STAFF AND PATRONS OF UNIDENTIFIED CINEMA)				
1955c					
16mm	b/w	silent	9ft		REF

Shots of the staff and patrons of a cinema.

0760	GALASHIELS HISTORICAL PEACE PAGEANT				
1919					
16mm	b/w	silent	216ft		VIEW

filmed by Fyfe and Fyfe

Scenes of the peace pageant in the Borders town of Galashiels.

0761	[CHILDREN'S PROCESSION GALASHIELS]				
1924					
16mm	b/w	silent	192ft		VIEW

[filmed as a local topical]

The children's procession at a pageant in the Borders town of Galashiels.

0762A	GALASHIELS WAR MEMORIAL, THE				
1925					
16mm	b/w	silent	170ft		VIEW

[filmed as a local topical]

The war memorial in the Borders town of Galashiels is unveiled by Field Marshall Earl Haig.

0762B	RUGBY LEAGUE CHAMPIONSHIP				
1912					
16mm	b/w	silent	154ft		VIEW

p.c. Gaumont News

The game in progress and onlooking crowds at a rugby league championship match in Galashiels in the Borders.

0763	OPENING OF OLD GALA HOUSE				
1949					
16mm	b/w	silent	226ft		VIEW

[filmed by Galashiels Film Society]

Opening of the Old Gala House in the Borders town of Galashiels and its first exhibition for the local Arts Festival.

0764	CROSSING THE TWEED				
1932*					
16mm	b/w	comopt	153ft		VIEW

p.c. Universal News
[filmed as a local topical]

The festival of the Braw Lads Gathering in Galashiels in the Borders.

0765	PICTURESQUE SCENES - 4TH ANNUAL BRAW LADS GATHERING				
1933*					
16mm	b/w	silent	170ft		VIEW

p.c. Universal News

The traditional ceremonies and procession at the Borders festival of the Braw Lads Gathering in Galashiels.

0766	GALASHIELS AND BRAW LADS GATHERING				
1952					
16mm	b/w	silent	230ft		VIEW

sp. Pavilion Theatre, Galashiels
p.c. Elder Film Productions

The festival of the Braw Lads Gathering in the Borders town of Galashiels; the historic flag is presented and carried on horseback through the town.

63

0767   BRAW LADS GATHERING
1947

| 16mm | b/w | silent | 306ft | VIEW |

p.c. Elder Dalrymple Productions

The historic flag of the Borders town of Galashiels is presented to the Cornet on the balcony of the burgh halls during the festival of the Braw Lads Gathering.

0768   (STANLEY L. RUSSELL'S WEDDING)
1950

| 35mm | b/w | silent | 150ft | REF |

Stanley L. Russell's wedding at the Registry Office in Lilybank Gardens, Glasgow, 24th April 1950.

0769   [KILMARNOCK]
1928-'33c

| 16mm | b/w | silent | 305ft | REF |

[amateur film]

The town of Kilmarnock, an industrial and tourist centre.

0770   [PEACE DAY CELEBRATION. KILMARNOCK 1919]
1919

| 35mm | b/w | silent | 615ft | VIEW |

[filmed as a local topical]

A Peace Day parade through the streets of Kilmarnock.

0771   GLIMPSE OF THE CAMPERDOWN WORKS, A
1912

| 35mm | b/w | silent | 125ft | VIEW |

[filmed by John Noble of the Oxford Picture House, Dundee.]

One of the earliest surviving local topicals in Scotland, the film shows workers leaving the Camperdown Jute Mill in Dundee.

0772   (STEAM LOCOMOTIVES AND SCENES AT LANARK RACECOURSE)
1964c

| 16mm | b/w | silent | 92ft | REF |

[filmed by Norman Pollock]

Footage of various steam locomotives around Glasgow, including the Glasgow to London train pulling out of Central Station. The film also includes scenes at Lanark race course.

0773   NORTHERN OUTPOST
1940

| 16mm | b/w | comopt | 570ft | VIEW |

p. & ph. by Jenny Brown and C.J. Cayley

Fishing, agriculture, transport, the archaeology and scenery of the Shetland Isles.

0774   (CONSTRUCTION OF THE RITZ CINEMA, EDINBURGH 1929)
1929

| 35mm | b/w | silent | 1000ft | VIEW |

filmed by James S. Nairn

The construction of the Ritz Cinema, from virgin site to opening day. The new projection facilities are shown and the cinema staff introduce themselves. [Film made by the first manager of the Ritz.]

0775   (LANARK RACECOURSE AND RENFREWSHIRE HUNT)
1931/*1937

| 16mm | b/w | silent | 372ft | REF |

[filmed by John P. Ritchie]

Scenes at Lanark racecourse; the Renfrewshire hunt; a ship being towed down the Clyde and animals in Manchester zoo.

0776   AILSA CRAIG - A SEABIRDS' ISLAND
1930c

| 16mm | b/w | silent | 270ft | REF |

[filmed by John P. Ritchie]

Bird life on the island of Ailsa Craig. [Film includes shots of horse-drawn ploughing.]

0777   (MISCELLANEOUS SCENES. RENFREWSHIRE)
1930s

| 16mm | b/w | silent | 345ft | REF |

[filmed by John P. Ritchie]

Miscellaneous scenes of Renfrewshire life, including trams, a wedding and family holidays.

0778   (SCENES AT RENFREWSHIRE HUNT)
1930c

| 16mm | b/w | silent | 432ft | REF |

[filmed by John P. Ritchie]

The Renfrewshire hunt assembling and in progress and shots of a blacksmith shoeing horses.

0779   (MORE SPEED FOR LESS BAWBEES)
1930

| 16mm | b/w | silent | 27ft | VIEW |

p.c. Gaumont Graphic

The new "Railplane" invented by George Bennie is demonstrated in front of Glasgow officials who enjoy a free ride.

0780   (HUNT)

1935c

| 16mm | b/w | silent | 72ft | | REF |

[filmed by John P. Ritchie]

Scenes at a hunt (possibly Renfrewshire) and of a race meeting.

0782   (TO SHOW WAR)

1935c

| 16mm | b/w | silent | 48ft | | REF |

[filmed by John P. Ritchie]

A small single-engined bi-plane taxiing in a private air field before taking off and landing.

0783   (FEEDING BIRDS)

1935c

| 16mm | b/w | silent | 72ft | | REF |

[filmed by John P. Ritchie]

Horses and hounds assembling before a hunt, and shots of a woman feeding birds.

0784   ("EMPRESS OF BRITAIN")

1931/'35c

| 16mm | b/w | silent | 54ft | | REF |

filmed by John P. Ritchie

A race meeting showing a race in progress. Shots of the liner "Empress of Britain" being towed down the River Clyde with crowds watching from the bank.

0785   HEART IS HIGHLAND, THE

1952

| 16mm | col | comopt | 755ft | | VIEW |

sp. British Transport Films
p. Edgar Anstey
d. John Taylor

Tourist attractions in the Highlands including Pitlochry, Rannoch Moor, Castle Urquhart on Loch Ness, and Ben Nevis Distillery.

0786   (RACE MEETING)

1935c

| 16mm | b/w | silent | 90ft | | REF |

[filmed by John P. Ritchie]

Scenes at the races, possibly Lanark.

0787   (HUNT NO. 2)

1935c

| 16mm | b/w | silent | 78ft | | REF |

[filmed by John P. Ritchie]

Coverage of an unknown hunt, possibly Renfrewshire.

0788   (MARQUIS OF BUTE/BUTE MOUNT STEWART)

1935c

| 16mm | b/w | silent | 102ft | | REF |

[filmed by John P. Ritchie]

Open day at the Marquis of Bute's estate.

0789   (BIRDS AND HORSE JUMPING)

1935c

| 16mm | b/w | silent | 100ft | | REF |

[filmed by John P. Ritchie]

Birds nesting and horses jumping.

0790   (TRIMS)

1935c

| 16mm | b/w | silent | 30ft. | | REF |

[filmed by John P. Ritchie]

Trims showing a hunt meeting, possibly Renfrewshire, and a shot of soldiers throwing grenades.

0791   [BORDERS LOCAL NEWSREELS NO. 1]

1897-1914

| 35mm | b/w | silent | 2100ft | | VIEW |

[filmed by D. Gaylor]

Scenes of Border life, including Hawick and Selkirk Common Riding, Lord Robert's visit to Hawick and laying the foundation stone of Jedburgh Town Hall.

0792   [BORDERS LOCAL NEWSREELS NO. 2]

1897-1914

| 35mm | b/w | silent | 2340ft | | VIEW |

p.c. Topical Budget News
[filmed by D. Gaylor]

Amateur footage of scenes of Border life, including the Selkirk and Hawick Common Riding Festivals, rugby matches and Victory at Pretoria procession. The latter part of the film contains a compilation of newsreel footage including President Wilson reviewing the troops and Investiture ceremonies at Buckingham Palace.

0793   EVACUATION OF ST. KILDA

1930

| 16mm | b/w | silent | 300ft | | VIEW |

[filmed by John P. Ritchie]

The preparations and evacuation of the island of St. Kilda which lies 50 miles off the Western Isles. 27th August 1930.

0794   (GLASGOW TRAMS C1902)

1902c

| 16mm | b/w | silent | 54ft | | VIEW |

Trams in the city centre of Glasgow.

65

0795	(ARRIVAL AT WHITEHART HOTEL. CAMPBELTOWN)

1914

| 35mm | b/w | silent | 350ft | VIEW |

[filmed by Randall Burnette]

Filmed by the owner of the De Luxe Cinemas in Rothesay and Glasgow, showing soldiers bound for camp arriving at Campbeltown, together with their supplies in horse-drawn carts and wagons.

0796	DUMFRIESSHIRE JOURNEY

1963*

| 16mm | col | mute | 570ft | REF |

filmed by SEFA (Dumfriesshire Group)

An introduction to Dumfriesshire in the Borders, including Gretna, Annan, the Solway Firth and Caerlaverock. Historical areas such as the Covenanters' monument, Robert Burns country and Maxwellton House.

0797	COASTS OF CLYDE, THE

1959

| 16mm | col | comopt | 770ft | VIEW |

p.c. British Transport Films
d. James Ritchie

A trip down the Clyde by passenger steamer to Millport including footage of the Cowal Games, Dunoon, Rothesay and the Isle of Arran.

0798	STRATHYRE TO BROADFORD. SKYE. BY TRAIN AND BOAT

1930

| 16mm | b/w | silent | 63ft | VIEW |

filmed by Revd. H. R. Harvey

Passengers travel from Perthshire to Broadford, Skye, by train and boat.

Lady Lauder in Rothesay, 1922. Holidaymakers at the seafront, Rothesay. Ref. 2339

0799   SINGING STREET, THE
1951

| 16mm | b/w | comopt | 654ft | VIEW |

[p.c. Norton Park Group]
[filmed by Nigel McIsaac, Raymond Townsend, James T. Ritchie]
Collection of children's street games filmed in the back streets of Edinburgh accompanied by traditional children's songs.

0800   [CAITHNESS, ORKNEY, KIRKWALL]
1965*

| 16mm | b/w | commag | 2457ft | REF |

p.c. Grampian Television
Stock footage of the North East including Grampian TV studios, life on the Orkney Isles, Caithness and local industries.

0801   [CAITHNESS, ORKNEY]
1964*

| 16mm | b/w | commag | 2358ft | REF |

p.c. Grampian Television
Life in the Highlands and Orkney Isles; residents talk about their reasons for leaving Thurso, including high food prices, and unemployment. Industries in the area, Dounreay Power Station, and tourism. [Rushes only.]

0802   WILL YE NO' COME BACK AGAIN
1965c

| 16mm | b/w | comopt | 1014ft | REF |

p.c. Grampian Television
d. & p. Edward Joffe
Scottish emigrants in Australia and how they settled into their new environment.

0803   (DANCE SEQUENCES)
1970c

| 16mm | col | comopt | 888ft | REF |

p.c. Grampian Television
d. & p. Anthony J. Bacon
Various types of dance, including 17th century in period costume, Highland and Basque dancing. [Rushes only.]

0804   GREAT SCOT - MARY SLESSOR
1965

| 16mm | b/w | comopt | 772ft | REF |

p.c. Grampian Television
The life and times of Church of Scotland missionary Mary Slessor. Her work in Africa and the lives she saved through religion and hospital care.

0805   (KIRKWALL, WICK, DOUNREAY)
1965*

| 16mm | b/w | mute | 1368ft | REF |

p.c. Grampian Television
Trims from a documentary including shots of Dounreay power station, and rural and urban scenes in Caithness and the Orkney Isles.

0806   SO MANY PARTINGS
1966*

| 16mm | b/w | comopt | 966ft | REF |

p.c. Grampian Television
d. Edward Joffe
Traditional songs reflecting emigration, set to scenes of farewells and the old ways of life.

0807   INVERNESS REMEMBRANCE SUNDAY
1949*

| 35mm | b/w | silent | 808ft | REF |

[filmed by James S. Nairn for the Playhouse, Inverness]
Memorial service and procession to commemorate Remembrance Sunday in Inverness.

0808   GORDONSTOUN SCHOOL GARDEN FETE
1949

| 35mm | b/w | silent | 935ft | VIEW |

[filmed by James S. Nairn for the Playhouse, Inverness]
Footage of Gordonstoun School garden fete. An obstacle race and various stalls are enjoyed by the boys. HRH the Duke of Edinburgh attends the fete.

67

0809   (GLASGOW ACADEMY SPORTS)
1917

| 35mm | b/w | silent | 605ft | REF |

[attributed to James Hart]
Coverage of Glasgow Academy Sports Day, including footage of the flat race, high jump, three legged race and prize giving.

0810A   (TAIN CARNIVAL 1935)
1935*

| 35mm | b/w | silent | 350ft | VIEW |

Scenes of carnival celebrations, floats procession and crowning of the Carnival Queen.

0810B   (TAIN CARNIVAL 1936)
1936

| 35mm | b/w | silent | 135 ft | VIEW |

Scenes of carnival celebrations, crowning of Carnival Queen, floats and procession.

0811   LOCHGELLY EQUITABLE CO-OPERATIVE SOCIETY'S SHOPPING WEEK

1927

35mm	b/w	silent	577ft	VIEW

The Co-op building and its staff. Fancy dress and floats procession. 4th - 9th July 1927.

0812   MOWER MADNESS

1939

16mm	b/w	silent	369ft	VIEW

filmed by C.E. Marshall and F.M. Marshall

One of a series of story films - this one about a lawn mower that goes out of control. [Won best fiction at 6th SAFF, and was the first British film to win an award at the international UNICA festival in 1947.]

0813   KIRKCALDY HOSPITAL PAGEANT

1925

35mm	b/w	silent	796ft	VIEW

sp. Opera House, Kirkcaldy
p.c. Pathe

Scenes of celebrations, including a fancy dress parade and decorated horse-drawn floats.

0814   QUEEN LAUDS SCOTTISH EXHIBITION, GLASGOW

1949

16mm	b/w	comopt	70ft	REF

p.c. Pathe News

The Queen opens the Scottish Industries Exhibition in the Kelvin Hall, Glasgow. Princess Margaret accompanies her.

0815   (GAUMONT SOUND MIRROR. 1927-1931)

1927-'31

16mm	b/w	comopt	181ft	REF

p.c. Gaumont

Cinema shots. Scenes of Highlands and tourist areas, also of a London dance band.

0816   AMERICAN AMBASSADOR SPEAKS OUT

1939

16mm	b/w	comopt	42ft	VIEW

p.c. Gaumont British News

US Ambassador Joseph Kennedy receives Freedom of the City of Edinburgh at the Usher Hall. In his speech he remarks on the war.

0817   AMBASSADOR KENNEDY IN EDINBURGH

1939

16mm	b/w	comopt	24ft	VIEW

p.c. Movietone News

US Ambassador Joseph Kennedy at the ceremony of the Freedom of the City in the Usher Hall, Edinburgh.

0818   PRIME MINISTER IN SCOTLAND

1942*

16mm	b/w	comopt	316ft	VIEW

p.c. Scottish Movietone News

Winston Churchill visits the Home Fleet in Scotland and receives the Freedom of the City of Edinburgh. Churchill speaks of German attitudes to the war.

0819   ROYAL VISIT TO SCOTLAND

1937

16mm	b/w	comopt	664ft	VIEW

p.c. Gaumont British News

King George VI and Queen Elizabeth's coronation visit to Scotland for the Ceremony of the Keys and the Order of the Thistle in Edinburgh. They visit Leith, Glasgow and the Musselburgh races.

0820   [ARGYLLSHIRE PIERS]

1935*

35mm	b/w	silent	255ft	VIEW

Piers in Argyllshire, in particular Rothesay and the entrance to the Crinan Canal at Ardrishaig. [Section from ref. 0253]

0821   (BOY SCOUTS PARADE, SCOTLAND)

1946*

35mm	b/w	silent	45ft	REF

A Boy Scouts' parade.

0822   (OTTER HUNTING AND PROCESSION)

pre-1916

35mm	b/w	silent	90ft	REF

[filmed by Mr. Gaylor]

Footage of otter hunt and unidentified civic procession, possibly in the Borders.

0823   (FAIR FESTIVAL)

1950*

35mm	b/w	silent	883ft	VIEW

Film of an unidentified Fair Festival. Fancy dress parade, fete, including a "penny farthing" bicycle.

0824	TROOPING OF THE COLOUR. 1ST BATTALION KOSB...				
1935*					
35mm	b/w	silent	530ft		VIEW

The 1st Battallion King's Own Scottish Borderers at Fort George troop the colour, Brigadier General D. A. Macfarlane takes the salute.

0825	[TAIN CARNIVAL AND ELGIN GALA WEEK]				
1950					
35mm	b/w	silent	1000ft		VIEW

sp. Caledonian Associated Cinemas
[filmed by James S. Nairn]

Tain and Elgin Carnival Queens are chosen. Parade of pipe bands and floats.

0826A	AT YOUR SERVICE - DUMFRIES AND GALLOWAY ROYAL INFIRMARY				
1935					
35mm	b/w	silent	873ft		REF

[filmed by Konomy Pictures]

The hospital services of Dumfries and Galloway Royal Infirmary.

0826B	AT YOUR SERVICE				
1935					
35mm	b/w	silent	860ft		VIEW

[filmed by Konomy Pictures]

Made to raise funds for Dumfries and Galloway Royal Infirmary, the film shows an emergency patient being treated in hospital, the out-patients department and the children's ward.

0827	(INVERNESS COMPILATION)				
1937-'40					
35mm	b/w	silent	1034ft		VIEW

[filmed as a local topical for the Playhouse, Inverness]

Events in Inverness; the Northern Counties Show and Inverness proclaims the new King, Edward VIII.

0828	(CAPTIONS AND ADVERTS)				
1955-'59c					
35mm	b/w&col	comopt	480ft		REF

Cinema confectionery and ice-cream adverts.

0829	BIRTHDAY GREETINGS TO QUEEN MARY				
1950c					
16mm	b/w	comopt	115ft		VIEW

p.c. Gaumont British News

Made to celebrate Queen Mary's 85th birthday, the newsreel is a compilation of events in her life, including meeting the troops during the 1st World War, celebrating the return of King George after his illness, and attending Wimbledon.

0830	(HUNTING)				
1930c					
16mm	b/w	silent	72ft		REF

filmed by John P. Ritchie

Scenes of a hunt with horse and hounds, possibly Renfrewshire.

0831	(RACING)				
1930c					
16mm	b/w	silent	90ft		REF

filmed by John P. Ritchie

Scenes of a hunt with horse and hounds, possibly Renfrewshire.

0832	(CINEMA SALES KIOSK)				
1950s					
35mm	b/w	silent	110ft		REF

Cinema advert for ice-cream sales in the Lyceum Cinema, Dumfries.

0833	MISS VIOLET HOPSON VISITS DUNDEE FIRE STATION				
1920c					
35mm	b/w	silent	400ft		VIEW

filmed as a local topical for La Scala Cinema, Dundee

Miss Violet Hopson and companion, probably Stewart Rome, visit Dundee fire station and watch a fire fighting display.

0834	[EUROPEAN COD FESTIVAL. GOUROCK]				
1978					
16mm	col	mute	100ft		REF

[filmed by Ricky Walker]

Anglers at Gourock pier line up to have their catches weighed at the European cod festival.

69

0835	RAILWAY JOURNEY				
1947c					
16mm	col	silent	312ft		VIEW

p.c. GB Instructional
p. John C. Elder

A train journey from Glasgow to Oban in the Highlands.

0836	CONSIDER THE CARPET				
1953*					
16mm	b/w	comopt	636ft		REF

sp. Hoover Limited
p.c. Oswald Skilbeck Productions
d. Winifred Holmes

The manufacturing of Axminster, Wilton and Chenille carpets and methods used for their cleaning.

0837	ENOUGH TO EAT? - THE NUTRITION FILM				
1936					
16mm	b/w	comopt	798ft		REF

sp. Gas Industry
p.c. Merton Park Studios
d. Edgar Anstey

Made in 1936, this documentary set out to promote the principles of healthy eating, as part of a wartime food policy.

0838	(DR. MACINTYRE'S X-RAY CABINET)				
1909c					
35mm	b/w	silent	15ft		VIEW

Single shot of a man behind an x-ray screen on which his x-ray is clearly visible. Another man sits on a chair to the right of the screen. [See also ref. 0520, 2714.]

0839	(STREET PROCESSION)				
1925c					
35mm	b/w	silent	122ft		VIEW

Street procession through George Square beside the City Chambers, Glasgow.

0840A	PROVOST JOHN SINCLAIR SHOWS ORKNEY GUIDES AROUND THE HARBOUR AT THURSO				
1949					
16mm	b/w	silent	274ft		REF

[filmed by the Silver Jubilee Girl Guides Association]

Provost John Sinclair shows the Orkney Girl Guides the harbour at Thurso as part of the Guides Silver Jubilee rally.

0840B	VISIT OF HER ROYAL HIGHNESS THE PRINCESS ROYAL TO WICK				
1949c					
16mm	b/w	silent	56ft		REF

The Princess Royal arriving at Wick airport escorted by the Lord Provost and local dignitaries.

0841	CHURCHILL RECEIVES FREEDOM OF PERTH				
1948					
16mm	b/w	silent	140ft		VIEW

[p.c. Scottish Film Productions]

Provost John Ure Primrose presents the freedom of the city of Perth to Churchill.

0842	(OPENING OF GREEN'S PLAYHOUSE. DUNDEE)				
1936c					
16mm	b/w	comopt	152ft		VIEW

Graphics used to describe the furnishings and facilities in the new Green's Playhouse, Dundee.

0843	CINEMA TRADE GOLF CHAMPIONSHIP				
1930c					
16mm	b/w	silent	40ft		REF

p.c. Gaumont Graphic News

A group of Scottish trade employees on a golf course watching play at the Cinema Trade Golf Championship.

0844	GLASGOW'S HOUSING PROBLEM AND ITS SOLUTION				
1917-'20c					
16mm	b/w	silent	81ft		VIEW

sp. Glasgow Corporation
p.c. Green's Film Service

Plans for new housing in Glasgow and building tradesmen at work on building sites.

0845	(RONNIE JAY WITH KING GEORGE V1)				
1940c					
16mm	b/w	silent	3ft		VIEW

[filmed by Ronald L. Jay]

Brief shot of Ronald L. Jay, news cameraman, showing King George VI how his camera works in the grounds of Balmoral.

0846	PORTRAIT D'UN OISEAU				
1950c					
16mm	b/w	comopt	73ft		VIEW

sp. SEFA and the SFC
p.c. Campbell Harper Films Ltd.

Francette Vernillat relates the story of the bird in French. [From "Pardes" by Jacques Prevert.]

70

0847 (STANLEY RUSSELL TALKS ABOUT SCOTTISH FILM PRODUCTIONS)
1937

16mm		sep opt	132ft		REF

[p.c. BBC radio]

Recording on film soundtrack of the BBC Radio interview with Stanley Russell concerning the activities of Scottish Film Productions. [Soundtrack only.]

0848 L'ANNIVERSAIRE
1950

16mm	b/w	comopt	504ft	VIEW

sp. SEFA and SFC
p.c. Campbell Harper Films Ltd.

The first film to be made in Scotland by a company of French players speaking their own language, it tells the story of a mother's birthday.

0849 SCOTTISH CUP FINAL. ABERDEEN V CELTIC AT HAMPDEN PARK, 24TH APRIL, 1937
1937

16mm	b/w	silent	250ft	VIEW

filmed by Jay's Film Service for Green's Playhouse, Glasgow

The Scottish Cup Final at Hampden Park, Glasgow where Celtic beats Aberdeen 2:1. Footage of the crowds making their way to the ground, watching the match in progress and the winning team having their photograph taken with the trophy.

0850 RIVER CREE, THE
1950c

16mm	b/w	comopt	248ft	VIEW

sp. SEFA in assoc. with Scottish Country Dance Association
p.c. Thames and Clyde Film Co.
d. Stanley Russell

Dancers demonstrate the various steps of the Scottish dance "The River Cree".

0851 TINY WINGS
1946*

16mm	b/w	comopt	248ft	REF

p.c. Thames and Clyde Film Co.
p. Stanley L. Russell

A "featurette" on model aircraft.

0852 (SNOW)
1947

16mm	b/w	silent	18ft	VIEW

The winter blizzards of 1947: blocked roads and abandoned vehicles in the snow. [See also ref. 0875.]

0853 (PRINCE AT COCONUT SHY)
1925c

16mm	b/w	silent	20ft	VIEW

p.c. Green's Film Service

The Prince of Wales at a coconut shy as police patrol the crowds.

0854 (SIR HENRY FOWLER)
1930c

16mm	b/w	silent	42ft	VIEW

Photograph and captions of Sir Henry Fowler, Chief Mechanical Engineer of the London Midland and Scottish Railway, and designer of the "Royal Scot", intercut with shot of engine turning.

0855 (NEWCOMEN ENGINE)
1935c

16mm	b/w	silent	126ft	REF

A demonstration of the model of the Newcomen engine for which James Watt in 1765 invented a separate condenser and thus, discovered the steam engine.

0856 OPENING INVERNESS MUNICIPAL AIRPORT BY HIS GRACE THE DUKE OF SUTHERLAND
1933

16mm	b/w	silent	122ft	VIEW

[filmed as a local topical for the Playhouse, Inverness]

The opening ceremony of Inverness municipal airport by his Grace the Duke of Sutherland, at which there is a demonstration jump by champion parachutist John Tranum.

0857 (SHIELDHALL PART TWO)
1930c

16mm	b/w	silent	384ft	REF

sp. SCWS

The manufacturing processes of the Co-op's products of coffee essence, 'Unitas' breakfast oats, cigarettes and hosiery at the Shieldhall factory in Glasgow.

0858 KEEPING STEP WITH THE TIMES
1933*

16mm	b/w	silent	642ft	REF

sp. SCWS
p.c. Jay's Film Service
d. Ronald L. Jay

The manufacturing processes involved in the production of shoes at the Co-op Shieldhall factory in Glasgow.

71

0859	HOW GUILD MARGARINE IS MADE				
1928c					
16mm	b/w	silent	246ft		VIEW

[sp. SCWS]

The production of SCWS Guild Margarine.

0860	(RED CROSS PRISONERS OF WAR PARCELS' FUND)				
1945					
16mm	b/w	silent	146ft		VIEW

[sp. Caledonian Associated Cinemas]

A "thank-you" from the directors of the Caledonian Associated Cinemas to their public and staff for raising money for the Red Cross Prisoners of War Parcels' Fund Film.

0861	(GLASGOW 1947)				
1947c					
16mm	b/w	comopt	18ft		REF

Sir Harry Lauder (at a dockside quay) accepts a gift from Boston to Scotland of 450 tons of food and clothing.

0862	GIRLS' CLUBS APPEAL				
1939*					
16mm	b/w	comopt	84ft		REF

An appeal for Scottish Girls' clubs highlighting the various activities offered.

0863A	(FRED ARCHER)				
1930c					
16mm	b/w	silent	27ft		REF

Shots of racehorses with their trainer, Fred Archer.

0863B	(AIR CIRCUS CAPTION)				
1934c					
16mm	b/w	silent	20ft		REF

A cinema trailer for the Scottish Flying Clubs' Annual Air Circus Joy Riding Festival.

0863C	(SPOT THE SPOT)				
1926*					
16mm	b/w	silent	42ft		REF

A cinema competition to "spot the spots" in Glasgow offering a prize of 10/6d for the first four correct answers sent in.

0864	(R101 AIRSHIP)				
1930					
16mm	b/w	silent	84ft		VIEW

p.c. Pathe Super Gazette

Newsreel footage of the ill-fated R101 before her last journey, aerial shots from the airship and shots of its twisted metal remains after the crash.

0865	(ALLOA ADVERTS)				
1935c					
16mm	b/w	silent	156ft		REF

Cinema adverts for various commercial establishments in the Alloa area including the County Laundry, Logie & Co. (ladies' wear), S.D. Cargill (newsagents) and the Royal Oak Hotel.

0866	(GIVE US MORE SHIPS)				
1942					
16mm	b/w	comopt	144ft		REF

sp. National Savings Committee
p.c. Merton Park Studios

An appeal for more warships and cargo ships "to win this war" featuring ships under construction and Nelson's flagship 'Victory'.

0867	(MINISTRY OF FOOD FLASHES)				
1939-'45c					
16mm	b/w	comopt	45ft		REF

Government sponsored promotion on how to save flour and an advert for powdered milk.

0868	(HAIR STYLIST)				
1936*					
16mm	b/w	silent	198ft		REF

Shots of women's hair being styled with examples of finished coiffures.

0869	PRINCESS LAUNCHES HMS ?				
1944					
16mm	b/w	comopt	45ft		VIEW

p.c. Movietone News

Launch of HMS "Vanguard" from John Brown's yard, Clydebank. [Information withheld in film due to wartime censorship.]

0870A	(TCC NO. 5: ASTLAND MARGERISON. VERA BARTON)				
1949					
16mm	b/w	silent	96ft		REF

[p.c. Thames and Clyde]

General shots of a dredger as it clears a river bed.

0870B   ("SAVICK")
1949*

16mm	b/w	silent	138ft	REF

[p.c. Thames and Clyde]

Interior and exterior shots of the dredger "Savick".

0870C   ("HAFFAZ MERSEY")
1949*

16mm	b/w	silent	36ft	REF

[p.c. Thames and Clyde]

Footage taken on board a dredger at work.

0871   (MAVOR COULSON)
1949*

16mm	b/w	silent	36ft	REF

[sp. Mavor and Coulson Limited]

Men working in engineering works, with some precision work being carried out.

0872   (DUMFRIES, GUID NYCHBURRIS DAY)
1949*

16mm	b/w	silent	200ft	REF

[filmed as a local topical for the Lyceum Cinema, Dumfries]

Crowning of the festival queen, the procession of floats and marching pipe band to cheering crowds at the annual Dumfries "Guid Nychburris Day".

0873A   ABERDEEN HIGH SCHOOL FOR GIRLS PRIMARY SPORTS
1940c

16mm	b/w	silent	96ft	REF

[filmed by Ernest Bromberg for the Newscine, Aberdeen]

At the primary school sports with shots of sprinting, the egg and spoon, skipping and sack races.

0873B   (HIGHLAND GAMES, ABERDEEN)
1940c

16mm	b/w	silent	42ft	REF

[filmed by Ernest Bromberg for the Newscine, Aberdeen]

Country dance displays and a pipe band at a Highland Games.

0873C   (TABLE TENNIS)
1940c

16mm	b/w	silent	48ft	REF

[filmed by Ernest Bromberg for the Newscine, Aberdeen]

A table tennis game in progress, amateur dramatics and a keep-fit class.

0873D   (WAITING CROWDS)
1940c

16mm	b/w	silent	18ft	REF

[filmed by Ernest Bromberg for the Newscine, Aberdeen]

Crowds waiting for the Duchess of Gloucester, in Aberdeen. [Trim only]

0874   (PRIEST'S FUNERAL)
1937*

16mm	b/w	silent	160ft	VIEW

[filmed by Ernest Bromberg for the Newscine, Aberdeen]

The funeral procession and the "last farewell " played by a piper at the graveside of a priest [unidentified.]

0875A   (SALVATION ARMY)
1940c

16mm	b/w	silent	35ft	VIEW

[filmed by Ernest Bromberg for the Newscine, Aberdeen]

The Salvation Army outside the Aberdeen Citadel celebrating a visit by General and Mrs Carpenter.

0875B   FLICKS ROYAL HIGHLAND GATHERING AT BRAEMAR
1937c

16mm	b/w	silent	90ft	VIEW

[filmed by Ernest Bromberg for the Newscine, Aberdeen]

King George VI, Queen Elizabeth and the two Princesses at the Royal Highland Gathering at Braemar.

0875C   (BUS OUTING, ABERDEENSHIRE)
1940c

16mm	b/w	silent	72ft	VIEW

[filmed by Ernest Bromberg for the Newscine, Aberdeen]

People on an outing, boarding buses with shots taken inside the buses and as they move off.

0875D   (MEN CLEARING ROAD)
1947

16mm	b/w	silent	42ft	VIEW

[filmed by Ernest Bromberg for the Newscine, Aberdeen]

Taken in Aberdeenshire during the winter blizzards of 1947, the film shows abandoned vehicles in snow and men clearing the road with shovels. [See also ref. 0852.]

73

Presentation of Freedom of the Burgh, Dingwall 1951. Waiting for the celebrities. Ref. 0596

74

0876   (HOW BLUEBELL MARGARINE IS MADE)

1927c

| 16mm | b/w | silent | 366ft | VIEW |

[sp. SCWS]

The manufacturing processes involved in the production of 'Bluebell' margarine at the Co-operative creamery in Wigtownshire. [Incomplete, Part I only.]

0877   (MAKING SOAP)

1927c

| 16mm | b/w | silent | 781ft | VIEW |

[sp. SCWS]

The manufacturing of soap at the Co-op's Grangemouth factory.

0878   (GUID NYCHBURRIS CELEBRATIONS)

1951*

| 35mm | b/w | silent | 885ft | REF |

[filmed as a local topical for the Lyceum Cinema, Dumfries]

Footage of the "Guid Nychburris Day" celebrations in Dumfries, festivities include the coronation of the festival queen and the cornet opening the "city gates".

0879   (KIRKCALDY PAGEANT WEEK 1951)

1951

| 35mm | b/w | silent | 1230ft | REF |

[filmed as a local topical for the Rio Cinema, Kirkcaldy]

The parade with decorated floats, a fancy dress competition and dancing display at Kirkcaldy Pageant Week.

0880   GLENROTHES FESTIVAL WEEK

1963

| 35mm | b/w | silent | 1140ft | REF |

filmed as a local topical for Caledonian Associated Cinemas

Events during Glenrothes festival week including the presentation of sashes to the festival "Lad and Lass", proclamation by the town crier, and a dance display.

0881	**(CINEMA ADVERTISEMENTS)**				
1953-'70c					
35mm	*col*	*comopt*	*c1000ft*		*REF*

sp. Langfords

Cinema adverts for local businesses in Leven, and confectionery ads. for 'Thunderbirds' 'Zoom', 'Orbit' and 'Captain Scarlet' ice lollies.

0882	**RIVER TWEED**			
1951				
16mm	*b/w*	*silent*	*385ft*	*VIEW*

sp. SEFA and SFC
p.c. Campbell Harper Films Ltd.

The River Tweed from source to sea; the agriculture, industry, landscape and people living by its banks.

0883	**[TAIN CARNIVAL 1937]**			
1937				
16mm	*b/w*	*silent*	*260ft*	*REF*

[filmed by James S. Nairn]

The carnival queen is chosen and the festival procession moves through the streets of Tain.

0884	**[TAIN CARNIVAL 1949]**			
1949				
16mm	*b/w*	*silent*	*240ft*	*REF*

[filmed by James S. Nairn]

The crowning of the carnival queen and procession of floats.

0885	**FIFE**			
1950				
16mm	*b/w*	*silent*	*414ft*	*VIEW*

sp. SEFA and the SFC
p.c. Campbell Harper Films Ltd.

A look at the agriculture, industries and the towns of Fife.

0886	**LEAGUE MATCH. QUEEN OF THE SOUTH V HIBERNIANS**			
1949c				
16mm	*b/w*	*silent*	*40ft*	*REF*

filmed as a local topical for the Lyceum Cinema, Dumfries
Shots of the crowd and league game in progress.

0887	**(CANOE RACE)**			
1930s				
16mm	*b/w*	*silent*	*215ft*	*VIEW*

Amateur footage of competitors taking part in a canoe race.

0888	**HOMES FOR THE PEOPLE**			
1947c				
16mm	*b/w*	*comopt*	*650ft*	*VIEW*

sp. Daily Herald
p.c. Basic Films

A discussion of the problems of housing in poverty stricken areas of Britain.

0889	**IMMORTAL MEMORY OF ROBERT BURNS**			
1946				
16mm	*b/w*	*comopt*	*756ft*	*VIEW*

p.c.Thames and Clyde
d. Stanley L. Russell

A tour of Burns' country illustrated with poems and songs.

0890	**(ARMISTICE DAY MEMORIAL SERVICE)**			
1949*				
16mm	*b/w*	*silent*	*39ft*	*VIEW*

[filmed as a local topical for the Lyceum Cinema, Dumfries]

Armistice day memorial service in the Borders town of Dumfries at the war memorial.

0891	**(EAST KILBRIDE DEVELOPMENT CORPORATION TRIMS 1947/'54)**			
1947/ '54*				
35mm	*b/w*	*mute*	*3086ft*	*REF*

sp. East Kilbride Development Corporation
p.c. Thames and Clyde

Material shot for a film entitled "A Town in the Making", 1962. Footage of the construction of East Kilbride new town and its factories.

0892	**ONCE BEFORE NOON**			
1948				
16mm	*b/w*	*comopt*	*340ft*	*REF*

Animation, with music, about a young girl's adventures in a Czechoslovak Co-op store.

0893	**SUNNY DAYS**			
1931				
16mm	*b/w*	*sep mag*	*1192ft*	*VIEW*

sp. Glasgow Necessitous Children's Holiday Camp Fund
filmed by Ronald L. Jay

One of the films annually made to raise money for the Glasgow Necessitous Children's Holiday Camp Fund showing Glasgow children enjoying a holiday on the East Coast.

75

0894   (ST. ENOCH STATION, GLASGOW)

1960

16mm	b/w	silent	42ft	VIEW

[filmed by Oliver F. Carter]

St. Enoch Station, Glasgow, with various steam locomotives in the station.

0895   THEY FOUND A FUTURE

1946c

16mm	b/w	comopt	1776ft	VIEW

sp. SCWS
p. Edward Cook

A promotional film to highlight the benefits of a career with the Scottish Co-operative Society, it shows the manufacturing processes involved in the production of Co-op goods and the work of some of its regional shops.

0896   (PRE MATCH DISPLAY. HAMPDEN STADIUM)

1949-'50c

16mm	col	silent	375ft	REF

[sp. Daily Record]

Pre-match displays of keep-fit by the Glasgow Keep-Fit Movement, Scottish Country Dancing, pipe-bands, community singing led by Robert Wilson and various athletic events.

0897   [CORONATION CUP, CELTIC V HIBS]

1953

16mm	b/w	silent	245ft	REF

Footage of the final of the Coronation Cup - a special tournament to celebrate the Coronation. Jock Stein, captain of the winning team Celtic, receives the cup. [There was a crowd of 116,000 at the match.]

0898   (AGRICULTURAL SHOW, ISLAY?)

1953*

16mm	b/w	silent	155ft	REF

[sp. Daily Record]

An agricultural show, possibly on Islay with shots of livestock, a floats procession and spectators.

0899   HAMPDEN STORY, THE

1956

16mm	col	silent	195ft	REF

Pre-match display of keep-fit, pipe bands, races and community singing led by Robert Wilson at Hampden Stadium, Glasgow.

0900   (PRE MATCH ENTERTAINMENT)

1965

16mm	col	silent	318ft	REF

[sp. Daily Record]

Pre-football match display of bicycle and go-cart racing, keep-fit and community singing, Hampden Stadium, Glasgow.

0901   (NEW PRINTING PLANT. DAILY RECORD)

1971

16mm		sep opt	204ft	REF

Sound track for news item on the introduction of new Webb offset printing plant in the Daily Record building in Glasgow.

0902   [DAILY RECORD GARDEN CHAMPIONSHIP 1958]

1958

16mm	col	silent	224ft	REF

filmed by Scottish Daily Record

Some of the "best gardens" in Forfar, Kilmarnock, Kelso and Bellshill taking part in the Daily Record Garden Championship.

0904   (TEAZIE WEAZIE)

1956

16mm	b/w	silent	185ft	REF

Displays of Highland dancing, ballet and scenes at a fashion show in St. Andrew's Halls, Glasgow. A poster reads "Television's Teazie Weazie (Raymond) presents the Ballet of the Hairpin".

0905   (POSSIBLY RANGERS V HEARTS 1952)

1952

16mm	b/w	silent	60ft	REF

Shots of a football match, possibly Rangers v Hearts.

0906   (POSSIBLY RANGERS V CELTIC 1955)

1955

16mm	b/w	silent	72ft	REF

Shots of a football match, possibly Rangers v Celtic at Hampden Stadium, Glasgow.

0907   (GEORGE YOUNG AD.)

1965c

16mm	col	silent	42ft	REF

sp. Daily Record

Advert for a football book by George Young, formerly Scotland's national team captain.

0908   INDUSTRIAL BRITAIN
1931

16mm	b/w	comopt	435ft		REF

sp. Empire Marketing Board
p.c. Gaumont British Picture Comporation Ltd.
p. Grierson and Flaherty

A survey of industry in Britain, emphasising the importance of craftsmanship. [Incomplete.]

0909   MIRROR FROM THE EAST
1951*

16mm	b/w	silent	390ft		VIEW

The secret of author George Gunter's successful Eastern plots for his books.

0910   GROWING CONCERN, A
1950c

16mm	col	comopt	1218ft	VIEW

sp. A. & G. Paterson Limited
p.c. Commercial and Educational Films Limited
d. John Oliver

Re-afforestation on Deeside.

0911   ST. KILDA - THE LONELY ISLANDS
1967*

16mm	col	comopt	1334ft	VIEW

sp. Films of Scotland
d. Christopher Mylne

Birdlife on St. Kilda, restoration by the National Trust for Scotland, and the military presence on the island, which lies 50 miles off the Western Isles.

0912   HEART OF SCOTLAND, THE
1962

16mm	col	comopt	840ft		VIEW

sp. Films of Scotland
p.c. Templar Film Studios
d. Laurence Henson

The history and industries of Stirlingshire. [Treatment by John Grierson.]

0913   WHAT ABOUT THE WORKERS
1965*

16mm	b/w	comopt	1242ft	VIEW

p.c. Mithras Films
p. Maurice Hatton

A history of the British Trade Union Movement since 1880.

0914   SOUTHERN SCOTLAND
1961

16mm	col	comopt	580ft		VIEW

sp. Educational Films of Scotland
p.c. Campbell Harper Films Ltd.

A geographical study of Scotland south of the Girvan/Dunbar fault line.

0915   GLASGOW
1963

16mm	col	comopt	726ft		VIEW

sp. Educational Films of Scotland
p.c. Park Film Studios
d. Douglas Gray

The early history and development of Glasgow, changes brought about by the Industrial Revolution and proposed plans for remodelling the city.

0916   PADDY'S MILESTONE
1947*

16mm	b/w	sep opt	1130ft		VIEW

sp. Andrew Kay and Company, Mauchline
p.c.Elder Dalrymple Productions
d. J. Blake Dalrymple

Ailsa Craig or "Paddy's Milestone" as the source of rock for the manufacture of curling stones.

0917   GLASGOW - MASS ASSAULT ON TB
1957

16mm	b/w	silent	114ft		VIEW

p.c. Pathe

The campaign against tuberculosis in Glasgow.

0918   DAY AT MORAY HOUSE NURSERY SCHOOL, A
1949c

16mm	b/w	silent	400ft		VIEW

[p.c. Visual and Aural Aids Committee]

Children enjoying various activities at Moray House Nursery School in Edinburgh. [See also ref. 0919.]

0919   (AT NURSERY SCHOOL)
1949-'50*

16mm	b/w	silent	252ft		REF

Activities at Moray House Nursery School, Edinburgh. [See also ref. 0918.]

0920   (BUS TOUR, THE)
1966*

16mm	col	silent	66ft		REF

filmed by Mr. Clark

An amateur film of a coach tour to Tomintoul, Dufftown and Rhynie.

0921   GREAT MILL RACE, THE
1975

16mm	col	comopt	1086ft	VIEW

sp. Films of Scotland
p.c. Edinburgh Film Productions
d. Robin Crichton

Dramatised account of a race between an unscrupulous modern woollen mill and a traditional mill to make up a garment from original fleece to finished article.

77

0922 PROGRESS REPORT NO. 2
1948

35mm	b/w	comopt	900ft	VIEW

sp. Corporation of Glasgow Housing Committee
p.c. Thames and Clyde

Progress report regarding new Pollok housing estate on the outskirts of Glasgow. The contrast between new semi-detached houses and older tenements is illustrated.

0923 BENNY LYNCH SMASHES HIS WAY TO VICTORY..
1935

16mm	b/w	comopt	105ft	REF

p.c. British Movietone News

Benny Lynch versus Jackie Brown in the World Flyweight title fight in Manchester.

0924 LYNCH BEATS JURICH AT CATCHWEIGHTS
1938

16mm	b/w	comopt	72ft	REF

p.c. British Movietone News

Benny Lynch fights Jackie Jurich of America at Love Street, Paisley.

0925 (BENNY LYNCH V PAT PALMER FOR WORLD FLYWEIGHT TITLE)
1936

16mm	b/w	comopt	63ft	REF

Boxing title fight in Glasgow won by Benny Lynch.

0926A WORLD FLYWEIGHT CHAMPIONSHIP. BENNY LYNCH V PETER KANE
1937

16mm	b/w	comopt	102ft	REF

p.c. Empire News

World flyweight championship between Benny Lynch and Peter Kane at Shawfield stadium in Glasgow. Lynch wins by a knockout.

0926B BENNY LYNCH V PETER KANE (LIVERPOOL)
1938

16mm	b/w	comopt	144ft	REF

p.c. Pathe

Return boxing match between Benny Lynch and Peter Kane of Liverpool, which ends in a draw at Anfield.

0927 BASS ROCK AND TANTALLON CASTLE
1959c

16mm	b/w	silent	500ft	VIEW

Footage of Tantallon Castle and bird life on the Bass Rock.

0928 LIFE IN THE HIGHLANDS
1936

16mm	b/w	silent	720ft	VIEW

p.c. GB Instructional Films
d. John C. Elder

A family at work on their highland farm; harvesting, shearing sheep, collecting peat and spinning wool.

0929 (SCOTLAND'S LAST TRAM)
1962

16mm	col	silent	20ft	REF

[filmed by George Williamson]

Scotland's last tram (Coronation no.1282) on its final journey from Glasgow to Dalmuir.

0930 HAND TRANSPORT OF THE INJURED
1941

16mm	b/w	silent	150ft	VIEW

[filmed by Dr. A.G. Mearns and B.H. Humble]

Glasgow Boy Scouts demonstrate techniques for transporting the injured.

0931 AROUND INVERNESS
1946

35mm	b/w	silent	1000ft	VIEW

[filmed by James S. Nairn and James Atterson]

Views of Inverness and surrounding countryside, including Culloden Moor, Ben Nevis and Loch Ness.

0932 ARDNAMURCHAN
1949/'50

16mm	col	silent	420ft	VIEW

filmed by Iain Dunnachie

A prize-winning film at the 1950 Scottish Amateur Film Festival, it shows life in the crofting community on the Ardnamurchan peninsula.

0933 BY BORDER BYWAYS
1961*

16mm	col	sep opt	402ft	VIEW

filmed by E.G. Cairns

Animal and bird life found the in the Borders, including linnets, goldfinches, moles and partridges.

0934 CROFTING IN SKYE
1939c

16mm	b/w	silent	403ft	VIEW

filmed by SEFA (Glasgow Group)

Daily life and activities on a croft in Skye.

0935	CRIEFF HIGHLAND GATHERING				
1950					
16mm	col	silent	450ft		VIEW

sp. Scottish Film Council
filmed by T.H. Thoms and J.R.L. Halley

Events at the 1950 Crieff Highland Gathering, the first held after 1939.

0936	CROFTERS OF WESTER ROSS				
1950c					
16mm	b/w	silent	348ft		VIEW

filmed by John Gray

A look at the crofting and fishing communities of Wester Ross.

0937	DUMFRIES, QUEEN OF THE SOUTH				
1961					
16mm	col	silent	264ft		VIEW

p.c. Educational Films of Scotland

A description of the town of Dumfries in the Borders, the "Queen of the South".

0938	GLASGOW'S DOCKLANDS				
1959*					
16mm	b/w	comopt	400ft		VIEW

sp. Educational Films of Scotland
filmed by Enrico Cocozza

Glasgow's docklands; its workers, transportation and daily life.

0939	GLASGOW WELCOMES THE QUEEN				
1953					
16mm	col	silent	396ft		VIEW

[p.c. SFC from film shot by SAAC]

The Coronation visit to Scotland. Queen Elizabeth visits Glasgow and attends a youth display at Hampden stadium.

0940	ST. KILDA 1929				
1929					
35mm	b/w	silent	930ft		VIEW

[filmed by Frank Lowe]

Scenes of life on the island of St. Kilda, including footage of islanders catching fulmars and at their cottages.

0941	NOTHING'S TOO GOOD FOR YOUR CHILDREN				
1963*					
35mm	col	comopt	210ft		REF

sp. ABC Minors' Club

Short film made for the ABC's Saturday morning matinees showing the shooting of a Children's Film Foundation film and a fancy dress/talent competiton.

0942	(BARRHEAD FESTIVAL AND OLD FOLKS' OUTING)				
1951c					
16mm	b/w	silent	204ft		REF

Barrhead Festival celebrations and an old folks' outing to a large country house.

0943	(JOURNEY THROUGH BARRHEAD AND REVIEW OF THE FESTIVAL YEAR 1951)				
1951					
16mm	b/w	silent	594ft		REF

Scenes of Barrhead and district with shots of a garden fete and the return home of the Barrhead Amateur Players with the Howard de Welden trophy.

0944	(ADVERT FOR "THE MAGGIE")				
1968*					
35mm	col	comopt	96ft		REF

Cinema advert for "The Maggie", a public house adjacent to the ABC cinemas in Sauchiehall Street, Glasgow.

0945	(SATURDAY MORNING MATINEE)				
1963c					
35mm	b/w	silent	175ft		REF

A children's cinema matinee with a "twisting" competition; the winner is decided by the volume of cheering each receives.

0946	NETHERTON'S CORONATION DAY PROCESSION				
1953					
9.5mm	b/w	silent	930ft		REF

Netherton's Coronation Day procession; the opening of a community hall, a sale of work, an outing to Girvan and a carnival.

0947	OPENING OF "A CENTURY OF ENTERTAINMENT", THE				
1979					
super 8mm	col	silent	c150ft		REF

[filmed by John Fletcher]

The opening reception of the exhibition "A Century of Entertainment", concerning the history of the ABC, Sauchiehall Street, Glasgow, on 26th November 1979.

0948   OCHILTREE TILE WORKS
1951

| 16mm | b/w | silent | 305ft | | VIEW |

filmed by SEFA (Ayrshire Group)

The manufacturing processes involved in producing clay tiles. [Commended at the Scottish Amateur Film Festival 1951.]

0949   STONEHOUSE - CENTRE FOR SUCCESS (NO. 1)
1974

| 16mm | col | sep opt | 2030ft | | REF |

sp. East Kilbride and Stonehouse Development Corporation
p.c. Edinburgh Films
d. Robin Crichton

Rushes for unfinished film on the planning and construction of Stonehouse New Town.

0950   STONEHOUSE - CENTRE FOR SUCCESS
1975

| 16mm | col | comopt | 282ft | | VIEW |

sp. East Kilbride and Stonehouse Development Corporation
p.c. Edinburgh Films

Rushes for unfinished film on the planning and construction of Stonehouse New Town.

0951   STONEHOUSE NEW TOWN FESTIVAL
1975

| 16mm | col | mute | 4228ft | | REF |

sp. East Kilbride and Stonehouse Development Corporation
p.c. Edinburgh Film Productions

Rushes for unfinished film on planning and construction of Stonehouse New Town.

0952   STONEHOUSE - CENTRE FOR SUCCESS (NO. 4)
1976

| 16mm | col | mute | 804 ft | | REF |

sp. East Kilbride and Stonehouse Development Corporation
p.c. Edinburgh Films
d. Robin Crichton

Rushes for unfinished film on planning and construction of Stonehouse New Town.

0953   STONEHOUSE TRIMS
1970s

| 16mm | b/w&col | sep mag | c1000ft | | REF |

sp. East Kilbride and Stonehouse Development Corporation
p.c. Edinburgh Films

Trims for unfinished film of the planning and construction of Stonehouse New Town.

0954   LAUREL BANK SCHOOL FILM
1952

| std.8mm | b/w | silent | 350ft | | REF |

[filmed by Colin Ure]

A compilation of events at Laurel Bank School, Glasgow including a Guide camp, school sports day and a Coronation cruise.

0955   WHY SCOTLAND. WHY EAST KILBRIDE
1970c

| 35mm | col | comopt | 2205ft | | VIEW |

sp. Films of Scotland & East Kilbride Developt. Corp.
p.c. IFA (Scotland) Limited
d. Edward McConnell

Dramatised account of two businessmen being shown round East Kilbride.

0956   (DUMFRIES CINEMA ADVERTS)
1935c

| 16mm | b/w | silent | 63ft | | REF |

Cinema adverts for various local businesses.

0957   MINISTRY OF INFORMATION TRAILERS
1943*-'46

| 16mm | b/w | comopt | 150ft | | VIEW |

sp. MOI (Scotland)

War trailers for war savings, schoolchildren's harvest holidays and the house building programme.

0958   MAKING A SPORRAN IN LEATHER
1955c

| 16mm | col | silent | 400ft | | VIEW |

filmed by SEFA (Glasgow Group)

The tools used and the materials and methods required to make a leather sporran.

0959   (ROTHESAY ENTERTAINERS' TRAILER 1918)
1918

| 35mm | b/w | silent | 130ft | | VIEW |

sp. Fyfe and Fyfe

Rothesay Entertainers trailer advertising their revue. Charlie Kemble, Renee and Billie Houston, J. W. Bowie and Sylvia Watt all feature.

0960A LOCHGELLY OLD AGE PENSIONERS DRIVE TO CROOK O' DEVON

1928*

16mm	b/w	silent	148ft	VIEW

[filmed by Tommy Timmons, for Cinema de Luxe, Lochgelly]

Crowds line the streets to see Lochgelly's old age pensioners leave on an outing to the Crook of Devon in a convoy of charabancs.

0960B LOCHGELLY CHILDREN'S GALA DAY

1927

16mm	b/w	silent	221ft	VIEW

[filmed by Tommie Timmons, for Cinema de Luxe, Lochgelly]

Lochgelly's Children's Gala Day with brass band and procession.

0960C CROWNING OF LOCHGELLY'S FIRST "QUEEN"...

1938

16mm	b/w	silent	223ft	VIEW

[filmed by Tommie Timmons, for Cinema de Luxe, Lochgelly]

Scenes at Lochgelly's Gala Day showing the crowning of the Gala Queen by the Countess of Elgin and the procession through the park accompanied by a brass band.

0961A LOCHGELLY V CELTIC FIRST ROUND SCOTTISH CUP

1922*

35mm	b/w	silent	320ft	VIEW

[filmed by Tommy Timmons for Cinema de Luxe, Lochgelly]

Coverage of a Scottish Cup first round football game between Lochgelly and Celtic; the latter wins.

0961B HOSPITAL/ FUND RAISING PAGEANT. LOCHGELLY

1930c

35mm	b/w	silent	440ft	VIEW

[filmed by Tommy Timmons for Cinema de Luxe, Lochgelly]

A parade and fete to raise funds for the local hospital.

0962 LOCHGELLY CORONATION YEAR CHILDREN'S GALA

1953

35mm	b/w	silent	500ft	REF

filmed by Tommy Timmons, proprietor of Cinema de Luxe, Lochgelly

Coverage of Lochgelly's coronation year children's gala.

0963 ST. PATRICK'S CHURCH, LOCHGELLY

1952-'53

35mm	b/w	silent	1080ft	REF

[filmed by Tommie Timmons for Cinema de Luxe, Lochgelly]

Laying the foundation stone of St. Patrick's Church, Lochgelly by Archbishop G.J. Gray of St. Andrews and Edinburgh, on the 8th. November 1952 and the procession of clergy and parishioners entering the newly opened chapel on 4th October 1953.

0964 CLOSE OF JUBILEE YEAR PROCESSION

1926

35mm	b/w	silent	92ft	VIEW

[filmed by Tommy Timmons for Cinema de Luxe, Lochgelly]

Footage of the Jubilee year procession with St. Patrick's brass band, Lochgelly.

0965 CHILDREN'S GALA AT LOCHGELLY

1928*

16mm	b/w	silent	147ft	VIEW

[filmed by Tommy Timmons for Cinema de Luxe, Lochgelly]

The procession for the Children's Gala in Lochgelly watched by crowds lining the streets.

0966 LOCHGELLY WAR MEMORIAL

1924

35mm	b/w	silent	220ft	VIEW

[filmed by Tommy Timmons for Cinema de Luxe, Lochgelly]

Ceremony to mark the unveiling of Lochgelly war memorial.

0967 LOCHGELLY AT WORK AND PLAY

1922-'23*

35mm	b/w	silent	900ft	VIEW

[filmed by Tommy Timmons for Cinema de Luxe, Lochgelly]

The people of Lochgelly at work and play, with footage of wash day and playing golf and bowls.

0968 ROYAL MILE EDINBURGH, THE

1944

16mm	b/w	commag	470ft	REF

sp. British Council
p.c. Merton Park Productions
d. Terence Egan Bishop

Historic Edinburgh with footage of the Royal Mile, St. Giles' Cathedral, John Knox's House and Holyrood Palace.

0969 HOLIDAY IN THE HIGHLANDS

1933

16mm	b/w	silent	432ft	REF

A holiday in the Highlands and Hebrides, visiting Skye, Oban and Iona Abbey.

0970   (EAST NEUK OF FIFE STEAM RAILWAY)
1960-'65c

16mm	col	silent	200ft		REF

[filmed by James W. Bryant]

An amateur film of various locomotives on the coastal route in Fife.

0971   (BLUEBELL BAKING MARGARINE)
1960*

35mm	b/w	comopt	50ft		REF

sp. SCWS

Advert for Bluebell margarine.

0974   GLASGOW 1980
1971

35mm	col	comopt	2700ft		VIEW

sp. Films of Scotland
p.c. Ogam Films
d. Oscar Marzaroli

A documentary on how Glasgow would look in the 1980's after the redevelopment of its traffic system and the construction of new housing developments, planned in the mid '70s.

0975   GLENROTHES
1957*

35mm	col	mute	870ft		REF

sp. BBC Television

Industry in Glenrothes New Town, and work at Rothes colliery.

0978   ISLAND OF ST. KILDA, THE
1917c

16mm	b/w	silent	190ft		VIEW

p.c. Imperium Film

How the inhabitants of St. Kilda lived on the land and from the sea. Fowling expeditions and village life on the island which lies 50 miles off the Western Isles.

0979   (CELTIC 2 INTER MILAN 1)
1967

16mm	b/w	comopt	654ft		REF

European Cup final between Celtic and Inter Milan, Lisbon. [Celtic win.]

0980   SCENES FROM A SHETLAND CROFT LIFE
1932

16mm	b/w	silent	246ft		VIEW

[d. by Jenny Brown]

How peat is cut using a "tushkar" and made ready for fuel on a croft in the Shetland Isles. [Bought by John Grierson for the GPO Film Library in the 1930s.]

0981   CROFTER'S LIFE IN SHETLAND, A
1931

16mm	b/w	silent	494ft		VIEW

filmed by Jenny Brown

A cyclical year on a croft in the Shetland Isles with scenes of islanders at work on their crofts, fishing and celebrations during the "Up Helly Aa" festival.

0982   ABERDEEN INFIRMARY. OPENING CEREMONY
1936

16mm	b/w	comopt	41ft		VIEW

p.c. Gaumont British News

The opening ceremony of Aberdeen Infirmary by the Duke and Duchess of York. 23rd September 1936.

0983   [PEOPLE OF MANY LANDS - THE ESKIMOS]
1977c

16mm	b/w	silent	60ft		REF

[sp. BBC Schools]
[d. Jenny Gilbertson for BBC Schools]

Trims and over material of a documentary about an Eskimo settlement at Coral Harbour, northern Canada.

0985   HEATHERY KNOWE SCHOOL
1953

35mm	b/w	mute	510ft		REF

The opening ceremony of Heathery Knowe School on the 5th October 1953.

0986   GLASGOW
1962

16mm	col	silent	315ft		VIEW

sp. Educational Films of Scotland
filmed by Louise Annand

An overview of the city of Glasgow, showing its buildings, industries, colleges, parks and football clubs.

0987   (LAST DAYS, GLASGOW TRAMS, THE)
1962

std.8mm	col	silent	125ft		REF

Footage of the last tram in public service on its route from Clydebank to Dalmuir and the accompanying farewell procession.

0988   ST. KILDA. ITS PEOPLE AND BIRDS
1908

35mm	b/w	silent	275ft		VIEW

filmed by Oliver G. Pike of Williamson Kinematograph Co.

Bird life on St. Kilda, including shots of islanders snaring young fulmars, the St. Kildans' staple food.

0989	CATTLE SALE, A

1932

35mm	b/w	silent	270ft	VIEW

[d. Jenny Brown]

Scenes at a cattle sale in the Shetland Isles. [Bought by John Grierson for the GPO Film Library c1936.]

0990	YOUNG GANNET, A

1932

35mm	b/w	silent	293ft	VIEW

[d. Jenny Brown]

A solan goose is caught by a crofter on Shetland, but is returned to the sea after a fortnight, "as it thought nothing of swallowing 20 fish to a meal".

0991	RUGGED ISLAND

1933

16mm	b/w	silent	2020ft	VIEW

d. Jenny Brown

The story of a young couple torn between the choice of emigration to Australia from Shetland or remaining to work their croft.

0992	(YOUNG AND OLD PASTIMES)

1969*

35mm	b/w&col	mute	327ft	REF

sp. SCWS

Rushes from an unidentified film, showing pensioners playing outdoor draughts, two men rock climbing and children playing in a castle.

0993	[AUSTRALIAN WEEK]

1959*

35mm	b/w	comopt	85ft	REF

sp. SCWS

Advert for Australian foodstuffs.

0994	[SHIELDHALL COFFEE]

1964*

35mm	b/w	comopt	15ft	REF

sp. SCWS

An advert for Co-op coffee.

0995	[COME CO-OP SHOPPING]

1963*

35mm	b/w	comopt	42ft	REF

sp. SCWS

An advert for the advantages of shopping at the Co-op.

0996	[BLUEBELL MARGARINE]

1960*

35mm	b/w	comopt	45ft	REF

sp. SCWS

An advert for Co-op Bluebell margarine.

0997	OUR POLICE

1947

16mm	b/w	silent	406ft	VIEW

sp. Glasgow Corporation Education Committee
p.c. Thames and Clyde

An illustration of the Police Force in action from patrolling the beat to catching a thief. The film also describes modern methods of crime detection.

0998	[LOFTY PEAK FLOUR]

1963*

35mm	b/w	comopt	80ft	REF

sp. SCWS

A woman demonstrates the advantages of the Co-op's Lofty Peak flour.

83

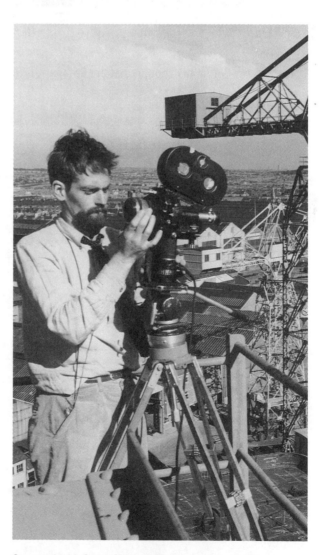

Seawards the Great Ships 1960. Scotland's only Oscar-winning film. Director, Hilary Harris and his camera high above a Clyde shipyard. Ref. 2230

0999	**[ORCHID MARGARINE]**				
1960c					
35mm	b/w	comopt	44ft		REF

sp. SCWS
An advert for Co-op Orchid margarine.

1000	**[LOFTY PEAK FLOUR]**				
1960c					
35mm	b/w	comopt	130ft		REF

sp. SCWS
An advert for Co-op flour accompanied by the Lofty Peak flour song.

1001	**[LOFTY PEAK SCRAPER OFFER]**				
1960c					
35mm	b/w	comopt	130ft		REF

sp. SCWS
An advert for Co-op Lofty Peak flour.

1002	**[COME CO-OP SHOPPING AT CHRISTMAS]**				
1964*					
35mm	b/w	comopt	48ft		REF

sp. SCWS
An advert for Christmas shopping at the Co-op.

1003	**[COPEX COOKING FAT]**				
1964					
35mm	b/w	comopt	45ft		REF

sp. SCWS
An advert for Co-op cooking fat.

1004	**[MONTRIL PARTY]**				
1960c					
35mm	b/w	comopt	23ft		REF

sp. SCWS
An advert for the Co-op's Montril orange juice.

1005	**[GOLDEN BALL MARMALADE]**				
1962*					
35mm	b/w	comopt	52ft		REF

sp. SCWS
An advert for saving 3d off Golden Ball marmalade at the Co-op.

1006	**[COME CO-OP SHOPPING]**				
1964*					
35mm	b/w	comopt	60ft		REF

sp. SCWS
A woman in her kitchen advertising the advantages of shopping at the Co-op.

1007	**[CO-OP SUGAR]**				
1960c					
35mm	b/w	comopt	25ft		REF

sp. SCWS
Co-op sugar is advertised at 1/6d for 2lbs.

1008	**[CHEDDAR CHEESE]**				
1960c					
35mm	b/w	comopt	25ft		REF

sp. SCWS
Two cheese wedges weighing half-a-pound are advertised for 3/11d at the Co-op.

1009	**[PINEAPPLE AND RICE]**				
1960c					
35mm	b/w	comopt	25ft		REF

sp. SCWS
Co-op pineapple and rice are offered at 2/2d a tin.

1010	**[CWS CENTENARY EXHIBITION]**				
1963c					
35mm	b/w	comopt	106ft		REF

sp. Co-operative Wholesale Society
An advert for the Co-operative Wholesale Society exhibition at Belle Vue, Manchester.

1011	**[SPRING SALE]**				
1960c					
35mm	b/w	comopt	60ft		REF

sp. SCWS
An advert for sale bargains at the Co-op.

1012	**[SAUCES]**				
1960c					
35mm	b/w	comopt	42ft		REF

sp. SCWS
An advert for Co-op sauce.

1013	**[COME CO-OP SHOPPING MK III]**				
1960c					
35mm	b/w	comopt	76ft		REF

sp. SCWS
Special Co-op offers advertised on oats, soup and sauces.

1014	**[COME CO-OP SHOPPING, MK IV]**				
1959*					
35mm	b/w	comopt	75ft		VIEW

sp. SCWS
A woman in her kitchen tells of the advantages of shopping at the Co-op.

84

1015	**[MARGARINE CARTOON]**				
1964*					
35mm	b/w	comopt	40ft		REF

sp. SCWS

Animated advert for Co-op Bluebell margarine.

1016	**[LOFTY PEAK CAKE MIX]**				
1960					
35mm	b/w	comopt	80ft		REF

sp. SCWS

Advert for Co-op chocolate cake mix.

1017	**[STAFF RECRUITMENT FILM]**				
1959*					
35mm	col	comopt	75ft		REF

sp. SCWS

A cartoon advertising vacancies within the Co-op.

1018	**[LEMON CURD]**				
1960c					
35mm	b/w	comopt	22ft		REF

sp. SCWS

An advert for Co-op Lemon Curd.

1019	**[STRAWBERRY JAM]**				
1959*					
35mm	b/w	comopt	22ft		REF

sp. SCWS

Advert for 3d off Co-op strawberry jam.

1020	**[GOLDEN BALL MARMALADE]**				
1960c					
35mm	b/w	commag	22ft		REF

sp. SCWS

Advert for 3d off the price of the Co-op's Golden Ball marmalade.

1021	**[ORCHID BUTTER]**				
1960c					
35mm	b/w	comopt	81ft		REF

sp. SCWS

An advert for the Co-op's Orchid butter, with shots of children eating bread and butter.

1022	**[JELLY CRYSTALS]**				
1960c					
35mm	b/w	comopt	22ft		REF

sp. SCWS

An advert for Co-op jelly crystals.

1023	**[CO-OP CARTOON]**				
1960c					
35mm	b/w	comopt	60ft		VIEW

sp. SCWS

A cartoon promoting Co-op products.

1024	**(SHAWLANDS CROSS)**				
1956*					
16mm	b/w	silent	100ft		REF

sp. SCWS

Pedestrians and shops around Shawlands Cross, Glasgow, with shots of trams and buses.

1025	**[SPOT THE LIKENESS]**				
1955*					
16mm	b/w	comopt	46ft		REF

sp. Co-operative Wholesale Society

Short advert using "spot the likeness" idea to illustrate Co-op products.

1026	**PRODUCTIVE GROCERY DEPARTMENT**				
1959*					
16mm	col	sep opt	378ft		VIEW

sp. SCWS
p.c. Gate Film Productions

The manufacturing processes for sauces, jams, coffee and sweets at the Co-operative's Shieldhall factory.

1027	**CLAN HAS ARRIVED, THE**				
1969c					
16mm	b/w	mute	100ft		REF

sp. SCWS

An advert for the Co-op's "Clan" grocery products.

1028	**HOMES IN BRITAIN**				
1959c					
35mm	col	comopt	510ft		REF

sp. SCWS
p.c. Merton Park Productions
d. George Wynn

A promotional film for Co-operative "Prescription" tea and "Curona" cocoa.

1029	**UNITAS OATS**				
1956*					
35mm	b/w	comopt	60ft		VIEW

sp. SCWS

An advert for Co-operative Unitas Oats; a family sing and dance at the breakfast table.

85

1030	KNITWEAR WITHOUT TEARS			
1956*				
35mm	col	comopt	270ft	REF

sp. SCWS

An advert for the "Knitmaster", the Co-op's knitting machine.

1031	CO-OP SHOPPING			
1957*				
35mm	b/w	sep opt	60ft	REF

sp. SCWS

A woman and a man discuss the benefits of shopping at the Co-op.

1032	SHIELDHALL SHOES			
1959*				
35mm	b/w	comopt	60ft	REF

sp. SCWS

An advert for the Co-op's Shieldhall shoes.

1033	[99 TEA]			
1959				
35mm	b/w	comopt	45ft	REF

sp. SCWS

A television advert for the Co-op's "99" tea at 1/9d per packet.

1034	[ORCHID MARGARINE]			
1965*				
35mm	b/w	comopt	45ft	REF

sp. SCWS

An advert for Co-operative Orchid margarine.

1035	[COGENT CIGARETTES]			
1956*				
35mm	b/w	sep opt	90ft	REF

sp. SCWS

An advert for the Co-op's "Cogent" cigarettes.

1036	[ETNA STEEL MILL]			
1967*				
16mm	col	silent	355ft	REF

Shot inside the former Etna steel mill in Motherwell, now demolished, the film shows the shaping of a steel square section bar from the original billet taken from the furnace.

1037	USS COR-TEN			
1964				
16mm	b/w	comopt	730ft	REF

sp. United States Steel
p.c. Jam Handy Pictures

An explanation and demonstration of the importance of Cor-ten; corrosion resisting, high-tensile steel of low alloy content.

1038	NATIONALISATION - TAKE IT AWAY			
1949				
16mm	b/w	comopt	610ft	REF

filmed by the Conservative and Unionist Films Association

An examination of the Socialist Party's attitude to the nationalisation of the steel and iron industries.

1039	[COLVILLE'S PRODUCTION NO. OF 20]			
1961*				
16mm	col	silent	2600ft	REF

p.c. Pera Film Unit (?)

Rushes and trims from documentary on steel production at David Colville's Limited.

1040	[COLVILLE'S HOT COILER]			
1965				
16mm	b/w	silent	2200ft	REF

Rushes and cuts for documentary on steel production at Colville's.

1044	OBEDIENT FLAME, THE			
1940				
16mm	b/w	comopt	540ft	REF

sp. British Commercial Gas Association
p.c. Science Films
d. Norman McLaren

A cartoon advertising the advantages of gas and gas cookers.

1048	EMPIRE EXHIBITION			
1938				
9.5mm	b/w	silent	360ft	REF

[filmed by William S. Manson]

Footage of the Empire Exhibition in Glasgow, including the King and Queen's visit, various pavilions, the fountain, amusement park and dancing waters.

1049	GLASGOW, NO MEAN CITY			
1951				
std.8mm	b/w	silent	600ft	REF

[filmed by William S. Manson]

Scenes of Glasgow including its streets with trams and buses, its shops, buildings, museums and parks, its shipyards, railway stations, theatres and cinemas.

1050   (ALL SCOTLAND CRUSADE)
1955

16mm	b/w	comopt	1989ft	VIEW

Billy Graham's Good Friday service in the Kelvin Hall, Glasgow. He preaches to the assembled crowd of 160,000 people.

1053   CHEMICAL SUNDRIES DEPARTMENT
1959*

16mm	col	sep opt	378ft	REF

sp. SCWS
p.c. Gate Film Production

Footage of the manufacture of various products in the Co-op's chemical sundries department, including "Snowdrop" salt and "Unitas" oats.

1054   (CO-OP DIVIDENDS)
1956*

16mm	b/w	comopt	36ft	REF

[sp. SCWS]
Advert for Co-op dividends.

1055   (CO-OP BUTTER)
1956*

16mm	b/w	comopt	36ft	REF

sp. SCWS
Advert for Co-op butter.

1056   (OUT OF SYNC. DIVIDENDS)
1956*

16mm	b/w	comopt	36ft	REF

sp. SCWS
Advert for Co-op dividends.

1057   TATTIE HOWKIN'
1951

35mm	b/w	comopt	92ft	REF

sp. COI for the Dept. of Agriculture for Scotland
Cinema trailer aimed at schoolchildren to persuade them to help pick the potato harvest.

1058   [POTATO PICKING TRAILER]
1951

35mm	b/w	comopt	93ft	REF

sp. COI for the Dept. of Agriculture for Scotland
Cinema trailer aimed at schoolchildren to persuade them to help pick the potato harvest.

1059   CHILDREN'S STORY, THE
1938

35mm	b/w	comopt	1350ft	VIEW

sp. Films of Scotland
p.c. Strand Film Company
d. Alexander Shaw

Made for screening at the 1938 Empire Exhibition under the supervision of John Grierson, the film shows children taking part in various educational activities in schools in Glasgow and Edinburgh.

1060   SEAFOOD
1938

35mm	b/w	comopt	1120ft	VIEW

sp. Films of Scotland
p.c. Pathe

Made for screening at the 1938 Empire Exhibition, the film features Scottish fishermen at work on their boats and trawlers, and the research work of the Fishery Board for Scotland.

1061   DUNDEE
1939

35mm	b/w	comopt	1750ft	VIEW

sp. Films of Scotland
p.c. Scottish Film Productions
d. Donald Alexander

The city of Dundee and its industries; jute, jam manufacturing and journalism.

1062   WEALTH OF A NATION
1938

35mm	b/w	comopt	1470ft	VIEW

sp. Films of Scotland
p.c. Scottish Film Productions
d. Donald Alexander

Made for screening at the 1938 Empire Exhibition, the film looks at the industries of Scotland, from the shipyards on the Clyde, to coal mining and housing construction.

1063   THEY MADE THE LAND
1941

35mm	b/w	comopt	1790ft	VIEW

sp. Films of Scotland
p.c. GB Instructional
d. Mary Field

A illustration of the various farming techniques in use in Scotland, from peat cutting to drystane dyking, forest plantation and sheep farming.

87

1065   AMONG THE CLOUDS

1952

16mm	b/w	silent	324ft		REF

The panoramic scenery of the Assiniboine Range in the Canadian Rockies, seen through the eyes of a climbing party. [This film was given to the film-maker Jenny Gilbertson by the Canadian Government in the 1950s to be used while lecturing in Canada.]

1066   (PENNYCOOK FAMILY FILM)

1949c

16mm	b/w	comopt	99ft		REF

[filmed by Jack Pennycook]

The Pennycook family enjoying a day on the beach.

1067   AMONG THE MANY VISITORS...

1938

9.5mm	b/w	silent	150ft		REF

[filmed by William S. Manson]

Scenes of events held in Glasgow during the Empire Exhibition; an historical pageant, a Boys' Brigade display and a Scout rally.

1068   SOME EVENTS IN GLASGOW 1937

1937

9.5mm	b/w	silent	360ft		REF

[filmed by William S. Manson]

Events celebrating the coronation in Glasgow, 1937, including illuminations in George Square, a firework display and a children's carnival.

1069   KIRKINTILLOCH

1946

std.8mm	b/w	silent	180ft		REF

[filmed by William S. Manson]

The streets of Kirkintilloch, a boat yard on the Forth and Clyde Canal, the Black Bull cinema and Peel Park are all featured in this amateur film.

1070   BLIZZARD, FEBRUARY 1947

1947

std.8mm	b/w&col silent	50ft		REF

[filmed by William S. Manson]

Shots of Kirkintilloch during a winter snowfall; its streets, park and boatyard on the Forth and Clyde Canal.

1071   INSPECTION OF PAISLEY FIRE BRIGADE BY PROVOST AND COUNCILLORS

1925c

16mm	b/w	silent	172ft		VIEW

sp. Paisley Fire Brigade
[attributed to Macrae & Drew, Paisley]

Inspection of Paisley Fire Brigade by the Provost and councillors, and a firefighting demonstration using horse-drawn vehicles. Firemaster Girdwood performs acrobatic stunts on top of an extension ladder.

1072   BARRHEAD ACCLAIMS DRAMA CUP WINNERS

1951

16mm	b/w	comopt	66ft		VIEW

sp. British Paramount News
p.c. Olympic Kinematograph

Celebrations in Barrhead as the town welcomes its Barrhead Players, the British Champions of the National Drama competition with their play "Displaced Persons".

1073A   NIGHT SWORD DANCE

1931*

16mm	b/w	comopt	39ft		REF

p.c. Paramount Sound News

Members of the Black Watch, on parade by torchlight and giving a performance of the sword-dance.

1073B   (DUKE AND DUCHESS OF YORK IN PERTH)

1935

16mm	b/w	comopt	42ft		REF

The Duke and Duchess of York inspect the guard of honour of the Black Watch and perform the opening ceremony for the new Art Gallery.

1073C   (KING GEORGE INSPECTS GUARD OF HONOUR, BLACK WATCH)

1935*

16mm	b/w	comopt	33ft		REF

King George V inspects the guard of honour of the Black Watch at Ballater Station.

1073D   2ND BATTALION BLACK WATCH REHEARSE FOR THE NAVAL AND MILITARY TOURNAMENT

1932

16mm	b/w	comopt	42ft		REF

The Black Watch rehearsing their drill with pipes and drums, for a military tournament.

1074 ST. JAMES' PARK

1934

| 16mm | b/w | silent | 211ft | | REF |

sp. Travel and Indust. Devel. Assoc. of GB and Ireland

Footage of London's St. James's Park, as seen through the changing seasons.

1075 PREVENTION IS BETTER

1954*

| 35mm | b/w | comopt | 1340ft | VIEW |

sp. National Association for the Prevention of Tuberculosis
p.c. Campbell Harper Films Ltd.
d. Henry Cooper

Made to encourage methods of prevention of TB, the film promotes the practice of regular chest x-rays.

1076 (EAST KILBRIDE TRIMS)

1959c

| 35mm | b/w | mute | 1800ft | | REF |

General shots of East Kilbride and of a council meeting discussing plans for the development of the town. [Trims only.]

1077 VOYAGEUR TRAILS

1949c

| 16mm | b/w | silent | 271ft | | REF |

A fishing party in Canada canoe up river.

1078 SAGA OF THE SILVER HORDE

1952c

| 16mm | b/w | silent | 406ft | | REF |

Salmon fishing in a Canadian lake.

1079 BIG TIMBER

1949c

| 16mm | b/w | silent | 342ft | | REF |

Lumberjacking in British Columbia, from timber cut and sawed to its shipment all over the world.

1080A ABERDEEN AWA' AUGUST 1949

1949

| std.8mm | b/w | silent | 100ft | | REF |

[filmed by William S. Manson]

Aberdeen, including the fish market, Marischal College, the River Dee and the Museum.

1080B RIVER CLYDE

1948

| std.8mm | b/w | silent | 100ft | | REF |

[filmed by William S. Manson]

Passenger steamers on the River Clyde, and their various ports of call.

1081 TAMMIE TWISTER

1933/'34

| 16mm | b/w | silent | 262ft | VIEW |

[filmed by George West and Friends]

Film of 'Tammie Twister Pantomime' which includes George West and Jack E. Raymond as Laurel and Hardy.

1082 FIRE FIGHTING

1942*

| 16mm | b/w | silent | 96ft | | REF |

[filmed by Ben H. Humble]

Comic display of fire fighting after an air raid.

1083 (WARTIME DUMBARTON)

1939-'43*

| 16mm | b/w | silent | 52ft | | REF |

[filmed by Ben H. Humble]

Dumbarton prepares for impending war as shown by the Glasgow Evening Times. Air Raid warning posters are shown.

1084 BOMB FELL, A

1941

| 16mm | col | silent | 296ft | VIEW |

sp. Glasgow Casualty and Rescue Party Services
[filmed by Ben H. Humble]

Shots of bomb damaged buildings during reconstruction of the aftermath of an air raid. Rescue services demonstrate their techniques and first aid methods.

1085 CROWD GATHERS, A

1941*

| 16mm | b/w | silent | 154ft | | REF |

sp. Knightswood First Aid Post
[filmed by Ben H. Humble]

The ARP demonstrates techniques in caring for an unconscious person. [Used as a test for First Aiders in Civil Defence.]

1086 CRAGSMAN'S DAY, A

1946

| 16mm | b/w | silent | 388ft | VIEW |

[filmed by Ben H. Humble]

Rock climbing on the "Cobbler". [Awarded first prize by Michael Powell in the 1948 Scottish Amateur Film Festival.]

1087 (HOLIDAY AT ARROCHAR)

1949*

| 16mm | b/w&col | silent | 298ft | | REF |

[filmed by Ben H. Humble]

A holiday in Arrochar, local events and sights.

90

1088   (MOUNTAIN RESCUE TRAINING)
1966*

16mm	b/w&col	silent	263ft		REF

[filmed by Ben H. Humble]

Mountain rescue techniques demonstrated at Glenmore Lodge.

1089   [KIDS KONCERT IN AID OF RED CROSS
1942*

16mm	b/w	silent	250ft		REF

[filmed by Ben H. Humble]

Children perform sketches in aid of Red Cross.

1090   FORUM FROLICS
1943*

16mm	b/w	silent	316ft		REF

[filmed by Ben H. Humble]

Various comedy sketches including a balancing act on a bicycle and the drinking of a glass of beer that never empties.

1091   (TRAMS IN EDINBURGH AND BRUSSELS)
1948-'49

std.8mm	b/w	silent	15ft		REF

[filmed by Dorothy Lynam]

Shot while on holiday in Edinburgh and Brussels, and intended as a film of buildings of architectural interest, the trams were incidental.

1092   MRS. MCLEOD
1950c

35mm	b/w	comopt	630ft		VIEW

sp. Scottish Country Dance Society
p.c. Thames and Clyde
d. Stanley Russell

A demonstration of the dance "Mrs. McLeod".

1093   [SCHOOLS STEEL]
1959*

35mm	b/w	mute	2150ft		REF

sp. BBC
p.c. Glasgow Films

Shots inside foundry of rolling press and various processes in steel manufacture. [Rushes for documentary.]

1094   (WESTERN INFIRMARY)
1959*

35mm	b/w	mute	3690ft		REF

sp. BBC
p.c. Glasgow Films

Interior shots of Western Infirmary; nurses, doctors, wards, patients, classrooms and operating theatre. [Rushes for television documentary.]

1095   (UNIDENTIFIED RURAL TOWN TRIMS)
1950c

35mm	b/w	mute	400ft		REF

p.c. Thames and Clyde

Shots of an unknown town with close-ups of the church tower. [Trims for documentary.]

1096   WAY THE MONEY GOES, THE
1957*

35mm	col	comopt	1545ft		VIEW

sp. Films of Scotland
p.c. Anglo-Scottish Pictures
d. David Paltenghi

The "travelling bank" in the Western Isles and Highlands, and its contribution to rural life.

1097   NATIONAL COMMERCIAL BANK OF SCOTLAND TRAINING FILM
1962*

35mm	b/w	mute	2745ft		REF

Training film for the National Commercial Bank of Scotland including vox pops on Colville's steel works.

1098   CAMERA MAKES WHOOPEE
1936

16mm	b/w	mute	664ft		VIEW

filmed by Norman McLaren, Willie MacLean, Violet Anderson

Student ball at Glasgow School of Art.

1099   HELL UNLTD
1936

16mm	b/w	silent	524ft		VIEW

filmed by Norman McLaren and Helen Biggar

Powerful anti-war film detailing the cost in dead and wounded, and the resultant economic depression of the 1914-1918 war. The film graphically illustrates the horrors of another war. [Entered for the 1937 Scottish Amateur Film Festival.]

1100   SEVEN TILL FIVE
1934

16mm	b/w	silent	348ft		REF

filmed by Glasgow School of Art Kinecraft Society

Filmed by Norman McLaren and Willie J. MacLean, it shows a day in the life of the Glasgow School of Art. [Awarded SAFF prize.]

1101 ("RIVER CREE" ENTERTAINS THE QUEEN, THE)
1953

35mm	b/w	mute	1070ft	VIEW

p.c. Thames and Clyde

Scottish Country Dance display during Coronation visit to Scotland. 2nd July 1953.

1102 CLEAN FOOD
1957

35mm	b/w	comopt	1410ft	VIEW

sp. COI/Dept. of Health for Scotland
p.c. Thames and Clyde
d. Stanley L. Russell

A demonstration of cleanliness when dealing with and when eating food.

1103 CINEMA ADVERTS
1960-'69

35mm	b/w	commag	407ft	REF

Various adverts, including Christmas greetings, Pearl and Dean advertising tickets for a grand ball, and the Entertainments Tax.

1104 (GLASGOW PARKS 1941)
1941

16mm	col	silent	255ft	REF

[filmed by Dr. T. J. Honeyman]

Footage of Glasgow's parks, including Pollok House, Rouken Glen and Queen's Park. Film made as an experiment with "new" colour film in and around March 1941.

1105 (FOUNDATION STONE)
1954

35mm	b/w	mute	270ft	REF

p.c. Thames and Clyde

Coverage of service held to celebrate the laying of a foundation stone for a new church [unidentified.] [Trims only.]

1106 (COUNTRYSIDE TRIMS)
1959*

35mm	col	mute	450ft	REF

p.c. Campbell Harper Films Ltd.

General views of Scottish countryside. [Trims only.]

1107 (DRINK AND DRIVE COMMERCIALS)
1965c

35mm	b/w	comopt	380ft	REF

Cinema commercials portraying the hazards of drinking and driving.

1108 INCIDENT AT LONGNIDDRY
1953

35mm	b/w	mute	615ft	REF

sp. British Transport Commission
p.c. Campbell Harper Films Ltd.

Re-railing a Pacific class locomotive after it had been completely detached and turned around. Two steam cranes take 47 minutes to re-rail the locomotive.

1109 1959 SCOTTISH INDUSTRIES EXHIBITION, THE
1959

16mm	b/w	comopt	c1000ft	REF

sp. Council of Management
p.c. Glasgow Films Limited

Scenes of the exhibition at the Kelvin Hall, Glasgow. Princess Margaret opens the event. [Mute cuts only.]

1110 PETROL
1957

16mm	b/w	silent	60ft	REF

[filmed by Enrico Cocozza]

A fictional horror story.

1111 ROBOT THREE
1951

16mm	col	silent	423ft	REF

filmed by Enrico Cocozza

Fictional story following the lines of a Frankenstein type horror movie.

1112 STATE ENTRY INTO EDINBURGH
1953

16mm	col	silent	1107ft	VIEW

sp. SFC
filmed by SAAC

Queen Elizabeth's state visit to Edinburgh. The Queen is presented with the key to Edinburgh Castle, watches a display at Murrayfield, and presents colours to the 1st Battn. Argyll and Sutherland Highlanders.

1113 HONOURS OF SCOTLAND
1953

16mm	b/w&col	silent	590ft	VIEW

sp. SFC
filmed by SAAC

The ceremony of the Honours of Scotland on the occasion of the state visit of Queen Elizabeth II.

1114 IN THE SHADOW
1957

16mm	b/w&col	silent	362ft	REF

[filmed by Enrico Cocozza]

Abstract experiments in low key lighting. [See also ref. 1122.]

91

1115   CAT, THE
1956

16mm	b/w	silent	144ft		REF

[filmed by Enrico Cocozza]

A story about a cat that turns into a man.

1116   FERRY FLIRT
1949

16mm	b/w	silent	300ft		REF

filmed by Enrico Cocozza

Fictional story of a young man and woman who fall in love on a ferry.

1117   CAMEO
1952

16mm	b/w&col	silent	232ft		REF

filmed by Enrico Cocozza

Fictional story of a golfer who finds a magic ring and dreams that he falls in love with the lady of the manor. [Highly commended at the 1953 SAAC Festival.]

1118   SCHERZO
1956

16mm	b/w	silent	170ft		REF

filmed by Enrico Cocozza

An amateur film of a fictional story set in Glasgow.

1119   PLUGGERS' PICNIC
1952

16mm	b/w	silent	335ft		REF

filmed by Wishaw Youth Club and Film Society

A drama about four schoolchildren playing truant to have a picnic. [Commended at the 1952 SAAC Festival.]

1120   SAIL TO INVERARAY
1952

16mm	col	commag	345ft		VIEW

filmed by Enrico Cocozza

A steamer trip from Wemyss Bay through the Kyles of Bute to Inveraray.

Seawards the Great Ships 1960. Shipyard workers relaxing at lunch break. Ref. 2230

1121   CRABBIT GRANNY
1953

16mm	b/w	silent	320ft		REF

filmed by Enrico Cocozza

Comedy about a young boy and his dog on holiday with his grandmother. [Highly commended at the 1953 SAAC Festival.]

1122   CAPRICCIO
1954

16mm	col	silent	290ft		REF

filmed by Enrico Cocozza

An amateur film experimenting in low key lighting. [See also ref. 1114.]

1123   BOTTLE, THE
1958

16mm	b/w	commag	220ft	VIEW

[filmed by Enrico Cocozza]

Fictional story about a group of boys playing in a park.

1124   RIC HAS A BATH
1949

16mm	col	silent	220ft	VIEW

[filmed by Enrico Cocozza]

An amateur film telling the story of a dog having a bath.

1126   INCUBO
1956

16mm	b/w	commag	310ft	VIEW

[filmed by Enrico Cocozza]

Fictional story of a man who commits suicide after losing his fight against alcoholism.

1127   DA MAKKIN O' A KESHIE
1932

16mm	b/w	silent	189ft	VIEW

[d. Jenny Brown]

A crofter in the Shetland Isles demonstrates how to make a 'keshie' to carry home his peat. [One of a group of films made by Jenny Brown and bought by John Grierson for the GPO Film Library in the 1930s.]

1128   SEABIRDS IN THE SHETLAND ISLANDS
1932*

16mm	b/w	silent	325ft	VIEW

[d. Jenny Brown]

Footage of the seabirds found in the Shetland Isles. [One of a group of films made by Jenny Brown and bought by John Grierson for the GPO Film Library in the 1930s.]

1129   IN SHEEP'S CLOTHING
1932

16mm	b/w	silent	270ft	VIEW

[d. Jenny Brown]

Crofters on the Shetland Isles are seen shearing sheep, carding and spinning wool to make Shetland jumpers. [One of a group of films about Shetland made by Jenny Brown and purchased by John Grierson for the GPO Film Library in the 1930s.]

1130   SHETLAND PONY
1969*

16mm	b/w	comopt	1116ft	VIEW

sp. BBC
d. Jenny Gilbertson

The rearing of Shetland ponies on island crofts.

1131   PROCESSION AND CROWNING OF THE QUEEN OF THE BONNIE LASSIES
1952

35mm	b/w	silent	720ft		REF

sp. Orient and Ritz Cinemas, Ayr
p.c. Elder Film Productions

The procession and crowning of the Queen of the Bonnie Lassies, Ayr.

1132   SOUTHERN SCOTLAND
1961

16mm	col	silent	486ft	VIEW

sp. Educational Films of Scotland
p.c. Thames and Clyde

An overview of southern Scotland showing its farming, industries and principal towns.

1133   [HALF PAST EIGHT SHOW]
1939c

16mm	b/w	silent	335ft		REF

[amateur film made by friend of Harry Gordon]

Filmed during the dress rehearsal of the "Half Past Eight Show" starring Harry Gordon, Betty Jumel, Margaret Holden, Georgina Jumel and Bunty Gordon.

1134   [ROBINSON CRUSOE]
1944

16mm	b/w&col	silent	423ft	VIEW

[amateur film made by friend of Harry Gordon]

Footage of a summer show, probably in Aberdeen's Beach Pavilion, starring Harry Gordon.

93

1135	[CINDERELLA 1950 ALADDIN 1951]				
1950/'51					
16mm	col	silent	387ft		VIEW

Scenes from pantomimes "Cinderella" and "Aladdin". Harry Gordon and Duncan Macrae are the Ugly sisters. The film ends with footage of animals at Edinburgh Zoo.

1136	[CINDERS 1950 AND ROAD SHOW. DUNDEE C1948]				
1946*-'50					
16mm	b/w&col	silent	369ft		REF

[amateur film made by friend of Harry Gordon]

Shots of a pantomime filmed from the wings and balcony of a theatre, probably the Alhambra in Glasgow. The film also includes footage of a road show in Dundee, starring Harry Gordon.

1137	[ROBINSON CRUSOE 1944/'45]				
1944/'45					
16mm	col	silent	400ft		REF

[amateur film made by friend of Harry Gordon]

Scenes from the pantomime "Robinson Crusoe" starring Harry Gordon and Will Fyffe.

1138	[ALADDIN 1938]				
1938					
16mm	b/w	silent	416ft		REF

[filmed by Harry Gordon]

Scenes from the pantomime "Aladdin" at the Glasgow Alhambra. Cast includes Harry Gordon, Alex Finlay and Jack Holden.

1139	[KING AND QUEEN OF HEARTS 1945]				
1945					
16mm	col	silent	399ft		VIEW

[amateur film made by friend of Harry Gordon]

Footage of the pantomime "Queen of Hearts", cast includes Harry Gordon and Will Fyffe.

1140	(VARIOUS ARTISTS C1948)				
1937/'45*					
16mm	b/w&col	silent	440ft		REF

[amateur film made by friend of Harry Gordon]

Scenes from various pantomimes and variety shows featuring Harry Gordon, Alec Finlay, Dave Willis, Florrie Ford, and Alec Lennox.

1141	[KING AND QUEEN OF HEARTS]				
1943*-'45					
16mm	b/w	silent	402ft		VIEW

[amateur film made by friend of Harry Gordon]

Scenes from the stage pantomime "King and Queen of Hearts" and various sketches featuring Harry Gordon, Jack Anthony, Will Fyffe and Jack Holden.

1142	[RED RIDING HOOD 1943]				
1937*-'43					
16mm	b/w&col	silent	345ft		VIEW

[amateur film made by friend of Harry Gordon]

Scenes from the stage pantomime "Red Riding Hood" including shots of Harry Gordon in his dressing room and Will Fyffe in costume.

1143	(PANTOMIME AND CHRISTMAS PARTY)				
1943					
16mm	b/w&col	silent	210ft		VIEW

Shots of pantomime troupe performing with Harry Gordon and their Christmas party in the Adelphi Hotel, Glasgow.

1144	[HALF PAST EIGHT SHOW 1945 AND ROBINSON CRUSOE 1944]				
1944/'45					
16mm	col	silent	401ft		REF

[amateur film made by friend of Harry Gordon]

Song and dance routines and comedy sketches from the "Half Past Eight Show" and "Robinson Crusoe" featuring Harry Gordon and Will Fyffe.

1145	[SLEEPING BEAUTY 1940, THE]				
1937*-'40					
16mm	b/w&col	silent	420ft		REF

[amateur film made by friend of Harry Gordon]

Shots of pantomime "Sleeping Beauty" featuring Harry Gordon as the "Queen" and Alec Finlay as the "King".

1146	BABES IN THE WOOD				
1936					
16mm	col	silent	267ft		REF

Filmed during the dress rehearsal of the pantomime "Babes in the Wood" featuring Harry Gordon in various sketches. [See also ref. 2180.]

1147	[HUMPTY DUMPTY]				
1947-'53					
16mm	b/w&col	silent	380ft		REF

[amateur film made by friend of Harry Gordon]

General views of the dress rehearsal of the pantomime "Humpty Dumpty", starring Harry Gordon, Duncan Macrae and Alec Finlay.

1148	[HARRY GORDON VISITS NEW YORK AND PANTOMIMES]

1943-'50*

16mm	b/w&col	silent	390ft	REF

Shots of Harry Gordon and his wife on the "Queen Elizabeth" on their frst visit to the USA. Scenes of New York and Harry Gordon and Will Fyffe on stage during rehearsal of "Babes in the Wood".

1149	DICK WHITTINGTON (1941)

1941-'58*

16mm	col	silent	300ft	VIEW

[amateur film made by friend of Harry Gordon]

Filmed during the dress rehearsal of the pantomime "Dick Whittington" featuring Harry Gordon and Will Fyffe.

1150	[PANTOMIME. SHOW PICNIC. AND VARIETY]

1939-'42*

16mm	b/w&col	silent	399ft	VIEW

Shots of Harry Gordon and Will Fyffe in the pantomime "Jack and the Beanstalk". The film also shows a picnic for members of the cast.

1151	[BEACH PAVILION. ABERDEEN AND FAMILY C1926]

1926/'27

16mm	b/w	silent	246ft	VIEW

Harry Gordon and company star in a variety show at the Beach Pavilion, Aberdeen.

1152	[BEACH PAVILION. ABERDEEN AND VARIETY C1925]

1925*-'37

16mm	b/w&col	silent	440ft	VIEW

[amateur film made by friend of Harry Gordon]

Scenes at a variety show in the Beach Pavilion, Aberdeen, Harry Gordon in "Puss in Boots" and a variety show in the Alhambra Theatre, Glasgow.

1153	WHEELWRIGHT, THE

1936c

16mm	b/w	silent	250ft	REF

[p.c. Elder Dalrymple Productions]

Demonstration of how a wooden cart wheel is made.

1154	[MURDOCHS-CAPOCCI-OBAN]

1952

16mm	col	silent	130ft	REF

[filmed by Enrico Cocozza]

Highland scenery, including shots taken from Oban promenade.

1155	PORPHYRIA

1959

16mm	b/w	mute	270ft	VIEW

filmed by Jimmy Craig

Based on a Robert Browning poem, the film tells the story of a doomed love affair between a photographer and his model.

1156	BONGO BUBBLE

1959

16mm	col	silent	300ft	REF

[filmed by Enrico Cocozza]

An amateur film telling the story of a boy who gets drunk on "bubbly" and has a fight with a chair.

1157	MIRROR, THE

1951

16mm	b/w	mute	200ft	VIEW

filmed by Enrico Cocozza

A short abstract film.

1158	MASQUERADE

1953

16mm	b/w	commag	390ft	VIEW

filmed by Enrico Cocozza

An amateur film of a girl dancing.

95

1159	AD INFERNUM BUDDY ?

1952

16mm	b/w	silent	210ft	VIEW

filmed by James Craig

An amateur production of a mock-up of a Roman story set in a studio.

1160	SILVER TRUMPET, THE

1961

16mm	col	commag	1340ft	VIEW

filmed by Enrico Cocozza

An amateur film telling the story of a young author and a magic trumpet.

1161	[LONDON 51]

1951

16mm	b/w	silent	396ft	REF

[filmed by Enrico Cocozza]

General shots around London, including the exteriors of the Empire and Carlton Theatres, a sea and ships exhibition, the Royal Mint and the Telekinema.

1162   LIVING GHOST, THE
1959

16mm	b/w	mute	920ft		VIEW

filmed by Enrico Cocozza

An amateur story film concerning the appearance of a "living ghost".

1163   TOURISTS, THE
1955

16mm	b/w&col	silent	1000ft		REF

filmed by Gavin and Enrico Cocozza

A holiday in Italy, including views of Genoa, Alassio, Naples and Filignano.

1164   ISLE OF CAPRI, THE
1955

16mm	col	silent	650ft		REF

filmed by Gavin Brown and Enrico Cocozza

Various scenes of Capri.

1165   BFI SUMMER SCHOOL (BANGOR 1949)
1949

16mm	b/w&col	silent	510ft		REF

filmed by Enrico Cocozza

General views of Bangor and surrounding countryside.

1166   MEET THE STARS
1960

16mm	b/w	silent	450ft		VIEW

[filmed by Enrico Cocozza]

A collection of Scottish footballing stars demonstrating how to play football; Alex Scott from Rangers FC and Bertie Peacock from Celtic FC at Cathkin Park, Glasgow.

1167   OLD AND THE NEW
1948

16mm	b/w	silent	830ft		REF

filmed by Astral Films

A record of the renovation work on the Bellhaven cafe, Wishaw, Lanarkshire.

1168   ALASSIO 1954
1954

16mm	col	commag	590ft		REF

filmed by Enrico Cocozza

General scenic shots around Alassio, Italy.

1169   ALASSIO 1947
1947

16mm	b/w&col	silent	720ft		REF

filmed by Enrico Cocozza

Panoramic views around Alassio, Italy.

1170   FANTASMAGORIA
1948

16mm	col	commag	1080ft		VIEW

filmed by Enrico Cocozza

A fictional story of a Dracula-type character who terrorises the Coltness Estate in Wishaw.

1171   SMART BOY WANTED
1960

16mm	b/w	mute	700ft		VIEW

filmed by Enrico Cocozza

The story of two teenagers given a job in a cafe.

1172   WHITE LADY, THE
1949

16mm	b/w	commag	350ft		REF

filmed by Enrico Cocozza

Story of a male hiker abducted by a "white lady".

1173   CHICK'S DAY
1949

16mm	b/w	commag	756ft		VIEW

filmed by Enrico Cocozza

The story of two young boys who commit a robbery.

1174   FILIGNANO
1955

16mm	b/w	silent	600ft		REF

filmed by Enrico Cocozza

General scenic shots of Filignano in Italy.

1175   CAPPELLA OF ENCHANTMENT, THE
1947

16mm	b/w&col	commag	720ft		VIEW

filmed by Enrico Cocozza

A love story set in Alassio, Italy.

1176   TWILIGHT
1955

16mm	b/w	commag	540ft		VIEW

filmed by Enrico Cocozza

The story of a group of people trying to survive after an atomic war.

1177   (COCOZZA TRIMS I)
1954c

16mm	b/w&col	silent	846ft		VIEW

[filmed by Enrico Cocozza]

Scenes of Pompeii and Brunati, Italy and the city of Paris. [Trims only.]

1178	COCOZZA TRIMS II

1954c

16mm	b/w	silent	720ft	VIEW

[filmed by Enrico Cocozza]

Shots of West Cross in Wishaw, and a polar bear at the Zoo. [Trims only.]

1179	[LOCAL WEDDINGS]

1959

16mm	b/w&col	silent	390ft	REF

[filmed by Enrico Cocozza]

Footage of various local weddings, probably in Wishaw, Lanarkshire.

1180	[HOUSE THAT JOHN BUILT]

1957*

16mm	b/w	silent	400ft	REF

[filmed by Enrico Cocozza]

Footage of two men building a house, including laying the foundations and bricklaying.

1181	BEFORE TIME GAME

1958

16mm	col	commag	710ft	VIEW

filmed by Enrico Cocozza

A love story set in a park.

1182	NINE O'CLOCK

1957

16mm	b/w	commag	720ft	REF

filmed by Enrico Cocozza

Story of a young man's last few hours before he commits suicide.

1183	CORKY

1957

16mm	b/w	commag	720ft	VIEW

filmed by Enrico Cocozza

The adventures of a young boy in Wishaw, Lanarkshire.

1184	THEME FOR SUNDAY

1957

16mm	b/w	commag	528ft	REF

[filmed by Enrico Cocozza]

Demonstrations of various camera and sound techniques.

1185	FAMILY RECORDS

1949

16mm	b/w&col	silent	770ft	REF

[filmed by Enrico Cocozza]

Compilation of various family events, including a wedding and a picnic in Kelvingrove Park.

1186	COCOZZA CUT AND TRIMS

1949

16mm	b/w	silent	600ft	VIEW

[filmed by Enrico Cocozza]

Family film. [Trims only.]

1187	[UNFINISHED WISHAW HIGH SCHOOL FILM]

1948

16mm	b/w	silent	660ft	REF

[filmed by Enrico Cocozza]

Shots of various sports at Wishaw High School and prize-giving ceremony.

1188	SECOND FOLLIES, THE

1953

16mm	b/w&col	commag	830ft	REF

filmed by Enrico Cocozza

Various song and dance routines.

1189	[SCENES AT WEST CROSS]

1954c

16mm	b/w	silent	550ft	REF

[filmed by Enrico Cocozza]

Compilation of views around West Cross in Wishaw, including shots of men tarring the roads, the Belhaven cafe and a gents' hairdressers.

1190	LAUNCH OF THE MV "RANGITANE"

1949

16mm	col	silent	286ft	REF

sp. John Brown and Company Limited, Clydebank

Launch of the MV "Rangitane" by HRH the Duchess of Gloucester at John Brown's shipyard, Clydebank.

1191	FAR FROM ALONE

1956

16mm	b/w	comopt		REF

[p.c. Kingswood Studios]

A film to promote temperance, it tells the story of an American football star who is against any form of alcohol.

97

1192 FAITH TRIUMPHANT

1950c

| 16mm | b/w | comopt | 811ft | | REF |

p.c. Pinewood Studios

Events in the life of St. Paul, after the crucifixion of Christ.

1193 LIQUID LORE

1959c

| 16mm | col | comopt | 540ft | | REF |

[sp. National Women's Christian Temperance Union (USA)]

A temperance propoganda film highlighting the comparison of alcohol and water in laboratory tests.

1194 BENEFICENT REPROBATE, THE

1945*

| 16mm | b/w | comopt | 720ft | | VIEW |

[sp. National Christian Women's Temperance Union (USA)]

A temperance propoganda film showing the chemicals present in the human body and the detrimental effect alcohol has on them.

1195 IT'S THE BRAIN THAT COUNTS

1943*

| 16mm | b/w | comopt | 540ft | | VIEW |

[p.c. Chicago Film Laboratory Incorporated]

Based on the writings of Bertha Rachel Palmer, the film tells the story of a young man injured after drinking too much. The doctor who is treating him explains the effect alcohol has on his body.

1196 ALCOHOL AND THE HUMAN BODY

1950c

| 16mm | b/w | silent | 378ft | | REF |

p.c. Encyclopaedia Britannica Films

An explanation of the specific effect of alcohol on the human body.

1198 WHICH IS BEST?

1945c

| 16mm | b/w | silent | 24ft | | REF |

A temperance propoganda film giving a comparison of the differences between alcoholic and non-alcoholic drinks.

1199 WHAT'S IN A GLASS?

1947*

| 16mm | b/w | silent | 285ft | | REF |

filmed by George J. Bowes

Dramatised account of how a man knocks down and kills a girl, after taking alcohol.

1201 [GOD OF CREATION]

1945

| 16mm | col | comopt | 900ft | | REF |

p.c. Moody Institute of Science

The story of God's creations, and Irwin A. Moon gives a sermon.

1202 ETHYL ALCOHOL. ITS NATURE AND ITS PROPERTIES

1940c

| 16mm | b/w | comopt | 1204ft | | REF |

sp. National Women's Christian Temperance Union (USA)
p.c. Burton Holmes Films Inc., Chicago, Illinois
d. Elmer Clifton

The effect of alcohol on the human body is defined through laboratory tests.

1203 TO YOUR HEALTH

1950c

| 16mm | col | comopt | 354ft | | REF |

sp. World Health Organisation
p.c. Halas and Batchelor

Cartoon showing the evils of alcohol.

1204 VOICE OF THE DEEP

1952c

| 16mm | col | comopt | 1024ft | | VIEW |

p.c. Moody Bible Institute (USA)
d. F. Acton Everest

The development of the hydro-phone (underwater microphone) and Irwin A. Moon's message of Christianity.

1205 NEMESIS

1949

| 16mm | b/w | silent | 342ft | | REF |

filmed by H. A. V. Bulleid

Dramatised account of a young man who knocks down his fiancee while drunk. He takes another car to go for help, but the man in the car reveals himself as Death.

1206 ROCK OF AGES

1942

| 16mm | b/w | comopt | 175ft | | REF |

The work and music of "Rock of Ages" by Toplady.

1207 TONI

n.d.

| 9.5mm | b/w | silent | 360ft | | REF |

p.c. Pathescope

A Pathescope comedy featuring Jack Buchanan.

1208	NO VACANT CHAIRS				
1957					
16mm	col	comopt	488ft		REF

p.c. Moody Bible Institute of Science (USA)

A training film for Sunday School teachers.

1209	DUST OR DESTINY				
1950*					
16mm	col	comopt	1400ft		REF

[p.c. Moody Institute of Science (USA)]

"A Sermon from Science with Irwin A. Moon", the film compares parts of the human body with man-made equivalents.

1210	[MOON'S ATOMIC ENERGY]				
1956					
16mm	col	comopt	1215ft		REF

[p.c. Moody Bible Institute of Science (USA)]

Irwin Moon lectures on atomic energy with shots of the preparation and aftermath of the dropping of the atom bomb on Bikini Island.

1211	HIGHLAND GATHERING, A				
1951					
16mm	col	silent	117ft		REF

[filmed by James S. Nairn and James Atterson]

Events at a highland games including a pipe band marching, competitors throwing the hammer, tossing the caber and highland dancing.

1212	SCOTTISH HOLIDAY, A				
1939					
16mm	col	silent	288ft		REF

A holiday film of city scenes of Glasgow and Edinburgh, and the Wallace Monument at Stirling.

1213	SLAUGHTER ON THE AVENUE (SEARCHLIGHT)				
1959					
16mm	b/w	comopt	980ft		REF

p.c. Granada TV
d. Mike Wooler

A television documentary on the prevention of accidents caused by drinking and driving.

1214	SUNSHINE CRUISE TO THE MEDITERRANEAN, A				
1936c					
16mm	b/w	silent	360ft		REF

sp. Anchor Donaldson

A cruise on board the "SS Tuscania" to the Mediterranean, starting from Yorkhill Quay in Glasgow.

1215	CANADA'S "QUEENS" CITY				
1936*					
16mm	b/w	silent	288ft		REF

sp. Department of Trade and Commerce
p.c. Canadian Government Motion Picture Bureau

Scenes around the city of Toronto.

1216	CANADA'S METROPOLIS: MONTREAL				
1936*					
16mm	b/w	silent	344ft		REF

sp. Department of Trade and Commerce
p.c. Canadian Government Motion Picture Bureau

Scenes of Montreal, Canada.

1217	NEW WAY TO THE NEW WORLD, THE				
1936c					
16mm	b/w	silent	342ft		VIEW

[sp. Anchor Donaldson]

Footage of the liner the "Cameronia" on her journey from Glasgow to her arrival at New York. Includes shots of games on board, such as deck tennis, shuffle board and a pillow fight.

1218	ISLES OF SUNSHINE				
1936c					
16mm	b/w	silent	378ft		REF

A description of how the White Fleet of Canadian National Steamships connect the ports of Canada with the West Indies.

1219	REGION OF ROMANCE, A				
1932*					
16mm	b/w	mute	360ft		REF

Panoramic footage of the Highlands of Ontario, Canada, highlighting the vantage points for tourists.

1220	[SEE CANADA THIS SUMMER]				
1936c					
16mm	b/w	silent	342ft		REF

[sp. Anchor Donaldson]

An advert for Anchor Line cruises to Canada on board the liners "Letitia" and "Athenia".

1221	(TOUR OF CANADA TRIMS)				
1936					
16mm	b/w	silent	460ft		REF

[p.c. Anchor Donaldsons]

Passengers boarding the liners the "Letita" and "Athenia"; scenes on board and shots of Toronto and Montreal in Canada.

1222   PRESBYTERIAN TOUR OF CANADA

1936

16mm	b/w&col silent	1438ft	REF

A tour of Canada on board the "Letitia" and "Athenia" with shots of the liners at Yorkhill Quay in Glasgow with Harry Lauder on board the "Letitia". The liners' arrival at Belfast and Quebec. Scenes of the tour in Canada.

1223   (SHIP GAMES)

1948c

16mm	b/w	silent	360ft	REF

Shots of a ship leaving Glasgow's Yorkhill Quay and of passengers on board playing various deck games.

1224   [WAYSIDE SCENES IN PALESTINE]

1941*

16mm	b/w	silent	355ft	REF

Footage of life in Palestine, with shots of local people and their customs.

1225   NEWS PARADE, THE

1939

16mm	col	silent	145ft	REF

p.c. Castle Films

Compilation of various news items concerning King George VI and Queen Elizabeth's visit to Canada and the U.S.A.

1226   FISHERMAN AND THE DJINN, THE

1947

16mm	col	silent	1200ft	VIEW

filmed by Frank M. Marshall

Story of the efforts of a drunken fisherman to ensure his country's success in an international yacht race. [A prize-winning film at the 1948 Scottish Amateur Film Festival.]

1227   CRUISING ON LOCH LOMOND

1959

9.5mm	b/w	silent	250ft	REF

[filmed by Donald Macpherson, Glasgow Cine Club]

Shots of Loch Lomond from the steamer "Maid of the Loch".

1228   HOLIDAYS AT ROTHESAY

1950c

9.5mm	b/w	silent	200ft	REF

[filmed by Donald Macpherson, Glasgow Cine Club]

Holidays in Rothesay, Isle of Bute.

1229   HOLIDAYS AT LARGS

1950c

9.5mm	b/w&col silent	250ft	REF

[filmed by Donald Macpherson, Glasgow Cine Club]

Street scenes in and around Largs; people playing pitch and putt, a local fair and a football match between Largs Thistle and Irvine Meadow.

1230   [ROUND AILSA CRAIG]

1950

9.5mm	b/w	silent	300ft	REF

[filmed by Donald Macpherson, Glasgow Cine Club]

Shot on the anniversary of the Caledonian Steam Packet Company, the film features the steamer "PS Duchess of Montrose", Ailsa Craig, Keppel pier and the sailing vessel the "Carrick" berthed at Custom House Quay, Glasgow.

1231   EDINBURGH

1950c

9.5mm	b/w&col silent	350ft	REF

p.c. Pathe [second section only]
[filmed by Donald Macpherson, Glasgow Cine Club]

The first section of the reel shows a holiday in Edinburgh, with shots of Princes Street and a family picnic. The second section is a Pathe newsreel featuring Edinburgh's Princes Street, Scott Monument, St. Giles' Cathedral and Holyroodhouse.

1232   [GLASGOW TRAMWAYS AND CLARKSTON TROLLEY BUSES]

1953-'67

9.5mm	b/w&col silent	350ft	REF

filmed by Donald Macpherson, Glasgow Cine Club

Tramways on the south side of Glasgow, in particular the last tram to Clarkston. Trolley buses and steam locomotives.

1233   GIRVAN ANNUAL ATHLETICS SPORTS MEETING

1930c

35mm	b/w	silent	180ft	VIEW

[filmed as a local topical for the Pavilion Cinema, Girvan]

A cartwheel race, sand castle competition and the Girvan Silver Band filmed at the annual athletic sports meeting.

1234   DALMELLINGTON FANCY DRESS PARADE

1927c

35mm	b/w	silent	240ft	VIEW

filmed as a local topical for the Pavilion and Picture House

People leaving the local butcher's shop, a band playing and a fancy dress procession.

1236	**(GREEN'S 1917 FILM SERVICE)**				
1917-'18					
35mm	b/w	silent	158ft		VIEW

p.c. Green's Film Service

The "tank bank" campaign in Aberdeen, an aerial display and sports at Powderhall, Edinburgh.

1237	**[SCENES OF LOCAL INTEREST]**				
1934c					
16mm	b/w	silent	466ft		VIEW

filmed as a local topical for the Regal Cinema, Girvan

"Paddy's Milestone", Bath parade with the Highland Light Infantry, the Prince of Wales visiting Girvan, and a Gala Day.

1238A	**SCOTTISH MOVING PICTURE NEWS NO. 32**				
1918					
35mm	b/w	silent	260ft		VIEW

p.c. Scottish Moving Picture News/ Green's Film Service

Scenes of flooding of the river Clyde and footage of the "Tank bank" week in Aberdeen to raise funds for the war effort. [£2 million was raised in a week in Aberdeen.] [See also ref. 1238B.]

1238B	**SCOTTISH MOVING PICTURE NEWS NO. 32**				
1918					
35mm	b/w	silent	420ft		VIEW

[p.c. Scottish Moving Picture News/ Green's Film Service]

Footage of "Julian the Tank Bank" in Edinburgh, Dundee and Aberdeen to raise money for the war effort. [See also ref. 1238A.]

1239	**MARYMASS PARADE, IRVINE**				
1931c					
35mm	b/w	comopt	270ft		VIEW

filmed as a local topical for the Palace Cinema, Irvine

The Marymass Parade, Irvine, showing the various races, including mothers' and grannies' races, the floats procession and spectators.

1240	**CAMERON HIGHLANDERS IN LONDON**				
1934					
16mm	b/w	comopt	33ft		REF

p.c. Pathe Gazette

The 2nd Battalion Cameron Highlanders take over guard duties at Buckingham Palace. [Incomplete.]

1241	**ROYAL MILE**				
1969					
16mm	col	comopt	700ft		VIEW

p.c. Educational Films of Scotland

The historical buildings and sites of the Royal Mile including Edinburgh Castle, Gladstone's Land, St Giles' Cathedral, Holyrood Palace and the Canongate.

1242	**(SCOTTISH SCENES)**				
1930c					
9.5mm	b/w	silent	c350ft		REF

A steam train at Bridgeton Cross in Glasgow and people enjoying a holiday on the seafront on the Clyde.

1243	**(LEISURE TIME)**				
1930s					
9.5mm	b/w	silent	c300ft		REF

A cricket match, a prayer meeting on a beach, a swimming pool, and people playing tennis.

1244	**(COASTAL SCENES)**				
1930s					
9.5mm	b/w	silent	350ft		REF

Scenes around Eyemouth and Berwick-on-Tweed including a Gala day with a pipe band and procession.

101

Da Makkin O' A Keshie, 1932. A Shetland crofter carrying peat in a 'keshie'. Ref. 1127

1245 NEWMILNS CIVIC WEEK
1949

| 16mm | col | silent | 2052ft | | REF |

filmed by Ronald L. Jay

Festival events during the Newmilns Civic Week, 28th May - 4th June 1949; the historical pageant, church parade, gala day, carnival night, a fireworks' display and an old folks' outing to Burns country.

1247 IT'S ABOUT TIME
1952*

| 16mm | b/w | comopt | 750ft | | VIEW |

in association with the Film Producers Guild
d. & p. Cecil Musk

An advert for Hoover vacuum cleaners showing the benefits to the housewife.

1248 STEEL GOES TO SEA
1941

| 16mm | b/w | comopt | 585ft | | VIEW |

sp. British Council
p.c. Merton Park Studios
d. John E. Lewis

The building of a ship during the war, the film shows each stage in its construction at Burntisland shipyard and emphasises the importance of the traditional skill of British shipbuilders.

1249 IT COMES FROM COAL
1941

| 16mm | b/w | comopt | 420ft | | VIEW |

sp. British Commercial Gas Assoc.
p.c. Realist Film Unit
p. Edgar Anstey

An essay on the synthetic substances derived from coal, including benzene for the Spitfire aircraft and other arms manufacture and plastics.

1250 JOYS OF THE OPEN ROAD
1961

| 16mm | col | silent | 100ft | | VIEW |

filmed by Frank M. Marshall

A humorous satire on the joys of motoring, the film was entered at the 1961 SAFF.

1251 LIFEBOAT DRILL
1936c

| 16mm | b/w | silent | 115ft | | VIEW |

[p.c. Elder Dalrymple Productions]

Demonstration of lifeboat drill on board the Royal Naval Lifeboat 'John Russell' at Montrose.

1252 FOCUS ON BRIDGETON
1948/'49

| 16mm | b/w | silent | 650ft | | REF |

filmed by William McKissock

Compiled and directed by the Revd. Ewart W. Lewis showing some aspects of the work of the East Glasgow Mission, Bridgeton.

1253 TWO GOOD FAIRIES
1943*

| 16mm | b/w | comopt | 540ft | | VIEW |

p.c. Normans Film Production
p. Edward Cook

Dramatised story of a demobbed soldier who takes out an insurance policy; possibly an indirect comment on the "Beveridge Report".

1254 (FASHION SHOW)
1959c

| 16mm | b/w | silent | 580ft | | REF |

sp. Scottish Co-operative Wholesale Society

A fashion show with women and men modelling the latest in fashion.

1256 [CO-OP ADVERTS I]
1955c

| 16mm | b/w | silent | 260ft | | REF |

sp. Scottish Co-operative Wholesale Society

Compilation of adverts for Co-op shoes, margarine, porridge oats, flour and bread.

1257 [CO-OP ADVERTS 11]
1955c

| 16mm | b/w | comopt | 180ft | | REF |

sp. Scottish Co-operative Wholesale Society

Christmas Co-op adverts for sweets, gents' slippers, food and drink etc. , part of their "Spot the Likeness" series.

1258 (HONEYMOON CARRIAGE RIDE)
1930s

| 9.5mm | b/w | silent | c20ft | | REF |

A couple leave for their honeymoon by horse-drawn carriage, they arrive at a cottage and the husband carries his wife over the threshold.

1259 EMMERSON MOUNTAINEERS, THE
1949c

| 16mm | b/w | comopt | 100ft | | VIEW |

A country style group sings "Listen to the Mocking Bird".

102

1260 [CO-OP ADVERTS 111]
1960s

| 16mm | b/w | comopt | c100ft | | REF |

sp. Scottish Co-operative Wholesale Society

Co-op adverts for Lofty Peak flour, Golden Ball marmalade, "Remember the Dividend", and tomato sauce.

1261 [CO-OP ADVERTS 1V]
1955c

| 16mm | b/w&col | comopt | 700ft | | REF |

sp. Scottish Co-operative Wholesale Society

Compilation of various Co-op food adverts, e.g.. Orchid margarine, digestive sweetmeal biscuits, cigarettes, furniture, clothes and dividend news.

1263 [SCWS WHEATSHEAF BREAD ADVERTISEMENT]
1947c

| 35mm | b/w | comopt | 140ft | | REF |

sp. Scottish Co-operative Wholesale Society

Several versions of Co-op bread adverts.

1264 CAR JOURNEY, A
1948c

| 16mm | col | silent | 360ft | | VIEW |

sp. GB Instructional Ltd.
p. John C. Elder

A boy and his uncle are given a lift home. The film shows how roadbuilders overcome obstacles with bridges, level crossings, ferries etc.

1265 LIFEBOAT COMING
1963*

| 16mm | col | comopt | 445ft | | REF |

filmed by William Guild, Dept. of Agric., Univ. of Edinburgh

The Arbroath lifeboat crew demonstrate a rescue from a ship in distress.

1266 (EMPIRE EXHIBITION. GLASGOW 1938)
1938

| 9.5mm | b/w | silent | c70ft | | REF |

The Empire Exhibition in Bellahouston Park, Glasgow. Shots of various pavilions, the tower and the dancing waters by night.

1267 (STATION FAREWELLS)
1930s

| 9.5mm | b/w | silent | c35ft | | REF |

A small Scottish railway station where a family waves farewell to friends before boarding a steam train.

1268 [YOKER SCHOOL FILM]
1930s

| 9.5mm | b/w | silent | c360ft | | REF |

Activities at Yoker School, Glasgow; pupils enjoying music and movement lessons, infants singing and dancing in the playground and senior pupils doing Scottish country dancing.

1269 SKYWAY AMBULANCE
1947

| 16mm | col | silent | 255ft | | VIEW |

sp. GB Instructional Ltd.
p.c. Junior Activity Films
p. John C. Elder

A boy becomes ill during a visit to the Western Isles, the Skyway ambulance is called and the boy is taken quickly to a hospital in Glasgow.

1270 VISIT TO A SHIPBUILDING YARD
1949

| 16mm | col | silent | 415ft | | REF |

sp. GB Instructional Ltd.
p.c. Junior Activity Films
p. John C. Elder

Children visit John Brown's shipyard in Clydebank and see vessels under construction and being fitted out.

1271 DOWN TO THE SEA
1950c

| 16mm | col | silent | 380ft | | VIEW |

sp. GB Instructional Ltd.
p.c. Junior Activity Films
p. John C. Elder

At Clyde docks three children watch the handling of cargo and movement of ships, coasters, tugs, tankers and liners. They board a ship and watch the crew at work.

1272 FLYING ABOVE THE CLOUDS
1941*

| 16mm | col | silent | 330ft | | VIEW |

sp. GB Instructional Ltd.
p.c. Junior Activity Films
p. John C. Elder

Two boys are taken on a flight from Renfrew airport. They are shown how the flight instruments work. The trip takes them over the Clyde estuary.

1273 (NOTRE DAME COLLEGE - MOVE TO BEARSDEN 1963-1970)
1963-'70

| 16mm | col | silent | 700ft | | REF |

Preparation of site, construction of buildings and removal to new college premises at Bearsden, Glasgow.

103

1274   OTHER MAN'S JOB, THE

1943

| 16mm | b/w | comopt | 100ft | VIEW |

sp. Ministry of Information
p.c. Paramount, Warwork News

How locomotives for "the second front" were constructed at the North British Locomotive Company, Springburn, Glasgow.

1275   DEAR GREEN PLACE

1960c

| 16mm | b/w | comopt | 520ft | REF |

p. & d. Oscar Marzaroli and Michael Pavett

Through a series of stills taken over a ten year period, a Glasgow photographer traces the rebirth of his city, through its social and structural changes.

1276   NORTH BRITISH

1949c

| 16mm | b/w | comopt | 1430ft | REF |

sp. North British Locomotive Company.
p.c. The Big Six Film Unit
d. John S. Abbott, Jnr.

Promotional film for North British Locomotive Company, Glasgow, with coverage on how the locomotive "Bartholomen Diaz" was manufactured and sent to South Africa.

104

1277   (NORTH BRITISH CUTTINGS)

1949*

| 16mm | col | mute | 390ft | REF |

sp. Locomotive Manufacturers Association

Shots inside foundry of men hammering a piston rod for a locomotive, using a machine hammer. [Rushes only.]

1278   (EMPIRE EXHIBITION. BELLAHOUSTON PARK, GLASGOW)

1938

| 9.5mm | b/w | silent | 310ft | REF |

[filmed by a member of the Thomson family]

General views of pavilions, the fair and exhibition tower at the Glasgow Empire Exhibition of 1938.

1279   (LIFEBOAT SERVICE)

1955c

| 35mm | b/w | comopt | 450ft | REF |

sp. Royal National Lifeboat Institution
p.c. Films of Fact Limited

A demonstration of a lifeboat crew bringing ashore survivors.

1280   (CORONATION? PARADE. BROXBURN C1910)

1910c

| 35mm | b/w | silent | 325ft | VIEW |

[attributed to Mr. Miller, for the Regal Cinema, Broxburn]

Street scenes in Broxburn, with brass bands and pipe bands accompanying the parade. Children carry Union Jacks and 'God Save the King' banners.

1281   [FERRY FAIR]

1930c

| 35mm | b/w | silent | 318ft | VIEW |

filmed by Mr. Miller for the Regal Cinema, Broxburn

A fancy dress parade in South Queensferry, with shots of the "Burryman" and the crowning of the Festival Queen. The Forth Rail Bridge is seen in the background.

1282   WINCHBURGH CHILDREN'S GALA DAY

1942

| 35mm | b/w | silent | 210ft | REF |

[filmed by Mr. Miller for the Regal Cinema, Broxburn]

A parade in the streets of Winchburgh, West Lothian. The Amateur Fire Service war units demonstrate fire fighting equipment. 1st. August 1942.

1283   STEWARTFIELD GALA DAY. BROXBURN

1942

| 35mm | b/w | silent | 160ft | REF |

[filmed by Mr. Miller for the Regal Cinema, Broxburn]

Events at the Gala Day in Stewartfield, West Lothian including the local "Tip Race" where the men race up and down a shale bing.

1284   UPHALL CHILDREN'S GALA ETC

1931*

| 35mm | b/w | silent | 908ft | REF |

[filmed by Mr Miller, proprietor of the Regal Cinema, Broxburn]

A compilation of films of gala days in West Lothian including Uphall Children's Gala day, Pumpherston Children's Gala and Broxburn pageant.

1285   (CINEMA TRAILERS II)

1960s,c

| 35mm | b/w&col comopt | 330ft | REF |

"God Save the Queen" cinema trailer and adverts for Lyons Maid ice cream and Vernon's Pools.

1286 SHETLAND, PEOPLE OF MANY LANDS
1967

16mm	b/w	comopt	745ft	VIEW

sp. BBC TV
d. Elizabeth Balneaves

Daily life on the Shetland Isles; cutting peat, making wicker fish baskets, shearing sheep and haymaking.

1287 GLASGOW CINEMA CLUB. 50TH ANNIVERSARY
1969

super 8mm	col	silent	300ft	REF

filmed by John Fletcher

Made during the celebrations to mark 50 years of the Glasgow Cinema Club, the first of its kind in the UK. The film includes shots of several well-known trade personalities from the west of Scotland.

1288A WICK SHOPPING WEEK - PRIMARY SCHOOL SPORTS
1933

35mm	b/w	silent	210ft	REF

Shots of Wick harbour as a fishing trawler enters, shots of Wick streets and a school sports.

1288B CARNIVAL PROCESSION AND CROWNING OF HERRING QUEEN
1938

35mm	b/w	silent	300ft	REF

filmed as a local topical for the Pavilion Cinema, Wick

Carnival procession and crowning of the "Herring Queen".

1288C YOU AND YOUR MONEY
1951*

35mm	b/w	comopt	120ft	REF

Cinema trailer on behalf of a petition to oppose an increase in the Entertainments Tax.

1289 SETTING UP THE BOLEX S-221 (PROJECTOR)
1961*

16mm	b/w	silent	305ft	REF

A demonstration of how to set up the Bolex S-221 projector.

1290 (ARRAN FARMERS SOCIETY ANNUAL FAIR 1951)
1951

35mm	b/w	silent	1000ft	REF

sp. Caledonian Associated Cinemas

The Arran Farmers' Society Annual Fair held at Lamlash with shots of supplies being unloaded from the steamer "Glen Sannox", horses and cattle in the paddock and the presentation of prizewinners' cups.

1291 BROXBURN GALA DAY AND CROWNING OF QUEEN
1954

35mm	b/w	silent	1200ft	REF

filmed by Mr. Miller for the Regal Cinema, Broxburn

Gala procession, children's fancy dress competition and the Gala Queen crowning ceremony.

1292 BROXBURN HIGH SCHOOL SPORTS AND DISPLAY
1954

35mm	b/w	silent	845ft	REF

filmed by Mr. Miller for the Regal Cinema, Broxburn

The first annual inter-house school sports day at Broxburn High School, West Lothian.

1293 BROXBURN HIGH SCHOOL SPORTS
1953

35mm	b/w	silent	c2000ft	REF

filmed by Mr. Miller for the Regal Cinema, Broxburn

School sports day with a brass band procession, races and other sporting events.

1294 UPHALL STATION CHILDREN'S GALA
1953

35mm	b/w	silent	670ft	REF

filmed by Mr. Miller for the Regal Cinema, Broxburn

Children's Gala Day, Uphall, West Lothian, with a fancy dress parade, races and dancing.

1295 FERRY FAIR 1955
1955

35mm	b/w	silent	770ft	REF

filmed by Mr. Miller for the Regal Cinema, Broxburn

Crowning of the Fair Queen, and the parade through South Queensferry.

105

1296	KIRKLISTON CHILDREN'S GALA AND CROWNING OF QUEEN				
1954					
35mm	b/w	silent	410ft		REF

[filmed by Mr. Miller for the Regal Cinema, Broxburn]

Procession of the Gala Queen and "The Champion" through the streets of Kirkliston, West Lothian.

1297	FERRY FAIR OF 1954				
1954					
35mm	b/w	silent	800ft		REF

[filmed by Mr. Miller for the Regal Cinema, Broxburn]

Crowning of the Fair Queen and the children's fancy dress competition at South Queensferry.

1298	GALA DAY AND CROWNING CEREMONY AT BROXBURN				
1953					
35mm	b/w	silent	960ft		REF

[filmed by Mr. Miller for the Regal Cinema, Broxburn]

The decorated floats procession and the crowning of Gala Queen at Broxburn, West Lothian.

1299A	BROXBURN HIGH SCHOOL SPORTS				
1955					
35mm	b/w	silent	720ft		REF

[filmed by Mr. Miller for the Regal Cinema, Broxburn]

School children in procession through Broxburn to the sports ground and competitions at the school sports.

1299B	HM QUEEN ELIZABETH AND HRH DUKE OF EDINBURGH PASSING THROUGH BROXBURN				
1955					
35mm	b/w	silent	405ft		REF

[filmed by Mr. Miller for the Regal Cinema, Broxburn]

The Royal motorcade passes through Broxburn where crowds line the streets with a welcoming banner.

1300	BROXBURN AND DISTRICT CHILDREN'S GALA DAY AND CROWNING CEREMONY				
1955					
35mm	b/w	silent	1140ft		REF

filmed by Mr. Miller for the Regal Cinema, Broxburn

Coronation of Gala Queen and procession of decorated floats.

1301	(UNIDENTIFIED GALA AND SPORTS DAY, BROXBURN AREA NO. 1)				
1953*					
35mm	b/w	silent	980ft		REF

[filmed by Mr Miller, Regal Cinema, Broxburn]

Unidentified Gala and Sports Day in the Broxburn area, includes footage of decorated floats procession, athletic camps, Scottish country dancing.

1302	(UNIDENTIFIED SPORTS DAY. BROXBURN AREA)				
1954c					
35mm	b/w	silent	805ft		REF

[filmed by Mr Miller, proprietor of Regal Cinema, Broxburn]

Unidentified sports day in the Broxburn area, West Lothian, with footage of festivities such as sports, country dancing and a fairground.

1303	(BROXBURN GALA DAY 1953)				
1953					
35mm	b/w	silent	720ft		REF

[filmed by Mr Miller, proprietor of Regal Cinema, Broxburn]

Fancy dress competition, and the crowning of the Gala Queen.

1304	(DUMFRIES - VISIT AND INSPECTION)				
1952*					
35mm	b/w	silent	100ft		REF

[filmed as a local topical for the Lyceum Cinema, Dumfries]

The Duchess of Gloucester inspects the King's Own Scottish Borderers.

1305	[SCOTTISH NATIONALISTS' BANNOCKBURN CELEBRATIONS]				
1948					
16mm	b/w	silent	300ft		VIEW

A recruitment appeal showing the Scottish Nationalists' Bannockburn celebrations in Stirling with Wendy Wood, R.E. Muirhead, and Dr. MacIntyre.

1306	(EMPIRE EXHIBITION: EXTERIORS AND INTERIORS)				
1938					
9.5mm	b/w	silent	175ft		REF

General views of the pavilions, stands and tower at the Glasgow Empire Exhibition in 1938 with shots of visitors touring the exhibition on "Lister's Auto Trucks" and at other engineering stands.

1307 (NOTRE DAME COLLEGE GRADUATES AND WEDDING)

1962

16mm	b/w&col silent	175ft		REF

Students graduation ceremony at Notre Dame College of Education, Glasgow. Featuring also a wedding and Christmas festivities.

1308 [ROOTES FILM] (WORKING TITLE)

1959*

16mm	b/w	silent	125ft	REF

p.c. Glasgow Films

Shot in the early stages of a documentary on the Rootes Car manufacturing plant at Linwood showing the virgin site for the factory. [See also refs. 0085 and 1480.]

1309 UP HELLY AA FESTIVAL 1949

1949

16mm	b/w	silent	216ft	VIEW

The Up Helly Aa festival in Lerwick in the Shetland Islands, with shots by night of the procession and ceremonial burning of the galley.

1310 WHALING

1930s/'40s

9.5mm	b/w	silent	174ft	REF

p.c. Pathescope

The hunting and harpooning of whales.

1311 (BAXTER FAMILY FILMS)

1929-'50*

9.5mm	b/w&col silent	1800ft		REF

A compilation of Baxter family activities including holidays in Orkney and the Shetland Isles.

1312 (HARRY MCSHANE. 90TH BIRTHDAY CELEBRATIONS)

1981

16mm	col	sep mag	560ft	VIEW

sp. Scottish Film Archive

Shot inside The Mitchell Theatre, Glasgow, Paul Foot addresses the audience before the presentation is made to Harry McShane. 7th May 1981.

1313 GLASGOW EMPIRE EXHIBITION

1938

16mm	b/w&col silent	390ft		REF

filmed by Mr. Dick, amateur cinematographer

Scenes at the Empire Exhibition in Glasgow 1938, with shots of the exteriors of pavilions, the Clachan, fairground amusements, and the dancing waters by night.

1314 (SUMMER SEASON IN DUNOON)

1936*

16mm	b/w	silent	300ft	VIEW

[attributed to George West]

A family film including shots on board a paddle steamer, the Cowal Highland Games, Dunoon and Jack E. Raymond's stage show.

1315 ST. ANDREWS 1916

1916-'22

35mm	b/w	silent	1145ft	VIEW

sp. Cinema House, St. Andrews
p.c. Pathe Gazette

A compilation of events in St. Andrews, Fife including the installation of Sir Douglas Haig as Lord Rector of St. Andrews University, and the Duke of York at St. Andrews golf course.

1316 [BO'NESS FAIR 1912]

1912

35mm	b/w	silent	390ft	VIEW

filmed by Louis Dickson, for Hippodrome Cinema, Bo'ness

Coronation of Bo'ness fair queen and fancy dress procession.

1317 [HOME GUARD, AYR - STAND DOWN]

1944

16mm	b/w	silent	460ft	REF

The Home Guard, during drill and on parade past the barracks. 3rd December 1944.

1318 CLYDE RESORT: AN INTRODUCTION TO GIRVAN

1959*

16mm	col	comopt	344ft	REF

[p.c. Anglo Scottish Pictures]

Made to highlight Girvan's potential as a holiday resort, the film features such activities as bowling, tennis, golf, putting, donkey rides and the beach.

1319 [PAGEANT OF AYR]

1948*

16mm	b/w	silent	200ft	REF

Shots of an open air historical pageant in front of the watch tower/castle in Ayr.

1320 PAGEANT OF AYR, JUNE 1934

1934

std.8mm	b/w	silent	180ft	REF

filmed by K. H. Stevenson

Open-air historical pageant in Ayr.

107

1321   AYR

1937

16mm	b/w	silent	450ft		REF

sp. Ayr Attractions Committee
p.c. Ayr Film Unit

The attractions of Ayr; its theatre, Burns' tours, shops, the beach and surrounding scenery.

1322   (TO IRELAND BY AIR)

1933

16mm	b/w	silent	400ft		REF

filmed by amateur cinematographer

To Ireland by Midlands and Scottish Air Ferries Ltd. Shots of Renfrew airport where the plane is pulled out from the hangar and passengers board. Aerial shots of Arran and views of Belfast, Galway, Westport, Sligo and Derry.

1323   STEAM LOCOMOTIVES IN SCOTLAND

1963c

16mm	b/w	silent	440ft		REF

filmed by Norman Pollock

Various shots of steam locomotives and railway stations in Scotland.

1324   FILM OF GLASGOW, A

1932*

16mm	b/w	silent	774ft		REF

filmed by amateur cinematographer

Scenes around Glasgow including the East End and south side.

1325   CRUACHAN HYDRO-ELECTRIC. ROYAL OPENING

1965

35mm	col	comopt	200ft		REF

p.c. Pathe News

HM Queen Elizabeth opens the Cruachan hydro-electric dam.

1326   (MAY DAY PARADE. EDINBURGH 1937)

1937

16mm	b/w	silent	60ft		VIEW

filmed by Thomas Murray

Parade in streets and crowds in King's Park, Edinburgh.

1327   SCOTTISH DAILY NEWS

1974/'75

16mm	col	commag	1220ft		VIEW

filmed by Norman Pollock

The story of the Scottish Daily News from the closure of the Scottish Daily Express to the last run of the Scottish Daily News. [A prize-winning film at the Scottish Amateur Film Festival 1976.]

1328   BEAUTY SPOTS IN GREAT BRITAIN

1929-'33*

16mm	b/w	silent	235ft		REF

filmed by amateur cinematographer

Stobo Castle, Kerrara, the west coast of Scotland and the Serpentine in London.

1329   [UNVEILING OF WAR MEMORIAL. SALTCOATS]

1922

35mm	b/w	silent	770ft		VIEW

filmed by Green's Topical Productions

The address and unveiling of the War memorial, Saltcoats by the Marchioness (of Ailsa), 27th May, 1922.

1330   SALTCOATS GETS NEW ESPLANADE

1933

35mm	b/w	comopt	535ft		VIEW

p.c. British Movietone News

Sir Josiah and Lady Stamp perform the opening ceremony of the new Sandilands esplanade in Saltcoats.

1331   MAIRI: THE ROMANCE OF A HIGHLAND MAIDEN

1912

35mm	b/w	silent	1140ft		VIEW

filmed by Andrew Paterson

Dramatised account of Mairi, a young girl in love with a Revenue Officer and caught up in a fight to catch smugglers. An amateur production, first shown to the public in the Central Hall Picture House, Inverness on 20th May 1912. [The film was re-edited by James S. Nairn in 1953.]

1332   GLASGOW 1938

1938

9.5mm	b/w	silent	75ft		REF

filmed by M. Blair

Shots of King George VI and Queen Elizabeth arriving at Ibrox Stadium for the opening ceremony of the Empire Exhibition in Glasgow. General views of the Exhibition.

1333	TRIP TO IONA AND STAFFA. OBAN DISTRICT AND GLENCOE				
1931*					
16mm	b/w	silent	510ft		REF

General views of scenery during a family holiday in the Hebrides and Highlands of Scotland.

1334	LAUNCH OF "QUEEN MARY" NO. 534 AT CLYDEBANK				
1934					
16mm	b/w	silent	244ft		REF

The launching ceremony of the "Queen Mary" at John Brown's shipyard.

1335	REMEMBRANCE DAY				
1926*					
35mm	b/w	silent	90ft		VIEW

[filmed as a local topical]

Remembrance Day ceremony at the Cenotaph, Aberdeen with shots of a pipe band and a boy's trumpet band.

1336	BOYS' BRIGADE RALLY IN ABERDEEN				
1925					
35mm	b/w	silent	135ft	VIEW	

p.c. Green's Film Service

The Lord Provost presents new colours to the Boys' Brigade.

1337	ROYAL VISIT TO ABERDEEN				
1925					
35mm	b/w	silent	90ft	VIEW	

[filmed as a local topical]

King George V and Queen Mary visit the "Granite City" and inspect the guard of honour of war veterans.

1338	(FAMILY HOLIDAYS 1936/'38)				
1936-'38					
9.5mm	b/w	silent	750ft		REF

filmed by James Ogg

A family holiday taken in the Scottish Highlands with shots of Fraserburgh, Inverness and Thurso.

1339	JUNIOR PIPERS AND BANDSMEN TRAINING IN EDINBURGH				
1975*					
16mm	col	comopt	138ft		REF

Massed pipes and drums on the Esplanade at Edinburgh Castle intercut with sequences of troop training and manoeuvres.

1340	BRITAIN WELCOMES THE KING OF NORWAY IN EDINBURGH				
1962					
35mm	col	comopt	1050ft		VIEW

p.c. British Movietone News

Queen Elizabeth, the Duke of Edinburgh and PM Harold McMillan welcome King Olav of Norway at Princes Street station, Edinburgh. The King visits the new Forth Road Bridge and is created Knight of the Thistle.

1341	GEORGE BENNIE RAILPLANE SYSTEM OF TRANSPORT				
1929-'30					
35mm	b/w	silent	1579ft		VIEW

Technical record of the construction of the railplane, invented by George Bennie. Opening of trial stretch of track and the railplane in operation. [See also ref. 0422.]

1342	(ROCKET RANGE, BENBECULA)				
1961c					
16mm	b/w	comopt	390ft		VIEW

commentary by Ludovic Kennedy

A documentary about the local people's reaction to the establishment of a Royal Artillery Guided Weapons Range in the Hebrides and how the presence of the base affects traditional life.

1343	HISTORIC EDINBURGH				
1956c					
std.8mm	b/w	silent	50ft		REF

p.c. Walten Films Production

Footage of Holyrood Palace, St Giles' Cathedral, the Forth Bridges and of the Military Tattoo on the Castle Esplanade.

1344	PASTEURISED MILK				
1938c					
16mm	b/w	silent	455ft		VIEW

sp. Glasgow Corporation Public Health Department
p.c. Campbell Harper Films Ltd.
d. Alan Harper

The transport, pasteurisation and testing of milk for public consumption.

1345	COUNTRY HOMES				
1938					
16mm	b/w	silent	450ft		VIEW

sp. Glasgow Corporation Public Health Department
p.c. Campbell Harper Films Ltd.

How "country homes" for needy children are run; recounted through one child's experience.

Images of Scotland

W̲hen the sun shines and the air is clear, there's no place quite like Scotland. But Scotland's climate is predictably unpredictable, often leaving producers plans and budgets weather-beaten.

But now there's the *Fairline* Tape Library!

Fairline Productions, perhaps best known for the Scottish BAFTA award winning BBC Scotland television series, *'Hooked on Scotland'*, have one of the most extensive video libraries in Scotland.

From our vast library of stock material, we are now able to offer programme makers and producers, the widest range of quality images covering all aspects of contemporary Scottish life. This includes landscapes, seascapes, aerials, the islands, historic and present day places of interest, wild life and natural history, sport, industry and crafts.

All library images are originated on superb broadcast quality, Betacam SP and already many productions world-wide have benefited from this new and low cost facility.

So, if you're looking for those special pictures to enhance your production, call *Fairline* and ask for Karen or Claire.

Also available to hire are our experienced film and video crews and our well equipped off-line and on-line edit suites.

1346	BATHING THE BABY				
1938					
16mm	b/w	silent	470ft		VIEW

sp. Glasgow Corporation Public Health Department
p.c. Campbell Harper Films Ltd.
An illustration of how to bathe a baby correctly.

1347	STOBHILL HOSPITAL: THE STORY OF A MODERN HOSPITAL				
1938					
16mm	b/w	silent	956ft		VIEW

sp. Glasgow Corporation Public Health Department
p. J. Campbell Harper
The work of a modern hospital with shots 'behind the scenes' showing the kitchens, dispensary, telephone switchboard and nurses relaxing off-duty.

1348	CITY'S FARMS, THE				
1940					
16mm	b/w	silent	400ft		VIEW

sp. Glasgow Corporation Public Health Department
p.c. Campbell Harper Films Ltd.
How cows are hygienically cared for before and after milking at farms owned by Glasgow Corporation and how their pasteurised milk is a 'safe' supply for hospitals.

1349	CHILD WELFARE				
1938					
16mm	b/w	silent	670ft		VIEW

sp. Glasgow Corporation Public Health Department
p.c. Campbell Harper Films Ltd.
The local authority's maternity and child welfare service in operation showing the benefits to mother and child.

1350	RIVER FORTH				
1956					
16mm	b/w	silent	130ft		VIEW

sp. SEFA &SFC
p.c. Templar Film Studios
The geography and industries of the river Forth from source to sea.

1351	COUNTY CLERK				
1950					
35mm	b/w	comopt	1860ft		VIEW

sp. Central Office of Information/Scottish Home Department
p.c. Campbell Harper Films Ltd.
The role of the County Clerk in a small Scottish town.

1352	(WELCOME TO OUR GENERAL)				
1948					
35mm	b/w	silent	100ft		REF

filmed by H. Kemp for the Regal Cinema, Saltcoats
Possibly the re-union of 4th and 5th Royal Scots Fusiliers in Saltcoats, January 1948. A banner reads "Welcome to our General".

1353	FIRES IN TENEMENT BUILDINGS				
1945c					
16mm	b/w	comopt	690ft		VIEW

sp. Scottish Home Department
p.c. Campbell Harper Films Ltd.
Various methods of fire fighting in tenement buildings in Edinburgh.

1354	STORY OF A STEEL WIRE ROPE				
1946					
16mm	b/w	comopt	1100ft		VIEW

sp. Martin Black and Company Limited
p.c. Russell Productions in assoc. with Thames and Clyde Film Co. Ltd.
How steel wire rope is manufactured at the Coatbridge works of Martin Black & Co. (Wire Ropes) Ltd.

1355	CALEDONIAN NEWS REVIEW				
1952					
35mm	b/w	comopt	285ft		VIEW

filmed by R. R. Bucknell for Kelburne Cinema, Paisley
Students working at the Scottish Hotel School, Glasgow and the construction and launch of passenger steamers at A. & J. Inglis shipyard, Glasgow.

1356	AMAZING MOMENTS OF THE GREAT TRACTION ENGINES				
1969					
35mm	col	comopt	1080ft		VIEW

sp. Films of Scotland Committee
p.c. IFA (Scotland) Limited
d. Edward McConnell
A small boy inherits a steam road roller. A film fantasy by Edward McConnell.

1357	SALTCOATS QUEEN OF THE SEAS 1929				
1929					
35mm	b/w	silent	300ft		REF

[filmed by Harry Kemp for Regal Cinema, Saltcoats]
The exterior of the Regal Picture House, Saltcoats as crowds gather to watch the procession of floats and the coronation of the "Queen of the Seas".

1358	SALTCOATS QUEEN OF THE SEAS 1931				
1931					
35mm	b/w	silent	105ft		REF

[filmed by Harry Kemp for the Regal Cinema, Saltcoats]
The crowning ceremony of the Saltcoats "Queen of the Seas".

111

1359	MINISTRY OF FOOD FLASHES				
1941-'45					
35mm	b/w	comopt	330ft		VIEW

sp. Ministry of Food

Compilation of food flashes including adverts for dried eggs, how to obtain vitamin C from swedes,how to use a ration book and how to keep milk during a storm.

1360	DUNFERMLINE CHILDREN'S GALA 1932				
1932					
35mm	b/w	silent	715ft		REF

[filmed as a local topical for the Regal Cinema, Dunfermline]

A boys' three-legged race, cartwheel race, "coal carry" fight, a pack race and a tug-o-war.

1361	DUNFERMLINE CHILDREN'S GALA 1933				
1933					
35mm	b/w	silent	765ft		REF

filmed as a local topical for the Regal Cinema, Dunfermline

Shot of exterior of the Regal Cinema, Dunfermline as the Gala procession sets off. Views of sports and games.

1362	DUNFERMLINE CHILDREN'S GALA DAY 1934				
1934					
35mm	b/w	silent	725ft		VIEW

[filmed as a local topical for the Regal Cinema, Dunfermline]

Views of the Dunfermline Children's Gala parade, watching crowds and children's sports.

1363	DUNFERMLINE CHILDREN'S GALA 1936				
1936					
35mm	b/w	silent	800ft		REF

filmed as a local topical for the Regal Cinema, Dunfermline

Footage of Dunfermline Children's Gala on 26th June 1936, with shots of Andrew Carnegie's birthplace.

1364	DUNFERMLINE CHILDREN'S GALA 1950				
1950					
35mm	b/w	silent	1000ft		VIEW

[filmed by James S. Nairn for the Regal Cinema, Dunfermline]

General views of Dunfermline Children's Gala, including shots of the regal cinema, the parade and children playing.

1365	DUNFERMLINE CHILDREN'S GALA 1951				
1951					
35mm	b/w	silent	1100ft		REF

filmed by James S. Nairn for the Regal Cinema, Dunfermline

Crowds line the streets of Dunfermline as the children's procession passes on its way to the public park. Shots of people relaxing in the park, children playing games and picnicking.

1366	[DUNFERMLINE CHILDREN'S GALA DAY 1952]				
1952*					
35mm	b/w	silent	1000ft		REF

filmed by James S. Nairn for the Regal Cinema, Dunfermline

Crowds line the main street of Dunfermline and in front of the Regal Cinema as the children's procession passes. Shots of people in the public park with children playing games and eating ice cream.

1367	DUNFERMLINE CHILDREN'S GALA 1954				
1954					
35mm	b/w	silent	1380ft		VIEW

[filmed by James S. Nairn for the Regal Cinema, Dunfermline]

The children's procession through the crowd lined streets of Dunfermline with a brass band playing. Shots of local schoolchildren outside school waving flags.

1368	PENICUIK CHILDREN'S GALA DAY 1953				
1953					
35mm	b/w	silent	770ft		REF

[filmed as a local topical for the Playhouse Cinema, Penicuik]

Penicuik Children's Gala Day with shots of the Gala Queen's coronation and the procession through the streets with accompanying pipes and drums, floats, horses and riders.

1369	BO'NESS SEA SCOUTS				
1935c					
35mm	b/w	silent	75ft		REF

filmed by Louis Dickson for the Hippodrome, Bo'ness

Sea scouts operating a small craft and enjoying a boxing match.

1370	[BO'NESS V FORTH RANGERS AND GRANGE ROVERS]				
1950					
35mm	b/w	silent	650ft		REF

[filmed by Louis Dickson for the Hippodrome, Bo'ness]

Coverage of a football match between Bo'ness and Forth Rangers and Grange Rovers with shots of spectators, the teams playing and the crowds leaving the match.

1371	ABERDEEN BY SEASIDE AND DEESIDE

1971

35mm	b/w&col	comopt	2100ft	VIEW

sp. Films of Scotland
p.c. Templar Films

An overview of Aberdeen and surrounding area, including the city's harbour, highland games, the fishing fleet, Kildrummy Castle, skiing, boat races and a water pageant.

1372	NEWMILLS. TORRYBURN AND CROMBIE GALA

1951

35mm	b/w	silent	900ft	VIEW

Shots of a cricket match between Fife and Clackmannan, the parade at the Crombie Gala Day and children playing.

1373	HUNTLY GALA DAY

1951

35mm	b/w	silent	990ft	VIEW

[filmed as a local topical for the Playhouse, Huntly]

The Huntly Gala Day, with shots of the Gala queen and sports competitions, a bonfire and fireworks display.

1374	LAYING FOUNDATION STONE. KIRKINTILLOCH PARISH CHURCH

1913

35mm	b/w	silent	225ft	VIEW

[filmed as a local topical for the Picture House, Kirkintilloch]

A brass band leads the parade towards the parish church followed by members of the Masonic Order. Close-up shots of the laying of the foundation stone by the Marquis of Tullibardine.

1375	PERTH HISTORICAL PAGEANT

1949

35mm	b/w	comopt	365ft	VIEW

p.c. British Paramount News

The final performance at Muirton Park of the Perth Historical Pageant, opened by Tom Johnston and watched by Anna Neagle and Herbert Wilcox.

1376	(MAY DAY PARADE, BO'NESS)

1918*

35mm	b/w	silent	90ft	VIEW

[filmed by Dickson's Pictures for the Hippodrome, Bo'ness]

General views of the May Day Parade and shots of a young girl tap dancing.

1377	INVERKEITHING LAMMAS FAIR AND GAMES 1951

1951

35mm	b/w	silent	360ft	VIEW

General views of a youth parade with the Boys' Brigade, Boy Scouts, and Girl Guides at the Inverkeithing Lammas Fair and Games.

1378	SCHOOL BANK, GLASGOW

1930c

35mm	b/w	silent	80ft	VIEW

Footage of one of the penny savings banks run by teachers in Glasgow schools with shots of children handing their money and bank books to the clerks and clerkesses of the school bank in a Govan School.

1379	LAYING FOUNDATION STONE. FREE GARDENERS' HALL

1923

35mm	b/w	silent	90ft	VIEW

[filmed by Dickson's Pictures for the Hippodrome, Bo'ness]

A foundation stone is layed at Free Gardener's Hall Bo'ness, with a procession and brass band as part of the festivities.

1380	OPENING OF BRIDGENESS MINERS INSTITUTE

1924

35mm	b/w	silent	95ft	VIEW

[filmed by Dickson's Pictures for the Hippodrome, Bo'ness]

The opening speech at the Bridgeness Miners Institute. Shots of two men playing bowls watched by the spectating crowd.

1381A	WOMEN'S GUILD OF EMPIRE 1934

1934

35mm	b/w	silent	100ft	VIEW

[filmed as a local topical for the Alex Cinema, Paisley]

Paisley Women's Guild of Empire enjoy a motor tour through Burns' country.

1381B	FERGUSLIE THREAD WORKS OUTING TO BRAEMAR

1934

35mm	b/w	silent	315ft	VIEW

[filmed as a local topical for the Alex Cinema, Paisley]

Ferguslie Thread Works Outing to Braemar. Also know as Sma' Shot Day, a privilege won by the workers of all thread mills in the Paisley area.

1382   LAUNCH OF THE "QUEEN MARY"

1934

35mm	b/w	comopt	320ft		VIEW

p.c. Universal News

King George V and Queen Mary at the launching ceremony of the liner the "Queen Mary".

1383   WOMEN'S GUILD OF EMPIRE C1933

1933c

35mm	b/w	silent	315ft		VIEW

[filmed as a local topical for the Alex Cinema, Paisley]

The Women's Guild of Empire enjoy a day trip to Walter Scott country; they leave Paisley in Alexander's motor coaches.

1384   PAISLEY CHILDREN'S HAPPY HUNTING GROUND

1929

35mm	b/w	silent	320ft		VIEW

filmed by R. Louis Jay for the New Alexandra Cinema, Paisley

A Saturday matinee at the "Alex Cinema" in Paisley with the local children queuing up eagerly outside.

1385   (ANCIENT MARINER'S FILM)

1915c

35mm	b/w	silent	200ft		VIEW

[filmed as a local topical for the Pavilion, Johnstone]

A prize-giving and passing out parade for the Boys' Brigade and the Navel Cadets.

1386   TENEMENT WARDEN

1941

35mm	b/w	comopt	1800ft		VIEW

sp. Edinburgh ARP Committee and Ministry of Home Security
p.c. Campbell Harper Films Ltd.
d. Alan Harper

An illustration of how to cope during an air raid, including first-aid and fire fighting procedures. The film also shows air raid shelters being built and put into practice.

1387   UNVEILING BO'NESS AND CARRIDAN WAR MEMORIAL

1924

35mm	b/w	silent	80ft		VIEW

[filmed by Dickson's Pictures for the Hippodrome, Bo'ness]

Lt .General Sir Walter Braithwaite unveils Bo'ness and Carriden war memorial.

1388   4TH CAMERON HIGHLANDERS AT BEDFORD

1915c

16mm	b/w	silent	162ft		REF

p.c. Gaumont Graphic

Not issued as a newsreel by Gaumont, and probably commissioned for the local cinema, the film shows the 4th Cameron Highlanders in battle kilts marching during training at Bedford.

1389   (GROSVENOR TOPICALS NO. 2)

1926c

35mm	b/w	silent	440ft		VIEW

filmed by James Hart (Grosvenor Topical News)

A compilation of various events, including a school sport's day, a trip to Aberfoyle, the Australian cricket team visiting Glasgow and shots of the Jury/Metro Goldwyn Ltd "trackless train".

1390   (GROSVENOR TOPICALS NO. 1)

1926-'27

35mm	b/w	silent	900ft		VIEW

filmed by James Hart (Grosvenor Topical News)

Various events in Glasgow, including a bowls competition at Willowbank Bowling Club, Kelvinside sports day, Hillhead High sports day and Dedication of Colours by the 157th Company Girl Guides.

1391   ["QUEEN MARY" LEAVES THE CLYDE]

1936

16mm	b/w	silent	100ft		REF

[filmed by Dr. John Humble]

The paddle steamer "Queen Mary" on a cruise down the Clyde towards Dunbarton Rock. This ship was called the 'Sunday Breaker', because she was the first passenger ship to run a pleasure cruise on a Sunday.

1392   GREAT WESTERN ROAD 1980

1980

16mm	col	sep mag	540ft		REF

filmed by the Scottish Film Archive

Filmed as a modern comparison to the amateur films "Great Western Road 1914" and "Great Western Road 1922". [See also refs. 0019 and 0570.]

1393   [GLASGOW AND THE CLYDE COAST 1980]

1980

16mm	col	mute	260ft		REF

filmed by the Scottish Film Archive

Filmed as a modern comparison to "Glasgow and the Clyde Coast 1910". [See also ref. 0044.]

1394   OIL FROM IRAN
1937

9.5mm	b/w	silent	560ft	REF

p.c. Strand Film Co
d. John Taylor

Originally shot in 1935 as "Oilfields of Iran", and re-issued in silent form in 1937, the film shows the work of the Anglo-Persian Oil Co. (BP). [See also ref. 1395.]

1395   IN THE LAND OF THE SHAH
1926

9.5mm	b/w	silent	360ft	REF

p.c. Pathe

Originally shot on 35mm as "Persian Oil Industry" by Topical Press [held by the National Film Archive.] This 9.5mm version filmed by Pathe shows the work of the Anglo-Persian Oil Co. [See also ref. 1394.]

1396   MESSAGE MUST GET THROUGH, THE
1940-'42

9.5mm	b/w	silent	750ft	REF

[filmed by Archie Craig and ? Nisbet]

A drama documentary about the Civil Defence services in wartime Edinburgh.

1397   (LAUNCH OF LIFEBOAT. "SIR ARTHUR ROSE")
1939

16mm	col	silent	150ft	REF

[filmed by Frederick Laing]

Mrs Federick Laing ceremonially launches the Royal Navy lifeboat "Sir Arthur Rose", at Tobermory Bay.

1398   (PS "LOCHMOR" AT KYLE)
1930s

16mm	b/w	silent	95ft	REF

[filmed by Frederick Laing]

Various shots of the paddle steamer "Lochmor" at Kyle of Lochalsh and of a turf cutting ceremony.

1399   (SALMON FISHING AT BRORA)
1937*

16mm	b/w	silent	99ft	REF

[filmed by Frederick Laing]

General views of Sutherland coastal scenery and salmon fishing at Brora.

1400   (SUTHERLAND)
1934*

16mm	b/w	silent	99ft	REF

[filmed by Frederick Laing]

Various scenes from Sutherland in the Highlands, including shots of bi-planes and naval vessels.

1401   (HONEST LAD AND LASS 1939)
1939

16mm	col	silent	50ft	REF

[filmed by Frederick Laing]

The "Honest Lad and Lass" are chosen at the Musselburgh Fair. Film also contains footage of Musselburgh racecourse.

1402   (HONEST LAD AND LASS 1935)
1935

16mm	b/w	silent	200ft	REF

[filmed by Frederick Laing]

The Musselburgh Fair as the "Honest Lad and Lass" ride past on horse-back followed by civic officials in their carriage, a brass band and the floats procession.

1403   (HONEST LAD AND LASS 1936)
1936

16mm	b/w	silent	98ft	REF

[filmed by Frederick Laing]

Shots of streets in Musselburgh as the "Honest Lad and Lass" ride past, followed by civic officials and the floats procession.

1404   (FISHERMAN'S WALK 1933)
1933

16mm	b/w	silent	98ft	REF

[filmed by Frederick Laing]

Footage of the "Fisherman's Walk" through the streets of Oxenfoord, Midlothian, by fishwives and others.

1405   (UNIDENTIFIED STEAMER ON CLYDE COAST)
1934*

16mm	b/w	silent	99ft	REF

[filmed by Frederick Young]

Various profile shots of a steamer and G-ACEC bi-plane.

1406   (TOBERMORY)
1939

16mm	col	silent	49ft	REF

General views of Tobermory harbour and of Sir Hugh Rose and his family at the quay side.

1407	BADMINTON LOOPS - STROKE PLAY				
1950s					
16mm	b/w	silent	200ft		VIEW

p.c. Scottish Instructional Films

Series of loop film on badminton stroke play.

1408	BADMINTON - INTERNATIONAL SELECT V DENMARK				
1951					
16mm	b/w	silent	380ft		VIEW

p.c. Scottish Instructional Films

Coverage of Badminton match on October 1951 between International Select and Denmark, the opening ceremony is performed by the Lord Provost.

1409	BADMINTON - INTERNATIONAL INVITATION TOURNAMENT				
1951					
16mm	b/w	silent	360ft		REF

p.c. Scottish Instructional Films

Coverage of various badminton matches in the Kelvin Hall, Glasgow. The Thomas Cup is presented by Sir George Thomas.

1410	GLADMINTON				
1951					
16mm	b/w	silent	110ft		VIEW

p.c. Scottish Instructional Films

Inside the Kelvin Hall Glasgow, Ken Davidson uses comedy tricks to demonstrate his skills at badminton.

1411	BADMINTON - INTERNATIONAL TOURNAMENTS 1954 &1956				
1954/'56					
16mm	b/w	silent	1030ft		REF

p.c. Scottish Instructional Films

Men's singles, doubles and mixed badminton tournaments.

1412	SWIMMING THE CRAWL WITH IAN BLACK				
1959					
16mm	b/w	silent	200ft		VIEW

sp. Amateur Swimming Association
p.c. Scottish Instructional Films

Ian Black, European Champion swimmer, demonstrates the front crawl.

1413	SMOCKING				
1953					
16mm	b/w	silent	85ft		VIEW

p.c. SEFA, SFC and Clark & Co., Paisley

A demonstration of various stitches used in smocking.

1414	CRICKET LOOPS				
1951					
16mm	b/w	silent	40ft		REF

p.c. Scottish Instructional Films

A series of uncut loop films demonstrating techniques in cricket.

1415	WATER POLO LOOPS				
1954					
16mm	b/w	silent	45ft		VIEW

p.c. Scottish Instructional Films

Set of five loop films, demonstrating methods of playing water polo.

1416	RUGBY UNION FOOTBALL				
1950c					
16mm	b/w	silent	c100ft		VIEW

p.c. Scottish Instructional Films

Series of loop films illustrating techniques in rugby skills.

1417	ASSOCIATION FOOTBALL				
1947					
16mm	b/w	silent	50ft		VIEW

p.c. Scottish Instructional Films

Series of twelve uncut loop films demonstrating methods of playing football. Demonstrators include W. Thorton (Rangers and Scotland) and Willie Waddel (Rangers and Scotland).

1418	LIFESAVING LAND DRILLS				
1937					
16mm	b/w	silent	48ft		VIEW

p.c. Scottish Instructional Films

Set of eight uncut loop films demonstrating the methods of life-saving.

1419	SWIMMING LAND DRILLS				
1937					
16mm	b/w	silent	30ft		VIEW

p.c. Scottish Instructional Films

Set of six uncut loop films demonstrating techniques in swimming.

1420	CREATIVE GYMNASTICS				
1959					
16mm	b/w	silent	400ft		VIEW

p.c. Scottish Instructional Films

Instructional film of creative gymnastics.

1421 AGILITY GYMNASTICS- BOYS
1949

16mm	b/w	silent	100ft		REF

p.c.Scottish Instructional Films

Demonstration of gymnastics by boys of Dalziel High School.

1422 TRAMPOLINING
1954

16mm	b/w	silent	75ft		VIEW

p.c. Scottish Instructional Films

Series of eight uncut loops illustrating the different movements in trampolining.

1423 AGILITY GYMNASTICS
1949

16mm	b/w	silent	50ft		REF

p.c. Scottish Instructional Films

Series of twelve uncut loops illustrating the various techniques in gymnastics.

1424 FEET OFF THE BOTTOM
1950s

16mm	b/w	silent	220ft		VIEW

p.c. Scottish Instructional Films

Shots by an open-air pool of learners practising swimming movements.

1425 SCHOOLBOY ATHLETICS
1950c

16mm	b/w	silent	150ft		REF

p.c. Scottish Instructional Films

Series of loop films, illustrating athletic sequences, hurdles, sprinting, etc.

1426 WOMEN'S ATHLETICS
1948c

16mm	b/w	silent	100ft		VIEW

p.c. Scottish Instructional Films

Series of eleven loop films, uncut, illustrating various techniques in athletics, hurdles, sprinting etc.

1427 HAMPDEN STARS 1949 NO. 1
1949

16mm	b/w	silent	50ft		REF

p.c. Scottish Instructional Films

Series of loop films illustrating techniques of high jumping.

1428 HAMPDEN STARS NO. 2
1949

16mm	b/w	silent	80ft		VIEW

p.c. Scottish Instructional Films

Set of loop films, uncut, illustrating techniques of sprinting, the high jump and long jump.

1429 J. & P. COATS - THREAD SPLICER
1950c

16mm	b/w	silent	50ft		REF

p.c. Scottish Instructional Films & J.&P. Coats Ltd.

Set of three loop films (uncut) demonstrating the techniques of splicing nylon thread by hand.

1430 WESTER ROSS
1953

16mm	col	silent	396ft		VIEW

p.c. Scottish Instructional Films

The fishing industry, lochs and towns of Wester Ross.

1431 ST. ANDREWS
1953*

16mm	col	silent	330ft		VIEW

p.c. Scottish Instructional Films

Footage of St. Andrews, including the harbour, Cathedral, the Royal and Ancient golf club, and University quadrangle.

117

1432 LOCH LOMOND
1957*

16mm	col	silent	375ft		VIEW

p.c. Scottish Instructional Films

Various scenic views of Loch Lomond, including Balmaha, the steamer (Maid of the Loch), Ben Lomond, Inversnaid and Ardlui.

1433 BOBBY JONES - NATIONAL OPEN GOLF CHAMPION
1936*

16mm	b/w	silent	200ft		REF

Bobby Jones demonstrates golfing techniques.

1434 LAUNCH OF THE "QUEEN ELIZABETH"
1931-'40

16mm	b/w&col	silent	360ft		REF

Launch of the "Queen Elizabeth" by HM the Queen on September 27th, 1938, at John Brown's yard, Clydebank. Film also includes footage of the "Queen Mary" leaving the fitting out basin, and arriving in New York.

1435   SAND RACING AND HILL CLIMB

1949

16mm	b/w	silent	235ft	VIEW

p.c. Templar Films

Footage of sand racing, shot during an event organised by the Royal Scottish Automobile Club, St. Andrews.

1436   ORKNEY - SCENES AROUND SHAPINSAY

1936-'38

16mm	b/w&col	silent	882ft	REF

[filmed by Revd. William Moore]

Everyday life in the Orkney Isles, with footage of crofting and lobster fishing.

1437   OUR PAPERS

1950

16mm	b/w	sep opt	1194ft	VIEW

sp. Outram Press

Compilation of news events reported by the "Bulletin", "Evening Times" and the "Glasgow Herald". The events reported include the Scotland v England football match at Hampden, political rallies and an election campaign. The Production of a newspaper is also shown.

1438   [NATIONAL SAVINGS TRAILER]

1943

35mm	b/w	comopt	112ft	VIEW

Advert for National Savings using an animated sequence with captions.

1439   SPORTS AT WEST OF SCOTLAND SCHOOLS OTC CAMP

1926

35mm	b/w	silent	130ft	REF

filmed by Grosvenor Topical

Sports day at the West of Scotland Schools OTC Camp at Gailes, Ayrshire.

1440   THATCHED CROFT

1949*

35mm	b/w	silent	65ft	REF

p.c. Elder Film Productions

Rushes showing two girls and a man outside a thatched croft.

1441   [KEITH SHOW, 14TH AUGUST, 1951]

1951

35mm	b/w	mute	1170ft	REF

sp. Caledonian Associated Cinemas
filmed by James S. Nairn

The Keith Show, with shots of the fairground, show jumping, football and a Charlie Chaplin imitator performing a comic bicycle stunt.

1442   PLUSCARDEN PRIORY RESTORATION FETE

1955*

35mm	b/w	mute	780ft	REF

[sp. Caledonian Associated Cinemas]
[atrributed to James S. Nairn]

The Pluscarden Priory Restoration Fete at Cooper Park, Elgin with amusement stalls, pony rides and a tea tent.

1443   LOSSIEMOUTH CORONATION TREE PLANTING

1953

35mm	b/w	mute	860ft	VIEW

[sp. Caledonian Associated Cinemas]
[filmed by James S. Nairn]

The Tree Planting ceremony by Lossiemouth local dignitaries, including the Laird of Pitgavney and the Provost Dean.

1444   HILLHEAD HIGH SCHOOL SPORTS DAYS 1925-1929

1925-'33

35mm	b/w	silent	570ft	VIEW

filmed by Grosvenor Topical

The three-legged race, balloon race, hurdles, sack race, pillow fight and presentation of prizes at Hillhead High Sports days.

1445   MOBILE CIVIL DEFENCE SURGICAL UNIT

1943c

16mm	b/w	silent	210ft	REF

[attributed to Ben H. Humble]

An illustration of Scotland's only mobile civil defence surgical unit.

1446   GLASGOW CASUALTY SERVICE

1942c

16mm	b/w&col	silent	430ft	REF

A record of Glasgow's casualty service highlighting it's First Aid posts at Gorbals Baths and at Riddrie.

1447   COWGLEN HOSPITAL CONSTRUCTION

1936

16mm	b/w	silent	200ft	REF

Shots of the construction site for Cowglen Hospital and the weekly staff doctors' meeting.

1448   [MAY DAY PARADES, ETC.]
1937-'40

9.5mm	b/w	silent	1000ft	VIEW

[filmed by Alex McGibbon]

An amateur film made for the Unemployed Workers Movement, Govan, it includes footage of the May Day Parades in Edinburgh and Glasgow, with a brief shot of John Maxton speaking in Glasgow's George Square.

1449   PERSONAL EPISODE
1950c

16mm	b/w	comopt	340ft	VIEW

sp. National Assoc. for Prevention of Tuberculosis
p.c. Campbell Harper Films Ltd.
d. Henry Cooper

A tour of the East Fortune Sanatorium showing the X-ray room, ward, and recreation room.

1450   EVER OPEN DOOR, THE
1938

16mm	b/w	silent	775ft	REF

sp. Royal Infirmary, Edinburgh
d. John N. Lauder

Various departments of the Royal Infirmary, Edinburgh are illustrated and the film extols the hospital's motto "the ever open door".

1451   LIFE IN THE HIGHLANDS
1946

16mm	b/w	silent	260ft	REF

Crofting and sheep farming in the Highlands.

1452   (CLYDE COAST STEAMERS)
1929

16mm	b/w	silent	115ft	REF

The steamer the "Duchess of Argyle" leaves for Brodick, Arran from the pier at Rothesay.

1453   LADY OF THE LAKE
1935

16mm	b/w	silent	350ft	REF

filmed by James S. Nairn and James Atterson

"The Lady of the Lake" tour of the Trossachs visiting Loch Doine, Loch Katrine and the Falls of Leny.

1454   BEE KEEPING IN THE NORTH
1946*

16mm	b/w	silent	870ft	REF

[filmed by James S. Nairn]

A demonstration of how to keep bees for heather honey.

1455   (9TH HIGHLAND LIGHT INFANTRY)
1935c

16mm	b/w	silent	645ft	REF

Footage of the 9th Highland Light Infantry on parade and at leisure.

1456   [CAMBUSLANG ORPHANED CHILDREN'S EXCURSION]
1938

16mm	b/w&col	silent	270ft	VIEW

[filmed by Mr. Kennedy]

An annual treat for the Cambuslang Ophaned Children, an excursion to Troon where races and and various games are held.

1457   HOPPITY HOP
1949

16mm	col	comopt	63ft	REF

filmed by Norman McLaren

Experimental film using coloured shapes to illustrate a dance to old fashion calliope music.

1458   FUNERAL OF LIEUTENANT GEORGE DINWOODIE
1917

35mm	b/w	silent	50ft	VIEW

p.c. Scottish Moving Picture News

The funeral procession of a young Glasgow airman, Lieutenant George Dinwoodie.

1459   JEDBURGH HANDBA'
1933

35mm	b/w	comopt	175ft	VIEW

p.c. Gaumont British News (Part B)
[filmed by local Universal cameraman] (Part A)

Part A contains footage of the Jedburgh Handba when the 'uppies' and the 'doonies' fight for the ball in the town square. Part B covers the boisterous celebrations of Candlemas.

1461   [ROYAL NAVY ON THE CLYDE]
1942c

super 8mm col		silent	66ft	REF

Shots of naval vessels, including an aircraft carrier on the Firth of Clyde.

1462   CHRISTMAS 1943
1943

35mm	b/w	comopt	160ft	VIEW

A cinema trailer for the Playhouse Elgin thanking patrons and wishing them a happy and victorious New Year.

119

1463	ELGIN CITY V CLACHNACUDDEN				
1935					
35mm	b/w	silent	380ft		VIEW

[filmed as a local topical for the Playhouse, Elgin]

The North of Scotland cup, semi-final replay between Elgin City and Clachnacudden.

1464	(ARP DISPLAY)				
1939					
35mm	b/w	silent	230ft		VIEW

[filmed as a local topical for the Playhouse, Elgin]

Soldiers practising mortar fire, the ARP parade through Elgin, a fly past by three planes and a fire fighting demonstration.

1465	KEITH V VALE OCOBA				
1936c					
35mm	b/w	silent	400ft		VIEW

[filmed as a local topical for the Playhouse, Elgin]

Scottish qualifying cup-final, Keith v Vale Ocoba at Borough Briggs, Elgin.

1466	ELGIN CHARCITY DAY 1933				
1933					
35mm	b/w	silent	470ft		VIEW

[filmed as a local topical for the Playhouse, Elgin]

Various events including a football match, a float parade and sports, at the celebrations of Elgin Charcity Day.

1467	ELGIN CHARCITY DAY 1935				
1935					
35mm	b/w	silent	500ft		VIEW

[filmed as a local topical for the Playhouse Elgin]

Shots of various events during Elgin Charcity Day including sports, a game of football, a baby competition and a fancy dress parade.

1468	ELGIN GALA WEEK 1950				
1950					
35mm	b/w	silent	870ft		VIEW

[attributed to James S. Nairn for the Playhouse, Elgin]

Coverage of Elgin Gala Week, including the children's fancy dress competition, parade and crowning of the Gala Queen.

1469	INVERNESS SWIMMING CLUB				
1949					
35mm	b/w	silent	630ft		VIEW

filmed by James S. Nairn for the Playhouse, Inverness

Various activities on offer at the Inverness Swimming Club, including the Ladies Formation Team, diving and the amateur swimming club.

1470	MORAY SEA SCHOOL				
1950					
35mm	b/w	comopt	720ft		VIEW

sp. Captain Tennant, Moray Sea School appeal
[filmed by James S. Nairn]

Some of the activities enjoyed by boys at the Sea School including rowing, sailing, fishing and climbing. [Made as part of an appeal on behalf of Moray Sea School.]

1471	(ELGIN GALA DAY NO. 1)				
1950					
35mm	b/w	silent	700ft		VIEW

[filmed as a local topical for the Playhouse, Elgin]

Elgin Gala Day including the parade, Highland dancing and tug-o-war. Shots of Morayshire Farmers' Club Show.

1472	(ELGIN GALA DAY NO. 2)				
1937					
35mm	b/w	silent	540ft		VIEW

[filmed as a local topical for the Playhouse, Elgin]

The motorcade, parade, ladies' football match, relay race and crowning of the Gala Queen.

1474	[INVERNESS FESTIVAL YEAR 1951]				
1951					
35mm	b/w	silent	1620ft		REF

sp. Caledonian Associated Cinemas
filmed by J. S. Nairn and J. Atterson

The Inverness Festival Year: open air gatherings, pipeband parades, and highland games.

1475	[EARL HAIG UNVEILS PEEBLES WAR MEMORIAL]				
1922					
35mm	b/w	silent	315ft		VIEW

[filmed as a local topical for the Playhouse, Peebles]

Earl Haig unveils Peebles War Memorial and lays a wreath after inspecting a parade of war veterans. Crowds line the streets to watch the pipes and drums lead the parade of veterans.

1476	[PEEBLES BELTANE FESTIVALS 1920/ '22]				
1920-'22					
35mm	b/w	silent	300ft		VIEW

[filmed as a local topical for the Playhouse, Peebles]

A compilation of Peebles Beltane Festivals including footage of a mounted procession with decorated floats, the Beltane Queen and her retinue leaving the podium and a horse-drawn decorated floats procession.

1477	PEEBLES MARCH RIDING AND BELTANE FESTIVAL1949				
1949					
35mm	b/w	silent	670ft		VIEW

[filmed as a local topical for the Playhouse, Peebles]

Peebles March Riding and Beltane Festival; the celebrations include a Piper who leads a procession of children and the Beltane Queen with her retinue through the Borders town.

1478	SCOTS ACCLAIM ROYAL FAMILY				
1947					
16mm	b/w	comopt	100ft		VIEW

p.c. British paramount News

Filmed during the 10 day royal visit to Scotland after the announcement of Princess Elizabeth's engagement.

1479	(MAVOR AND COULSON SITE CONSTRUCTION)				
1957c					
16mm	b/w	silent	270ft		REF

sp. Mavor and Coulson

Shots of the demolition of the The Easson Brothers factory in Bridgeton and the construction site for the new Mavor and Coulson factory.

1480	YOUNG IN HEART				
1963					
35mm	b/w&col	comopt	2120ft		VIEW

sp. Films of Scotland
p.c. Glasgow Films

The development and production of the Hillman Imp at the Linwood industrial plant.

1481	CLYDESCOPE				
1974					
35mm	col	comopt	2800ft		VIEW

sp. Films of Scotland
p.c. VIZ Ltd.
d. Murray Grigor

A panorama of the Clyde, from Biggar to Brodick, with Billy Connolly as guide.

1482	(SCOTTISH HOTEL SCHOOL)				
1959*					
16mm	b/w	comopt	306ft		REF

p.c. BBC Scotland

Students seen working at various practical sessions at the Scottish Hotel School, Ross Hall: The film includes an interview with John Fuller, director of the School.

St. Kilda – Britain's Loneliest Isle, 1923. Anne Gillies outside her door spinning, watched by a group of passengers. Ref. 0418

1483	EDINBURGH FESTIVAL OPENING CEREMONY				
1952					
35mm	b/w	comopt	1170ft		REF

p.c. Gaumont British News and Universal Irish News

The Edinburgh Festival opening ceremony is performed by the Duke of Edinburgh on the Esplanade of Edinburgh Castle, Douglas Fairbanks is amongst the crowd.

1484	(GLASGOW "DISCARDS")				
1968-'71					
std.8mm	col	silent	750ft		REF

[filmed by Willie and Avril Murdoch]

Glasgow scenes including shots of tenements, the Citizens Theatre, Glasgow Green, St. Enoch's Station, Sauchiehall Street, Paddy's Market, the University, Templeton's carpet factory and Kelvingrove Art Gallery.

1485	(GUILD OF AID ANNUAL TREATS)				
1960c					
std.8mm	col	silent	220ft		REF

[filmed by Miss Marald Grant]

Footage of the Women's Guild of Aid the Gorbals, enjoying a Christmas Party and outings to "Barcapel" house in Newton Mearns, Callander and Largs.

1486   EDINBURGH FESTIVAL - PATHE
1963

| 35mm | col | comopt | 900ft | | REF |

p.c. Pathe News

A compilation of various events held during the Edinburgh Festival including the Film Festival, a demonstration by the Royal Scottish Country Dance Society, the Budapest Ballet Company, and shots of the Tattoo on the Castle esplanade.

1487   EDINBURGH
1952

| 35mm | col | comopt | 1620ft | | REF |

p.c. London Films
d. David Eady

Some of Edinburgh's famous sites are visited including the Tolbooth, Holyrood Abbey, Princes Street, the Botanic Gardens, Dean Village, Charlotte Square, Fettes College, Leith Docks and Edinburgh Castle.

1488   EXCURSION TO WEMBLEY
1924

| 35mm | b/w | silent | 450ft | | VIEW |

sp. Pullars of Perth

Made for Pullars of Perth, and taken during a works outing to the British Empire Exhibition at Wembley, London, 1924.

1489   PERTH PRESENTATION
1936

| 35mm | b/w | comopt | 60ft | | VIEW |

p.c. Gaumont British News

The presentation of the King George Memorial Film to the Lord Provost of Perth.

1490   WATER DISPLAYS AT THE EMPIRE EXHIBITION
1938

| 16mm | col | silent | 510ft | | REF |

sp. Couch & Hogg MM Inst.
p.c. Jay's Film Service Ltd.

The water displays at the Empire Exhibition Glasgow, including the royal fountain, the lake fountain, south cascade and the 'an clachan'.

1491   ROYAL JUBILEE CELEBRATIONS
1935

| 16mm | b/w | silent | 300ft | | REF |

filmed by T.C. Davidson

Perth's Royal Jubilee celebrations, with the town decorated in bunting and a firework display with illuminations.

1492   PSNS EXCURSION
1934

| 16mm | b/w | silent | 50ft | | VIEW |

[filmed by John Ritchie]

PSNS excursion to Howietoun trout fisheries.

1493   FESTIVAL IN EDINBURGH
1954

| 35mm | col | comopt | 1255ft | | VIEW |

sp. Films of Scotland Committee
p.c. Associated British Pathe Ltd
d. Douglas Clarke

Compilation of various events, people and shows at the Edinburgh Festival. Footage contains extracts from "Macbeth", the National Youth Orchestra, and Margot Fonteyn in "The Firebird".

1494   HOLIDAYS AT HOME 1942-'44
1942-'44

| 16mm | col | silent | 1026ft | | REF |

sp. Edinburgh Corporation "Holidays at Home" Committee
p. Robert J. Black

Made to promote Edinburgh as a holiday area for its local people.

1495   [SAVING OF A SHABBY COAT]
1930c

| 16mm | b/w | silent | 740ft | | REF |

p.c. Jay's Film Service
d. Ronald L. Jay

Dramatised account of how the 'Franco Barbie' method of cleaning transforms old garments into new. The film was shot inside Castlebank dye works.

1496   SUN PICTURES, THE
1964

| 35mm | b/w | comopt | 1350ft | | VIEW |

sp. Films of Scotland
p.c. Campbell Harper Films Ltd.
d. David Bruce

A history of the pioneers of photography, David Octavius Hill and Robert Adamson, including examples of their calotypes of the city of Edinburgh and its people from 1843-1848.

1497   [GLASGOW'S PROGRESS]
1968-'78

| 35mm | col | mute | 8500ft | | VIEW |

sp. Films of Scotland
p.c. Ogam Films

Rushes from an unfinished production intended as a sequel to Glasgow 1980. [See also ref. 0974.]

1498	NEW SITES FOR OLD			
1950c				
16mm	b/w	comopt	70ft	REF

p.c. Wallace Productions, London

Shots of waste ground in Glasgow overgrown with grass before being improved and cultivated by local children.

1499	[SCOTT CENTENARY, PERTH]			
1932				
16mm	b/w	silent	145ft	VIEW

Shots of Perth's celebrations to mark the centenary of the death of Sir Walter Scott.

1500	LAMPLIGHTER, THE			
1956				
35mm	b/w	silent	180ft	REF

[filmed by Stanley L. Russell]

Dramatisation of Robert Louis Stevenson's poem in which a small boy watches the "leerie" doing his rounds lighting gas street lamps.

1501	BEYOND THE GRAMPIANS			
1963				
35mm	col	comopt	1800ft	VIEW

sp. Films of Scotland
p.c. Templar Films
exec. p. R. Riddell Black

A look at the lives of the people of the North East of Scotland; the farming and fishing industries and leisure activities available.

1502	[SINGER'S FOUNDRY]			
1959c				
16mm	b/w	sep opt	720ft	REF

sp. Singer Manufacturing Co. Ltd
p.c. Thames & Clyde
[d. Stanley L. Russell]

An illustration of the various technical processes associated with casting and dressing on the 201K aluminium arm and bed for sewing machines.

1503	OPENING OF A NEW ALUMINIUM WORKS			
1944				
16mm	b/w	silent	300ft	VIEW

p.c. Scottish Films Presentation

The opening of a new aluminium works by Sir Stafford Cripps, June 1944. The film also shows women workers in the factory.

1504	(WARTIME PRODUCTION - H. MORRIS & CO.)			
1937-'41*				
16mm	b/w&col silent		596ft	REF

Shot inside the H. Morris & Co. factory during wartime production of rifle stock, fuse boxes, aircraft plywood, etc, with a workforce of both men and women.

1505	(EXPERIMENTAL HELICOPTER AND AUTOGYRO BLADES)			
1941*				
16mm	b/w&col silent		450ft	REF

Shot inside the Glasgow factory of H. Morris & Co., the film shows the firm's experimental designs for helicopter blades, R46 autogyro blades and other wartime products.

1506	PRINCESS MARGARET SEES IDEAL HOME			
1951				
16mm	b/w	comopt	105ft	REF

p.c. Movietone News

Princess Margaret visits the Ideal Home Exhibition at the Olympia, London.

1507	(GLASGOW'S WEDDING GIFT)			
1949				
16mm	b/w&col silent		96ft	REF

Shot inside the factory of H. Morris & Co. the film shows the construction and display of a fitted bedroom suite that was gifted by the City of Glasgow to HRH Princess Elizabeth and Lieutenant Mountbatten on the occasion of their wedding.

1508	(H. MORRIS FURNITURE FACTORY)			
1939/'59				
16mm	b/w	silent	720ft	REF

Shots inside the H. Morris & Co. furniture factory, Milton Street, Glasgow showing the different sorts of machinery and processes.

1509	WOOD GOES TO WAR			
1942-'43				
16mm	col	silent	830ft	REF

A film highlighting the work of the Glasgow furniture-making firm of H. Morris & Co. during the Second World War, producing rifle stocks and prototype bomb casings for the "bouncing bomb".

123

1510   [CROWNING OF QUEEN OF THE BONNIE LASSIES, AYR]
1935

16mm	b/w	silent	85ft	REF

Footage of the coronation of the 'Queen of the Bonnie Lasses', including the historical pageant, dancing and football games.

1511   OVER THE ESK
1967-'68

super 8mm col	silent	150ft	REF

[filmed by David Steele]

The opening of the New Bridge over the river Esk by the Lord Provost of Musselburgh with shots of the construction of the New Bridge and demolition of the Old Bridge.

1512   (MISS DE COURCEY DEWAR)
1931-'35*

16mm	b/w	silent	50ft	REF

 Miss De Courcey Dewar and her sister ran a house in Bellshill for destitute women and the film shows the visit of HRH the Prince of Wales to see the work of Harkness House.

1513   QUEEN'S OWN CAMERON HIGHLANDERS, THE
1958

35mm	b/w	mute	835ft	REF

[filmed by James S. Nairn for the Playhouse, Inverness]

The Queen's Own Cameron Highlanders' new recruits take part in a passing-out parade Inverness, before joining their Battalion at Dover.

1514   [THURSO HIGH SCHOOL OPENING]
1958

35mm	b/w	silent	735ft	VIEW

[filmed by James S. Nairn for Caledonian Cinemas]

The official opening of Thurso High School including footage of pupils at work in their classrooms.

1515   FORTROSE CELEBRATES ITS 500TH ANNIVERSARY
1955

35mm	b/w	mute	440ft	REF

[filmed by James S. Nairn for CAC]

Coverage of the celebrations surrounding the 500th anniversary of Fortrose. Provost John Anderson receives the Burgh's new chain of office and the Countess of Middleton gains the Freedom of the Burgh.

1516   [CORONATION DAY. PARADE. INVERNESS]
1953

35mm	b/w	mute	860ft	VIEW

[filmed by James S. Nairn for the Playhouse, Inverness]

À parade of Youth Organisations headed by pipebands marching through the streets of Inverness to celebrate Coronation Day.

1517   [HOME AND AWAY NO. 2]
1955-'59*

16mm	b/w	comopt	620ft	REF

sp. Babcock and Wilcox (Steam) Ltd
p.c. Technical and Scientific Films in assoc. with Film Producers Guild

One of a series of 20 films made for Babcock and Wilcox (Steam) Ltd. between 1954 and 1961. It illustrates the use of Babcock and Wilcox boilers for steam ships, and includes footage of pay day and workers leaving the Renfrew plant. [See also refs. 1518-1531.]

1518   HOME AND AWAY NO. 4
1955

16mm	b/w	comopt	290ft	REF

sp. Babcock and Wilcox (Steam) Ltd.
p.c. Technical and Scientific Films Ltd. in assoc. with Film Producers Guild
d. Derrick Knight

A review of the work and recreation for members and friends of the Babcock and Wilcox family. [See also refs. 1517-1531.]

1519   HOME AND AWAY NO. 8
1956

16mm	b/w	comopt	485ft	REF

sp. Babcock and Wilcox (Steam) Ltd
p.c. Technical and Scientific Films Ltd. in assoc. with Film Producers Guild
d. Peter Dixon

Members and friends of the Babcock and Wilcox family at work and leisure. [See also refs. 1517-1531.]

1520   HOME AND AWAY NO. 10
1956c

16mm	b/w	comopt	540ft	REF

sp. Babcock and Wilcox (Steam) Ltd.
p.c. Technical and Scientific Films Ltd in assoc. with Film Producers Guild
d. Peter Ward

Featuring the Babcock and Wilcox Cyclone furnace, the Renfrew staff association magazine going to press and staff and their families boarding the "holiday special" steam train to Blackpool and Morcambe. [See also refs. 1517-1531.]

124

1521   HOME AND AWAY NO. 11
1957

| 16mm | b/w | comopt | 500ft | | REF |

sp. Babcock and Wilcox (Steam) Ltd.
p.c. Technical and Scientific Films Ltd in assoc. with Film Producers Guild
d. Peter Ward

The 1957 Industrial Fair and Exhibition in Sydney, Australia where Babcock and Wilcox Australian Co. featuring a stand. [See also refs. 1517-1531.]

1522   HOME AND AWAY NO. 12
1957c

| 16mm | b/w | comopt | 510ft | | REF |

sp. Babcock and Wilcox (Steam) Ltd.
p.c. Technical and Scientific Films in assoc. with the Film Producers Guild
d. Peter Ward

Shots of Babcock and Wilcox boilers being installed in the Kodak factory, Essex. [See also refs. 1517-1531.]

1523   HOME AND AWAY NO. 13
1958c

| 16mm | b/w | comopt | 495ft | | REF |

sp. Babcock and Wilcox (Steam) Ltd.
p.c. Technical and Scientific Films Ltd. in assoc. with Film Producers Guild
d. Peter Ward

A meeting held by the Auto section of the Babcock and Wilcox Club, members of their Renfrew Club at a dog training class and Babcock boilers at work in Ravenscraig Steel Works, Motherwell. [See also refs. 1517-1531.]

1524   HOME AND AWAY NO. 14
1958

| 16mm | b/w | comopt | 510ft | | REF |

sp. Babcock and Wilcox (Steam) Ltd.
p.c. Technical and Scientific Films Ltd. in assoc. with Film Producers Guild

Shots of the firm's various products at work and shots of the Babcock and Wilcox industrial stand at the Brussels Exhibition. [See also refs. 1517-1531.]

1525   HOME AND AWAY NO. 16
1959

| 16mm | b/w | comopt | 504ft | | REF |

sp. Babcock and Wilcox (Steam) Ltd.
p.c. Technical and Scientific Films Ltd. in assoc. with Film Producers Guild
d. Peter Ward

A tea party for members of Babcock and Wilcox staff held at Turnberry Hotel where they also play golf for the inter-departmental sheild. Footage of the installation of the Babcock and Wilcox pressure vessel for the atomic furnace at Hinkley atomic power station. [See also refs. 1517-1531.]

1526   HOME AND AWAY NO. 17
1959

| 16mm | b/w | comopt | 375ft | | REF |

sp. Babcock and Wilcox (Steam) Ltd.
p.c. Technical and Scientific Films Ltd. in assoc. with Film Producers Guild
d. Peter Cantor

The Babcock and Wilcox tower crane involved in building the new sports stadium, Crystal Palace, London. [See also refs. 1517-1531.]

1527   HOME AND AWAY NO. 18
1960c

| 16mm | b/w | comopt | 450ft | | REF |

sp. Babcock and Wilcox (Steam) Ltd.
p.c. Technical and Scientific Films Ltd. in assoc. with Film Producers Guild
d. Cyril Randell

A look at the Scottish Gas Board Works at Westfields and ferries using Babcock and Wilcox steam engines. [See also refs. 1517-1531.]

1528   HOME AND AWAY NO. 19
1960c

| 16mm | b/w | comopt | 520ft | | REF |

sp. Babcock and Wilcox (Steam) Ltd.
p.c. Technical and Scientific Films Ltd. in assoc. with Film Producers Guild
d. Phil Dennis

An illustration of the Babcock and Wilcox' involvement with atomic power and their construction of a reactor pressure vessel at Hickley Point Atomic Power Station and at Sizewell. [See also refs. 1517-1531.]

1529   FOUNDRY PRACTICE
1953*

| 16mm | b/w | comopt | 940ft | | REF |

sp. Babcock and Wilcox Ltd.
p.c. Technical and Scientific Films Ltd. in assoc. with Film Producers Guild
d. George H. Sewell

Used for training purposes, the film shows the casting process from pattern design to the finished article moulded by hand, at the Babcock and Wilcox Renfrew works. [See also refs. 1517-1531.]

1530   WELDING IN BOILER MANUFACTURE
1955*

| 16mm | b/w | comopt | 650ft | | REF |

sp. Babcock and Wilcox Ltd
p.c. Technical and Scientific Films Ltd. in assoc. with Film Producers Guild
d. George H. Sewell

A demonstration in Babcock and Wilcox's welding school of different methods of fusion welding by hand and by machine. [See also refs. 1517-1531.]

125

126

1531 STEAM
1955*

16mm	b/w	comopt	1495ft		REF

sp. Babcock and Wilcox (Steam) Ltd
p.c. James E. Rogers Prduction in assoc. with Film Producers Guild

The development of Babcock and Wilcox boilers from their early 19th C design to the Ceres design. A new boiler is shown being constructed and installed at a power station. [See also refs. 1517-1530.]

1532 RAIL STRAIGHTENER
1954

16mm	b/w	silent	216ft		VIEW

sp. Lamberton & Co. Ltd.
p.c. Thames & Clyde Film Company Ltd.
d. Stanley L. Russell

A demonstration of the trial roller straightening of six rolls of steel at the Glengarnock Works of Colvilles Ltd.

1533 AUTOMATIC FEEDING DEVICE FOR HORIZONTAL FORGING MACHINES
1955

16mm	b/w	mute	300ft		VIEW

sp. Lamberton & Co. Ltd., Coatbridge
p.c. Thames and Clyde Film Company Ltd.

A demonstration of the automatic feeding device for horizontal forging machines.

1534 CABLE BELT CONVEYOR, THE
1951

16mm	b/w	sep opt	740ft		REF

sp. Cable Belt Ltd.
[filmed by James S. Nairn]

A technical film on the operation of cable belt conveyors in mines and for movement of bulk materials.

1535 [LOCAL EVENTS, INVERNESS AREA]
1952/'53*

16mm	b/w&col silent	880ft		REF

Compilation of local events in the Highlands; soldiers on parade in Inverness, net fishing and the Highland Orphanage celebrating Easter.

1536 QUEEN'S OWN CAMERON HIGHLANDERS 79TH FOOT
1953

16mm	col	silent	200ft		REF

[filmed by James S. Nairn and James Atterson]

The Queen Mother attends the presentation of the Freedom of the Burgh of Inverness to the Cameron Highlanders 79th Foot.

1537 IN THE CLEAR
1955*

35mm	b/w	comopt	330ft		VIEW

sp. National Association for the Prevention of Tuberculosis
p.c. Campbell Harper Films Ltd.
d. Henry Cooper

A cinema trailer on behalf of the National Association for the Prevention of Tuberculosis. Jimmy Logan and Stanley Baxter demonstrate how easy it is to have your chest x-rayed.

1538 LOCH LOMOND
1939c

16mm	col	silent	230ft		VIEW

p.c. SEFA (Dunbartonshire branch)

Panoramic views of Loch Lomond and the surrounding area including Inchmurrin (the largest island), Inchcailleach (the burial island) and the villages of Rowardennan, Tarbet and Inversnaid.

1539 (LOCH LOMOND PILOT FILM)
1963*

16mm	col	silent	280ft		VIEW

[filmed by Stanley Russell]

Profile of the loch steamer "Maid of the Loch" on Loch Lomond, showing the steamer tied up at Tarbet pier and shots on board.

1540 STEAMER JOURNEY
1950c

16mm	col	silent	340ft		VIEW

sp. GB Instructional Limited
p.c. Junior Activity Films
p. John C. Elder

A boy and his uncle go sailing among Scottish islands on cargo and passenger coastal ships.

1541 (CLAY PIGEON SHOOT)
1935

16mm	b/w	silent	100ft		REF

[filmed by J.A. Thomson]

Competitors and spectators at a clay pigeon shoot.

1542 (VISIT TO STAFFA)
1927*

16mm	b/w	silent	100ft		VIEW

[filmed by J.A. Thomson]

A visit by steamer to the island of Staffa and Fingal's Cave.

1543 LAUNCH OF THE PADDLE STEAMER "GLEN GOWER"

1922

| 35mm | b/w | silent | 210ft | VIEW |

sp. P. & A. Campbell
p.c. Gaumont

Launch of the paddle steamer "Glen Gower" at Troon. Built for P. & A. Campbell Ltd., Bristol, by the Ailsa Shipbuilding Company.

1544 OIL BLASTING IN SCOTLAND

1938*

| 35mm | b/w | comopt | 60ft | VIEW |

p.c. British Pictorial Productions Limited

Footage of the first land oil-well to be struck in Britain, near Dalkeith, Midlothian.

1545 QUEEN'S OWN CAMERON HIGHLANDERS 50TH ANNIVERSARY

1935

| 35mm | b/w | silent | 390ft | VIEW |

p.c. Pathe

Celebrations surrounding the Queen's Own Highlanders 50th Anniversary "At Home" including a firework and firearm display.

1546 (HIPPODROME CINEMA, BO'NESS)

1931*

| 35mm | b/w | silent | 85ft | VIEW |

[filmed by Louis Dickson]

Footage of the exterior of the Hippodrome Cinema in Bo'ness as patrons emerge.

1547 CROWNING OF THE DARVEL LACE QUEEN 1952

1952

| 35mm | b/w | silent | 1125ft | REF |

filmed by Elder Film Productions for the Picture House, Darvel

The coronation of the Lace Queen with a parade of floats and a pipe band.

1548 [CROWNING OF LACE QUEEN. DARVEL, 22ND AUG, 1953]

1953

| 35mm | b/w | silent | 1300ft | VIEW |

[filmed by Elder Film Productions for the Picture House]

Footage of the coronation of the Lace Queen, Darvel. The queen and her retinue parade along the streets followed by pipebands and floats.

1549 HOW A FILM IS MADE

1949*

| 16mm | b/w | silent | 820ft | VIEW |

d. Ernst Niederreither

A german production showing all aspects of film making from script reading to sound testing.

1550 INSPECTION AND MARCH PAST ATC

1940

| 35mm | b/w | comopt | c200ft | REF |

[filmed by James S. Nairn for the Playhouse, Inverness]

Inspection and march past ATC, Inverness.

1551 (CAMERONS PARADE THROUGH INVERNESS)

1949

| 35mm | b/w | mute | c200ft | REF |

The Cameron Highlanders parade through Inverness.

1552 SCOTTISH QUALIFYING CUP 1949

1949

| 35mm | b/w | mute | c300ft | REF |

sp. Caledonian Associated Cinemas

Scottish qualifying cup 1949, unknown game.

1553 INTER SCHOOL SPORTS DAY. INVERNESS

1951

| 35mm | b/w | mute | c300ft | REF |

sp. Caledonian Associated Cinemas
[filmed by James S. Nairn]

An inter-school sports day, Inverness.

1554 INVERNESS THANKSGIVING PARADE TO EAST CHURCH

1945*

| 35mm | b/w | mute | c200ft | REF |

[filmed by James S. Nairn for the Playhouse, Inverness]

Inverness thanksgiving parade to East Church.

1555 INVERNESS GALA QUEEN 1950

1950

| 35mm | b/w | mute | 900ft | VIEW |

[filmed by James S. Nairn for Caledonian Associated Cinemas]

The Inverness Gala Queen parade, 1950.

1556 EMPIRE YOUTH, SUNDAY PARADE

1949*

| 35mm | b/w | mute | c200ft | REF |

filmed by James S. Nairn for Caledonian Associated Cinemas

Coverage of the Empire Youth Sunday Parade, Inverness.

1557 (AGRICULTURAL SHOW, GHILLIE)
1937*

| 35mm | b/w | silent | c300ft | | REF |

Coverage of an Agricultural show in Ghillie near Inverness.

1558 ATC INTERNATIONAL
1944

| 35mm | b/w | comopt | c200ft | | REF |

Footage of the ATC International, Inverness.

1559 (CINEMA ADVERTS)
1938*

| 35mm | b/w | comopt | c100ft | | REF |

Various cinema adverts.

1560 [RED CROSS APPEAL/LOCAL ADS]
1936-'45*

| 35mm | b/w | mute | c100ft | | REF |

A Red Cross appeal and local ads.

1561 QUEEN'S OWN CAMERON HIGHLANDERS LEAVE LA SCALA
1934*

| 35mm | b/w | silent | 122ft | | VIEW |

[filmed as a local topical for La Scala Cinema, Inverness]

The Queens Own Cameron Highlanders enjoy a film programme at La Scala, Inverness, before returning to their barracks.

1562 DALKEITH GALAS 1926. 1933/ LAUREL AND HARDY VISIT EDINBURGH
1926/'32

| 35mm | b/w | silent | 780ft | | VIEW |

[filmed as a local topical for the Picture Palace, Dalkeith]

Spectators watch the fancy dress procession and the Gala Queen being crowned at Dalkeith 1926 and 1933. Laurel and Hardy visit Edinburgh in 1932, arriving at Waverley Station, and visiting the Castle.

1563 SCOTTISH CUP FINAL 1952
1952

| 35mm | b/w | comopt | 400ft | | REF |

p.c. Universal News

Coverage of the Scottish Cup final at Hampden Park, Glasgow, between Motherwell and Dundee. Film includes footage of Motherwell's triumphant return to their home town.

1564 (FERRARI FAMILY FILM)
1946-'50*

| 16mm | b/w | silent | 260ft | | VIEW |

[filmed by various members of the Ferrari family]

A compilation of films taken between 1945-'49 including a procession of Cistercian monks, a Catholic communion service, shots of the staff of the Ferrari's Restaurant and a boat race at Oxford.

1565 INVERGORDON HIGHLAND GATHERING
1949

| 35mm | b/w | mute | 710ft | | REF |

[filmed as a local topical for the Playhouse, Invergordon]

Coverage of the Invergordon Highland gathering, Inverness.

1566 (WEDDING FILM NO.1)
1963c

| 16mm | col | silent | 190ft | | REF |

[filmed by Stanley L. Russell]

A record of the wedding of John McGarrity and Sheila Morrison.

1567 (WEDDING FILM NO. 2)
1961

| 16mm | col | silent | 360ft | | REF |

[filmed by Stanley L. Russell]

A record of the wedding of Patricia Boyd Martin to Peter Anderson, August 1961, at Trinity Church, Uddingston.

1568 MINE CAR HANDLING AT BOWHILL
1953

| 16mm | b/w | silent | 288ft | | VIEW |

sp. National Coal Board
p.c. Data Film Unit
d. Francis Gysin

How a mine car is operated at Bowhill Pit, Fife.

1569 LAMBERTON COLD BILLET SHEAR
1962

| 16mm | col | comopt | 334ft | | REF |

sp. Lamberton & Co. Ltd., Coatbridge
p.c. Thames and Clyde Film Co.

Demonstration of the Lamberton cold billet shearing machine in operation cutting blocks of steel.

1570 [RUSSELL'S LIBRARY FOOTAGE]
1959c

| 35mm | b/w&col | mute | 1560ft | | REF |

[filmed by Stanley L. Russell]

Stockshot material compiled by Stanley Russell for his own use, including shots of industry, farming, the river Clyde, Glasgow, St. Andrews and Stirling.

Stanley Russell behind camera, 1940s

1571 PARTNERS IN PROGRESS
1964

16mm	col	sep mag	715ft	REF

sp. Bank of Scotland
p.c. Clyde Film. Co Ltd

A promotional film for the Bank of Scotland featuring a newly-wed couple opening an account with the Bank, and staff at work at the various operations in the Bank.

1572 CARPETS OF DISTINCTION
1951c

16mm	col	sep opt	1080ft	VIEW

sp. James Templeton & Co.
p.c. Thames and Clyde
d. Stanley Russell

The production line of Templeton's Carpets beginning with the initial design stages to the repairing of flaws in the finished carpets.

1573 PROUD SPIRIT, THE
1962*

16mm	b/w&col	silent	380ft	REF

sp. Wm. Grant (Whisky) Ltd.
p.c. Thames and Clyde

A depiction of the whisky industry in Scotland from the distilling processes to the final product at home, and in the pub.

1575 ROOM FOR MORE
1962c

16mm	b/w	sep opt	930ft	VIEW

sp. SSPMH
p.c. Thames & Clyde Film Co.

Narrated by the actor Roddy McMillan, the film shows various centres for the handicapped and their importance for handicapped children. Curran House Glasgow, the Stirling Centre, and Eversly House Edinburgh are all visited.

1576 [CELTIC V RANGERS]
1962c

16mm	b/w	commag	400ft	REF

sp. BBC Scotland
p.c. Thames and Clyde Film Co.

General views of football match between Rangers and Celtic at Parkhead Stadium, Glasgow.

1577A (MOTHERWELL PEDESTRIANS)
1938*

35mm	b/w	silent	35ft	VIEW

A tiny fragment from a local topical showing close-up shots of pedestrians/spectators on a pavement in Motherwell looking towards the camera.

1577B SOME BEAUTY SPOTS IN NORTH SCOTLAND
1912c

35mm	b/w	silent	75ft	VIEW

Panoramic views of Scotland including Tomintoul, Balmoral Castle and the ruins of Elgin Cathedral.

1578 (MAVOR FAMILY FILM)
1932

16mm	b/w	silent	280ft	VIEW

Family film shot mostly by Jack Mavor, of Mavor and Coulson, showing holidays at Brodick Arran, walking at Glen Sannox, and at the family home "Gateside" at Drymen.

1579 [HANDICAPPED BUT HAPPY]
1962c

16mm	b/w	comopt	830ft	REF

sp. SSPMH
p.c. Thames and Clyde Film Co.
d. Stanley Russell

An illustration of how young handicapped people can enjoy activities such as painting, cooking, ironing and sewing at Laurieston House, Glasgow.

129

1580   ON THE SPOT WITH FIRST AID
1956c

16mm	b/w	comopt	600ft	VIEW

p.c. Thames & Clyde Production
d. Stanley Russell

An illustration of the St. Andrews Ambulance Association in action demonstrating their first aid techniques.

1581   (HOLIDAY SCOTLAND)
1930c

16mm	b/w	silent	400ft	VIEW

A compilation of scenes from various holiday areas in Scotland including Edinburgh, Glasgow, Rothesay, Wemyss Bay, The Trossachs and Loch Lomond.

1582   DOON THE WATER
1960

16mm	col	comopt	820ft	REF

filmed by Gabriel Donald

A sail down the River Clyde on the 100th anniversary of the founding of the Glasgow and West of Scotland Mission to the Outdoor Blind.

1583   BOYS' BRIGADE
1915

35mm	b/w	silent	80ft	VIEW

p.c. Pathe Gazette

Coverage of a Boys' Brigade parade at Queen's Park, Glasgow. Lord Rosebery takes the salute.

1584   SINGER SPORTS GALA 1952
1952

16mm	col	silent	280ft	REF

Footage of the Singer Sports Day, Clydebank including shots of procession of youth organisations and the Singer Gala Queen.

1585   [SINGER SPORTS AND GALA 1954]
1954

16mm	col	silent	400ft	REF

Shots of Singer Sports Day at Dalmuir and the coronation ceremony of the Singer Gala Queen.

1586   [SINGER SPORTS AND GALA 1957]
1957

16mm	col	silent	275ft	REF

Footage of Singer Sports Day and coronation of their Gala Queen.

1587   [SINGER] SPORTS GALA 1961
1961

16mm	col	silent	420ft	REF

Coverage of Singer Sports Gala, Dalmuir and the procession led in by the pipes and drums of the Argyll and Sutherland Highlanders.

1588   (CLYDEBANK. ARMISTICE DAY AND SINGER GALA)
1963c

std.8mm	col	silent	200ft	REF

Visuals of Clydebank, including parks, new housing and the industrial skyline. Also coverage of Armistice Day celebrations and Singer Sports day celebrations.

1589   CLYDEBANK BURGH JUBILEE 1936
1935

35mm	b/w	silent	1100ft	REF

Clydebank's Burgh Jubilee 1816-1936 including footage of the Jubilee Queen's Coronation Pageant and Procession.

1590   TULLIS OF CLYDEBANK
1966

16mm	col	mute	255ft	VIEW

sp. Tullis Clydebank

A demonstration of laundry machines operating at Lily Laundry, Darlington, manufactured by Tullis Clydebank.

1591   INDUSTRY ON PARADE - THE DEFENDING CHAMPION
1961

16mm	b/w	comopt	480ft	VIEW

p.c. Arthur Lodge Productions Inc.

Propaganda film on behalf of US sewing machine manufacturers in the face of competition from Japanese and Asian imports.

1592   BIRTH OF A SEWING MACHINE
1934c

16mm	b/w	silent	2010ft	VIEW

sp. Singer Sewing Machine Co. Ltd.

The manufacturing processes involved in making a Singer sewing machine at Clydebank, Glasgow.

1593   NEEDLE BRUSHING MACHINE USED AT SINGER
1930s

16mm	b/w	silent	285ft	REF

A needle brushing machine in operation. Technical captions and graphics illustrate the methods and processes involved.

1594   (YMCA CAMP)
1935*

16mm	b/w	silent	280ft		REF

sp. YMCA, Glasgow
p.c. Meteor Film Producing Society

A group of boys enjoy a YMCA camp in the country and participate in a Sports Day.

1595   FISHING FLEET
1940

16mm	b/w	silent	480ft		VIEW

filmed by J. Evans Gordon

An illustration of Lossiemouth's fishing industry detailing the preparations before, during and after a catch. The Seine fishing method is highlighted.

1596   GRANITE
1949

16mm	b/w	silent	200ft		VIEW

p.c. Scottish Educational Film Assocation, Aberdeen

The mining of granite used for sculpture, road making, stone bridges and housing.

1597   (SCENES ON THE RIVER CLYDE)
1927-'34*

16mm	b/w	silent	1155ft		REF

[filmed by Professor Percy Hillhouse]

Scenes from the River Clyde including the launch of the "Queen Mary" from John Brown's shipyard and on board the steamer "Empress of Britain".

1598   (GLASGOW UNIVERSITY CHARITIES DAY)
1932-'33

16mm	b/w	silent	370ft		REF

[filmed by Professor Percy Hillhouse]

Glasgow University students enjoying Charities Day and the Duke and Duchess of York receiving an honorary LLD.

1599   NORTH AMERICAN IMP
1966

16mm	col	comopt	720ft		VIEW

sp. Rootes Car manufacturing Co. Ltd.
p.c. Stanley Schofield production

A journey taken by a Hillman Imp from Miami to Alaska.

1600   OPENING OF HAMILTON LA SCALA PICTURE HOUSE
1921

16mm	b/w	silent	120ft		VIEW

[filmed by Green's Topical Productions]

Opening of Hamilton's La Scala picture house 14th March, 1921. General views of patrons and staff.

1601   BETWEEN THE WARS
1919-'39

16mm	b/w	comopt	600ft		VIEW

sp. University of Glasgow for C. A. Oakley
p.c. Rank Film Studios

Compilation of Glasgow University events that occurred during the inter-war period.

1602   BONNETS OVER THE BORDER
1959

35mm	col	comopt	1665ft		VIEW

sp. Films of Scotland and the National Benzole Co.
p.c. Random Production

TheVeteran Car Club Rally, starting in Edinburgh, passing through Perth, the Trossachs, Glasgow and arriving finally at Turnberry airfield. [The rally includes a 1913 "Argyle" tourer.]

1603   PADDY BLACK MEMORIAL MISSION DISTRICT TRIP
1922/'39*

16mm	b/w&col	silent	435ft		VIEW

Footage of children on their way to a day out at Bellahouston Park in the years 1922 and 1939, as part of the Paddy Black charity to give children from poor families a day out in the country. [See also ref. 1662.]

1604   [DUNDEE COURIER 1911]
1911

35mm	b/w	silent	1560ft		VIEW

sp. D.C.Thomson & Co. Ltd.
p.c. Gaumont

Commissioned to celebrate the Dundee Courier's 50 years as a daily newspaper, the film illustrates the various newspaper activities from reporting, editing, setting the linotype to the final printing.

1605   [EDWARD VII LAYS FOUNDATION STONE]
1903

35mm	b/w	silent	40ft		VIEW

King Edward VII lays the foundation stone for the Glasgow and West of Scotland Technical College. Queen Alexandra is also present.

1606   (DALYELL FAMILY FILM)
1930-'40s

16mm	b/w&col	silent	1332ft		REF

Compilation of events including a Highland show, an archery display by the Royal Company of Archers, 1937 Coronation day, Girl Guides rally 1939, Ayr races 1933, and the Duke and Duchess of York's visit to Edinburgh in 1935.

131

1607   THEATRE FIRE IN EDINBURGH
1911

| 35mm | b/w | silent | 60ft | VIEW |

[unidentified newsreel]

General scenes of men and women amid the burnt out wreckage of the Empire Palace Theatre in Edinburgh's Nicolson Street and the charred remains of the "Great Lafayette's Lion". May 9, 1911. [See also ref. 1620.]

1608   (LOCK GATES AT BOWLING)
1960s

| std.8mm | col | silent | 100ft | REF |

[filmed by N. Shannon]

The Forth and Clyde canal lock gates in operation at Bowling, Dunbartonshire.

1609   SCOTTISH TROOPS FOR THE FRONT
1914

| 16mm | b/w | silent | 269ft | VIEW |

Footage of the 5th Royal Scots involved in training before going to the front line. J. L. Dewar 4th Royal Scots winner of the King's Prize is seen entering Hawick camp in the Borders. Scouts demonstrate their skills.

1610   EDUCATION AUTHORITY OF GLASGOW SPECIAL SERVICES
1925

| 35mm | b/w | silent | 835ft | VIEW |

Some of the Education authority special services; the preparation of school meals, transporting handicapped children to school, the work of Woodburn Hostel for blind children and Langside School for the deaf.

1611   ROYAL HIGHLAND SHOW. DUNDEE 1957
1957

| 16mm | col | silent | 885ft | REF |

filmed by Norman Brown

Annual show of the Royal Highland and Agricultural Society of Scotland. The Queen Mother visits the show.

1612   CONSTRUCTION OF THE BACKWATER DAM
1968/'69

| 16mm | col | commag | 1080ft | REF |

sp. East of Scotland Water Board
d. Norman Brown

The construction of the Backwater Dam, Angus. HM Queen Elizabeth opens the dam on the 9th October, 1969.

1613   OVER THE CAPEL TO BIRKHALL
1960

| 16mm | col | mute | 865ft | REF |

sp. The Black Watch (Royal Highland Regiment)
d. Norman Brown

Footage of the march from Cortachy Castle to Royal Deeside, Birkhill by the 4/5th Battalion of the Black Watch, to parade in front of their Colonel-in-chief the Queen Mother. [Shot on Kodachrome.]

1614   [STANDING AT THE GATE]
1942

| 16mm | b/w | silent | 415ft | REF |

sp. Dundee Education Committee

To commemorate the work of Bellfield Nursery School, the first purpose built nursery in Dundee, the film shows the children enjoying themselves, taking part in lessons and taking a nap.

1615   (SHETLAND SCENES)
1943-'56

| 16mm | b/w&col | silent | 415ft | REF |

[filmed by Theo Kay]

Scenes from the Shetland Isles - a man making by hand a pair of cowskin moccasins known as "rivkins", fishing at Lerwick, and shots of the Skerry Lighthouse.

1616   [SHETLAND - A FEW ASPECTS]
1934-'51*

| 16mm | b/w&col | silent | 1110ft | REF |

[filmed by Theo Kay]

Scenes of some of the industries on the Shetland Isles - handline fishing, how 'Fair Isle' jumpers are produced and cutting peat using a tushkar.

1617   (SHETLAND AND FAIR ISLE SCENES)
1934/'50

| 16mm | b/w&col | silent | 320ft | REF |

[filmed by Theo Kay]

An island family on Fair Isle - Fair Isle's first baby girl for 21 years, the family and friends building a haystack and gathering in the sheep.

1618   FAIR ISLE, THE
1951c

| 16mm | col | silent | 660ft | REF |

[filmed by Theo Kay]

The arrival of Fair Isle's mail boat the "Good Shepherd" and the work of the Fair Isle Bird Observatory.

1619	GANNETS AT LERWICK			
1946				
16mm	b/w	silent	300ft	REF

[filmed by Theo Kay]

The gannets' habitat on the Shetland Isles is observed between January and February 1946.

1620	FUNERAL OF THE GREAT LAFAYETTE. EDINBURGH			
1911				
35mm	b/w	silent	73ft	VIEW

Funeral of the Great Lafayette, Piershill Cemetery, Edinburgh. A brass band leads the funeral procession behind the horse- drawn hearse. May 14, 1911. [See also ref. 1607.]

1621	GEORGE HERIOT'S SCHOOL. EDINBURGH			
1938				
16mm	b/w	silent	732ft	VIEW

sp. George Heriot's School
p.c. Campbell Harper Films Ltd.

The activities and facilities offered by George Heriot's School, Edinburgh.

1622	(OUR ROMANY FRIENDS)			
1933*				
16mm	b/w	silent	55ft	REF

A group of travelling people as they pull and push their horse-drawn caravan up a slope.

1623	[DONALD ELLIOT RETIRES]			
1968				
16mm	b/w	silent	150ft	REF

filmed by John Torrance

Made by John Torrance, a member of the Scottish Film Council's technical staff on the occasion of the retiral of the Director, D.M. Elliot.

1624	SCOTS HONOUR THE PRINCE			
1933				
35mm	b/w	comopt	205ft	VIEW

p.c. British Paramount News

HRH the Prince of Wales is made a Freeman of Rothesay.

1625	TRIBUTE TO WARTIME PRODUCTION			
1941				
35mm	b/w	comopt	100ft	VIEW

[attributed to Scottish Films]

King George VI and Queen Elizabeth tour Templeton's carpet factory in Glasgow where women are seen working on the manufacture of army blankets.

1626	TEMPLETON'S CARPETS			
1939				
16mm	b/w	mute	315ft	VIEW

sp. James Templeton & Co.
p.c. Scottish Film Productions

The manufacture of Templeton's Carpets is detailed from the initial design to the finished article.

1627	PRINCESS IN STIRLING, THE			
1947				
35mm	b/w	comopt	660ft	VIEW

p.c. Universal News

Princess Elizabeth inspects the Argyll and Sutherland highlanders of which she is their Colonel-in-Chief, at Stirling Castle and receives the Freedom of the Burgh.

1628	SHOTTS HIGHLAND GAMES			
1952				
35mm	b/w	silent	c400ft	REF

Coverage of Shotts Highland Games in a football stadium on the 6th Sept, 1952. Footage of the Chieftains parade and the procession along Main Street.

1629	AULDHOUSE CINEMAGAZINE			
1938				
9.5mm	b/w	silent	400ft	REF

filmed by Robert Allison

Footage of the Allison family in their garden, holidaying in Arran and at the Empire Exhibition.

1630	BELL'S TRAILER			
1968				
16mm	col	sep opt	27ft	REF

p.c. Campbell Harper Films Ltd.

Advert for Bell's whisky.

1631	THIS LITTLE WORLD			
1954				
16mm	b/w	comopt	940ft	REF

sp. National Association for Prevention of Tuberculosis
p.c. Campbell Harper Films Ltd.
d. Henry Cooper

The work of the East Fortune Sanatorium, East Lothian, showing the staff at work, patients waiting to be x-rayed and the facilities enjoyed by patients including the library and leisure activities such as golf and snooker.

1632	[OPENING COOPER PARK. ELGIN. AUGUST 1903]			
1903				
35mm	b/w	silent	130ft	VIEW

The opening of Cooper Park, Elgin with shots of the procession and onlooking crowds.

133

1633 DESTRUCTION BY FIRE OF THE TOWN HALL, ELGIN

1939

35mm	b/w	silent	250ft	VIEW

Shots of the fire and the firemen fighting the blaze which destroyed Elgin Town Hall.

1634 (MIDSUMMER QUEEN GALA)

1917*

16mm	b/w	silent	265ft	REF

Galashiel's Midsummer Gala with shots of the children's procession, the maypole dance, flower girls parade and the crowning of the Gala Queen.

1635 GLENGARNOCK IRON AND STEEL WORKS

1965c

16mm	b/w	silent	145ft	REF

Steel making processes at Glengarnock Iron and Steel works.

1636 HOUSEWIVES OF TOMORROW

1951

16mm	b/w	silent	496ft	VIEW

[sp. Glasgow Education Committee]
filmed by staff of Albert Secondary School, Springburn

Domestic Science- as taught in a Glasgow School.

1637 SNOW PLOUGH, THE

1936*

16mm	b/w	silent	120ft	VIEW

sp. Educational and General Services
p.c. Elder Dalrymple Productions

A history of the snow plough from the earliest wooden wedge drawn by a man, the horse-drawn plough and the snow plough attached to a lorry.

1638 WIRE LINES

1950c

16mm	b/w	comopt	840ft	VIEW

sp. Martin Black & Co. (Wire Ropes Ltd.)
p.c. Thames and Clyde Film Company
d. Stanley Russell

An illustration of the manufacture of Martin Black's wire ropes. Their use in coal mining is highlighted. [See also ref. 1639.]

1639 (MARTIN BLACK AND COMPANY - UNUSED MATERIAL)

1950c

16mm	b/w	mute	900ft	REF

sp. Martin Black & Co. (Wire Ropes Limited)
p.c. Thames and Clyde Film Company Limited

General views inside Martin & Black's Speedwell Works, Coatbridge. [Rushes from Thames & Clyde's production of WIRE LINES.] [See also ref. 1638.]

1640 INSANE

1955

16mm	b/w	silent	112ft	REF

filmed by the Pearce Institute Cine Club

One of a series of films made during an exercise in production at a week-end school for film-makers organised by the Scottish Association for Amateur Cinematographers. Shot at Crieff Hydro.

1641 ISLES OF YOUTH, THE

1950

16mm	col	silent	1066ft	VIEW

sp. David Macbrayne Limited
d. John C. Elder

A tour of the Hebrides and Highlands of Scotland including a visit to Iona and views of the island of Staffa.

1642 GREAT WATERS MIGHTY ORGAN HARMONIES

1940

35mm	b/w	comopt	600ft	VIEW

Reginald Foort at the organ console, introducing songs including "Let's all go down the Strand" and "The Sunshine of Your Smile".

1643 CAIRNGORMS, THE

1965*

16mm	col	silent	200ft	REF

p.c. Campbell Harper Films Ltd.

A & B Rolls from a documentary on the Cairngorms.

1644 HAWICK COMMON RIDING

1952*

16mm	col	mute	234ft	REF

p.c. Campbell Harper Films Ltd.

Footage of Hawick Common Riding in the Borders including the procession through the streets, the Cornet on horseback, the flagbearer receiving the sword and the Cornet and others being carried shoulder high through the streets of Hawick. [Shot on Kodachrome.]

1645 CORONATION PAGEANT PARADE AND CROWNING OF PAISLEY'S

1953

35mm	b/w	silent	1420ft	REF

The Coronation Day procession passing the Kelburne Cinema, Paisley and the crowning ceremony of Paisley's "Thread Queen".

1646 DUNFERMLINE CHILDREN'S GALA 1953

1953

35mm	b/w	silent	1620ft	REF

[filmed by James S. Nairn for the Regal Picture House]

Dunfermline week 1953 celebrating Elizabeth II's coronation, and featuring the Dunfermline Children's Gala.

1647 BO'NESS CHILDREN'S FAIR FESTIVAL 1957

1957

35mm	b/w	silent	1270ft	REF

The Bo'ness Children's Fair Festival Queen getting ready for the procession, the coronation ceremony and floats procession.

1648 KIRKCALDY YOUTH PAGEANT 1952

1952

35mm	b/w	mute	1085ft	REF

[filmed as a local topical for the Palace and Rio Cinemas]

An archery competition, fancy dress competition, procession and decorated floats at the Youth Pageant. The Pageant Queen visits patients in the children's ward of the local hospital.

1649 (BISCUIT FACTORY AND WEDDING)

1930-'33*

16mm	b/w	silent	306ft	REF

Interiors of a biscuit factory as dough is mixed for custard creams and chocolate biscuits. The film also shows a society wedding.

1650 SALMON FISHING IN SKYE

1938

16mm	col	silent	195ft	VIEW

p.c. Scottish Educational Film Association

Salmon fishermen at work on the shores of Skye; mending and sorting their nets and bringing in the catch. [Entered for the Scottish Amateur Film Festival 1941.]

1651 TO THE TOP OF BEN NEVIS

n.d.

16mm	col	silent	375ft	VIEW

sp. GB Instructional Limited
d. John Elder

Two boys climb Ben Nevis, and are given some rock climbing instruction.

1652 BROWNIE PACK HOLIDAY, A

n.d.

16mm	col	silent	212ft	REF

A brownie pack holiday in Girvan with the brownies taking part in various activities including peeling potatoes, cleaning shoes, washing dishes and sweeping up. The brownies also go for a swim and enjoy the amusements at the funfair.

1653 EDINBURGH

1948c

16mm	b/w	silent	274ft	REF

sp. JPC
filmed by SEFA

Edinburgh's history, industry, and educational life is illustrated with particular reference to the distillation of whisky, the city's university and colleges and the production of the Edinburgh Evening News.

1654 GOLDEN EAGLE, THE

1946c

16mm	col	silent	310ft	VIEW

Scenes from the life of the golden eagle showing an eyrie with newly hatched chicks, two eagles fighting for supremacy and the young eagles learning to fly.

1655 BARRA

1955c

16mm	col	silent	378ft	VIEW

filmed by J.H. Thomas

Scenes on the island of Barra; Castlebay and the MacNeil's Kisimul Castle, the Bay of Traigh Vais, shell gathering and crofting.

1656 RUGBY HINTS NO. 2

1950c

16mm	b/w	comopt	260ft	REF

Summary of rugby skills such as the tackle, dribbling and catching.

1657 RUGBY HINTS NO. 5

1950c

16mm	b/w	comopt	300ft	REF

Players demonstrating different techniques used in the game of rugby.

135

1658	**WEEKEND QUARTET**			
1952				
16mm	*col*	*silent*	*400ft*	*REF*

filmed by W.S. Dobson

A humorous fiction film telling of the adventures of four grass widowers who decide to spend the week-end in a country cottage. [A prize-winning film at the 1952 Scottish Amateur Film Festival.]

1659	**WEDDING OF ALYS COUPER AND DOUGLAS LINDSAY**			
1920				
35mm	*b/w*	*silent*	*135ft*	*VIEW*

p.c. Scottish Moving Picture News

The wedding of Alys Couper and Douglas Lindsay, son of Sir John Lindsay the Town Clerk of Glasgow. Glasgow Cathedral, June 1920. [See also ref. 2833.]

1660	**SPORTS CARNIVAL AT HAMPDEN**			
1925*				
35mm	*b/w*	*silent*	*85ft*	*VIEW*

filmed by Grosvenor Topical

A Sports Carnival at Hampden, with Lord Birkenhead an interested spectator.

1661	**PROMINENT PAISLEY WEDDING**			
1932				
35mm	*b/w*	*silent*	*370ft*	*VIEW*

Wedding at Martyr's Church, Paisley, of Mary McGeorge (daughter of Baillie McGeorge) to Daniel Sinclair, in February 1932.

1662	**(GORBALS PROCESSION)**			
1922				
35mm	*b/w*	*silent*	*90ft*	*VIEW*

Rushes edited into logical sequence of events from "Paddy Black Memorial Mission District Trip". [See also ref. 1603.]

136

Scottish Film Productions on location in Midcalder filming The Glen is Ours, 1946. Ref. 0486

1663	LITTLE GREATHEART

1950c

| 16mm | col | silent | 1000ft | | REF |

filmed by Frank M. Marshall

The dramatised account of a young girl tormented by two youths who are in turn saved by her when they are trapped in a fire.

1664	(W6 FIRST FLIGHT)

1940

| 16mm | b/w | silent | 255ft | | REF |

[p.c. Lizars, Glasgow]

Footage of the W6 helicopter's first flight.

1665	(MOTHERWELL FOOTBALL CLUB COLLECTION)

1938-'54c

| 16mm | b/w&col | silent | 7400ft | | REF |

A combination of amateur film and newsreel footage showing various football games including the Scotland team's Scandinavian tour of 1952, the 1954 World Cup in Brazil, Scotland v England matches 1944 to 1953, Rangers v Moscow Dynamo 1945, and Great Britain v Europe 1948.

1666	CAPITAL GARDEN

1970s

| 16mm | col | comopt | 1320ft | | VIEW |

p.c. Grange Films
d. Ian Brock

An historical introduction to the Royal Botanic Gardens of Edinburgh. All aspects of the work of the Gardens are shown, including the herbarium, laboratories, glasshouses and library. The general public are seen enjoying the gardens.

1667	HEALTHY HOLIDAYS

1950

| 16mm | b/w | silent | 372ft | | REF |

p.c. GB Instructional Limited
d. Donald Carter

Made to promote healthy holidays, the film shows a couple walking in the countryside, people swimming, playing hockey, volleyball and leap-frog.

1668	CHRISTMAS

1937

| 16mm | b/w | silent | 380ft |

filmed by Frank M. Marshall

A children's Christmas Eve and Christmas morning. [An amateur prize-winning film of 1937.]

1669	ST. ANDREWS

1965c

| 16mm | col | comopt | 400ft | | REF |

filmed by Iain Dunnachie

An historical trip round St. Andrews visiting St. Rules's church and tower, the Cathedral, University, Kate Kennedy procession and the golf course.

1670	KIDS IN CLOVER

1940

| 16mm | col | silent | 342ft | | VIEW |

filmed by Frank M. Marshall

The story of two children who visit a farm with their mother and get into all kinds of mischief. [Commended at the 7th Scottish Amateur Film Festival 1940.]

1671	LIVINGSTONE

1925

| 16mm | b/w | silent | 1230ft | | REF |

Filmed by The Religious Film Society
p M A Wetherell

A film biography of the African explorer David Livingstone.

1672	SCHOOL MASTER, THE

1953

| 16mm | b/w | comopt | 684ft | | REF |

p.c. Anglo Scottish Pictures

The daily life of a school master including taking woodwork class, giving a film show, on a field trip and at a council meeting.

1673	UNDAUNTED: THE TREFOIL SCHOOL

1947

| 16mm | b/w | silent | 288ft | | REF |

sp. The Trefoil School
p.c. Campbell Harper Films Ltd.

The work of the Trefoil School for handicapped children with shots of children at summer camp, children at meal time, learning crafts and playing various sports. [An updated version of this film was made in 1956. See ref. 1674.]

1674	UNDAUNTED: THE TREFOIL SCHOOL

1956

| 16mm | b/w | comopt | 740ft | | VIEW |

sp. The Trefoil School
p.c. Campbell Harper Films Ltd.

Film details the facilities that the Trefoil school offers disabled children. [See also ref. 1673.]

137

1675   STRATHNETHY IN SPRING
1959

16mm	col	comopt	400ft		VIEW

p.c. Educational Films of Scotland

Shot in the valley of Nethy, between the Cairngorms and Speyside, the film shows the animal and plant life of the area including golden plovers, wheatears and red stags.

1676   BRIDGE TOWN, THE
1956

16mm	col	silent	334ft		VIEW

p. John C. Elder

A look at the river Clyde, its bridges, ships, and buildings and traffic along its banks.

1678   THERE'S NAE LUCK ABOUT THE HOOSE
1950c

16mm	col	comopt	156ft		REF

p.c. Scottish Educational Film Association

Interpretation of a traditional Scots ballad which tells the story of a family in the nineteenth century awaiting the return of the man of the house.

1679   POWER AND PULSE OF SCOTLAND, THE
1968

16mm	col	silent	552ft		REF

sp. Scottish Standing Conference of Voluntary Youth Organisations
filmed by Mary MacRae

Young people enjoying various activities at Butlin's camp at Ayr.

1680   [1938]
1938

16mm	col	silent	480ft		REF

[filmed by D.G. Russell]

One of a series of 'annuals' made by the filmmaker between 1933 and 1980, it includes footage of the Empire Exhibition, D. G. Russell's family at Redlands and a wedding at Bearsden.

1681   SALMON FISHING BY THE RING NET METHOD
1952

16mm	b/w	silent	135ft		VIEW

filmed by Iain Dunnachie

Salmon fishing by the ring net method on Loch Feochan, Argyllshire.

1682   NURSERY SCHOOLDAYS
1953*

16mm	col	silent	430ft		VIEW

filmed by T. H. Thomas

An award winning film, showing children enjoying various activities at nursery school.

1683   OLD COLLEGE, THE
1957*

16mm	col	sep opt	380ft		VIEW

sp. Glasgow University Graduates Association
p.c. Scottish Film Council

Glasgow University's Old College as seen through illustrations, paintings and photographs.

1684   NEW LIVES
1941

16mm	b/w	silent	550ft		REF

sp. Church of Scotland Home Board
p.c. Campbell Harper Films Ltd.
d. Alan Harper

Some aspects of the Church of Scotland Extension work are shown in this story of a family's evacuation from an Edinburgh slum to a new housing area.

1685   THREE MUST-GET-THERE'S, THE
1949

16mm	col	silent	200ft		VIEW

[filmed by W. Nimmo]

A prize-winning film at the 1949 SAFF, it shows three young boys on bicycles coping with traffic.

1686   CALEDONIAN CANAL, THE
1960s

16mm	col	silent	360ft		REF

[filmed by D.G. Russell]

Passage through the Caledonian Canal from east to west in the motor yacht "Ormidale". Filmed over a period of twelve years during annual visits to the canal.

1687   FORTH AND CLYDE CANAL, THE
1962

16mm	col	silent	400ft		REF

[filmed by D.G. Russell]

The Forth and Clyde Canal's operations on it's last year of use.

1688	SCOTTISH NATIONAL ZOOLOGICAL PARK				
1931/'32					
16mm	b/w	silent	420ft		REF

sp. Scottish National Zoo
[filmed by D.G. Russell]

Made for screening at an international zoological meeting in Paris, the film shows the work of the Scottish National Zoological Park, highlighting its naturalistic methods of exhibition.

1689	(BENNY LYNCH COMPILATION)				
1935/'38					
35mm	col	comopt	410ft		REF

p.c. Movietone and British Movietone News

A compilation of newsreel footage of Benny Lynch boxing matches, including his fights with Jurich and Peter Kane. [Commentary missing.]

1690	[FINNART OCEAN TERMINAL]				
1957*					
35mm	b/w	mute	135ft		REF

Footage possibly originally acquired by John Grierson at Scottish Television for inclusion in the series "This Wonderful World", showing the construction area for the Finnart Ocean Terminal.

1691	GREENOCK PLANS AHEAD				
1948					
16mm	b/w	comopt	855ft		VIEW

sp. Corporation of Greenock
d. Hamilton Tait

Highlighting the main industrial and housing problems facing the Corporation of Greenock and solutions proposed.

1692	TRAMPING AND CAMPING				
1948c					
16mm	col	silent	423ft		VIEW

p.c. GB Instructional Ltd.
p. John C. Elder

A camping expedition by an uncle and his nephew, showing the do's and don'ts of the countryside code.

1693	OUR CITIZEN ARMY				
1935c					
16mm	b/w	comopt	760ft		REF

p.c. Strain Limited
d. Clifford J. Strain

A promotional film for the Territorial Army in Scotland, the TA's training techniques are highlighted.

1694	INDUSTRIAL CLYDESDALE				
1938					
16mm	b/w	silent	387ft		VIEW

p.c. Elder-Dalrymple Productions

Using diagrams, working models, and actuality footage the film outlines the industrial development of Clydesdale, including its iron and steelworks, textile mills and shipbuilding.

1695	MAKING TWEED				
1955*					
16mm	col	silent	288ft		VIEW

sp. SEFA & SFC
p.c. Joint Production Committee

The various processes in the production of tweed, from the gathering of wool to the finished product.

1696	ROYAL SCOTLAND				
1946					
16mm	col	comopt	327ft		REF

p.c. Crown Film Unit

A record of Royal visits to Scotland, including shots of King George VI and the Royal Family visiting Balmoral and Queen Elizabeth and Princess Margaret at the Braemar Highland games.

1697	[ARBROATH HISTORICAL PAGEANT 1947]				
1947					
9.5mm	b/w	silent	150ft		REF

The grounds and ruins of Arbroath Abbey during its historical pageant. Shots of the decorated floats procession in the streets of Arbroath.

1698	[ARBROATH HIGH SCHOOL SPORTS AND OPENING OF BATHING POOL]				
1935					
9.5mm	b/w	silent	100ft		VIEW

The opening day of Arbroath Bathing Pool and a diving display by the world champion, the American Pete Desjardins.

1699	SCOTTISH NATIONAL EXHIBITION				
1908-'11					
35mm	b/w	silent	138ft		VIEW

p.c. Gaumont Company and Pathe Freres

Footage of the Scottish National Pageant, Edinburgh and of the Edinburgh Music Hall Fire.

139

1700 [CIVIL DEFENCE SCOTTISH]
1950*

| 16mm | b/w | comopt | 114ft | REF |

A recruiting film for the Civil Defence Corps.

1701 ERISKAY - A POEM OF REMOTE LIVES
1935

| 35mm | b/w | comopt | 1710ft | VIEW |

filmed by Dr. Werner Kissling

A study of Eriskay's crofting life, filmed by Dr. Kissling during a sailing holiday.

1702 ENCHANTED GLADE, THE
1933

| 16mm | b/w | silent | 220ft | REF |

filmed by the Bearsden Film Club

A drama involving witches casting a spell over a group of picnicers.

1703 BLOOD TRANSFUSION SERVICE
1941

| 16mm | b/w | silent | 480ft | REF |

filmed by Frank M. Marshall

The work of the Blood Transfusion Service in Glasgow.

1704 (SCOTTISH WEDDING, A)
1956

| 35mm | b/w | mute | 300ft | REF |

Wedding ceremony between the Hon. Flora Marjory Fraser (daughter of Lord Saltoun) to Captain Alexander Ramsay at St. Peter's Episcopal Church, Fraserburgh.

1705 HIGHLAND TOUR. CROOKSTON STREET SCHOOL
1956

| 16mm | col | silent | 650ft | REF |

Record of Crookston Street School Highland Tour. The group visits Skye and Dunvegan Castle where they meet Dame Flora MacLeod; Pringles Mill, Inverness; Elgin Cathedral; the Queen's Church, Crathie and Balmoral Castle.

1706 DUNDEE WAR WEAPONS WEEK
1941

| 35mm | b/w | comopt | 180ft | REF |

p.c. Scottish Films

Lord Provost Wilson promoting the need to invest in War Savings certificates.

1707 DUCHESS OF YORK NAMES NEW LIFEBOAT
1932

| 35mm | b/w | silent | 430ft | VIEW |

[filmed as a local topical for the Palace Theatre, Arbroath]

The Duchess of York names the new lifeboat "John and William Mudie", boards the lifeboat and is taken on a trip around the harbour.

1708 ARBROATH HISTORICAL PAGEANT/ THE STONE RETURNS
1947*/'51

| 35mm | b/w | sil/comopt | 400ft | VIEW |

p.c. Pathe News

Silent footage of Arbroath Historical Pageant, and sound footage of an interview with Arbroath councillors Thornton and Gardner talking about their role in returning the Stone of Destiny to Arbroath Abbey.

1709 [ST. LEONARD'S AND ST. KATHARINE'S SCHOOL]
1932*

| 16mm | b/w | silent | 400ft | REF |

School activities at St. Leonard's girls' school, St. Andrews.

1710 ST. LEONARD'S SCHOOL 50 YEARS JUBILEE 1927
1927

| 16mm | b/w | silent | 290ft | REF |

[filmed by Margaret S. Baron]

Footage of celebrations surrounding St. Leonard's school 50 years Jubilee 1927, including the Duchess of York opening the new library.

1711 AD VITAM
1937

| 16mm | b/w | silent | 1000ft | VIEW |

filmed by Jan Read and Oscar Oeser

Early photographs depict the history of St. Leonard's School for girls and the film shows the arrival of girls for a new term by steam train, motor coach and horse-drawn cabs.

1712 (ST. LEONARD'S 1940)
1940

| 16mm | b/w | silent | 150ft | REF |

[filmed by Miss Strathairn]

Shots of pupils exercising, playing cricket and taking part in a school play, at St. Leonard's School for girls, St. Andrews.

1713 [OPENING OF NEW SCIENCE LABORATORIES]
1962

| 16mm | col | silent | 150ft | | REF |

HM Queen Elizabeth the Queen Mother visits St. Leonard's School, St. Andrews, to open the school's new science laboratory.

1714 QUEEN MOTHER VISITS ST. ANDREWS 1977
1977

| super 8mm col | | commag | 400ft | | REF |

filmed by Morris Allan

HM Queen Elizabeth the Queen Mother visits St. Andrews, including St. Leonard's School for girls, celebrating its centenary.

1715 [ST. LEONARD'S EXPEDITION TO SIKKIM]
1977

| super 8mm col | | silent | 400ft | | REF |

Pupils from St. Leonard's School for girls on an expedition to Sikkim.

1716 ST. LEONARD'S SCHOOL
1972

| super 8mm col | | silent | 350ft | | REF |

St. Leonard's School for girls, St. Andrews during its Open Day showing classes in progress, a lacrosse match and a fireworks display.

1717 LANIMER DAY, LANARK 1968
1968

| std.8mm col | | silent | 200ft | | REF |

[filmed by James Kerr Hill]

Shots of the Lanimer Day celebrations in Lanark.

1718 ROYAL HIGHLAND SHOW, INGLISTON
1967

| std.8mm col | | silent | 200ft | | REF |

[filmed by James Kerr Hill]

Shots at the Royal Highland Show, Ingliston.

1719 [LUSS HIGHLAND GATHERING]
1966

| std.8mm col | | silent | 200ft | | REF |

[filmed by James Kerr Hill]

General views of Luss Highland Gathering.

1720 [NAMING CEREMONY. THE "DUKE OF MONTROSE"]
1958

| 16mm | col | silent | 250ft | | REF |

Naming ceremony at Arbroath harbour of the lifeboat "Duke of Montrose" by HRH the Duchess of Kent.

1721 LET GLASGOW FLOURISH
1952/'56

| 16mm | b/w | silent | 420ft | | VIEW |

filmed by the Dawn Cine Group

Made to highlight housing conditions in Glasgow using footage shot in 1952 during the proposed sale of Council houses in Merrylee.

1722 GLASGOW MAY DAY 1937
1937

| 16mm | b/w | silent | 400ft | | VIEW |

filmed by Glasgow Clarion Club Film Society

Promotional film for the Clarion Film Society. Members are seen involved in the Glasgow May Day procession, filming the march for "fallen comrades" in the Spanish Civil War.

1723 PROCESSION IN COMMEMORATION OF CALTON WEAVERS/ROBERT SMILLIE CENTENARY
1957

| 16mm | b/w | silent | 340ft | | VIEW |

filmed by the Dawn Cine Group

Glasgow Trades Council commemorate the martyrdom of the Calton weavers and lay a plaque in the Calton graveyard. Robert Smillie founding member of the Scottish Labour Party has a park opened in his honour.

1724 [PARENTS AT SCHOOL]
1956/'58

| 16mm | b/w | silent | 300ft | | REF |

[filmed by the Dawn Cine Group]

Trims from a film made for the Parents Club of Toryglen School, Glasgow.

1725 [LOST TREASURES]
1956

| 16mm | b/w | silent | c1000ft | | REF |

[filmed by the Dawn Cine Group]

Sequences shot for a film on Highland depopulation; interiors of houses in Sutherland and in Glasgow, the lime kilns at Eriboll, fishing boats at Lochinver, Dounreay under consruction and the hydro board work at Altnabreac, Golspie.

141

1726   [BOYS' BRIGADE RECRUITING MARCHES, LEITH]

1925c

| 35mm | b/w | silent | 800ft | VIEW |

[filmed by Topical Productions, Glasgow]

The Boys' Brigade recruiting march Leith with shots of the flag-bearers marching, a gymnastics display, and a parade by former BB's.

1727   [AT THE SMIDDY/THE ROAD TO BRAEMAR]

1947

| 16mm | b/w | silent | 255ft | VIEW |

[filmed by John Todd]

Account of a scenic journey to Braemar and the arrival of the Royal family to the Braemar Highland games.

1728   UNVEILING OF KIRKCALDY WAR MEMORIAL

1920c

| 16mm | b/w | silent | 345ft | REF |

p.c. Gaumont

The unveiling of Kirkcaldy War Memorial and the ceremonial tree planting ceremony by Admiral Lord Wester Wemyss. The general public enjoy a fete.

1729   [STARKS PARK]

1920/'25c

| 16mm | b/w | silent | 135ft | REF |

Sports day at Starks Park, Kirkcaldy, including a bicycle race, tug-o-war and a competition to win a leg of ham.

1730   FINE FLOORS

1963c

| 16mm | col | comopt | 915ft | REF |

A promotional film for the linoleum manufacturers Michael Nairn and Company Ltd., Kirkcaldy. It shows the processes involved in the making of linoleum and highlights the export trade of the company.

1731   SRDA CONFERENCE, GLENEAGLES

1957

| 16mm | b/w | silent | 360ft | REF |

Scottish Retail Drapers' Association conference at Gleneagles, 22nd to 25th of April, 1957. Guests enjoy the hotel's grounds and golf course.

1732   SCOTTISH GAS BOARD. WESTFIELD WORKS

1961

| 35mm | col | comopt | 804ft | REF |

p.c. Glasgow Films Ltd

HM the Queen opens the Scottish Gas Board Westfield Works. The film also shows men laying gas pipes, furnace workers, and home gas users.

1733   GREAT GLASGOW FIRES

1925

| 35mm | b/w | silent | 210ft | VIEW |

p.c. Green's Film Service, Glasgow and London

Footage of the fire at the Kelvin Hall and Kelvingrove UF Church, Glasgow.

1734   (KELVIN HALL EVENTS)

1929*

| 35mm | b/w | silent | 130ft | VIEW |

p.c. Topical Budget News

A compilation of events at the Kelvin Hall, Glasgow, including Sir James Barrie opening the Housing and Health Exhibition and the comedian Tommy Lorne entering Bostock and Wombwell's lion's den.

1735   EDINBURGH TRAMWAYS [EXTRACT]

1920/'30s

| 16mm | b/w | silent | 90ft | VIEW |

Various shots of Edinburgh trams travelling along Princes Street, North Bridge, and George Street.

1736   [WESTERN AREA FIRE STATIONS]

1948/'66c

| 16mm | b/w&col | silent | 1660ft | REF |

Fire fighting procedures, how to prevent fire and methods of escaping from a fire.

1737   WESTERN AREA FIRE BRIGADE (BARRHEAD)

n.d.

| 16mm | b/w | mute | 90ft | REF |

Exterior and interior shots of Barrhead fire station.

1738   [FIRE AT PAPER MILL, LINWOOD]

1968

| 16mm | b/w | silent | 72ft | REF |

General views of firemen fighting the fire at the paper mill in Linwood on 7th. October 1968.

142

1739   FIRE-FIRE-FIRE
1969c

16mm	b/w	comopt	216ft		REF

p.c. Thomson Foundation Television College
d. John Mwakitawa

Demonstration of firemen reacting to an emergency call and an interview with the firemaster.

1740   (CRAWFORD'S BISCUITS)
1935

16mm	b/w	silent	505ft		REF

[filmed by George P. May]

Crawford's Biscuits sales campaign in 1935 at the time of the Bakery and Biscuits trade Exhibition in the Kelvin Hall, Glasgow.

1741   [SCOTTISH CND PROTEST]
1960/'62c

16mm	col	silent	60ft		REF

[filmed by Hugh Dunlop]

Shots of Scottish CND marchers during a protest against Polaris.

1742   CINE HOLIDAY
1955*

16mm	col	silent	280ft		REF

[filmed by Hugh Dunlop]

Taken by cameraman whilst visiting members of the Dawn Cine Group during the shooting of their film "Lost Treasures". They discuss scenes and act them out.

1743   FAMILY PARTIES
1957*

16mm	b/w&col	silent	200ft		REF

[filmed by Hugh Dunlop]

Children enjoy a Hallowe'en fancy dress party and a family celebrates Christmas.

1744   (TEN GLASGOW ARTISTS EXHIBITION)
1956

16mm	col	silent	160ft		REF

[filmed by Hugh Dunlop]

Shots of paintings by J.M. McChlery, W. Rennie, C. Sinclair, T. Macdonald and Bet Low with close-ups of some of the artists.

1745   PORT HEALTH AUTHORITY
1928/'30c

16mm	b/w	silent	710ft		VIEW

Demonstration of the role of the Port Health Authority and the work it undertakes from the supervision of food imports to the inspection of ships' holds.

1746   [FLAX FACTORY, TURRIFF]
1942c

16mm	b/w	silent	1170ft		REF

[filmed by L.S. Gorrie]

The production of flax fibre and by-products.

1747   (JUTE MACHINERY - TECHNICAL RECORDS)
1935-'36c

16mm	b/w	silent	4000ft		REF

[filmed by L.S. Gorrie]

Compilation of reels demonstrating jute machinery in action, manufactured by Urquhart Lindsay and Robertson Orchar Ltd., Dundee

1748   [ULRO KIDDIES PICNIC]
1951

16mm	b/w	silent	280ft		REF

[filmed by L.S. Gorrie]

Employees and friends of Urquhart, Lindsay and Robertson Orchar Ltd., manufacturers of jute machinery, on a day out in Balmore Park, Dundee.

1749   [BURNS CLUB AND ULRO PICNIC]
1956

16mm	b/w&col	silent	400ft		REF

[filmed by L.S. Gorrie]

The ULRO Annual 1956 Burns Club Dinner and Dance with the piping in and addressing of the Haggis.

1750   [ULRO GOLF CLUB 1956]
1956

16mm	b/w&col	silent	300ft		REF

[filmed by L.S. Gorrie]

Members of Urquhart Lindsay and Robertson Orchar's club playing golf at Gleneagles.

1751   SCOTTISH CUP FINAL 1963
1963

35mm	b/w&col	comopt	545ft		REF

p.c. Pathe News

Coverage of the Scottish Cup Final 1963 between Celtic and Rangers at Hampden Park, with Rangers winning the Cup.

1752   MAKING SWEETS
1952*

16mm	col	silent	279ft		VIEW

p.c. Educational Films of Scotland

The different stages involved in the manufacturing of sweets.

143

1754   LACE MAKING

1927*

| 16mm | b/w | silent | 331ft | VIEW |

sp. British Instructional Films Ltd
p.c. Pathe Production

Lace making, from the creation of designs to the winding and weaving of cotton to produce widths of curtaining. Women stretch and dry the material before folding and packing it.

1755   BROXBURN CHILDREN'S GALA DAY 1924/'25

1924/'25

| 35mm | b/w | silent | 690ft | REF |

The children's procession, decorated floats, races and a pillow fight at Broxburn Children's Gala Days.

1756   BROXBURN CHILDREN'S GALA DAY 1934/'35

1934/'35

| 35mm | b/w | silent | 630ft | REF |

The children's prcession, mothers and baby competition and fancy dress competition at Broxburn Children's Gala Days.

1757   (BROXBURN CHILDREN'S GALA DAY 1952)

1952

| 35mm | b/w | silent | 355ft | REF |

[filmed as a local topical for the Regal Cinema, Broxburn]

The gala procession, coronation of the gala queen and decorated floats at Broxburn Children's Gala Day.

1758   HORSE AND HARNESS

1934*

| 16mm | b/w | silent | 124ft | VIEW |

sp. Glasgow Education Authorities
p.c. Elder Dalrymple Productions

A demonstration of how to harness a Clydesdale horse.

1759   BY BUS TO THE HILLS

1950c

| 16mm | col | silent | 317ft | VIEW |

p.c. GB Instructional Limited Production
p. John C. Elder

A group of children join a bus tour party at Edinburgh for an outing to Tweedside. They visit Peebles and Neidpath Castle in the Borders, tracing the Tweed to its source.

1760   KIPPERS

1952

| 16mm | b/w | silent | 228ft | VIEW |

sp. Scottish Educational Film Assocation
p.c. Joint Production Film

The herring catch is unloaded, gutted, pickled and cured.

1761   FAIR RENT

1947

| 16mm | b/w | comopt | 400ft | VIEW |

sp. Department of Health for Scotland
p.c. Central Office of Information
p. Donald Alexander

How rents could be more fairly applied within Aberdeen by means of a tribunal system.

1762   RIVER IS SPANNED, THE

1950

| 16mm | b/w | comopt | 370ft | VIEW |

filmed by Harry Birrell

A reconstruction of the building of the Forth Railway Bridge using contemporary footage and stills. [The film was a prize winner at the Scottish Amateur Film Festival.]

1763   AMONG THE HILLS

1949*

| 16mm | col | silent | 303ft | VIEW |

sp. GB Instructional Limited
p. John C. Elder

Three children on holiday trace the River Clyde from its source at Little Clydesburn to the sea.

1764   LOTHIANS PART 1, THE

1955*

| 16mm | b/w | silent | 250ft | VIEW |

sp. SEFA and SFC
p.c. Campbell Harper Films Ltd.

Hill farming, harvesting, dairy farming and small holdings in the Lothians. Golfers at North Berwick, horse racing at Musselburgh and the beach at Portobello are also featured.

1765   LOTHIANS PART II, THE

1955*

| 16mm | b/w | silent | 360ft | VIEW |

sp. SEFA and SFC
p.c. Campbell Harper Films Ltd.

Fishing ports at Granton and Newhaven, the docks at Leith, shale mining, a new pit at Bo'ness and some of the towns of the Lothians; Edinburgh, Linlithgow, Haddington and Musselburgh.

144

1766   [SCOTT FAMILY FILM]
1928-'39

16mm	col	silent	1700ft	REF

[filmed by George Scott]

The Scott family (of Peter Scott & Co. hosiery manufacturers, Hawick) on holiday in North Berwick, Largs, Hawick, the Highlands and Edinburgh. A family wedding is included.

1767   HEATHER HONEY
1959

16mm	col	silent	1119ft	REF

p.c. Edinburgh and East of Scotland Agricultural College

The work of the beekeeper, from preparing the hives to the marketing of the honey.

1768   JOB FOR THE FUTURE, A
1958*

16mm	col	sep opt	276ft	REF

p.c. National Cash Register Company

A promotional film for the National Cash Register Co, showing the workforce in their Dundee factory.

1769   SCOTTISH TRANSPORT
1942*

16mm	col	silent	72ft	REF

p.c. BBC

Various methods of transport including single decker and double decker buses in Edinburgh, a "Mother's Pride" truck collecting grain in Glasgow, cart horses at the Glasgow docks and a tractor being used to harvest potatoes.

1770   [WARTIME TRAILERS]
1944c

35mm	b/w	comopt	120ft	VIEW

Government trailer attempting to instill the virtue of the wise shopper and saver during wartime, promoting National Savings Certificates, and the use of skimmed milk from the USA.

1771   (RENTS PROTEST MARCH, GLASGOW)
1972/'73c

16mm	b/w	silent	400ft	VIEW

[filmed by the Dawn Cine Group]

General views of Glasgow's Blythswood Square and streets in the city centre as marchers assemble and demonstrate against rents increases. Shots of speakers at the rally including Jimmy Reid.

1772   [BOAT OF GARTEN 1932]
1932

16mm	b/w	silent	339ft	REF

[filmed by J.D. Urie]

A tennis match, a game of golf, swimming in a loch and a family wedding.

1773   [602 CITY OF GLASGOW SQUADRON]
1936

16mm	b/w	silent	345ft	REF

[filmed by J.D. Urie]

The 602 City of Glasgow Squadron training at North Cotes in Lincolnshire. A Hawker Hart takes off and lands at Abbotsinch airport and a flight display by No. 43 Squadron (Bull-dogs).

1774   ["QUEEN MARY"]
1936

16mm	b/w&col	silent	250ft	REF

[filmed by J.D. Urie]

Aerial shots of the liner the "Queen Mary" in the fitting out basin, taken from an aircraft of the 602 Squadron; the liner is seen passing the Cloch lighthouse and approaching Gourock.

1775   [PHOTOGRAPHIC CONVENTION. GLASGOW 1898]
1898

35mm	b/w	silent	100ft	VIEW

[filmed by E.P. Prestwich]

Members of the photographic convention carrying tripods and cameras file past a waiting room on the deck of the Clyde steamer "Lady Rowena".

1776   (REGAL CINEMA, DUNFERMLINE)
1976

super 8mm col	silent	c50ft	REF

[filmed by Neil Castell]

General views of the exterior of the Regal Cinema, Dunfermline, with "Sold" notice. Shots inside the auditorium after a fire.

1777   NEILSTON REEL / CATTLE SHOWS
1950-'57

9.5mm	b/w&col	silent	1220ft	REF

[filmed by Mr. Laws]

Compilation of events, including footage of the Moderator of the Church of Scotland visiting Neilston, the Neilston Show, and Coronation Day 1953.

1778   FREEDOM OF BURGH CEREMONY QUEEN'S OWN HIGHLANDERS

1961

16mm	col	silent	225ft		REF

[filmed by James S. Nairn and James Atterson]

The Freedom of the Burgh Ceremony in the Playhouse Cinema on 11th March, 1961. The Queen's Own Highlanders march through the streets of Inverness.

1779   WITH CAR AND CAMERA THROUGH THE LAKE DISTRICT TO SOUTHERN SCOTLAND

1936

16mm	b/w&col	silent	320ft		REF

filmed by F.L. Unwin

A car journey through the Lake District, a visit to the Blacksmith's Shop Gretna Green, on to Glasgow and the Empire Exhibition, Edinburgh and finally to Loch Lomond.

1780   OBAN

1951

16mm	col	silent	336ft		REF

A prize-winning film at the Scottish Amateur Film Festival of 1952, telling of the adventures of two children on holiday in Oban.

1781   SMOKIES

1958*

16mm	col	silent	216ft		VIEW

sp. Educational Films of Scotland
filmed by SEFA, Dundee Branch

A description of the fishing industry on the east coast of Scotland.

1782   STEEL WORKS, THE

1948c

16mm	col	silent	378ft		VIEW

p.c. GB Instructional Limited Production
p. John C. Elder

Two children visit a steel works where they see the furnace in action.

1783   RIVER TAY

1950s

16mm	b/w	silent	390ft		VIEW

sp. SEFA and SFC
p.c. Thames and Clyde Film Co. Ltd.

Following the river Tay showing the countryside and towns situated on its banks.

1784   HIGHLAND CASTLES

1959c

16mm	col	silent	828ft		REF

filmed by James S. Nairn

Inverness Castle, Castle Stuart, Castle Leys, Eilean Donan, Dunvegan, Achnacarry and Aldourie Castle.

1785   GREEN'S PLAYHOUSE BALLROOM

1927c

35mm	b/w	silent	45ft		VIEW

[sp. Green's Playhouse]

A series of advertisements for Green's Playhouse ballroom.

1786   (FIRST COMMUNION CEREMONY)

1920s

9.5mm	b/w	silent	160ft		REF

[filmed by Mr. Lawrie]

Young Roman Catholic girls dressed up for their first communion parading with banners through the streets of Glasgow.

1787   [CLYDE RIVER]

1939

16mm	b/w	comopt	565ft		REF

sp. LMS Railway
p.c. LMS Advertising and Publicity Department

The River Clyde from source to sea highlighting its industry, history, the city of Glasgow and its nearby holiday areas.

1788   (BERTRAMS LTD.)

1960s

std.8mm	col	silent	200ft		REF

Machinery at work in Bertrams Ltd, papermaking machinery engineers of Edinburgh.

1790   (CEA CONFERENCE. GLENEAGLES C1949)

1949c

35mm	b/w	comopt	180ft		VIEW

Coverage of a CEA (Cinematograph Exhibitors' Association) Conference at Gleneagles Hotel.

1791   WEDDING AT ALL SOULS

1936

35mm	b/w	mute	200ft		VIEW

p.c. Gaumont British News

The wedding of Mr. J. Poole and Miss I. Storck at All Souls, Langholm Place, London, on 3rd of September, 1936.

Movietone news cameraman and Jimmy Rich, manager of the Palace Kinema, filming Dunfermline Children's Gala Day c1932

1792   SOLWAY COUNTIES, THE

1955/'58c

16mm	b/w	silent	372ft	VIEW

sp. Joint Production Committee and SEFA, SFC
p.c. Thames and Clyde Film Co.

A survey of three Solway Counties, Wigtown, Kirkcudbright and Dumfries. Farming and industries are highlighted.

1793   (CONSTRUCTION OF DUNFERMLINE'S WAR MEMORIAL)

1953

std.8mm col	silent	150ft	REF

[filmed by Mr. Blackie]

Stonemasons build and engrave the war memorial in Dumfermline.

1794   NETTING SALMON

1936c

16mm	b/w	silent	84ft	VIEW

sp. Glasgow Education Authority
p.c. J. C. Elder-Dalrymple Productions

Fishermen netting a fish and making ready for the next catch.

1795   TASK FORCE

1962

16mm	col	comopt	396ft	VIEW

p.c. Research Film Unit, Edinburgh

A look at the work of the Conservation Corps at Aberlady Bay Local Nature Reserve, East Lothian.

1796   GB NEWS REVIEW 1948

1948

16mm	b/w	comopt	270ft	REF

p.c. Gaumont British News

A record of events of 1948 including the Olympic Games at Wembley, the British Open, the departure of Mountbatten from India, Truman's victory parade in Washington and the Royal Silver Wedding.

1797   MOVIES GREATEST HEADLINES

1950

16mm	b/w	comopt	269ft	REF

p.c. GB Movie Paks

Preview of features on film, shots of the Hindenburg disaster, Winston Churchill meeting Roosevelt, the funeral of F. D. Roosevelt and the first underwater atomic bomb test.

1798   FENWICK EVENTS OF 1931

1931

16mm	b/w	silent	350ft	REF

[filmed by Revd. George Allan]

Scenes of community life centred on activities associated with the local church in Fenwick.

1799   PRINCESS STREET CHURCH [PORT GLASGOW]

1938

9.5mm	b/w	silent	350ft	REF

[filmed by Revd. George Allan]

A Sunday School picnic to Kilmun, junior Bible class excursion to Largs, a bowling match and the crowning of the Temperance King and Queen.

1800   PRINCESS STREET CHURCH EVENTS OF 1937

1937

9.5mm	b/w	silent	350ft	REF

[filmed by Revd. George Allan]

A compilation of Princess Street Church events of 1937; the Women's Guild trip to Inveraray, a Sunday School picnic to Blairmore, and the office bearers' outing to Girvan.

1801	PRINCESS STREET CHURCH SNAPSHOTS OF 1935				
1935					
9.5mm	b/w	silent	350ft		REF

[filmed by Revd. George Allan]

Record of events relating to Princess Street Church, Port Glasgow, including an outing on the "Waverley" paddle steamer, a Sunday School picnic to Kirn, and a Boy Scouts' camp at Kilchattan Bay.

1802	PRINCESS STREET CHURCH SNAPSHOTS OF 1939				
1939					
9.5mm	b/w	silent	300ft		REF

[filmed by Revd. George Allan]

Snapshots of Princess Street Church events including a Sunday School picnic to Kilmun, a sports day, a cricket match and a wedding.

1803	HONEYMOON TOUR				
1932					
9.5mm	b/w	silent	250ft		REF

[filmed by Revd. George Allan]

A tour round the Highlands by steam train taking in Loch Fyne, Ballachulish, Loch Ness, Killin and Callander.

148

1804	IN THE LAND OF LORNE				
1936					
9.5mm	b/w	silent	250ft		REF

[filmed by Revd. George Allan]

A family holiday in Argyll, and a boat trip to Staffa and Iona.

1805	FENWICK EVENTS OF 1933				
1933					
9.5mm	b/w	silent	350ft		REF

[filmed by Revd. George Allan]

Compilation of Fenwick events of 1933 including the Film Society at work, a choir trip to Kilmarnock, a Sunday School trip and Boy Scouts at camp.

1806	FENWICK EVENTS OF 1932				
1932					
9.5mm	b/w	silent	300ft		REF

[filmed by Revd. George Allan]

Various events associated with the local church in Fenwick including a school trip to Girvan, and a Boy Scouts' visit to Glenapp Castle.

1807	FENWICK EVENTS OF 1934				
1934					
9.5mm	b/w	silent	350ft		REF

[filmed by Revd. George Allan]

Fenwick events associated with the local church including a Bible Class excursion, a Sunday School picnic at Bruntland Bridge and Boy Scouts on holiday in West Kilbride.

1808	(ALLAN FAMILY HOLIDAYS)				
1933-'37					
9.5mm	b/w	silent	1000ft		REF

[filmed by Revd. George Allan]

A camping holiday at West Kilbride, family outings to Strathlachlan and Inveraray.

1809	ART AND MOVEMENT				
1965					
16mm	col	sep opt	288ft		REF

sp. Educational Films of Scotland
p.c. Campbell Harper Films Ltd.

A film tracing the introduction of movement as a factor in 20th century art. It records various ways in which artists have tackled this development such as Gabo, Calder and Soto.

1810	CENTRAL SCOTLAND				
1962					
16mm	col	sep opt	684ft		REF

sp. Educational Films of Scotland
p.c. Park Film Studios

One of a series of regional geography films, looking at farming and industries including engineering, shipbuilding, textiles and coal mining in the areas from Stonehaven to Helensburgh and Girvan to Dunbar.

1811	CLIMBERS, THE				
1971					
16mm	col	mute	c432ft		REF

sp. Educational Films of Scotland

An educational film for young people, explaining the skills necessary to gain experience in hill climbing.

1812	CREEL FISHING IN SCOTLAND				
1960					
16mm	col	comopt	720ft		REF

sp. Educational Films of Scotland
p.c. Park Film Studios

A description of various methods of fishing for lobsters and crabs around the coast of Scotland. Includes footage of a lobster "moulting" or casting its shell.

1813 CLYDE VALLEY

1972

16mm	col	comopt	c500ft		REF

sp. Educational Films of Scotland
p.c. Lanarkshire Production Group

The first part of a short series on the River Clyde, studying the geography, social distribution and industry from the source of the river to the outskirts of Glasgow.

1814 DISCOVERING THE SEASHORE

1966

16mm	col	sep opt	540ft		REF

sp. Educational Films of Scotland
p.c. Park Film Studios

An introduction to seashore collecting showing children how to explore the flora and fauna at the seaside.

1815 DUNBAR - THE A1 RESORT

1970c

16mm	col	comopt	720ft		VIEW

sp. Dunbar Joint Publicity Committee
p.c. Campbell Harper Films Ltd.
d. James Hickie

A promotional film for the holiday resort of Dunbar showing holiday-makers arriving by train, visitors exploring the harbour and castle, amusements and sports available and shots of nearby Tantallon Castle.

1816 ORIGINAL ELECTROVALENCY

1965

16mm	col	comopt	720ft		REF

sp. Educational Films of Scotland
p.c. Campbell Harper Films Ltd.

A guide to new teaching techniques, particularly in the Sciences.

1817 LAUNCH OF MR. WILKIE'S GOOD SHIP "DORRIMEE"

1933

35mm	b/w	silent	100ft		REF

filmed by Zest Film Company

The launch of a family yacht the "Dorrimee".

1818 FIFTEEN TO SIXTEEN

1972

16mm	col	sep opt	720ft		REF

sp. Educational Films of Scotland
p.c. Campbell Harper Films Ltd.

A look at the work both practical and recreational, undertaken during the extra year at school to hold the interest of pupils, with the emphasis on individual pursuits.

1819 FLUORINE

1968

16mm	col	sep opt	288ft		REF

sp. Educational Films of Scotland
p.c. Campbell Harper Films Ltd.

A scientific definition of fluorine. Melting and boiling points are analysed and types of protective clothing described.

1820 FORTH - POWERHOUSE FOR INDUSTRY

1968

16mm	col	comopt	756ft		REF

sp. Educational Films of Scotland
p.c. Campbell Harper Films Ltd.

A look at the development of sources of power, industries, and new towns along the borders of the River Forth.

1821 GEOGRAPHER AT WORK

1975c

16mm	col	sep opt	c400ft		REF

sp. Educational Films of Scotland

A look at the work of a geographer towards the improvement of the urban environment and the location and use of natural resources for industry and tourism.

1822 INTRODUCING MAMMALS

1964

16mm	col	comopt	396ft		REF

sp. Educational Films of Scotland
p.c. Park Film Studios

An introduction to four of the smaller mammals of Britain, the field vole and bank vole, the shrew and woodmouse.

1823 MACDIARMID

1969

16mm	col	sep opt	600ft		REF

sp. Educational Films of Scotland
p.c. Park Film Studios

Hugh Macdiarmid talks about his life and work to fellow Scottish poet, George Bruce.

1824 TOWARDS NEW HORIZONS

1960

16mm	col	sep opt	900ft		REF

sp. Educational Films of Scotland
p.c. Park Film Studios

A demonstration of the importance of outdoor activities as an aid to lessons and the well-being of the pupil.

150

1825	**NEW SCOTLAND**				
1964					
16mm	col	sep opt	864ft		REF

sp. Educational Films of Scotland
p.c. Thames and Clyde

The demolition of old property and the construction of new towns and new industries following the 1964 economic survey of Scotland.

1826	**NEW TOWNS**				
1969					
16mm	col	comopt	864ft		REF

sp. Educational Films of Scotland
p.c. Park Film Studios

A study of Scotland's four new towns. The film considers how each new town has developed and grown in its own way.

1827	**RED DEER**				
1971					
16mm	col	sep opt	c600ft		REF

sp. Educational Films of Scotland
p.c. Park Film Studios

A study of the red deer in its natural habitat. The control and preservation of the species are also looked at.

1828	**SCIENCE FOR THE SEVENTIES**				
1966					
16mm	col	comopt	648ft		REF

sp. Educational Films of Scotland
p.c. Campbell Harper Films Ltd.

A look at the techniques being developed in courses in physics, chemistry and biology for non-certificate pupils.

1829	**[OPENING OF GLASGOW EMPIRE EXHIBITION 1938]**				
1938					
16mm	b/w	silent	100ft		REF

[filmed by John A. Wilkie]

Footage of the opening of the Glasgow Empire Exhibition at Bellahouston Park with shots of the royal procession, the royal party meeting guests, visitors inside a refreshment tent and horse riding.

1830	**SEABIRDS IN SCOTLAND**				
1974					
16mm	col	comopt	720ft		REF

sp. Educational Films of Scotland
filmed by C.E. Palmar

A look at nine different species of cliff-breeding seabirds.

1831	**SHORENESTING BIRDS OF SCOTLAND**				
1975					
16mm	col	comopt	650ft		REF

sp. Educational Films of Scotland
p.c. Park Film Studios

A look at the life-style of birds whose natural habitat is found at the edge of the sea.

1832	**SIR WILLIAM BRUCE**				
1971					
16mm	col	comopt	c600ft		REF

The life of Sir William Bruce as seen through his buildings and his career as a diplomat.

1833	**(WILKIE FAMILY COLLECTION)**				
1930-'33					
16mm	b/w&col	silent	3900ft		REF

[filmed by John A. Wilkie]

A compilation of family holidays on board the family yacht, at the Cowal Highland Games and on a Mediterranean cruise.

1834	**[BARNARDO'S CHILDREN'S PARTY]**				
1933/'46*					
16mm	b/w&col	silent	100ft		REF

[filmed by John A. Wilkie]

Barnardo's children playing and eating ice-cream at a party.

1835	**2ND BATTALION BLACK WATCH SAYS FAREWELL TO PAKISTAN**				
1948					
16mm	b/w&col	silent	180ft		REF

The 2nd Battalion Black Watch march through Karachi to Government House where they give the royal salute to Mohammed Ali Jinnah, the Governor General. The Colours are taken on board the SS "Empire Holladale".

1836	**KING IN SCOTLAND**				
1935					
35mm	b/w	comopt	90ft		VIEW

p.c. Pathe Gazette

King George V arrives at Ballater station and inspects the guard of honour of the Black Watch.

1837	**(TAKING CHARGE OF THE KEYS. MAY 1936)**				
1936					
35mm	b/w	comopt	45ft		VIEW

Shots of the 2nd Battalion Black Watch as they escort the "Keys" of Edinburgh Castle through the streets of the city [incomplete.]

1838   EMPIRE EXHIBITION, GLASGOW 1938
1938

9.5mm	b/w&col	silent	360ft		REF

filmed by Revd. George Allan

The amusements and exhibits including the Scenic Railway and the Stratosphere at the Empire Exhibition.

1839   ROYAL VISIT [TO RAF LEUCHARS]
1957

16mm	col	comopt	450ft		REF

p.c. PRB Film Unit, Air Ministry, London

A visit by Queen Elizabeth and Prince Philip to Royal Air Force Leuchars. It includes a display of air aerobatics and an address by the Queen.

1840   LOOK AROUND NORTH LANARK. SEVENTH DISTRICT
n.d.

16mm	col	sep opt	700ft		REF

ph. James Marzella

A look at North Lanark and its industry, land, history and people.

1841   GUIDE THEM ON THEIR WAY
1960s

16mm	col	comopt	500ft		REF

sp. Lanarkshire Spastics Association
filmed by Scottish Educational Film Association

An appeal film for the Alexander Anderson Home for Spastics in Wishaw. Fund raising events, including shots of a miner at Kingshill Colliery diving into a twenty foot deep shaft known as the "Wishing Well" to retrieve coins thrown in by miners on pay day. The open day is attended by local MPs and Max Bygraves.

1843   REFORM AND REACTION
n.d.

16mm	b/w&col	sep opt	c1000ft		REF

p.c. Dundee College of Education

A discussion of the trial of Thomas Muir and the writings of Paine and Burke and their influence on reform societies.

1844   [HAMILTON MAUSOLEUM]
1985c

16mm	col	silent	20ft		REF

Aerial shots of Hamilton mausoleum under scaffolding and of the glass dome being lowered into position by helicopter.

1845   POLECATS, WEASELS AND STOATS
1965

16mm	col	comopt	396ft		REF

sp. Educational Films of Scotland
p.c. Park Film Studios

The weasel, stoat and domesticated rat are the subjects of this educational film.

1846   WORLD OUTSIDE, THE
1968

16mm	col	comopt	684ft		REF

sp. Educational Films of Scotland
p.c. Park Film Studios

A training film for teachers showing how biology and geography lessons were integrated into two Scottish schools, one primary and one secondary.

1847   WATER SHREW, RATS AND VOLES
1966

16mm	col	comopt	426ft		REF

sp. Educational Films of Scotland
p.c. Park Film Studios

A study of the water shrew, rat and water vole in their natural habitat.

1848   RED SQUIRREL
1965

16mm	col	sep opt	c300ft		REF

sp. Educational Films of Scotland

A study through the different seasons, of the red squirrel in its natural habitat.

1849   LOCH LOMOND NATURE RESERVE
1970

16mm	col	comopt	690ft		VIEW

sp. Educational Films of Scotland
p.c. Park Film Studios

A study of the Loch Lomond Nature Reserve, set up in 1962.

1850   HIGHLAND BUZZARD
1968

16mm	col	sep opt	c700ft		REF

sp. Educational Films of Scotland
p.c. Park Film Studios

A study of the highland buzzard, one of Scotland's larger birds of prey.

1851   FISHING FOR FUN
1964

16mm	col	comopt	c360ft		REF

[amateur film]

An amateur film of the joys of the sport of angling.

151

1852   FOXES, THE
1967

16mm	col	sep opt	c800ft		REF

sp. Educational Films of Scotland
p.c. Park Film Studios

A study of the fox, showing the adult animals and the development of cubs from four weeks to the break-up of the family unit.

1853   DIXINE NEWS
1931

16mm	b/w	silent	380ft		REF

A compilation of amateur footage of news items under the name 'Dixine news', including the launch of the "George and Mary Strachan" lifeboat in Dunbar, a Punch and Judy show and a sports day at Dollar Academy.

1854   (PROVOST FLETT COLLECTION)
1943-'56*

16mm	b/w&col silent	2160ft		REF

[filmed by Provost James Flett]

Various events in Kirkwall in the Orkney Islands including an Agricultural Show, the unveiling ceremony of the war memorial, Kirkwall, the Queen Mother's visit to the islands in 1956, the Orkney Festival of Britain, 1951 and the opening of the power station.

1855   REVIEW OF THE YEAR 1950
1950

16mm	b/w	comopt	360ft		VIEW

p.c. Pathe News

A compilation of news events including the election of the Labour government, the wedding of Moira Shearer, the Knockshinnoch mine disaster, riots in Belgium and footage of the Korean war.

1856   (DIXINE MISCELLANY)
1934-'36*

16mm	b/w	silent	500ft		REF

Amateur footage of a compilation of news events and family occasions including shots of Culross in Fife, Scouts and Brownies on parade in Glasgow, the building of a bonfire, a display by the Japanese amateur judo team in Glasgow and a firework display.

1857   DIXINE PICTORIAL
1933

16mm	b/w	silent	410ft		REF

Amateur footage of miscellaneous events; Dalbeth swimming club, 1933 Boys' Brigade Jubilee Review at Queens Park, Glasgow and the 1933 annual golf outing of the Scottish Iron and Steel Scrap Merchants.

1858   HOSPITALS FOR ALL
1948c

16mm	b/w	comopt	780ft		VIEW

sp. Department of Heath for Scotland
d. Hamilton Tait

Made to promote the new nationalised health services, the film looks at a number of hospitals throughout central Scotland including the Edinburgh Royal Infirmary, Ballochmyle, Strathcathro and Killearn Hospitals; their medical staff at work and the services the hospitals provide.

1859   RING, THE
1930s

16mm	b/w	silent	540ft		REF

filmed by Dumfries and Galloway Amateur Film Assoc.

A story about a young graduate who leaves Glasgow to work in Dumfries.

1860   PROGRESS OF A DUNDEE JUTE MILL
1950

16mm	b/w	silent	400ft		REF

filmed by J.R.L. Halley, Director, Wm. Halley & Sons

An illustration of the historical development of William Halley & Sons Limited, jute manufacturers.

1861   SHOTTS FARMERS' ANNUAL BALL 1951
1951

35mm	b/w	silent	270ft		VIEW

p.c. Thames and Clyde Production

Dancing at the Shotts Farmers' Annual Ball, 2nd February 1951.

1862   HERIOT WATT COLLEGE, EDINBURGH
1938

16mm	b/w	silent	400ft		REF

p.c. Campbell Harper Films Ltd.
d. Alan Harper

A look at the facilities and courses at Heriot Watt College, Edinburgh.

1863   SCHOOL WITHOUT WALLS
1970c

16mm	col	comopt	420ft		VIEW

p.c. Universities of Glasgow and Strathclyde
d. Peter Coltman

Shots of the interior and exteriors of classrooms, shops, factories, playgrounds, houses and hospitals during the "School Without Walls" experiment, where 15 year olds worked in a variety of jobs for a few days at a time.

1864 SPRINGHILL PRIMARY SCHOOL
1969

| 16mm | col | comopt | 650ft | REF |

filmed by Falconer Houston

Filmed during a working day at Springhill primary school, Barrhead, Renfrewshire, showing the children taking part in various activities and lessons.

1865 THIS HEARING WORLD
1970-'73

| 16mm | col | comopt | 810ft | REF |

filmed by Paisley Round Table

Children in the classroom and at play at Gateside School for the Deaf, Renrewshire.

1866 RENFREWSHIRE SCHOOL CRUISE 1971
1971

| 16mm | col | comopt | 800ft | REF |

Footage of a school trip on board the SS "Uganda" to Oslo and Helsinki.

1867 NURSERY TEACHING AT TODHOLM
1971

| 16mm | b/w | comopt | 865ft | REF |

p.c. Jordanhill College TV Outside Broadcast Unit

Shots of a teacher at Todholm nursery school teaching crafts to a class of infants.

1868 BANK FOR SCOTLAND
1974c

| 16mm | col | comopt | 780ft | VIEW |

sp. Bank of Scotland
d. Ian Brock

Made to promote the Bank of Scotland, the film uses Scotland's history and its industries as a backdrop to the Bank's role within the country.

1869 BUSINESSWISE
1976c

| 16mm | col | comopt | 648ft | VIEW |

sp. Bank of Scotland
p.c. Grange Film Production
d. Ian Brock

Made to promote the importance of the Bank of Scotland to the business community.

1870 MONEYWISE
1973c

| 16mm | col | comopt | 460ft | VIEW |

sp. Bank of Scotland
d. Ian Brock

An illustration of the various Bank of Scotland customer services.

1871 DUMBARTON 1944-1946
1944-'46

| 16mm | col | silent | 445ft | REF |

[attributed to Ben H. Humble]

Events in Dumbarton including the "Norwegian Week" festival and VE Day celebrations.

1872 RURAL ROUND ABOUT
1950

| 16mm | b/w | silent | 260ft | REF |

filmed by W.E. Richardson

The Dalry annual Grand Collie Dog Trials, a bowling match and the Galloway Gala.

1873 THORNHILL SHOW
1950

| 16mm | b/w | silent | 400ft | REF |

filmed by W.E. Richardson

The Thornhill agricultural show and Thornhill Gala Day in the Borders.

1874 [FILM OF MONIAIVE 1950-1955]
1950

| 16mm | b/w | silent | 350ft | REF |

[filmed by W.E. Richardson]

A children's parade, sheep dog trials, a local football match and a dinner dance in Moniaive, Dumfriesshire.

1875 CHILDREN'S EXCURSION 1952
1952

| 16mm | col | silent | 260ft | REF |

[filmed by W.E. Richardson]

A children's excursion from the Borders to Edinburgh, visiting the Castle, the Zoo and the Forth Rail Bridge.

1876 NEW GALLOWAY GALA WEEK
1951

| 16mm | b/w | silent | 260ft | REF |

[filmed by W.E. Richardson]

Amateur footage of the Borders celebrations surrounding the New Galloway Gala Week, including a handicraft exhibition, a children's fancy dress parade, carnival floats and a Highland dancing display.

1878 (TABLEAUX PARADE/HORSE RIDING)
1950*

| 16mm | col | silent | 90ft | REF |

[filmed by W.E. Richardson]

Shots of the Moniaive tableaux parade illustrating "Songs of the Golden West" with floats and spectators.

153

1879   VILLAGE VARIETIES
1949-'53

| 16mm | b/w&col | silent | 1300ft | REF |

filmed by W.E. Richardson

A compilation of local events in the Borders town of Moniaive including school sports, Remembrance day, a Sunday school outing, sheep dog trials, a bowling competition and the show day parade.

1880   UPPER DEESIDE
1949*

| 16mm | col | silent | 360ft | VIEW |

sp. Scottish Youth Hostel Association
filmed by Harry C. Hampton

The youth hostels and surrounding walking country of Upper Deeside taking in Lochanagar, Lairig Ghru, Braeriach and Aviemore.

1881   RATAGAN/TORRIDON
1955*

| 16mm | col | silent | 400ft | VIEW |

sp. Scottish Youth Hostel Association
filmed by Harry C. Hampton

Youth hostellers are seen enjoying their accommodation at Ratagan Hostel and Inveralligin Hostel in the Highlands; they climb the Saddle, visit Dunvegan Castle on Skye and watch a game of Highland shinty.

1882   WESTERN PERTHSHIRE
1955c

| 16mm | col | silent | 350ft | REF |

filmed by SEFA, a Glasgow Group Production

Various shots of hostellers and hillwalkers in the countryside by Killin.

154

Elder Dalrymple Productions on location in Africa, 1937.

1883	[ROAD TO CARBISDALE, THE]			
1946*				
16mm	col	silent	360ft	REF

Highland landscape views including the Cuillins on Skye, Gruinard Bay, Ullapool, and the youth hostels at Achininver and Carbisdale.

1884	BORDER RAID			
1957*				
16mm	col	silent	300ft	VIEW

sp. Scottish Youth Hostels Association
[filmed by A.C. Cromer, Edinburgh]

A group of hostellers enjoying a tour of the Borders, visiting Melrose, Selkirk, Cauldshiels Loch, Mungo Park's birthplace, Newark Castle, and Broadmeadow and Snoot youth hostels.

1885	[YOUTH GOES HOSTELLING]			
1953*				
16mm	b/w	silent	300ft	REF

Two men on a youth hostelling holiday; they visit Monachyle and Killin hostels where they are seen preparing their meals, and taking part in various hostel duties.

1886	SCHOOLBOY HOSTELLERS			
1951				
16mm	b/w	silent	360ft	VIEW

filmed by Charles McKenzie

A group of young people on a cycling holiday in Scotland, staying in various youth hostels. They visit Dunblane, Doune and Callander, climb Ben A'an, walk in Glen Finglas and cycle across the Duke's Pass.

1887	[GLENCOE AND NEVIS]			
1949*				
16mm	col	silent	400ft	REF

Groups of climbers are seen hillwalking and rock-climbing in the Highlands in the Glencoe and Ben Nevis areas.

1888	TOURING THE TROSSACHS			
1959				
16mm	col	silent	450ft	REF

[p.c. Corporation of Glasgow]

An educational journey through the Trossachs by schoolchildren from the Sacred Heart Secondary School, Glasgow. The children are seen preparing for their trip, hostelling and hiking, taking the steamer on Loch Katrine and visiting Inchmahome priory on Lake of Menteith.

1889	LOCH LOMOND AND THE TROSSACHS			
1949*				
16mm	col	silent	400ft	REF

filmed by SEFA, a Glasgow Group Production

Youth hostels at Loch Ard, Inverbeg and Rowardennan, with footage of hostellers climbing Ben Lomond and the Cobbler, canoeing on Loch Lomond and enjoying a dance.

1890	(LOCH LOMOND. QUEEN OF SCOTTISH LOCHS)			
1950c				
16mm	col	silent	250ft	REF

Scenic views of Loch Lomond and surrounding countryside, the National Forest Park and youth hostels at Inverbeg, Ardgartan and Lochgoilhead.

1891	(HOSTEL SKI TRIP)			
1949				
16mm	col	silent	380ft	REF

A group of hostellers on a ski-ing trip to Glenmore where they are seen skiing and sledging.

1892	[PONY TREKKING]			
1950c				
16mm	b/w	silent	400ft	REF

Ponies being groomed and riders being given handling instructions before setting out on a hillside trek.

1893	PICK-A-BACK DEMONSTRATION FLIGHT			
1937				
9.5mm	b/w	silent	30ft	REF

p.c. Pathe Gazette

Footage of a demonstration of the Mercury/Maia aircraft in flight over the Firth of Tay. [The Mercury aircraft flew nonstop from Dundee to Cape Town in 1937.]

1894	CRUISE TO SCOTTISH GARDENS, A			
1953				
16mm	col	silent	1821ft	REF

[filmed by R. Endall]

Footage of the first gardens cruise organised by the National Trust for Scotland, visiting Iona, Colonsay and Inverewe.

1895	EXOTIC FRINGE, THE			
1953c				
16mm	col	comopt	450ft	REF

sp. National Trust for Scotland
filmed by Tom Steel

The gardens and flora of the island of Colonsay and at Inverewe and Crarae Gardens.

155

1896   ST. KILDA
1957

16mm	col	mute	815ft		REF

sp. National Trust for Scotland
p.c. Film Unit, Edinburgh University

A depiction of St. Kilda after it's evacuation, showing the remains of the village buildings, the naval encampment and the animal and bird life on the island.

1897   "DANDIE DINMONT" TRACTION ENGINE
1963

std.8mm col		silent	25ft		REF

[filmed by James Houston]

Test run of the newly restored Burrill traction engine, the "Dandie Dinmont", prior to exhibiting at the 1963 Royal Highland Show.

1900   (GREEN'S NEWSREEL)
1920c

35mm	b/w	silent	106ft		VIEW

p.c. Greens Film Service

A compilation reel including footage of the fairground ride "The Whip", at Green's Amusements during the Carnival in the Gallowgate, Glasgow. The film also shows the marriage of Edward MacMahon to Mary Frances Green, daughter of George Green.

1901   WEE DRAM, A
1959c

16mm	col	comopt	900ft		REF

sp. Scotch Whisky Association
p.c. Chetwynd Films Limited

The distillation process of Scotch Whisky (Vat 69).

1902   TIME WAS THE BEGINNING
1959c

16mm	col	comopt	650ft		REF

sp. Scotch Whisky Association
p.c. Ace Film Production
d. John Green

An explanation of whisky distillation.

1903   ACCIDENTALLY YOURS
1959*

16mm	col	comopt	650ft		REF

sp. Distillers Company Limited
p.c. Elder Film Productions Ltd
d. John C. Elder

A training film made for the Distillers Company on safety procedures.

1904   JOB TO BANK ON, A
1974

16mm	col	comopt	612ft		VIEW

sp. Bank of Scotland
p.c. Grange Film Prods.

A recruitment film for the Bank of Scotland.

1905   PORTRAIT OF THE ROYAL BANK
1979

16mm	col	comopt	765ft		REF

sp. Royal Bank of Scotland
p.c. Cinecosse
d. Don Walker

The various services offered by the Royal Bank of Scotland including the mobile bank in Skye, and its international division in Glasgow.

1906   ALL TO YOUR CREDIT
1978

16mm	col	comopt	648ft		REF

sp. Access
p.c. Wadlow Grosvenor Productions
d. Anthony Squire

An illustration of the various uses of credit cards, particularly when abroad.

1907   FARMS AND BANKS
1966c

16mm	col	comopt	100ft		REF

sp. Barclays Film
p.c. Worldwide Picture in assoc. with Charles Barker & Sons

A detailed look at the banking needs of farmers in England and Scotland, and how Barclays Bank attempts to help them.

1908   WELCOME TO SCOTLAND
1978

16mm	col	comopt	906ft		REF

p.c. Viz Limited
d. Andrew Homes

The attractions of Scotland as a holiday destination.

1909   FROM THE PROJECTION BOX
1938-'39*

35mm	b/w	silent	130ft		VIEW

Advertising film made for Cadburys confectionery - as sold in cinemas.

1910   (EDINBURGH'S HOUSING CONDITIONS)
1969c

16mm	b/w	sep mag	340ft		REF

p.c. Dolphin Films Production

A documentary on the poor housing conditions in the tenements and flats in Leith.

156

1911 FLOODTIDE

1949

| 16mm | b/w | comopt | 3200ft | VIEW |

d. Frederick Wilson p. Donald B. Wilson

Featuring Gordon Jackson, Rona Anderson, John Laurie and Jimmy Logan. Set in Clydeside, the film tells the story of a farmer's son who comes to the Clyde, works his way up in the shipyard from apprentice to naval architect and falls in love with the boss's daughter.

1912 (WILLIE GALLACHER. FUNERAL PROCESSION)

1965

| std.8mm | col | silent | 20ft | REF |

[filmed by Harry Scott]

Shots of funeral procession for Willie Gallacher, former leader of the Scottish Communist Party. [See also ref. 2508.]

1913 WINTER ON THE FARM

1934*

| 16mm | b/w | silent | 100ft | VIEW |

sp. Glasgow Education Authority
p.c. Elder Dalrymple Productions Ltd.

An educational film showing the variety of jobs done on a mixed farm throughout the seasons.

1914 [ERSKINE BRIDGE]

1970

| std.8mm | col | silent | 400ft | REF |

[filmed by R.B. Macluskie]

Various stages of the construction of the Erskine Bridge in Renfrewshire, using a combination of live action and still photography.

1915 HAYMAKING

1934c

| 16mm | b/w | silent | 155ft | VIEW |

sp. Glasgow Education Authorities
p.c. Elder Dalrymple Productions Ltd.

Horse-drawn mowing and raking machines at work in a field.

1916 VILLAGE BLACKSMITH

1935*

| 16mm | b/w | silent | 100ft | REF |

sp. Glasgow Education Authority
p.c. Elder-Dalrymple Productions Limited

One of a series of educational films produced for the Glasgow Education Authority, showing a blacksmith working at his anvil and fitting a new shoe to a horse.

1917 MODERN BAKERY

1934*

| 16mm | b/w | silent | 155ft | REF |

sp. Glasgow Education Authority
p.c. Elder-Dalrymple Productions Limited

Shot inside a bakery showing the ingredients and processes used in the baking of loaves of bread.

1918 MODERN BAKERY

1946*

| 16mm | b/w | silent | 210ft | VIEW |

sp. British Instructional Films
p.c. Pathe Production

Shots of the harvesting of wheat, the baking of bread in a bakery and the selling of the final product in a baker's shop.

1919 QUEEN OPENS THE FORTH ROAD BRIDGE, THE

1964

| 35mm | col | comopt | 610ft | REF |

p.c. Pathe News

Coverage of the opening ceremony of the Forth Road Bridge. The Royal Company of Archers and the 1st Battn. Cameronians form the guard of honour. The royal party includes Willie Ross MP.

157

1920 CHILDREN'S DAY 1951

1951

| 16mm | b/w | silent | 230ft | REF |

filmed by Lionel Butler, John Boyle and Adam Malcolm

Amateur film of the Children's Day festival in Pilton, Edinburgh.

1921 WEST PILTON GALA DAY 1952

1952

| 16mm | b/w | silent | 370ft | REF |

An amateur film of the West Pilton Gala Day, Edinburgh, including the gala procession, a display of Scottish country dancing, a football match, and people taking refreshment in the tea tent.

1922 CHILDREN'S GALA DAY 1953

1953

| 16mm | b/w | silent | 325ft | REF |

filmed by West Pilton Community Association

Amateur footage of West Pilton's Children's Gala Day, Edinburgh, including the procession of children through the streets of Pilton, the crowning of the Gala Queen and races.

1923	CHILDREN'S GALA DAY 6TH JUNE 1954				
1954					
16mm	b/w	silent	360ft		REF

filmed by West Pilton Community Association

The selection of the Gala Queen, the crowning ceremony and races in the park at the West Pilton Children's Gala Day.

1924	CHILDREN'S ANNUAL GALA				
1955					
16mm	b/w	silent	330ft		REF

The gala procession into Recreation Park, West Pilton, Edinburgh, dancing and boxing displays, races and spectators at the Children's Gala Day.

1925	GALA WEEK AND CROWNING CEREMONY				
1956					
16mm	b/w	silent	300ft		REF

filmed by West Pilton Community Association

Amateur footage of West Pilton's Gala week including the church parade, a bowling competition, a football match and the Gala Queen crowning ceremony.

1926	LOCAL COLOUR				
1939/'40					
9.5mm	b/w	silent	720ft		REF

filmed by Henry Cocozza

An amateur film of a garden fete, a family wedding, and scenes at a zoo.

1927	GEORGE THE BLOOD DONOR				
1948					
16mm	b/w	silent	560ft		REF

sp. Blood Transfusion Service
filmed by George Maran

Set in Edinburgh, the film tells the story of George, giving blood for the first time.

1928	TRIP TO SKYE. ORKNEY AND SHETLAND				
1932*					
16mm	b/w	silent	420ft		REF

[filmed by the Duchess of Montrose]

Ploughing on Skye, the launching of a lifeboat on Shetland, Lerwick's fishing and wool industries, and the Pictish dwellings at Skarra Brae, Orkney.

1929	[CUMNOCK CELEBRATION. JUNE 1951]				
1951					
16mm	col	silent	940ft		REF

[filmed by John Nimmo]

Festivities at the Cumnock Celebration including a BBC variety concert, a fireworks display, an angling competition, and a carnival.

1930	MIGHTY CUNARDER LAUNCHED, THE				
1934					
16mm	b/w	silent	100ft		REF

p.c. Fox Photos

The launch of the "Queen Mary" from John Brown's Shipyard at Clydebank.

1931	FARMER IN THE FIELDS, A				
1936c					
16mm	b/w	silent	111ft		VIEW

[p.c. Elder-Dalrymple Productions]

The ploughing, sowing, harrowing and rolling of fields using horse-drawn ploughs and hand sowing methods. [See also ref. 2161.]

1932	SOVEREIGN "SCOTCH", THE				
1928*					
35mm	b/w	silent	390ft		VIEW

p.c. Morgan Film Services Limited

An advertising film for King George IV whisky, shot in the company's Edinburgh bottling stores.

1933	DUNDEE POLICE SPORTS				
1921					
35mm	b/w	silent	363ft		VIEW

sp. Dundee City Police Sports
filmed by C.F. Partoon, Dundee

Coverage of Police Sports day at Dens Park Stadium in Dundee. Includes shots of a women's football team, a pillow fight, gymnastic display, hammer throwing and a display of Highland dancing.

1934	DUMBARTON CASTLE				
1966					
16mm	b/w	commag	750ft		REF

filmed by David Iain Harvie

A historical survey of Dumbarton Castle and its environs with commentary and on-the-spot narrative by local historian Dr. I. M. Macphail. [Made as a student film for Central London Polytechnic.]

1935	FORGE, THE

1962c

16mm	b/w	silent	175ft		REF

sp. British Instructional Films
p.c. Pathe BIF

A blacksmith is seen shaping hot metal to form a hook, using his hammer and anvil.

1936	FILM-MAKING IN THE SCHOOL

1965

16mm	b/w	silent	138ft		REF

Introduction to film-making in school; scripting, exterior shooting, interior shooting, and editing. [Compiled from material shot at Cornwell Secondary Modern School.]

1937	BRIDE AND GROOM

1956

16mm	col	comopt	282ft		REF

filmed by the Grasshopper Group

Surrealistic view of the "Honeymoon couple", interrupted by salesmen, consumer goods, jealousy, anger and infidelity. [Award winner in the 1957 Scottish Amateur Film Festival.]

1939	LOWLANDS OF SCOTLAND

1946

16mm	b/w	comopt	555ft		REF

sp. Travel Assoc. of GB, NI, and Scottish Tourist Board
p.c. Paul Barralet Productions Ltd

A travelogue on the lowlands of Scotland, including footage of Burns' country, the Trossachs, and the towns of Stirling, Linlithgow, Edinburgh, and Glasgow.

1940	FLYWEIGHT CHAMPIONSHIP OF THE WORLD, LYNCH V MONTANA

1937

35mm	b/w	comopt	1434ft		REF

p.c. Featurettes Ltd., London

Exclusive pictures of the contest for the flyweight championship of the world between Benny Lynch and Small Montana of the USA at the Empire Arena, Wembley 19 Sept 1937.

1942	FACES

1957

35mm	b/w	comopt	1325ft		REF

p.c. Templar Film Studios
d. Edward McConnell

An abstract film, set in and around Glasgow's Botanic Gardens. [Shown at London Film Festival and Brussels Experimental Film Festival.]

1943	ENCHANTED ISLES

1957

35mm	col	comopt	1513ft		VIEW

sp. Films of Scotland Committee
p.c. Anglo-Scottish Pictures Ltd.

The route to the Hebrides taken by Bonnie Prince Charlie with footage of Iona, Staffa, the Outer Hebrides and Skye.

1947	GRANTON TRAWLER

1934

35mm	b/w	comopt	969ft		REF

p.c. GPO Film Unit
ph. John Grierson

The working conditions on board the trawler "Isabella Greig" as the men fish, haul, gut and sort the catch.

1948	JOHN NEWLAND'S DAY, BATHGATE

1953

35mm	b/w	silent	1310ft		REF

p.c. Elder Film Productions Limited, Glasgow

Footage of John Newlands' Day, Bathgate with the crowning of the Gala Queen, racing and sporting events, and the laying of a wreath on John Newlands' plaque.

1949	FOURTH IN HAND

1935

16mm	b/w	silent	500ft		VIEW

filmed by Meteor Film Producing Society

A drama telling the story of a young man, late for a bridge game, who is replaced by a stranger who then disappears, leaving only a joker card on his chair. [Exhibited at the International Amateur Movie Show.]

1950	QUEEN ELIZABETH'S VISIT TO POSB

1942

35mm	b/w	mute	166ft		VIEW

[p.c. British Pictorial Productions Limited. Universal News.]

Queen Elizabeth visits the Post Office Savings Bank in Blythe Road, Kensington, London.

1951	OPENING OF BALMUIDY PRIMARY SCHOOL

1962

16mm	col	silent	160ft		REF

Shots of various events on the opening day of Balmuidy Primary School.

159

1952	BATHGATE FESTIVAL WEEK 1951

1951

35mm	b/w	silent	900ft		REF

p.c. Thames and Clyde Limited

Footage of Bathgate Festival Week, June 1951, including the coronation of the festival queen, the floats procession, and various sports.

1953	SERVICE COMMEMORATING 750TH ANNIVERSARY/ OPENING OF QUEEN'S BRIDGE PERTH

1960

16mm	b/w	silent	425ft		REF

The commemoration ceremony of the 750th Anniversary of the granting of the charter to Perth and the opening of the Queen's Bridge, Perth, by HM Queen Elizabeth.

1954	KING GEORGE V1

1953c

35mm	b/w	comopt	360ft		VIEW

A cinema trailer advertising King George VI National Memorial Week with an appeal for donations.

1956	INDUSTRIAL STIRLINGSHIRE

1950*

16mm	b/w	silent	1025ft		REF

[filmed by SEFA, Stirlingshire Branch]

A study of the principal industries of Stirlingshire including coal mining, brick making, soap making and oil refining.

1957	LANARK

1956

std.8mm col	silent	200ft		REF

[filmed by H.J. Blackie]

A prize-winning film which records various events in the Lanark area including Lanimer Day festivities, sheepshearing, and the Lanark racecourse.

1958	IN THE FOOTSTEPS OF DAVID LIVINGSTONE

1955

std.8mm col	mute	200ft		REF

filmed by H.J. Blackie (Scotland) Bob Janson (Africa)

An account of the life of the explorer David Livingstone, the film returns to his birthplace and retraces his footsteps through Africa. [The winner of the Marshall Quaich cup at the 1956 Scottish International Amateur Film Festival.]

1959	GLASGOW IN THE SIXTIES

1960s

std.8mm col	silent	200ft		REF

filmed by W. and A. Murdoch

Compilation of scenes from Glasgow in the sixties including footage of the Gorbals, Paddy's Market, the Broomielaw, the Alhambra Theatre and Glasgow Green.

1960	GLASGOW'S INTERNATIONAL GARDENS

1983*

16mm	col	sep opt	650ft		REF

p.c. Antonine Productions
p. Paddy Higson

[Not shotlisted.]

1961	GLASGOW - CITY THAT WORKS

1981

16mm	col	sep opt	720ft		REF

p.c. QMR Productions
p. Paddy Higson

[Not shotlisted.]

1962	A9 HIGHLAND [HIGHWAY]

1982

16mm	col	comopt	1150ft		REF

sp. Films of Scotland
p.c. QMR Productions
p. Paddy Higson

A documentary on the remaking, over ten years, of the A9 between Perth and Inverness - the highest trunk road in Britain.

1963	THRU' THE KYLES

1957*

16mm	col	silent	300ft		REF

Amateur footage of a trip by the steamer "Queen of Scots" through the Kyles of Bute, stopping at Dunoon and Rothesay.

1964	LOCOMOTIVE, THE

1949c

16mm	col	comopt	1070ft		REF

sp. The Locomotive Manufacturers Assoc. of Great Britain
p.c. Furneaux-Weber Ltd
d. Cecil Musk

An historical look at the development of steam locomotion from 1800 to 1927; shots of the manufacturing processes, workers leaving a yard [possibly North British Locomotive Company in Glasgow] and a locomotive being hoisted by crane onto a cargo ship.

1965	[SCOTTISH MISSION HOSPITAL. TIBERIAS]				
1937-'39*					
16mm	b/w&col	silent	195ft		REF

[filmed by Dr. Herbert Watt Torrance]

Filmed at the Scottish Mission Hospital in Tiberias, Palestine by Dr. Herbert Torrance, the film shows various medical cases being treated at the hospital. [See also refs. 0346-0361.]

1966	HUNTLY GALA QUEEN				
1950					
35mm	b/w	silent	655ft		REF

filmed as a local topical for the Playhouse, Huntly

The exterior of the Playhouse Cinema Huntly, town streets decorated, crowds in Christie Park and the crowning of the Festival Queen.

1967	SHOTTS FESTIVAL 1951				
1951					
16mm	b/w	silent	675ft		REF

filmed by J.S. Roy

Coverage of the Shotts Festival in Lanarkshire with exhibitions, choral concerts, dramatic productions, opera and sports events.

1968	UNDERWATER STORY				
1951					
16mm	b/w	comopt	720ft		REF

sp. Scottish Office
p.c. Crown Film Unit

Made in collaboration with the Scottish Home Department's Marine Laboratory at Torry, Aberdeen, the film shows how marine scientists are attempting to overcome declining fish stock in the North Sea.

1969	CAER-PEN-TULACH				
1961-'64*					
16mm	col	silent	1800ft		REF

filmed by John and Irene Rodger

The 750th Anniversary of Kirkintilloch and the celebrations and events to mark it, including a football match, swimming competition, and a church parade.

1970	(COMING OF AGE OF EARL HAIG)				
1939					
35mm	b/w	mute	130ft		VIEW

The young earl Haig is presented with various gifts in the grounds of the family home at Bemersyde. [Unidentified newsreel footage.]

1971	(LEITH ATHLETIC FOOTBALL MATCH)				
1920s					
35mm	b/w	silent	40ft		VIEW

A football match between Leith Athletic football club and an unidentified team.

1972	SHINTY IN THE HIGHLANDS				
1934					
35mm	b/w	silent	555ft		VIEW

[filmed by James S. Nairn for the Playhouse, Inverness]

A shinty match in the Highlands between Kingussie and Newtonmore on 3rd February, 1934, abandoned due to spectators rushing onto field. Footage of the replay match on 17th February.

1974	UNVEILING OF RUTHERGLEN WAR MEMORIAL				
1924/'25					
35mm	b/w	silent	890ft		VIEW

sp. Royal Burgh of Rutherglen
p.c. Gaumont

A compilation of events including the unveiling of Rutherglen war memorial, a Boys' Brigade demonstration, sports day in Ballochmill Park, and a competition between a 'spoof' football team and the local team.

1975	SNAPPY SNAPS OF RUTHERGLEN				
1926					
35mm	b/w	silent	855ft		VIEW

sp. Exclusive Film
p.c. Topical Productions, Glasgow

Some of the events surrounding the Royal Burgh of Rutherglen Octocentenary Celebrations including the unveiling of the new Mercat Cross by Lord Fleming, the historical pageant and coronation of the pageant Queen.

1976	(ANTI-ALCHOHOL CAMPAIGN/ USSR VISIT?)				
1930s					
9.5mm	b/w	silent	720ft		REF

The Soviet Union's anti-alcohol campaign involving brigades of teetotallers organised at factories and firms to speed up the rate of recruiting. Footage of the Russian vessel "Felix Dzezhinsky" with passengers on board preparing to leave.

1977	(WILSON COLLECTION)				
1930s					
9.5mm	b/w&col	silent	c1270ft		REF

[filmed by Mr. Wilson]

Family scenes in the garden, at the seaside, the Jubilee celebrations of 1935 and the opening of the Empire Exhibition.

161

1978   (CINEMA ADVERTS)
1960-'70s

35mm	col	comopt	2000ft		REF

Beer and spirit commercials featuring actors Joanna Lumley and Anthony Andrews.

1979   VITAL STATISTICS
1940*

16mm	b/w	silent	432ft		REF

sp. Glasgow Corporation Public Health Department
p.c. Campbell Harper Films Ltd.

The work of the Public Health Department; checking imported foodstuffs, sanitary inspection of housing, hospital care and child welfare.

1980   TIME OUT OF SCOTLAND
1960c

16mm	col	comopt	356ft		REF

sp. Smiths Clock and Watch Division
p.c. Smiths Film Unit Production
d. David Everitt

Shots of Smith's Wishaw factory where clocks are seen on the production line.

1981   BROWNIAN MOVEMENT, THE
1940

16mm	b/w	silent	70ft		VIEW

filmed by Thos. Smith Wylie, Francis G. Conway

An illustration of the work of Scottish botanist Robert Brown.

1982   EFFECTS OF SURFACE TENSION
1943c

16mm	b/w	silent	120ft		REF

[filmed by Matthew Blair, T.S. Wylie, Frank Conway]

Cinematographic record illustrating the effects of surface tension.

1983   LAND-SHIP, THE
1942c

16mm	b/w	silent	100ft		VIEW

[filmed by Thomas S. Wylie]

The Land-Ship; a mock navigation bridge on the roof of the School of Navigation, Royal Technical College, Glasgow, used to teach students the points of the compass.

1984   SHARK FISHING
1940c

9.5mm	b/w	silent	c800ft		REF

[filmed by Thomas Smith Wylie]

Various scenes and events including herring boats at sea, a steamer pulling up to Carradale pier and the catching of a basking shark.

1985   LIGHT IN OUR DARKNESS
1955c

16mm	b/w	comopt	500ft		REF

p.c. Big Six Film Unit
d. John S. Abbot

Shots of Lloyd's steel foundry and the company's Medical Health Department.

1986   HIAWATHA
1933

16mm	b/w	silent	720ft		REF

filmed by Sydney W. Carr, & Andrew Simpson

Shots of a performance of "Hiawatha" on stage at the Empire Theatre, Edinburgh.

1987   (HOME GUARD, "A" COY., 1ST BATTN)
1939-'42

16mm	b/w&col	silent	700ft		REF

[filmed by Andrew Simpson]

Film record of manoeuvres, exercises and parades by the "A" Coy., 1st Battn.

1988   (EDINBURGH OPERA COMPANY)
1934*

16mm	b/w	silent	300ft		REF

[filmed by Andrew Simpson]

Shots of performance on stage, possibly either "The Tales of Hoffman" or "The Bartered Bride", by members of the Edinburgh Opera Company.

1989   (SIMPSON FAMILY FILM)
1932-'42*

16mm	b/w&col	silent	c600ft		REF

[filmed by Andrew Simpson]

A family film which includes footage of holidays in Staffa, North Berwick, Edinburgh, the Borders, Gleneagles and festivities at Christmas.

1990   [LAUNCH OF THE MTV "KINGENNIE"]
1958

16mm	b/w	silent	100ft		REF

The launch of the "Kingennie" by Mrs. J.R. Cowper at Greenock shipyard.

1991   [LAUNCH OF MV "LOCHEE"]
1937

16mm	b/w	silent	150ft		REF

Launch of the MV "Lochee" and her maiden voyage on the river Tay on the 27th August 1937.

162

1992   LAUNCH OF "LONDON"
1950

16mm	b/w	silent	150ft		REF

General views of the launch of the "London". Shots of other cargo vessels.

1993   (LAUNCH OF "BROUGHTY")
1956

16mm	b/w	silent	200ft		REF

Launch of the boat "Broughty", at J. Koster's shipyard, Dundee.

1994   [WITCH CRAFT]
1938

16mm	col	silent	125ft		REF

[filmed by Jean L. Gray, Edinburgh]

A prizewinner at the British Empire Amateur Film Festival, Glasgow, the film gives a series of effects using animated figures and reflected light.

1995   OPENING OF WELLMEADOW SUPERMARKET
1960s

super 8mm col	silent	50ft		REF

filmed by John Cowan

The official opening of the Wellmeadow Supermarket by Rikki Fulton and Jack Milroy.

1996   (QUARRIER'S HOMES)
1936-'49*

16mm	b/w&col silent	760ft		REF

An illustration of the role of Quarriers homes for orphans.

1997   FALKIRK
1938

16mm	b/w	silent	780ft		REF

filmed by J.S. Nairn and James Atterson

Made as a promotional film for screening at the 1938 Empire Exhibition in Glasgow, documenting the history and industries of the town of Falkirk.

1998   LAUNCH OF "QUEEN ELIZABETH"
1938

16mm	b/w	silent	250ft		REF

[filmed by J. McRoberts]

The launching of the "Queen Elizabeth" from John Brown's shipyard, Clydebank, by HM the Queen.

1999   (EDINBURGH)
1949/'52

16mm	b/w	silent	270ft		VIEW

Various scenes of Edinburgh including the Castle, Princes Street, the Botanic Gardens, Dean Village and "Robert the Bruce" ferry on the river Forth.

2000A   BENS, THE
1967

16mm	col	comopt	810ft		VIEW

sp. Ben Line Shipping Company
p.c. Campbell Harper Films Ltd.

The Ben Line shipping fleet at work in the Far East.

2000B   BENS, THE
1967

16mm	col	mute	342ft		REF

sp. Benline Shipping Co.

Launching ceremony of Ben Line ship "Bencruachan" at Leith.

2001   [NORTH OF SCOTLAND - WESTER ROSS]
1958c

16mm	col	mute	324ft		REF

[p.c. Campbell Harper Films Ltd.]

Landscape shots of the western Highlands including Inverewe National Trust Park.

2002   COUNTRY OF THE BLIND
1967

16mm	col	comopt	891ft		VIEW

sp. Films of Scotland
p.c. Campbell Harper Films Ltd.
d. Henry Cooper

The work of the Scottish National Institution for the War Blinded.

2003   [ST. CUTHBERT'S NINETIETH BIRTHDAY]
1949c

16mm	col	silent	519ft		REF

sp. St. Cuthbert's Co-operative Association
p.c. Campbell Harper Films Ltd.

The work of the St. Cuthbert's Association.

2004   [CATTLE FROM THE UPLANDS]
1955c

16mm	b/w	silent	720ft		REF

[p.c. Campbell Harper Films Ltd.]

Cattle farming in the Uplands of Scotland, from hillside to market.

163

2005 [JUTE INDUSTRIES]
1962c

16mm	col	silent	300ft		REF

[p.c. Campbell Harper Films Ltd.]

A tour of the Douglas Field jute mill by HM Queen Elizabeth.

2006 CAMERON IRON WORKS
1960

16mm	col	silent	150ft		REF

[sp. Cameron Iron Works]
[p.c. Campbell Harper Films Ltd.]

Shots of the interior and exterior of the Cameron Iron Works. [Rushes only.]

2007 KING AND THE WHISKY, THE
1965c

16mm	col	comopt	535ft		REF

sp. Films of Scotland and Distillers Agency Limited
p.c. Campbell Harper Films Ltd.

General views of Edinburgh and the Port Edgar "George IV Old Scotch Whisky" distillery at South Queensferry.

2008 [LEITH DREDGER]
1962c

16mm	col	silent	144ft		REF

[p.c. Campbell Harper Films Ltd.]

Dredgers and tugs at work in Leith.

2009 LIFE IN THE ORKNEYS
1957

16mm	b/w	comopt	362ft		VIEW

sp. Films of Scotland
p.c. Campbell Harper Films Ltd.
d. Alan Harper

An impression of life in the Orkney Isles - street scenes in Stromness and Kirkwall, lobster fishing, the gathering of seaweed, harvesting and the Highland Park Distillery.

2011 EPSTEIN IN EDINBURGH
1961

16mm	b/w	comopt	738ft		REF

sp. Educational Films of Scotland
p.c. Campbell Harper Films Ltd.
d. Henry Cooper

Footage of Edinburgh and the Epstein exhibition of sculpture at the Edinburgh International Festival.

2012 "PROJECT EAST MAINS"
1968

16mm	col	sep opt	726ft		REF

sp. Arthur Bell and Sons Limited
p.c. Campbell Harper Films Ltd.

Construction and subsequent operation of Bell's whisky distillery at East Mains, Edinburgh, with the official opening by Sir Alec Douglas-Home.

2016 [SIMON SQUARE EXHIBITION]
1970

16mm	b/w	silent	214ft		REF

[p.c. Campbell Harper Films Ltd.]

Exhibition of works by the disabled in Edinburgh.

2017 [NATIONAL COMMERCIAL BANK]
1965c

16mm	b/w	silent	468ft		REF

sp. National Commercial Bank
[p.c. Campbell Harper Films Ltd.]

The National Commercial Bank of Scotland, its staff and customers.

2018 IN THY HANDS
1967c

16mm	col	mute	378ft		REF

sp. Church of Scotland Social and Moral Welfare Department
p.c. Campbell Harper Films Ltd.

The patients and staff in the homes for the elderly run by the Church of Scotland.

2019 CLYDE FITTINGS
1960c

16mm	col	silent	531ft		REF

sp. Clyde Tube Forgings
p.c. Campbell Harper Films Ltd.

Steel pipes are manufactured at the Shaw Petrie works with shots of the finished product.

2020 [ORDER OF ST. JOHN, THE]
1972

16mm	col	sep mag	738ft		REF

[p.c. Campbell Harper Films Ltd.]

Memorial service by members of the Order of St John. [Rushes only.]

2021 VIEWS OF PERTH
1935c

16mm	b/w	silent	70ft		REF

p.c. Campbell Harper Films Ltd.

Various views of Perth. [Rushes only.]

Charlie Chaplin and Fred Green on a Hollywood film set during one of several trips to the USA by the Glasgow film exhibitor, c1916

2022   SCOTTISH MINERS GALA DAY

1953

16mm	col	comopt	1044ft		REF

sp. National Union of Mineworkers
p.c. Campbell Harper Films Ltd.
p. James Dickson, the National Union of Mineworkers

The miners' gala day in Edinburgh, with the Scottish Miners Youth contingent, procession and rally, pipe band and sports competitions.

2023   BETTER HAY

1964

16mm	col	sep opt	936ft		REF

sp. South of Scotland Electricity Board
p.c. Campbell Harper Films Ltd.
p. James Eddlestone

An electric barn hay drier in operation at Auchencruive Agricultural College, Ayrshire.

2024   FORTH - POWERHOUSE FOR INDUSTRY

1967

16mm	col	mute	740ft		REF

sp. Educational Films of Scotland
p.c. Campbell Harper Films Ltd.
d. Henry Cooper

The sources of power, industries and new towns on the borders of the river Forth.

2025   GATEWAY TO SECURITY

1953

16mm	b/w	comopt	200ft		REF

sp. Dunfermline Building Society
p.c. Campbell Harper Films Ltd.

A promotional film for the Dunfermline Building Society showing how it can help a young couple buy their own home.

2026   QUEST, THE (GIRLS' GUILDRY)

1937

16mm	b/w	mute	876ft		REF

p.c. Campbell Harper Films Ltd.
d. Robert L. Fairfoull

The various activities of the Girls' Guildry, including summer camp.

2027   DIAMOND JUBILEE BRISBANE QUEEN, LARGS

1936

35mm	b/w	silent	600ft		VIEW

p.c. Pathe Gazette

The pageant and crowning ceremony of the Diamond Jubilee "Brisbane Queen", Largs.

2028   "HARE BUILDS A HOUSE"

1960

16mm	col	sep opt	334ft		REF

p.c. Campbell Harper Films Ltd.
d. Liam Hood

Puppets demonstrate how to build a house. [Based on the book of the same title by Ronald MacKin and Myles Lee.]

2029   MARY'S LAMB

1950

16mm	col	silent	320ft		REF

sp. SEFA/SFC
p.c. Campbell Harper Films Ltd.

An educational film to show infants how clothes are made from sheep's wool.

2030   "IT'S NEVER TOO LATE TO LEARN"
1961

16mm	col	sep opt	330ft		REF

p.c. Campbell Harper Films Ltd.
d. Liam Hood

The dangers of quicksand. [Based on the book of the same title.]

2031   ROYAL BOTANIC GARDENS PLANT HOUSE, EDINBURGH
1962c

16mm	col	comopt	488ft		REF

sp. COI/Ministry of Public Building and Works
p.c. Campbell Harper Films Ltd.

The planning and construction of the new plant houses for Edinburgh's botanical gardens, and the royal opening by Princess Margaret.

2032   PHYSICS FOR ALL (AN EXPERIMENTAL APPROACH)
1967c

16mm	b/w	silent	966ft		REF

sp. EFS/SED
p.c. Campbell Harper Films Ltd.
d. Henry Cooper

Staff and pupils carrying out physics experiments in Kirkcaldy High School and Heriot Watt College.

2033   [PARAPLEGIC GAMES]
1970

16mm	col	mute	1045ft		REF

sp. Scottish Paraplegic Association
p.c. Campbell Harper Films Ltd.

Teams compete in the paraplegic games in Edinburgh which are opened by Edward Heath. Team members visit Edinburgh Zoo.

2034   [ROYAL VISIT CO-OPERATIVE CENTENARY]
1964c

16mm	col	silent	192ft		REF

p.c. Campbell Harper Films Ltd.

Queen Elizabeth and Prince Philip attend the Co-operative centenary.

2036   RAIN ON THE ROOF
1964

16mm	col	silent	710ft		REF

sp. Edinburgh Corporation Water Department
p.c. Campbell Harper Films Ltd.
d. Henry Cooper

The work of the water department in providing water used for domestic purposes in Edinburgh.

2037   ST. KILDA - JULY 1956
1956

16mm	col	silent	432ft		REF

p.c. Campbell Harper Films Ltd.

The journey from Mallaig to St. Kilda in the Western Isles and shots of the island's flora and fauna.

2038   SUN, WIND AND RAIN
1968

16mm	col	sep opt	410ft		REF

sp. Educational Films of Scotland
p.c. Campbell Harper Films Ltd.
d. Henry Cooper

An educational film about the weather.

2039   SCIENCE SECOND CYCLE
1970

16mm	col	silent	236ft		REF

p.c. Campbell Harper Films Ltd.

Science experiments in Barrhead High School.

2040   FIBRE WEB, THE
1964

35mm	col	mute	1935ft		VIEW

sp. Tullis Russell
p.c. Campbell Harper Films Ltd.
d. Henry Cooper

The processing of the raw materials required for paper-making and some of the end products.

2042   UNIROYAL LTD.
1966

35mm	col	silent	700ft		REF

Shots of Uniroyal building site and North British Rubber's Newbridge factory. [Rushes only.]

2043   HIGHLAND FACE LIFT
1959c

35mm	col	silent	365ft		REF

General scenes of the Highlands and young people at work cleaning up the hillsides.

2044   DISTANCE NO OBJECT
1959

35mm	b/w	comopt	646ft		REF

sp. Cable Belt Limited
p.c. Campbell Harper Films Ltd.
d. Henry Cooper

The cable belt rope driven conveyor at work.

2045 FISHING AND THE SEINE NET
1953

35mm	b/w	comopt	375ft		REF

sp. Scottish Home Department
p.c. Campbell Harper Films Ltd.

A demonstration of the correct method of handling the specially designed seine net, used by the fishing industry to catch fish which live on or near the sea bed.

2046 MAGIC KEY, THE
1951

35mm	b/w	comopt	576ft		REF

sp. COI/Scottish Home Department
p.c. Campbell Harper Films Ltd.

A catalogue of the industries and inventions of Scotland.

2049 OUR THREE R'S
1961

35mm	col	mute	2070ft		VIEW

sp. Educational Films of Scotland
p.c. Campbell Harper Films Ltd.
d. Henry Cooper

The educational services provided in Glasgow, including work in primary schools, secondary schools and technical training for day release students.

2050 [FARM IN SOUTHERN SCOTLAND, A]
1960s

35mm	b/w&col	silent	387ft		REF

p.c. Campbell Harper Films Ltd.

Activities on a farm including sheep shearing, harvesting and ploughing.

2053 [OBAN, IONA, STAFFA AND HARRIS]
1950c

16mm	col	silent	384ft		REF

p.c. Campbell Harper Films Ltd.

Shots of Iona Abbey, Fingal's Cave and McCaig's Tower in the Highland town of Oban.

2054 EVERYTHING BY DESIGN
1967

16mm	col	comopt	549ft		REF

p.c. Campbell Harper Films Ltd.

A demonstration of how we as individuals are responsible to some degree for the appearance of everything in the world in which we live.

2056 (ABBOTT'S WHISKY COMMERCIAL)
1968

35mm	b/w&col	sep mag	50ft		REF

sp. Abbot's Whisky
[p.c. Campbell Harper Films Ltd.]

Advert for Abbott's whisky.

2057 BEARDMORE STORY, THE
1961c

16mm	col	mute	800ft		REF

Interior shots of Beardmore's factory, probably at Parkhead in Glasgow. [Rushes only.]

2058 MORAY HOUSE CUISENAIRE
1964

16mm	col	sep opt	1260ft		REF

The teaching of arithmetic using Cuisenaire materials at Moray House College, Edinburgh.

2061 VOLCANOES
1956

16mm	b/w	mute	800ft		REF

sp. SEFA/SFC

An explanation of the volcanic origins of Castle Rock and Arthur's Seat in Edinburgh, the Isle of Arran and the cauldron subsidence of Glencoe.

2062 [SCOTTISH YOUTH HOSTEL TRAILER]
1960c

35mm	b/w	sep opt	23ft		REF

sp. Scottish Youth Hostel Association
p.c. Campbell Harper Films Ltd.

A trailer for the Scottish Youth Hostel Association.

2063 (HILLFOOT PICTURE HOUSE ADVERTS, ETC.)
1960/'70s

35mm	b/w&col	comopt	c700ft		REF

Various adverts, including Lyons Maid products and local businesses.

2064 (LA SCALA TRAILERS, ETC.)
1960s,c

35mm	b/w&col	comopt	c700ft		REF

Possible trailer for the Blackpool Hippodrome, including Cilla Black singing "Tonight" and "Anyone Who Had a Heart".

2065 (MISCELLANEOUS CINEMA ANNOUNCEMENTS)
1960s,c

35mm	b/w	silent	c700ft		REF

Various cinema announcements.

167

2066	ACTION FOR DISASTER				
1973					
16mm	b/w	sep opt	1700ft		VIEW

[p.c. University of Glasgow]

The work of the emergency services in Glasgow, dealing with a hypothetical train disaster in Pollokshaws Road.

2067	TECHNIQUES OF ETCHING				
1975					
16mm	col	comopt	1045ft		REF

p.c. University of Glasgow Audio-Visual Service

Made for a first year university course on the History of Art, the film gives a detailed demonstration of the processes involved in creating an etching.

2068	SURGERY OF THE ABSENT THUMB				
1970s					
16mm	col	comopt	720ft		REF

p.c. University of Glasgow Audio-Visual Service

An instructional film for nurses and students in orthopaedics and plastic surgery.

2069	LIVING SEDIMENTS				
1970s					
16mm	col	comopt	830ft		REF

p.c. University of Glasgow Audio-Visual Service

An educational film made for palaeontology and sedimentology classes, it gives an introduction to the setting up of an actualistic model for interpreting ancient environments.

2070	(CASTLECARY EVENTS)				
1932/'37					
16mm	b/w	silent	650ft		VIEW

[filmed by Norman Stein]

Events in the life of the Stein family and their family-owned brickworks at Bonnybridge. Includes the opening of Castlecary bowling green, a gala day, staff garden party and coronation day celebrations. [See also refs. 2071-2075.]

2071	(BRICKMAKING)				
1937-'45*					
16mm	b/w&col silent		265ft		REF

[filmed by Norman Stein]

Brick-making at the Bonnybridge Stein family brickworks. [See also refs. 2070-2075.]

2072	[WALLHOUSE - MINING CLAY]				
1963					
16mm	col	silent	280ft		REF

[filmed by Alaistair Stein]

Mining for clay and the making of hand-made bricks at the Stein Manuel brickworks, Linlithgow. [See also refs. 2070-2075.]

2073	(STEIN FAMILY LIFE)				
1932-'34					
16mm	b/w	silent	720ft		REF

[filmed by Norman Stein]

Family scenes at the home of the Stein family, owners of the Stirlingshire Stein Brickworks. [See also refs. 2070-2075.]

2074	(STEIN FAMILY - SCHOOL LIFE)				
1933					
16mm	b/w&col silent		690ft		REF

[filmed by Norman Stein]

Sports days at Glenalmond and Hurst Grange Boys' Schools. [Part of collection of Stein family films, see also refs. 2070-2075.]

2075	(STEIN FAMILY HOLIDAYS)				
1932					
16mm	b/w&col silent		2880ft		REF

[filmed by Norman Stein]

Various holidays enjoyed by the Stein family including scenes at Brodick, jubilee celebrations in Stirling and yachting on the Clyde. [See also refs. 2070-2074.]

2076	(BB'S DIAMOND JUBILEE)				
1943					
16mm	b/w	silent	680ft		

Events during the Boys' Brigade diamond jubilee year.

2077	STONES OF GLASGOW, THE				
1980c					
16mm	col	silent	540ft		REF

p.c. University of Glasgow
d. Michael Rigg

A review of the architecture of Victorian Glasgow and specifically the work of Alexander "Greek" Thompson.

2078	GILMOREHILL RETROSPECT, A				
1973					
16mm	b/w	sep opt	1820ft		REF

p.c. University of Glasgow Television Service

A studio discussion introduced by Roderick McLean to record the memories of Glasgow University life of former graduates.

2079   HECTOR VALE!
1956-'60

16mm	b/w&col comopt	1000ft		REF

[filmed by Glasgow University Graduates' Association]

Put together from cuts of university film records to pay tribute to the Principalship of Sir Hector Hetherington, events highlighted include Commemoration Day, Sir Hector going for a flight in a jet aircraft, and the opening of the new engineering building by Field Marshall Viscount Montgomery.

2080   INTESTINAL BY-PASS FOR OBESITY
1970s

16mm	col	comopt	300ft	REF

filmed by Stephen Joffe, Glasgow Royal Infirmary

Record of the various treatments prescribed for the clinical problem of obesity.

2081   [UNIVERSITY OTC]
1970s

16mm	col	mute	570ft	REF

Footage of the various activities of the Glasgow and Strathclyde Universities Officer Training Corps.

2082   [ARCHIVAL SNIPPETS]
1970s

16mm	b/w&col silent	600ft		REF

Miscellaneous events in the life of the University of Glasgow.

2083   JUBILEE CELEBRATION
1950

35mm	b/w	silent	1620ft	REF

sp. James Jones & Son Limited
p.c. Commercial and Educational Films

1700 employees of James Jones and Sons board two chartered steamers at Bridge Wharf, Glasgow for a cruise down the Clyde as a celebration to mark fifty years of service of J.C. Jones, the Chairman and Managing Director of the company.

2084   SALUTE THE SOLDIER WEEK
1944

16mm	b/w	silent	475ft	VIEW

Events during Renfrew and Inchinnan's "Salute the Soldier" week.

2085   FIRE AT ROTHESAY PIER
1962c

std.8mm col	silent	250ft		REF

[filmed by Mr. Hunter]

Family holidays in Rothesay. The film also includes footage of a fire on Rothesay pier with shots of the building ablaze and fire fighters at work.

2086   (CINEMA ADVERTS)
1950/'60s

35mm	col	comopt	500ft	REF

Miscellaneous confectionery adverts and cinema announcements. [Found in former Regal Cinema, Girvan.]

2087   GLASGOW TENEMENTS WRECKED IN BLITZ
1941

35mm	b/w	mute	278ft	VIEW

p.c. British Paramount News

Un-issued news footage of the aftermath of the Clydebank Blitz. March 1941.

2088   FAIR COUNTY OF AYR
1949*

16mm	b/w	comopt	1180ft	REF

sp. Ayr County Council
p.c. Anglo Scottish Pictures
d. Charles Heath

General views of the county of Ayr, including its farming and fishing industries, mills, distilleries and mines. The film also looks at Burns' country, the county's beaches and golf courses.

2089   ("QUIET WEDDING" TRAILER NO. 1)
1949

35mm	b/w	comopt	272ft	REF

A cinema trailer for the production of the comedy "Quiet Wedding" by the Ayr Amateur Players. [See also ref. 2090.]

2090   ("QUIET WEDDING" TRAILER NO. 2)
1949

35mm	b/w	comopt	140ft	VIEW

[p.c. Elder Dalrymple Films]

Cinema trailer for the production of the comedy "Quiet Wedding" by Ayr Amateur Players. [See also ref. 2089.]

2091   GOVERNOR OF THE CASTLE
1936c

35mm	b/w	mute	135ft	VIEW

p.c. Universal Talking News

Extract from newsreel story concerning the installation of the new governor of Edinburgh Castle.

2092   SERVICE OF THANKSGIVING
1945

16mm	b/w	silent	160ft	REF

A service of thanksgiving and commemoration to mark the cessation of hostilities, Hampden Park, Glasgow, Sunday 13th May 1945.

169

2093	DEMONSTRATION BY GLASGOW BATTALION				
1945					
16mm	b/w	silent	320ft		REF

Boys' Brigade demonstration at Hampden Park prior to Scotland v England football international.

2094	BOYS' BRIGADE JUBILEE REVIEW 1933				
1933					
16mm	b/w	silent	150ft		REF

Boys' Brigade review in Queen's Park recreation ground in Glasgow. Prince George takes the salute.

2095	LET'S GO SKI-ING				
1957*					
16mm	col	silent	380ft		REF

filmed by Charlie Bukelis

Ski-ing in Glencoe and the Cairngorms by members of the Glasgow Ski-ing and Outdoor Group, the first organised working class ski club in Scotland. [See also refs. 2096 and 2097.]

2096	(SOC CLUB RACES)				
1962					
16mm	col	silent	200ft		REF

People on ski slopes and group members and banners for the Ski-ing Outdoor Club races. The Club was the first organised working class Ski Club in Scotland. [See also refs. 2095 and 2097.]

2097	CAMPING AND OUTDOOR CLUB				
1957					
16mm	col	silent	180ft		REF

Members of the Ski-ing Outdoor Club at summer camp at Inchmurrin on Loch Lomond. A party are seen leaving the Ardgarten Youth Hostel preparing to climb the Cobbler. [See also refs. 2095 and 2096.]

2098	CARRICK KNOWE - CHURCH OF SCOTLAND				
1953					
9.5mm	b/w	silent	350ft		REF

[filmed by Robin Chalmers]

The construction of Carrick Knowe church in Edinburgh, the first stone-built church to be built after World War II.

2099	(JOSEPH HISLOP COLLECTION)				
1927					
16mm	b/w	silent	1080ft		REF

[filmed by Joseph Hislop and friends]

Family film made by Joseph Dewar Hislop, Scotland's international operatic tenor. It includes footage of a train derailment in South Africa, a winter holiday in Denmark, a tennis party attended by King Gustav V of Sweden and shots of the family relaxing during a concert tour of New Zealand.

2100	RAILWAY RIDE OVER THE TAY BRIDGE				
1897					
35mm	b/w	silent	292ft		VIEW

Shot from the engine front, the film shows a steam train pulling away from Wormit station in Fife, crossing the Tay rail bridge and passing south bound trains.

2101	IF ONLY WE HAD THE SPACE				
1974					
16mm	col	comopt	580ft		VIEW

sp. Films of Scotland and the Corporation of Glasgow
p.c. Tree Films
w .& d. Charles Gormley

Made to demonstrate how improvements to Glasgow city tenements could be achieved with the aid of Home Improvement Grants.

2102	MUNGO'S MEDALS				
1961c					
16mm	col	comopt	710ft		REF

sp. Corporation of the City of Glasgow
p.c. Elder Film Productions
d. John C. Elder

An illustration of the efforts made to rehouse families from sub-standard tenement flats in Glasgow, and to alleviate the housing shortage in the city.

2103	(SCENIC PICTURE HOUSE CLOSURE)				
1939					
35mm	b/w	silent	190ft		VIEW

pc. Topical Productions
d. Paul Robello

Shots of children queuing for the last matinee performance of "The Adventures of Robin Hood" at the Scenic Picture House, Glasgow. Shots of the building being demolished.

2104	BUILDING THE NEW CHRYSLER				
1976					
16mm	col	comopt	1200ft		REF

sp. Chrysler Corporation
p.c. Formula One Films

Promotional film celebrating the introduction of the production of the new Chrysler Alpine car model to Britain and the plans for its production in Europe and the UK.

2105	HEIL OSTERREICH			
1936				
16mm	b/w	silent	960ft	REF

filmed by Violet Anderson

An entry for the 1938 Scottish Amateur Film Festival. Shot in Austria, it includes scenes of local festivals and Goebbels' presence in the country.

2106	GLASGOW JUNIOR INSTRUCTION CENTRE, A			
1934c				
16mm	b/w	silent	360ft	REF

filmed by Violet Anderson

An entry for the 1937 Scottish Amateur Film Festival, showing daily life at South Carntyne junior instructional centre, one of several in Glasgow for unemployed people.

2107	POTTERY			
1936				
16mm	col	silent	260ft	REF

filmed by Violet Anderson

An entry for the 1937 Scottish Amateur Film Festival, showing a potter at work in a small house and yard in Somerset.

2108	JUNGLE JINKS, ETC.			
1934/'37				
16mm	b/w&col silent		600ft	REF

[filmed by Violet Neish

Composite reel of family film and footage from other titles by film-maker. [Trims only.]

2109	ANCIENT CRAFT. AN /ASK NO QUESTIONS			
1936c				
9.5mm	b/w	silent	360ft	REF

filmed by Violet Anderson

A compilation of brief shots of plough horses, rural pottery in Somerset and an animated film.

2110	(VIOLET ANDERSON FILM)			
1930s				
9.5mm	b/w	silent	600ft	REF

[filmed by Violet Anderson]

Various scenes taken around the country, including the West of England Academy and School of Art, a puffer, firemen called to a burning haystack and a wrecked boat beached at Ailsa Craig.

2111	PEERIE HORSES OF SHETLAND, THE			
1985				
16mm	b/w&col sep mag		310ft	REF

d. Jenny Gilbertson

Re-working of the original b/w footage shot by Jenny Gilbertson in the 1930s and 1960s of the Peerie horses. Specially filmed colour prologue and epilogue added in 1985.

2112	WEDDING DAY 1936			
1936				
16mm	b/w&col silent		276ft	REF

filmed by IAC

A wedding at the Church of St. John the Evangelist, Edinburgh with the reception in the Freemasons' Hall and a wedding at St. Serfs, Burntisland, Fife.

2113	TRAPPED			
1973				
35mm	col	comopt	2340ft	VIEW

sp. Scottish Society for the Prevention of Vivisection
p.c. Edinburgh Films
d. Robin Crichton

A fashion model and her husband go into partnership in a chain of beauty salons. Disillusionment sets in when they discover how the cosmetics are being produced.

2114	NINE DALMUIR WEST			
1962				
16mm	b/w	comopt	500ft	VIEW

filmed by Kevin Brownlow

Shots of the route of the No. 9 service to Dalmuir on the last day of the trams in Glasgow; the crew at work, in the depot and at a dance to mark the end of the services. Enthusiasts are seen lining the streets watching the last cavalcade.

2115	(LAUNCH AT DENNY'S - "SHAMROCK III")			
1903				
35mm	b/w	silent	92ft	VIEW

The launch of Sr Thomas Lipton's yacht "Shamrock III" from William Denny's yard in Dumbarton.

2116	HAPPY THE MAN			
1987				
16mm	col	sep opt	1200ft	REF

p.c. Antonine Productions
d. Jim Gillespie

A post-holocaust fable set in the Highlands of Scotland.

171

2117   KELVIN, MASTER OF MEASUREMENT

1946

| 16mm | b/w | comopt | 1800ft | REF |

sp. Kelvin, Bottomley and Baird
p.c. James E. Rogers in assoc. with the Film Producers' Guild

A dramatised documentary of the life and work of William Thompson, Lord Kelvin.

2118   FLYING SCOTSMEN

1975

| 16mm | col | comopt | 1550ft | VIEW |

p.c. BBC Scotland
p. Michael Marshall

The inter-island air services on the Orkney and Shetland Isles and helicopter services from Inverness to the Western Isles. Retrospective sequences on the early days of both.

2119   REST-AND-BE-THANKFUL HILL CLIMB 1949

1949

| 16mm | col | silent | 180ft | REF |

Shots of spectators on the slopes overlooking the road as vintage racing and sports cars compete in the hill climb.

2120   REST-AND-BE-THANKFUL HILL CLIMB 1950

1950

| 16mm | col | silent | 258ft | REF |

Preparations for the hill climb, shots of the race and presentation of the trophy to the winner.

2121   SKI-ING IN SCOTLAND

1934-'61*

| 16mm | b/w&col silent | 740ft | REF |

[filmed by P.F. Carmichael, Harry MacRobert]

Scenes of ski-ing in Scotland in the early 1930s - 1960s.

2122   "MAREEVE"

1946*

| 16mm | col | silent | 440ft | REF |

A motor cruise off the West Coast of Scotland on the "Mareeve", including views of Tobermory Bay, going through the lock at the Crinan Canal and shots of yachts, cruisers and steamers.

2123   (FFORDE COLLECTION)

1931*/'52

| 16mm | col | silent | 1000ft | REF |

[filmed by James Graham and Lady Mary Douglas-Hamilton]

Collection of family film made by the 6th Duke and Duchess of Montrose including shots of a deer hunt, the Duke of Montrose at Holyrood House, the home farm at Buchanan Castle and Donald Campbell's "Bluebird" on Loch Lomond.

2124   BUCHAN CLUB AT FYVIE CASTLE, THE

1938

| 16mm | b/w | silent | 330ft | REF |

Members of the Buchan Field Club enjoy an outing to Fyvie Castle.

2125   JUBILEE CELEBRATIONS OF THE BUCHAN CLUB

1937

| 16mm | col | silent | 430ft | REF |

The 50th anniversary celebrations of the Buchan Field Club.

2126   BIRTH OF A NEW SOUND

1980

| super 8mm col | commag | 350ft | REF |

filmed by Colin Jonston

Amateur documentary about the opening of the independent radio station, Radio Tay. [Prize-winning film at SAFF 1980.]

2127   HOMESPUN

1934*

| 16mm | b/w | silent | 100ft | REF |

sp. Glasgow Education Authority
[p.c. Elder Dalrymple Productions]

A demonstration of teasing, carding, spinning and weaving wool.

2128   PRESTWICK AIRPORT ARRIVAL

1951

| 16mm | col | silent | 120ft | REF |

[attributed to Harry Birrell]

Scots from overseas arriving at Prestwick airport on a BOAC aeroplane. The visitors are escorted from the airport by pipes and drums.

2129   OUR HIGHLAND HERITAGE
1958*

16mm	col	silent	420ft		REF

sp. David MacBrayne Limited
p.c. Elder Film Productions

Promotional film for MacBrayne's steamship operators, showing a coach excursion to Glencoe, a visit by train and steamer to Mallaig, Loch Scavaig via Glenfinnan and a coach trip to Loch Ness.

2130   AIR CANADA SILVER BROOM 1969
1969

16mm	col	comopt	1120ft		REF

sp. Air Canada

Coverage of the Silver Broom curling matches with a short introduction on the host town of Perth. [The Scottish team were beaten in the final by the USA.] [See also ref. 2131.]

2131   AIR CANADA SILVER BROOM 1975
1975

16mm	col	comopt	1120ft		VIEW

sp. Air Canada

Coverage of the Silver Broom curling matches with a short sequence on the origins of the sport of curling. [See also ref. 2130.]

2132   STRANRAER ROYAL VISIT 1955
1955

35mm	b/w	silent	990ft		REF

filmed as a local topical by Kinema News

Coverage of the royal visit to Stranraer by Queen Elizabeth and the Duke of Edinburgh.

2133   (SCOTTISH SCENES 1931-'35)
1931

16mm	b/w	silent	400ft		REF

[filmed by A. Adams]

Various scenes of Scotland, including Strathallan Highland Games and a scout camp.

2134   GLASGOW'S SUNDAY 1963
1963

std.8mm col		commag	100ft		REF

filmed by A. & W. Murdoch

Street scenes of Glasgow, stall holders at the "barras", families in Queen's Park and sunset on the Clyde.

2135   FILM-MAKING AT CRIEFF
1969

super 8mm col		commag	125ft		REF

filmed by W. & A. Murdoch

A weekend at Crieff Hydro for members of the Scottish Association of Amateur Cinematographers where film-makers are seen preparing for a shoot.

2136   [STEAM EXCURSIONS 1959]
1959

16mm	b/w	silent	300ft		REF

[filmed by J.S. Bauchop]

Shots of North British and Caledonian Railway locomotives.

2137   (MACNEILL TRACTORS DEMONSTRATION FILMS)
1940-'60

16mm	b/w&col	silent	1850ft		REF

[filmed by J.S. Bauchop]

Demonstrations of the various tractors manufactured by MacNeill's Tractors of Glasgow. [Film-maker was the Managing Director of MacNeill Tractors.] [See also refs. 2138, 2139.]

2138   (MACNEILL TRACTORS DEMONSTRATION FILMS)
1940c

16mm	b/w	silent	500ft		REF

[filmed by J.S. Bauchop]

Demonstration of the various tractors manufactured by MacNeill Tractors of Glasgow. [See also refs. 2137, 2139.]

2139   PLOUGHING DEMONSTRATION
1940s

16mm	b/w	silent	100ft		VIEW

[filmed by J.S. Bauchop]

A demonstration of a MacNeill tractor ploughing furrows. [See also refs. 2137 - 2138.]

2140   (GSA KINECRAFT SOCIETY)
1932-'34

16mm	b/w	silent	180ft		REF

filmed by Glasgow School of Art Kinecraft Society

Two dramas filmed by the Glasgow School of Art Kinecraft Society.

2141   [TV COMMERCIALS]
1954*

16mm	b/w	comopt	100ft		VIEW

Various TV commercials including Scott's Porridge Oats, Haliborange, Eskimo Fish Fillets and Dunsade lemonade.

2142   GLASGOW AND DISTRICT CO-OPERATIVE ASSOCIATION
1953

16mm	b/w	silent	210ft		REF

Some of the activities organised by the Glasgow and District Co-operative Association's Education Department during an exhibition week in Glasgow's Palace of Art.

173

2143   ABERFELDY AGRICULTURAL SHOW 1952

1952

| 35mm | b/w | silent | 400ft | | REF |

p.c. Elder Film Productions

General views of the agricultural show, including scenes in the livestock ring, the horse show, and Scottish country dancing.

2144   AULD TAM MCGUIRE

1951*

| 35mm | b/w | comopt | 1250ft | | VIEW |

p.c. Campbell Harper Films Ltd.
d. Alan Harper

The dramatised enactment of a comic poem. [Tam McGuire is played by Duncan Macrae.]

2145   (STRANRAER LOCAL EVENTS)

1950s

| 16mm | b/w | silent | 360ft | | VIEW |

[filmed as a local topical for the Kinema, Stranraer]

Various local events in Stranraer including an agricultural show and gala day.

2146   KEEK AT THE HIGHLANDS, A

1931

| 16mm | b/w | silent | 95ft | | REF |

[filmed by Ian S. Drew]

A ski-ing and mountaineering trip on Ben Nevis by members of the Scottish Ski Cub. [See also refs. 2121, 2147-2149.]

174

Interior of Green's Playhouse, Renfield Street, Glasgow

2147　(SKI-ING ON BEN LAWERS)

1935*

16mm	b/w	silent	180ft		REF

[filmed by Ian S. Drew]

Members of the Scottish Ski Club on a ski-ing party on Ben Lawers. [See also refs. 2121, 2146-2149.]

2148　SCOTTISH SKI CLUB DINNER

1958

16mm	b/w	silent	92ft		REF

filmed by J.V. Dewar

The Scottish Ski Club's 50th Anniversary dinner and dance. Shots of ski tow trials. [See also refs. 2121, 2146-2149.]

2149　[SKI-ING IN SCOTLAND]

1939-'48*

16mm	b/w	silent	245ft		REF

[filmed by Ian S. Drew]

A group of skiers being filmed by a British Movietone News cameraman, and general views of skiers on the slopes. [See also refs. 2121, 2146-2148.]

2150　IN DAYS OF OLD

1958

16mm	b/w	silent	360ft		REF

[filmed by Ben H. Humble]

Made to commemorate the 50th Jubilee of the Ladies' Scottish Climbing Club, the film shows how women climbers dressed in Edwardian times. [See also ref. 2155.]

2151　GLENMORE AND THE CAIRNGORMS

1966

16mm	col	silent	260ft		REF

[filmed by Ben H. Humble]

An illustration of various outdoor activities by youth groups at Glenmore Lodge in the Cairngorms.

2152　OUT FOR VALUE

1931-'32c

35mm	b/w	silent	1050ft		VIEW

sp. Isaac Benzie's Department Store
p.c. Jay's Film Service

A promotional film for the Aberdeen department store Isaac Benzie, showing a 'family enjoying a day's shopping in the store, visiting all its various departments, taking lunch and tea in the tearoom, and even taking a bath! [See also refs. 2525-2536.]

2153　(RENFREW FERRY'S FINAL WEEK)

1972

super 8mm	col	silent	200ft		REF

filmed by J.D. Paterson

Amateur footage of various types of trams at Fleetwood, Lancashire and shots of the Renfrew Ferry crossing the Clyde.

2154　BOYS' BRIGADE JUBILEE CELEBRATIONS AT GLASGOW

1933

16mm	b/w	comopt	770ft		REF

p.c. Gaumont British Equipment Limited

Record of the celebrations in Glasgow to mark the Jubilee of the Boys' Brigade.

2155　RHUM AND WATER/LSCC 50TH ANNIVERSARY

1958

16mm	b/w	silent	200ft		REF

[filmed by Louise Annand]

The Ladies' Scottish Climbing Club on the island of Rhum, and the Club's 50th anniversary at Lix Toll near Killin in 1958. [See also ref. 2150.]

2156　AEROPLANE, AN

1936c

16mm	b/w	silent	95ft		REF

sp. Glasgow Education Committee
p.c. Elder-Dalrymple Productions

A bi-plane taking off from an aerodrome, aerials of the city below, and shots of the plane landing.

2157　[DENNY CLOSURE]

1963

super 8mm	col	silent	152ft		REF

[filmed by Robert Black]

Taken during the last few days prior to the closure of William Denny's shipyard in Dumbarton.

2158　PUPPIES

1936*

16mm	b/w	silent	84ft		VIEW

sp. Glasgow Education Committee
p.c. Elder-Dalrymple Productions

A fox terrier and her puppies. The film portrays aspects of the care of the mother animal for her young.

2159　WIRE ROPE-MAKING

1945c

16mm	b/w	silent	180ft		REF

[sp. Glasgow Education Committee]
[p.c. Elder-Dalrymple Productions]

An illustration of the various stages in the manufacturing of wire rope.

175

2160   LEADED LIGHTS
1936

16mm	b/w	silent	201ft	REF

[sp. Glasgow Corporation Education Committee]
[p.c. Elder-Dalrymple Productions]

The various stages in the assembly of pieces of coloured glass into a door or window pane, the application of lead moulding and polishing with blacklead.

2161   SPRING IN THE FIELDS
1936c

16mm	b/w	silent	115ft	REF

[p.c. Elder-Dalrymple Productions]

A farmer at work in the fields; ploughing with a horse-drawn plough, sowing seed by hand, harrowing and rolling. [See also ref. 1931.]

2162   ON THE POULTRY FARM
1936c

16mm	b/w	silent	94ft	REF

sp. Glasgow Education Committee
[p.c. Elder-Dalrymple Productions]

Hens and chickens in a poultry farmyard.

2163   PIGS
1936c

16mm	b/w	silent	95ft	VIEW

[sp. Glasgow Corporation Education Committee]
[p.c. Elder-Dalrymple Productions]

One of the Carrick Classroom Series, the film shows pigs in a farmyard being fed, rounded up and driven into their sty.

2164   SHEPHERD AND HIS DOG, THE
1938c

16mm	b/w	silent	105ft	VIEW

[sp. Glasgow Education Committee]
p.c. Elder-Dalrymple Productions

Scenes in the Southern Uplands of Scotland as a Lowland shepherd and his dog round up sheep.

2165   BLIND BASKET MAKER, THE
1936c

16mm	b/w	silent	130ft	VIEW

[sp. Glasgow Education Committee]
[p.c. Elder-Dalrymple Productions]

A blind man demonstrates the technique of wicker-work.

2166   MILK AT THE CREAMERY
1935c

16mm	b/w	silent	110ft	VIEW

[sp. Glasgow Education Committee]
[p.c. Elder-Dalrymple Productions]

A demonstration of cooling, bottling and discing of milk at a creamery.

2167   HIGHLAND CATTLE
1935c

16mm	b/w	silent	109ft	VIEW

[sp. Glasgow Education Committee]
p.c. Elder-Dalrymple Productions

Shots of Highland cattle in a field.

2168   SAWMILL IN THE FOREST, THE
1935c

16mm	b/w	silent	106ft	VIEW

[sp. Glasgow Education Committee]
[p.c. Elder-Dalrymple Productions]

Shots of men felling trees and transporting logs by horse to a small sawmill, where the timber is cut into lengths.

2169   SOAP MAKING
1936c

16mm	b/w	silent	174ft	VIEW

sp. Glasgow Education Committee
p.c. Elder-Dalrymple Productions

Inside a soap works where the different manufacturing processes are explained.

2170   WATER WHEEL, THE
1936c

16mm	b/w	silent	92ft	REF

[sp. Glasgow Corporation Education Committee]
[p.c. Elder-Dalrymple Productions]

A water wheel is shown in operation.

2171   WOODCRAFT
1936c

16mm	b/w	silent	180ft	VIEW

[sp. Glasgow Corporation Education Committee]
[p.c. Elder-Dalrymple Productions]

A woodcraft class in school where pupils use home-made, treadle and power lathes.

2172   GRAIN HARVEST
1936

16mm	b/w	silent	276ft	VIEW

sp. Gaumont-British Instructional
d. John C. Elder

Part Two of the series "Agricultural Scotland", showing a field of oats being scythed to clear a path for the horse-drawn reaping and binding machines, and the threshing machine at work in the farmyard. [See also ref. 0652.]

2173   OPENING BRIDGE
1936c

16mm	b/w	silent	180ft	REF

[sp. Glasgow Education Committee]
[p.c. Elder-Dalrymple Productions]

The Kincardine bridge opening to let boats pass through, and closing again for the traffic to proceed across it.

176

2174	LORD AND LADY OVERTOUN'S VISIT TO MACINDOE'S SHOW

pre-1908

35mm	b/w	silent	75ft		VIEW

Lord and Lady Overtoun visit a fairground booth. [Probably John Campbell White, the 1st Baron Overtoun, and his wife Grace.]

2175	LAND OF THE WHITE RHINO

1939

16mm	b/w	comopt	360ft		VIEW

[p.c. Elder-Dalrymple Productions]

Shot during a Cape to Cairo expedition, October 1937 to January 1939, the film shows Blake Dalrymple and J. Stirling Gillespie being taken into the bush by Zulu tracker Charlie Ninela to film white rhino. [See also refs. 2176-2177, 2183.]

2176	(CAPE TO CAIRO - ANIMALS)

1936-'38

16mm	b/w	silent	340ft		REF

[p.c. Elder-Dalrymple Productions]

General views of animals in the bush, including zebra, buffalo, wart-hogs and rhinos. [See also refs. 2175, 2177, 2183.]

2177	(CAPE TO CAIRO - NATIVE LIFE)

1936-'38

16mm	b/w	silent	295ft		REF

p.c. Elder-Dalrymple Productions

Shot during a Cape to Cairo expedition, the film shows tea picking, villagers cooking, men dancing and a 'witch doctor'. [See also refs. 2175-2176, 2183.]

2178	FORTY THIEVES PANTOMIME, THE

1937

16mm	col	silent	316ft		VIEW

[filmed by Horace H. Collins, Fred Collins Variety Agency]

Stage routines and sketches in the Pavilion Theatre, Glasgow on 20th December 1937.

2179	SNATCHES FROM THE FORTY THIEVES PANTOMIME

1931

16mm	b/w	silent	290ft		REF

[filmed by Horace H. Collins, Fred Collins Variety Agency]

Sketches and routines from the pantomime at the Theatre Royal, Edinburgh.

2180	SINBAD THE SAILOR/BABES IN THE WOOD

1936-'37

16mm	b/w&col	silent	440ft		REF

[filmed by Horace H. Collins, Fred Collins Variety Agency]

Stage routines and sketches from two pantomimes, with Dave Willis starring in "Sinbad the Sailor" and Harry Gordon in "Babes in the Wood".

2181	QUEEN OF HEARTS PANTOMIME, THE

1937

16mm	col	silent	266ft		VIEW

[filmed by Horace H. Collins, Fred Collins Variety Agency]

Stage routines, sketches and the finale of the pantomime at the Theatre Royal, Edinburgh.

2182	POTTERY, THE

1936c

16mm	b/w	silent	168ft		REF

[sp. Glasgow Education Committee]
[p.c. Elder-Dalrymple Productions]

A potter shaping a vase at a potter's wheel, glazing the vase and firing it in the kiln.

2183	(CAPE TO CAIRO - WILDLIFE AND NATIVE SCENES)

1936-'38

16mm	b/w	silent	375ft		REF

[sp. Glasgow Education Committee]
[p.c. Elder-Dalrymple Productions]

Scenes at a pottery in South Africa where the clay is prepared, shaped, decorated and fired. Shots also of animals in the bush. [See also refs. 2175-2177.]

2184	[ISLE OF BUTE CARNIVAL]

1949

16mm	col	silent	258ft		REF

[filmed by J. Stirling Gillespie and Mr. Aitken]

General scenes of the Isle of Bute carnival in Rothesay.

2185	AT THE ZOO (A. A. MILNE)

1940*

16mm	col	silent	300ft		REF

An early educational film showing various animals at the zoo intercut with lines of poetry read by A.A. Milne.

2186	AREAS OF SCOTLAND - HIGHLAND

1935*

16mm	b/w	silent	285ft		REF

Highland scenery, hill-walkers, a fishing village and fishermen at work.

177

2187   XMAS LIGHTS
1964

std.8mm col	silent	300ft	REF

[filmed by John Cowe]

Amateur footage of Glasgow streets at night with Christmas decorations and illuminations, the exterior of the Odeon Cinema and the carnival at the Kelvin Hall.

2188   RAINBOW TRAILS
1932*

16mm	b/w	mute	261ft	REF

filmed by James Blair

A tour of the Highlands and Hebrides including footage of a Highland Gathering on the isle of Skye, Loch Shiel and Glenfinnan, and a trip on the sea plane the "Cloud of Iona".

2189   [SCENES AROUND HALFWAY AND DISTRICT]
1933

9.5mm/16mm	b/w	silent	450ft	REF

[filmed by James Blair]

Places and events in and around the Lanarkshire village of Halfway, including street scenes, the tram terminus, construction of council housing, an amateur dramatic club production and a wedding.

2190   DEEP SEA DAYS
1930*

16mm	b/w	silent	153ft	REF

filmed by James Blair

Amateur footage of life on board a deep sea trawler as the fishing grounds are selected, the trawl is dropped and the catch landed and cleaned.

2191   VIRGINIA
1938

16mm	b/w	silent	149ft	REF

[filmed by James Blair]

The Minerva Operatic Club's presentation of "Virginia" at the Lyric Theatre in Glasgow.

2192   [MAKING A SPINNING WHEEL AT PORTSONACHAN]
1941*

16mm	b/w	silent	100ft	REF

[filmed by James Blair]

In a rural workshop a man hand turns and shapes wood to make a spinning wheel.

2193   [GLASGOW, JUBILEE 1935]
1935

16mm	b/w	silent	42ft	REF

[filmed by James Blair]

Various activities in Glasgow to mark the Silver Jubilee of King George V, including an exhibition in the Kelvin Hall, and the Regal Cinema's promotion of "Royal Cavalcade".

2194   "MAURETANIA" AND" QUEEN MARY"
1936

16mm	b/w&col	silent	54ft	REF

[filmed by James Blair]

Clyde docks and various vessels on the river including the "Mauretania", and the "Queen Mary".

2195   (AIR DISPLAY, RENFREW)
1935-'39*

16mm	b/w&col	silent	180ft	REF

[filmed by James Blair]

General views of an air show, possibly Allan Cobham's Air Circus, at Renfrew.

2196   [RIDING OF THE MARCHES, ANNAN]
1960

35mm	b/w	silent	2500ft	REF

[sp.United Kingdom Atomic Energy Authority]
[p.c. United Kingdom Atomic Energy Authority Prod. Group]

Riding of the Marches annual celebrations in Annan, including the "snuffing" ceremony and coronation of the Queen of the Border. [Believed to have been made as a public relations exercise for the local community.]

2197   (EMPIRE EXHIBITION)
1938

16mm	col	silent	85ft	REF

[filmed by Alston Dunderdale]

General scenes during the opening ceremony of the Empire Exhibition in Glasgow with interior shots of the pavilion as the royal party arrives.

2198   ZOO, THE
1936-'37*

16mm	b/w	silent	183ft	REF

[filmed by Alston Dunderdale]

General views inside a zoo with shots of various animals and birds.

2199   HOLIDAY SHOTS 1936
1936

16mm	b/w	silent	239ft	REF

[filmed by Alston Dunderdale]

A car tour through Hexham, the Lake District, the Rhinns of Galloway and Corsewall Point. Shots of horses and hounds preparing for a meet at Armathwaite Hall.

2201	DRAM LIKE THIS, A				
1972					
16mm	*col*	*comopt*	*800ft*		*VIEW*

sp. Films of Scotland on behalf of William Grant and Sons Limited
p.c. IFA (Scotland) Ltd.

Distilling whisky at William Grant's Glenfiddich, Girvan and Ladyburn distilleries.

2202	BY LOCHABER I WILL GO				
1957					
35mm	*col*	*comopt*	*1150ft*		*VIEW*

sp. Films of Scotland
p.c. Anglo-Scottish Pictures Limited
d. David Paltenghi

A documentary on the travelling bank as seen in Lochaber and Lewis in the Western Isles.

2203	CHAMPIONS IN THE SUN				
1964					
16mm	*col*	*comopt*	*603ft*		*VIEW*

sp. Films of Scotland
p.c. Templar Film Studios
p. R. Riddell-Black

The Royal Highland Show at Ingliston where the cattle and sheep are judged and paraded in the show ring.

2204	COUNTY OF THE CLYDE				
1963					
35mm	*col*	*comopt*	*1745ft*		*VIEW*

sp. Films of Scotland
p.c. Anglo Scottish Pictures
d. Gordon Stewart

A documentary showing the changing pattern of life in Lanarkshire; fruit picking in the Clyde valley, street scenes in Rutherglen, Airdrie, Coatbridge and Motherwell, interiors of factories, construction of housing and children playing.

2205	COUNTY ON THE MOVE				
1966					
35mm	*col*	*comopt*	*1710ft*		*VIEW*

sp. Films of Scotland and West Lothian County Council
p.c. IFA (Scotland)
d. Laurence Henson

The towns, industries and places of interest in and around the county of West Lothian including Linlithgow Palace, the Forth Rail and Road Bridges, Hopetoun House, a clay mine, engineering factory and colliery.

2206	EDINBURGH TATTOO, THE				
1959					
16mm	*col*	*comopt*	*873ft*		*VIEW*

sp. Films of Scotland
p.c. Campbell Harper Films Ltd.

The military displays of the Tattoo on the esplanade of Edinburgh Castle during the Edinburgh Festival.

2207	FETTES				
1970					
16mm	*col*	*comopt*	*576ft*		*REF*

sp. Films of Scotland for the Old Fettesian Association

Activities and events at Fettes College, Edinburgh including a visit by HM the Queen Mother.

2208	FORTH ROAD BRIDGE, THE				
1965					
35mm	*col*	*comopt*	*4973ft*		*VIEW*

sp. Films of Scotland and Shell and BP Scotland
p.c. Random Productions
d. Gordon Lang

The story of the Forth Road Bridge, from the initial survey and different stages of construction, to the official opening by HM the Queen. [See also ref. 2222 for alternative version.]

2209	FROM GLASGOW GREEN TO BENDIGO				
1961					
35mm	*col*	*comopt*	*1662ft*		*VIEW*

sp. Films of Scotland Committee
p.c. Anglo Scottish Pictures Ltd.
d. Robert Irvine

A look at the processes involved in the manufacturing of carpet in the Templeton factory in Glasgow.

2210	GEORGE IV'S EDINBURGH				
1960					
35mm	*col*	*comopt*	*1305ft*		*VIEW*

sp. Films of Scotland
p.c. Campbell Harper Films Ltd.
d. Henry Cooper

An account of the history of the New Town of Edinburgh.

2211	GOOD SERVANT, THE				
1958					
35mm	*col*	*comopt*	*1800ft*		*VIEW*

sp. Films of Scotland and the Royal Highland & Agricultural Society
p.c. Campbell Harper Films Ltd.
d. Alan Harper

The story of a Clydesdale horse, from foal to champion at the Royal Highland Show.

2212	HEBRIDEAN HIGHWAY				
1966					
35mm	*col*	*comopt*	*1800ft*		*VIEW*

sp. Films of Scotland
p.c. Glasgow Films

The Inner and Outer Hebrides with scenes of Iona, Mull, Skye and Harris.

179

2213 HIGHLAND CAPITAL
1968

| 35mm | col | comopt | 1800ft | VIEW |

sp. Films of Scotland
p.c. Campbell Harper Films Ltd.
p. Alan Harper

Inverness as a focal point for Highland life past and present: from St.Columba and King Bruce to the Loch Ness Monster and the World Pipe Band Championships.

2214 HOLLOW MOUNTAIN, THE
1966

| 35mm | col | comopt | 1260ft | VIEW |

sp. Films of Scotland
p.c. Templar Film Studios

The story of the building of the Ben Cruachan pumped-storage hydro-electric scheme with a detailed description of the civil and electrical engineering work involved. [See also ref. 2790.]

2215 IN GOOD HEART
1961

| 35mm | col | comopt | 1890ft | VIEW |

sp. Films of Scotland
p.c. Campbell Harper Films Ltd.
d. Henry Cooper

The farming year in Scotland - in the Borders, Ayrshire, the Highlands and Angus with scenes of sheep and dairy farming, and the harvesting of potatoes.

2216 INVERGORDON SMELTER, THE
1972

| 16mm | col | comopt | 738ft | VIEW |

sp. Films of Scotland and the British Aluminium Co. Ltd.
p.c. Ogam Films
d. Oscar Marzaroli

The story of the conception and construction of the aluminium smelter at Invergordon.

2217 LAND LIVED IN, A
1957

| 35mm | col | comopt | 1400ft | VIEW |

sp. Films of Scotland
p.c. Campbell Harper Films Ltd.
d. Alan Harper

Castles and country houses in the care of the National Trust for Scotland, including Culzean Castle, Falkland Palace, Crathes Castle and Gladstone's Land.

2218 LEATHERNECK AMBASSADORS
1961

| 16mm | col | comopt | 519ft | REF |

sp. US Marine Corps
p.c. US Naval Photographic Centre

An account of the visit paid by the US Marines in Edinburgh in 1958 and their participation in the Edinburgh Tattoo.

2219 LIVINGSTON - A TOWN FOR THE LOTHIANS
1969

| 16mm | col | comopt | 752ft | VIEW |

sp.Films of Scotland
p.c. IFA (Scotland) Ltd.

Made to promote Livingston New Town, the film shows the countryside round the town, its new housing, industries and schools.

2220 PLAYING AWAY
1961

| 35mm | col | comopt | 1764ft | VIEW |

sp. Films of Scotland
p.c. Thames and Clyde Film Co. Ltd.
d. Stanley Russell

Spotlight on various sporting events and personalities in Scotland, including a rugby international at Murrayfield, the British Open at St. Andrews and a Scotland v England football match at Hampden.

2221 QUEEN IN SCOTLAND, THE
1960

| 35mm | col | comopt | 2160ft | VIEW |

sp. Films of Scotland
p.c. Templar Film Studios

A royal visit to Scotland including the Shetland and Orkney Isles, Balmoral, Braemar Highland Games, the opening of the Kincardine generating station and the General Assembly of the Church of Scotland.

2222 CONSTRUCTION OF THE FORTH ROAD BRIDGE
1965

| 35mm | col | comopt | 4320ft | VIEW |

sp. Films of Scotland
p.c. Campbell Harper Films Ltd.
d. Henry Cooper

The engineering work-in-progress of the construction of the Forth Road Bridge. [See also ref. 2208 for alternative version.]

2223 BORDERS, THE
1970

| 16mm | col | comopt | 612ft | VIEW |

sp. Films of Scotland
p.c. Edinburgh Film Productions
d. Mike Pavett

The changing forces in the traditional borderland, in the fishing and textile industries, farming, forestry and housing.

2224 SCOTLAND DANCES
1957

| 16mm | col | comopt | 486ft | VIEW |

sp. Films of Scotland Committee
p.c. Campbell Harper Films Ltd.
d. Alan Harper

The tradition of Scottish country dancing filmed in Ayrshire, Blair Castle, Princes Street Gardens, and the forecourt of Holyroodhouse.

2225 SILVER CITY, THE
1960

| 16mm | col | comopt | 714ft | VIEW |

sp. Films of Scotland
p.c. Anglo Scottish Pictures

The city of Aberdeen; its university, fishing industry and leisure facilities.

2226 MACKINTOSH
1968

| 35mm | col | comopt | 2939ft | VIEW |

sp. Films of Scotland and the Scottish Arts Council
p.c. IFA (Scotland) Ltd.
d. Murray Grigor

The life and work of Charles Rennie Mackintosh.

2227 CUMBERNAULD. TOWN FOR TOMORROW
1970

| 35mm | col | comopt | 2295ft | VIEW |

sp. Films of Scotland and Cumbernauld Development Corp.
p.c. Edinburgh Film Productions
d. Robin Crichton

The New Town of Cumbernauld; its housing, recreational facilities and industries.

2228 PLAN FOR LIVING, A
1976

| 35mm | col | comopt | 1800ft | VIEW |

sp. Films of Scotland and Livingston Development Corp.
p.c. Pelicula Films
d. Michael Alexander

A young family take a look round the new town of Livingston and discover what it has to offer both inhabitants and industry.

2229 DUNA BULL, THE
1972

| 35mm | col | comopt | 2830ft | VIEW |

sp. Films of Scotland
p.c. IFA (Scotland) Ltd.
d. Laurence Henson

A light-hearted comedy where Duna is an imaginary island lying far west of the Hebrides. When the islanders' only bull has to be destroyed they are faced with the problem of getting another to the island. [Films of Scotland first story film.]

2230 SEAWARDS THE GREAT SHIPS
1960

| 35mm | col | comopt | 2610ft | VIEW |

sp. Films of Scotland
p.c. Templar Films
d. Hilary Harris

The Oscar-winning documentary of shipbuilding on the Clyde, with treatment by John Grierson.

2231 SMITHS IN SCOTLAND, THE
1966

| 16mm | col | comopt | 810ft | VIEW |

sp. Films of Scotland
d. Laurence Henson

An overview of places, industries and sports enjoyed in Scotland.

2232 I REMEMBER, I REMEMBER
1968

| 35mm | b/w&col | comopt | 4789ft | VIEW |

sp. Films of Scotland and Scottish Television
w. John Grierson

A personal account by John Grierson of a life spent in documentary film-making, including his early life in Stirling, and his first films.

2233 KEEP YOUR EYE ON PAISLEY
1975

| 35mm | col | comopt | 2815ft | VIEW |

sp. Films of Scotland and Corporation of Paisley
p.c. Tree Films
d. Charles Gormley

The town of Paisley, its industries and people.

2234 KIND OF SEEING, A
1967

| 16mm | col | comopt | 544ft | REF |

sp. Films of Scotland
p.c. IFA (Scotland) Ltd.
d. Edward McConnell

The colour of Scotland as seen through the eyes of Edward McConnell. Abstract shapes in nature.

2235 SONGS OF SCOTLAND
1963

| 35mm | col | comopt | 1440ft | VIEW |

sp. Films of Scotland
p.c. IFA (Scotland) Ltd.
d. Laurence Henson and Edward McConnell

Against a backdrop of Scottish scenes, traditional songs of Scotland are sung by Elizabeth Robson, Dolina MacLellan, Hamish Henderson, Duncan Robertson, Robin Hall and Jimmy MacGregor.

2236	SEA CITY GREENOCK				
1974					
35mm	col	comopt	1900ft		VIEW

sp. Films of Scotland and Corporation of Greenock
p.c. IFA (Scotland) Ltd.
d. Laurence Henson

A promotional film for the town of Greenock, it features the Scott Lithgow shipyard, the town's industries, houses and parks.

2237	ONE DAY IN IRVINE				
1971					
35mm	col	comopt	1870ft		VIEW

sp. Films of Scotland and Irvine Development Corporation
p.c. IFA (Scotland) Ltd.
d. Mark Littlewood

The Ayrshire town of Irvine as seen through the eyes of a young Canadian.

2238	HIGHLAND FOLK				
1962					
35mm	col	comopt	860ft		VIEW

sp. Films of Scotland
p.c. Anvil Films (Scotland) Ltd.

Folk traditions of the Highlands including the Folk Museum of Kingussie and caber tossing at Highland gatherings.

2239	METAL IN HARMONY				
1962					
35mm	col	comopt	1850ft		VIEW

sp. Films of Scotland
p.c. Anglo-Scottish Pictures Ltd.
d. Kenneth Fairbairn

The story of aluminium production, from bauxite mining in Ghana, transportation to Burntisland in Fife and the product's various uses.

2240	RIVERS AT WORK				
1958					
16mm	col	mute	1800ft		VIEW

p.c. Greenpark Productions
d. Lew Davidson

Water power and its development in Scotland. Commentary by John Grierson.

2241	HEALTH OF A CITY				
1965					
16mm	b/w	comopt	890ft		VIEW

sp. Films of Scotland
p.c. Templar Film Studios
p. Riddell Black

The health services of Glasgow and the work of the Medical Officer of Health in housing, schools and hospitals.

2242	IN GREAT WATERS				
1974					
35mm	col	comopt	2004ft		VIEW

sp. Films of Scotland and HIDB
p.c. IFA (Scotland) Ltd.
d. Laurence Henson

The fishing industry in the Shetlands and Outer Hebrides.

2243	TAY ROAD BRIDGE				
1967					
35mm	col	comopt	2659ft		VIEW

sp. Films of Scotland and Esso Petroleum Co. Ltd.
p.c. Campbell Harper Films Ltd.
d. Henry Cooper

The building of the Tay Road Bridge from the initial stages to the official opening by HM the Queen Mother.

2244	MAKE WAY FOR STEEL				
1966					
35mm	col	comopt	1112ft		REF

sp. Films of Scotland
p.c. Templar Film Studios

The construction of Ravenscraig and Gartcosh steel works, David Colvilles Limited.

2245	WEAVE ME A RAINBOW				
1962					
35mm	col	comopt	2532ft		VIEW

sp. Films of Scotland
p.c. Templar Film Studios
d. Edward McConnell

The designing and weaving of woollen cloth.

2246	HAND OF ADAM				
1975					
35mm	col	comopt	1190ft		VIEW

sp. Films of Scotland and the Scottish Arts Council
p.c. Viz Limited

A detailed study of the many architectural works of the Scottish architect Robert Adam, including Culzean Castle and many parts of the New Town of Edinburgh.

2247	ST. ANDREWS BY THE NORTHERN SEA				
1974					
35mm	col	comopt	2057ft		VIEW

sp. Films of Scotland and Royal Burgh of St. Andrews
p.c. Pelicula Films
d. Mark Littlewood

A look at the town of St. Andrews; its University and traditions, the Royal & Ancient Golf Course and the Lammas Fair.

2248	CALTREX CALENDERING LINE				
1978					
16mm	col	sep opt	380ft		REF

sp. Films of Scotland
p.c. Edinburgh Film Productions
p. Robin Crichton

The partnership of an Edinburgh based firm of metal box manufacturers Wilkie and Paul, with Francis Shaw of Manchester, to produce the PVC calendering line for the manufacture of PVC film for packaging.

2249	QUIET COUNTRY, THE				
1972					
35mm	col	comopt	c1600ft		VIEW

sp. Films of Scotland

An exploration of south-west Scotland; the Mull of Galloway, its rich farming land, and coastal holiday places.

2250	LOCH LOMOND				
1967					
35mm	col	comopt	2790ft		VIEW

sp. Films of Scotland
p.c. IFA (Scotland) Ltd.
d. Laurence Henson

The changing seasons are seen on Loch Lomond; the animals, and the lives of the people who live on the lochside.

2251	WATER OF LIFE, THE				
1972					
16mm	col	comopt	540ft		VIEW

sp. Films of Scotland

An explanation of how whisky is distilled.

2253	WATER, WATER EVERYWHERE				
1967					
35mm	col	comopt	1000ft		VIEW

sp. Films of Scotland
p.c. IFA (Scotland) Ltd.
d. Edward McConnell

Scotland's water resources and the wide range of uses made of water for industry, health and recreation.

2254	ERSKINE BRIDGE, THE				
1972					
35mm	col	sep opt	2000ft		VIEW

sp. Films of Scotland
p.c. IFA (Scotland) Ltd.
Documentary on the building of the Erskine road bridge.

2256	SONG FOR PRINCE CHARLIE, A				
1959					
35mm	col	comopt	1650ft		VIEW

sp. Films of Scotland
p.c. Anvil Films

Story of the '45 Stuart Rising. Told in song, the film follows the route taken by Bonnie Prince Charlie after the Battle of Culloden.

2257	TAYSIDE				
1974					
35mm	col	comopt	2700ft		VIEW

sp. Films of Scotland
p.c. Ogam Films
d. Oscar Marzaroli

An overview of Tayside, looking at its industries, towns, landscape and people.

2258	LOTHIAN LANDSCAPE				
1974					
35mm	col	comopt	1890ft		VIEW

sp. Films of Scotland
p.c. Pelicula Films
d. Mark Littlewood, Mike Alexander

The towns, castles and farmland of East Lothian.

2259	PRIDE OF ISLANDS, A				
1973					
35mm	col	comopt	2687ft		VIEW

sp. Films of Scotland and HIDB
p.c. Ogam Films
d. Oscar Marzaroli

The changing pattern of life in the Hebrides, Orkney and Shetland.

2260	LINE TO SKYE, THE				
1973					
35mm	col	comopt	1440ft		VIEW

sp. Films of Scotland and Ross & Cromarty County Council
p.c. IFA (Scotland) Ltd.
d. Ed. McConnell

The stations, landscape, flora and fauna along the Inverness to Kyle railway line.

2261	TOWN CALLED AYR, A				
1975					
35mm	col	comopt	2000ft		REF

sp. Films of Scotland
The town of Ayr, past and present.

183

184

Gordon Highlanders Leave for the Boer War, 1899. The local regiment leaving Aberdeen. Ref. 0449

2262	CASTLE AND CAPITAL

1979

35mm	col	comopt	1616ft	VIEW

sp. Films of Scotland
p.c. Pelicula Films
d. Mike Alexander

A descriptive essay on the city of Edinburgh, and in particular of Edinburgh Castle.

2263	THREE SCOTTISH PAINTERS

1963

35mm	col	comopt	2000ft	VIEW

sp. Films of Scotland

A documentary on the work of the artists John Maxwell, Joan Eardley and Robin Philipson.

2264	PRACTICAL ROMANTIC. SIR WALTER SCOTT

1969

16mm	col	comopt	840ft	VIEW

sp. Films of Scotland
p.c. Anvil Films (Scotland)

The life of Sir Walter Scott, and the hills, castles and countryside that inspired him.

2266	KIRKCALDY

1975

35mm	col	comopt	1974ft	REF

sp. Films of Scotland Committee
p.c. Sidhartha Films
d. Steve Clark-Hall

Guided by a cartoon disc jockey, the films looks at the Fife town of Kirkcaldy. Its townspeople tell of their town, their attitudes to it, its oddities, pleasures and problems.

2267 DUNFERMLINE

1974

| 35mm | col | comopt | 1800ft | VIEW |

sp. Films of Scotland

The town of Dunfermline, its past and present, at work and at play.

2268 HOLIDAYS 1934

1934

| 9.5mm | b/w | silent | 360ft | REF |

[filmed by Alston Dunderdale]

Holidays on the islands of Jura and Gigha.

2269 TWO BIG EVENTS

1938

| 16mm | col | silent | 300ft | REF |

filmed by James Robertson

Amateur footage of the launch of the "Queen Elizabeth" from John Brown's shipyard in Clydebank, and of the Empire Exhibition.

2270 [GLASGOW UNIVERSITY NORTH RONA EXPEDITION]

1958

| 16mm | b/w | silent | 1010ft | REF |

[filmed by Dr. Robert Morrison]

A scientific expedition mounted by Glasgow University to North Rona and Sula Sgeir. The expedition was supported by the yacht "Mary Rose of Moran" captained by Dr. Robert Morrison.

2271 UNICA, BRUXELLES 1953

1953

| 16mm | b/w | silent | 306ft | REF |

sp. Cineastes Amateurs Bruxelles
filmed by J.M. Dumont

Coverage of the Congress of UNICA (International Union of Amateur Cinematographers) in Brussels 1953.

2272 (WATERSIDE AND DISTRICT)

1935*-'40

| 16mm | b/w | silent | 295ft | REF |

Some events around the villages of Waterside and Lethan Hill, Ayrshire.

2273 MAILLEY FAMILY FILM

1951

| 16mm | b/w | silent | 400ft | REF |

Family holidays in Argyllshire with picnics, and paddling at the beach.

2274 ROYAL SCOTTISH MUSEUM. EDINBURGH

1939?

| 16mm | b/w | silent | 490ft | REF |

p.c. J. Campbell Harper Films Ltd.

The Royal Scottish Museum in Edinburgh, its history and the work of its various departments.

2275 AN EMPIRE MEETS

1938

| 16mm | col | silent | 288ft | REF |

filmed by James Blair

General scenes of the Empire Exhibition in Glasgow's Bellahouston Park.

2276 [JOYCE AND IRENE ON THE CLYDE. SUMMER 1955]

1955

| 35mm | b/w | silent | 210ft | REF |

Two girls enjoy a holiday at the seaside.

2277 LOYAL GLASGOW

1953

| 16mm | col | silent | 100ft | REF |

filmed by James Robertson

The Coronation visit of Queen Elizabeth and the Duke of Edinburgh to Glasgow.

2278 [HIGHLAND FUND IN ACTION. HIGHLAND INITIATIVE]

1981

| 16mm | col | silent | 1080ft | REF |

[p.c. Glasgow and Strathclyde Universities A-V Services]
[d. Calum Ferguson]

Unedited rushes of a tape/slide production, including footage of McLean's marine repair yard in Kyle of Lochalsh, a cheese factory, and crofting scenes in Wester Ross.

2279 AMONG THE ISLES

1937*

| 16mm | b/w | silent | 286ft | REF |

Life on board the SS "Tuscania" including lifeboat drill and deck games. Shots of St. Kilda and Cape Wrath.

2280 RESTORATION OF PROVOST SKENE'S HOUSE

1953

| 16mm | col | mute | 528ft | REF |

sp. City of Aberdeen Corporation
p.c. City of Aberdeen's Architect's Department

The opening ceremony of Provost Skene's House in Aberdeen by HM the Queen Mother.

185

186

2281   WHEELS OF CHANCE
1960s

16mm	col	comopt	1000ft		VIEW

sp.Scottish Development Dept. & NCPS
p.c. Transworld International Inc.
d. Robert Thorpe

Promotional film for the National Cycling Proficiency Scheme presented by Jackie Stewart.

2282   [STONES]
1970s,c

16mm	col	comopt	468ft		VIEW

[p.c. Glasgow University A-V Service]

Professor Mackie of the University of Glasgow at the site of standing stones on the west coast of Kintyre, talking about the astronomical theory and archaeology of the stones.

2283   IMAGE RECONSTRUCTION OF SEBACEOUS GLANDS
1983

16mm	col	comopt	80ft		REF

[p.c. Glasgow University A-V Service]

Demonstration of the reconstruction of sebaceous glands using graphics and animation.

2284   ELECTRON MICROSCOPE
1970c

16mm	b/w	mute		REF

[p.c. Glasgow University A-V Service]

An educational film on the electron microscope.

2285   OSMOSIS
1978c

16mm	col	mute	468ft		VIEW

[p.c. Glasgow University A-V Service]

The process of osmosis illustrated by animation.

2286   GOING TO MARKET
1975*

16mm	col	comopt	1000ft		REF

[p.c. Glasgow University A-V Service]

An instructional film on the methods of marketing products.

2287   POTTERY AS A SCHOOL CRAFT
1951

16mm	b/w	silent	860ft		VIEW

filmed by Allan Glen's School Film Unit

Art master and pupils of Allan Glen's School demonstrate various methods of making pottery. [Prize-winner at the 1951 Scottish Amateur Film Festival.] [See also ref. 2288.]

2288   ALLAN GLEN'S SCHOOL CAMP
1931-'32

16mm	b/w	silent	160ft		REF

Allan Glen's school camp at Loch Awe in 1931 and at Gullane in 1932. [See also ref. 2287.]

2289   (TAYPORT PARISH CHURCH SALES OF WORK)
1934-'50

16mm	b/w&col	silent	390ft		REF

[filmed by R. Robertson]

Scenes at the Tayport parish church sale of work and garden fete. [See also refs. 2290-2307.]

2290   JUBILEE DAY IN TAYPORT. 6TH MAY 1935
1935

16mm	b/w	silent	230ft		REF

[filmed by R. Robertson]

The celebrations in Tayport to mark Jubilee Day, including a church parade, a picnic and royal toast in the Council Chambers. [See also refs. 2289-2307.]

2291   CORONATION DAY. TAYPORT. 12TH MAY 1937
1937

16mm	b/w&col	silent	445ft		REF

[filmed by R. Robertson]

The coronation celebrations in Tayport; streets decorated in bunting, a children's parade, a bowling match and fireworks display. [See also refs. 2289-2307.]

2292   (LOCAL EVENTS, TAYPORT)
1937

16mm	b/w	silent	166ft		REF

[filmed by R. Robertson]

Events in the Fife village of Tayport; the demolition of the mill factory chimney, construction of the new bridge at Guardbridge, and the Burgh Jubilee Dinner in the Masonic Hall. [See also refs. 2289-2307.]

2293   (WARTIME IN TAYPORT)
1940*-'44

16mm	b/w&col	silent	303ft		REF

[filmed by R. Robertson]

Footage of the Polish forces in Tayport, Tayport Flight 1302 Squadron ATC drill and women railway workers at Tayport station. [See also refs. 2289-2307.]

2294	(TAYPORT EVENTS 1946-'49)

1946-'49

16mm	b/w&col silent	465ft	REF

[filmed by R. Robertson]

The coming of electric light to the streets of Tayport, a local pageant and the Royal Highland Show in Dundee attended by HM Queen Elizabeth. [See also refs. 2289-2307.]

2295	RED LETTER DAY FOR TAYPORT, A

1950

16mm	b/w&col silent	173ft	REF

[filmed by R. Robertson]

The visit of HM the Queen Mother to Tayport on 19th September 1950. [See also refs. 2289-2307.]

2296	INDUSTRIES OF TAYPORT, THE

1947*

16mm	b/w	silent	340ft	REF

[filmed by R. Robertson]

Women at work in the Scott & Fyfe jute factory in Tayport, and the village blacksmith shoes a horse. [See also refs. 2289-2307.]

2297	TAYPORT AND ITS INDUSTRIES

1948

16mm	b/w	silent	304ft	REF

[filmed by R. Robertson]

Shoe repairs are done at Smith & Kays' shoe shop in Tayport. [See also refs. 2289-2307.]

2298	INDUSTRIES OF TAYPORT, THE

1949*

16mm	b/w	silent	100ft	REF

[filmed by R. Robertson]

Work at the foundry yard and iron works of James Ferguson & Sons, Tayport, Fife. [See also refs. 2289-2307.]

2299	TAYPORT TOWN HALL OPENING

1950

16mm	b/w&col silent	158ft	REF

[filmed by R. Robertson]

The opening ceremony of Tayport Town Hall and the crowning of the Gala Queen. [See also refs. 2289-2307.]

2300	"MERRIE ENGLAND"

1950

16mm	b/w	silent	202ft	REF

[filmed by R. Robertson]

Tayport amateur musical society in rehearsal for the production of "Merrie England". [See also refs. 2289-2307.]

2301	TAYPORT PICNICS 1951/'52

1951

16mm	b/w&col silent	260ft	REF

[filmed by R. Robertson]

A picnic at Craigtown Park, St. Andrews and at Bottomcraig Farm, Balmerino. [See also refs. 2289-2370.]

2302	OPENING NEW COUNCIL CHAMBERS. TAYPORT

1952

16mm	b/w	silent	195ft	REF

[filmed by R. Robertson]

Provost Wilkie opens the new Burgh Chambers in Tayport, and the first council meeting is held in the new room. [See also refs. 2289-2370.]

2303	(CHURCH HUT, TAYPORT)

1953*

16mm	b/w&col silent	335ft	REF

[filmed by R. Robertson]

The conversion of the Battery Factory canteen hut into Tayport's Sunday School. [See also refs. 2289-2370.]

2304	CORONATION YEAR 1953

1953

16mm	b/w&col silent	400ft	REF

[filmed by R. Robertson]

The celebrations in Tayport on Coronation Day, including a church service, the jute mill and streets decorated with bunting, a gala procession and a swimming race in the river Tay. [See also refs. 2289-2370.]

2305	"QUAKER GIRL, THE"

1954

16mm	b/w	silent	255ft	REF

[filmed by R. Robertson]

Stage performance of "The Quaker Girl" as presented by Tayport amateur musical society. [See also refs. 2289-2370.]

2306	"COUNTRY GIRL"

1955

16mm	b/w	silent	216ft	REF

[filmed by R. Robertson]

Tayport amateur musical society present "A Country Girl". [See also refs. 2289-2370.]

187

2307	IN SEARCH OF TAYPORT				
1934					
16mm	b/w	silent	325ft		REF

[filmed by R. Robertson]

Various scenes in Tayport, Fife; the arrival of the ferry in Tayport harbour, machinery at work in the sawmill, a swimming gala in the harbour, a sand building competition and golfing at the Scotscraig golf club. [See also refs. 2289-2370.]

2308	[GALLIPOLI]				
n.d.					
16mm	b/w	silent	220ft		REF

Believed to be footage of the return visit by war veterans to scenes of battle during the Gallipoli campaign in 1915.

2309	STEALING AWAY TO STORNOWAY				
1937					
16mm	b/w	silent	370ft		VIEW

filmed by R.V. Brown

Steamer journey from Mallaig to Stornoway, with views of Skye, the standing stones at Callanish, blackhouses and the Hospital Carnival in Stornoway.

2310	PRETTY DART, A				
1939					
16mm	b/w	silent	160ft		REF

A wedding at St. Clement's church, Rodel on the island of Harris.

2311	HEATH VISITS THE WEAVERS				
1970c					
16mm	b/w	comopt	120ft		REF

[p.c. Pathe News]

Edward Heath visits Stornoway where he meets crofter Neil MacLean at his weaving loom and visits a weaving company mill.

2312	SEALING WAX AND WAFERS				
1966					
16mm	col	comopt	730ft		REF

sp. George Waterston and Sons Ltd.
p.c. Grange Film Productions
d. Ian Brock

A promotional film for George Waterston and Sons of Edinburgh, wax chandlers. Shot inside the firm's wax making factory at St. John's Hill, just prior to demolition it shows the machinery and traditional processes in the making of sealing wax.

2313	BRIGHT FUTURE				
1970c					
16mm	col	comopt	670ft		REF

sp. Bank of Scotland
p.c. Grange Film Productions
d. Ian Brock

A promotional film for a career in banking with the Bank of Scotland.

2314	QUEEN IN OBAN, THE				
1956					
35mm	b/w	silent	630ft		REF

[filmed as a local topical for the Playhouse Cinema, Oban]

The visit of HM the Queen and Prince Philip to Oban.

2315	[MELROSE FESTIVALS 1956-'61]				
1956-'60					
16mm	col	silent	800ft		REF

filmed by Mysie Hargrave

Events at the Melrose Festivals of 1956, 1957, 1959 and 1960.

2317	GLASGOW AIRPORT				
1969					
16mm	col	sep opt	686ft		REF

filmed by SEFA (Lanarkshire Production Group)

A comprehensive picture of a modern airport showing flight movements, radar, passenger flow, and emergency services at work.

2318	LIFE IN THE SCOTTISH HIGHLANDS				
1968					
16mm	col	sep opt	720ft		REF

filmed by SEFA (Lanarkshire Production Group)

A look at the population and social problems of the seven crofting counties of Scotland.

2319	BATTLE OF THE STYLES				
1968					
16mm	col	sep opt	630ft		REF

sp. Educational Films of Scotland
p.c. Park Film Studios

Nineteenth century Scottish architecture and the battle between those who found their inspiration in Classic or Gothic methods, leading to the development of new ideas and expertise.

2320	ABERDEEN				
1970					
16mm	col	sep opt	675ft		VIEW

sp. Educational Films of Scotland
p.c. Campbell Harper Films Ltd.

The historical background to the growth of the city of Aberdeen.

2321	THOMAS TELFORD				

1963

16mm	col	sep opt	c700ft		REF

sp. Educational Films of Scotland
p.c. Park Film Studios

A study of the work of the Scottish engineer Thomas Telford.

2322	[HALFWAY TO PARADISE: D.C. THOMSON]			

1988

16mm	b/w	sep mag	160ft	VIEW

[sp. Channel 4]
[p.c. Big Star in a Wee Picture]
[series p. Don Coutts, Stuart Cosgrove]

Interviews with writers Bill Graham and Martin Lindsay who talk about their story lines for D.C. Thomson's illustrated "Football Picture Monthly".

2323	[HALFWAY TO PARADISE: GRANT MORRISON]			

1988

16mm	col	sep mag	265ft	VIEW

[sp. Channel 4 Television]
[p.c. Big Star in a Wee Picture]
[series p. Don Coutts, Stuart Cosgrove]

Comic story writer Grant Morrison talks about comics, how they have changed since the 1950s and his contribution to "Zenith" and "Animal Man".

2324	[HALFWAY TO PARADISE: JAMES KELMAN]			

1988

16mm	col	sep mag	230ft	VIEW

[sp. Channel 4 Television]
[p.c. Big Star in a Wee Picture]
[series p. Don Coutts, Stuart Cosgrove]

Author James Kelman reads extracts from his book "A Greyhound for Breakfast" and talks about his writing.

2325	[HALFWAY TO PARADISE: AL JOLSON]			

1988

16mm	col	sep mag	277ft	VIEW

[sp. Channel 4 Television]
[p.c. Big Star in a Wee Picture]
[series p. Don Coutts, Stuart Cosgrove]

Interview with Hugh Dempster who talks about his career as a drag and mime artist. Shots of Dempster as Al Jolson in Glasgow streets. He defends his act against accusations of racism.

2326	[HALFWAY TO PARADISE: GREENOCK PUB]			

1988

16mm	col	sep mag	144ft	VIEW

[sp. Channel 4 Television]
[p.c. Big Star in a Wee Picture]
[series p. Don Coutts and Stuart Cosgrove]

"Danny's Place", a "pub" in Greenock where teenagers and youngsters are served soft drinks. The role of the pub in the campaign to reduce alcohol abuse.

2327	[HALFWAY TO PARADISE: THE CUT]			

1988

16mm	col	sep mag	180ft	VIEW

[sp. Channel 4 Television]
[p.c. Big Star in a Wee Picture]
[series p. Don Coutts and Stuart Cosgrove]

Interview with Alan Campbell concerning the magazine's style and intended readership of the magazine "The Cut". Gavin Evans, the magazine's photographer, at work in his studio.

2328	[HALFWAY TO PARADISE: JOHN COLQUHOUN]			

1988

16mm	col	sep mag	220ft	VIEW

[sp. Channel 4]
[p.c. Big Star in a Wee Picture]
[series p. Don Coutts and Stuart Cosgrove]

Footballer John Colquhoun talks about his politics and his life before football. Shots of young athletes and footballers training at Meadowbank Stadium.

2329	[HALFWAY TO PARADISE: IRN BRU]			

1988

16mm	col	sep mag	360ft	VIEW

[sp. Channel 4 Television]
[p.c. Big Star in a Wee Picture]
[series p. Don Coutts and Stuart Cosgrove]

Interview with Robin Barr on the history of "Irn Bru" with shots of old bottle labels and packaging. Robin Barr mixes the Irn Bru "essence".

2330	[HALFWAY TO PARADISE: CHIC MURRAY]			

1988

16mm	col	sep mag	170ft	VIEW

[sp. Channel 4 Television]
[p.c. Big Star in a Wee Picture]
[series p. Don Coutts and Stuart Cosgrove]

Voice-over of Chic Murray telling jokes intercut with vox pops, people in street wearing Chic Murray style 'bunnets' telling his kind of gags and how they remember him.

190

2331 [HALFWAY TO PARADISE: NAKED RADIO]

1988

| 16mm | col | sep mag | 315ft | VIEW |

[sp. Channel 4 Television]
[p.c. Big Star in a Wee Picture]
[series p. Don Coutts and Stuart Cosgrove]

Interviews with producer Philip Differ and actors Tony Roper and Jonathon Watson on the show "Naked Radio", specifically the spoof history of Scottish football, its audience reaction and how it was received by the professional footballers.

2332 ROTHESAY ACADEMY. CHRISTMAS 1928

1928

| 35mm | b/w | silent | 230ft | VIEW |

[filmed as a local topical for Palace Picture House, Rothesay]

Children leaving Rothesay Academy's school building and close-ups of several prominent local citizens.

2333 (DUNOON AND ROTHESAY PIER)

1920c

| 35mm | b/w | silent | 60ft | VIEW |

[filmed as a local topical for Palace Picture House, Rothesay]

Shots of Dunoon pier from approaching steamer, passengers pass through the ticket gate.

2334 HOLIDAY SCENES AT ROTHESAY

1922c

| 35mm | b/w | silent | 200ft | VIEW |

sp. Palace Picture House, Rothesay
p.c. Green's Topical Productions, Glasgow and London

Holiday-makers arriving in Rothesay by the steamer "Columba". Beach scenes, the ladies' bathing pond, the putting green.

2335 ROTHESAY FANCY DRESS PARADE

1928

| 35mm | b/w | silent | 305ft | VIEW |

[filmed as a local topical for the Waverley Picture House]

One of a collection of local topicals commissioned from cameraman in Glasgow by James Gillespie, proprietor of the Palace and later Waverley Picture Houses, Rothesay. The film shows children in fancy dress and the parade of decorated floats.

2336 ROTHESAY PEACE CELEBRATIONS

1919

| 35mm | b/w | silent | 355ft | VIEW |

p.c. Green's Film Service, British Moving Picture News

Footage of the peace celebrations, including the parade, crowds and band. General Sir Hunter Weston takes the salute at Rothsay Town Hall. An effigy of Kaiser Bill is hoisted up the mast of a boat.

2337 (MACEWAN'S FREEDOM OF ROTHESAY)

1922

| 35mm | b/w | silent | 310ft | VIEW |

[filmed as a local topical for the Palace Picture House]

Passengers disembark from steamer, including Sir William MacEwan and party. General scenes of the freedom ceremony in the grounds of Rothesay Castle.

2338 (ROTHESAY 1918)

1920*

| 35mm | b/w | silent | 290ft | VIEW |

[sp. Palace Picture House, Rothesay]
p.c. Green's Topical Productions

A parade through the streets of Rothesay led by a pipe band, the colour party outside a church, with the Marquis of Graham and other prominent citizens.

2339 (LADY LAUDER IN ROTHESAY)

1922

| 35mm | b/w | silent | 285ft | VIEW |

[filmed as a local topical for the Palace Picture House]

Beach scenes on the island of Bute. A tram approaches Ettrick Bay, and Lady Lauder and party arrive to judge the sand modelling competition.

2340 [KILSYTH RAILWAY STATION]

1920c

| 35mm | b/w | silent | 12ft | VIEW |

Two men alight from a North British first class carriage onto Kilsyth station platform. [Fragment of film.]

2341 (TOWERS FAMILY FILM PART 1)

1952/'57

| 35mm | b/w | silent | 290ft | VIEW |

Exterior and interior shots of the Prize Cinema in Gretna, run by the Towers family.

2342 (TOWERS FAMILY FILM PART 2)

1956

| 35mm | b/w | comopt | 370ft | VIEW |

[p.c. Pathe Pictorial]

Pathe News footage of the film premiere of "Now and Forever" at the Empire, Leicester Square. The film portrays a couple, played by Janet Scott and Vernon Gray, who elope to Gretna Green.

2343 IONA COMMUNITY YOUTH GROUP, THE

1959*

16mm	b/w	comopt	415ft		REF

p.c. ABC Television

Filmed for the television programme "The Sunday Break Film Report" featuring the international camp on Iona as seen through the eyes of two young visitors. Dr. George MacLeod talks about what the Community means to him.

2344 THAT SACRED ISLE IONA

1959c

16mm	b/w	comopt	620ft		REF

[p.c. BBC Television]
p. Bill Northwood

History of Iona Abbey and the rebuilding programme since 1938. Dr. George MacLeod relates how it all began. Service of thanksgiving and re-dedication of the chapel. [See also ref. 2742 for longer version.]

2345 [COMMUNITY HOUSE]

1967

16mm	b/w	mute	800ft		REF

[p.c. Templar Film Studios]

Members of staff and various activities at the Iona Community House in Govan, Glasgow. [Rushes only.]

2346 CAN THESE STONES LIVE?

1964

16mm	b/w	comopt	920ft		REF

p.c. BBC Television
p. Vernon Sproxton

The story of Dr. George MacLeod, leader of the Iona Community, including the early days of his ministry in Govan, and the reconstruction work of Iona Abbey.

2347 ALF GOES TO WORK

1960

16mm	b/w	mute	1650ft		VIEW

sp. National Council of Churches, USA
d. & p. Robert Newman

Dr. George MacLeod talks about the origins of the Iona Community and the re-building of Iona Abbey.

2348 [IONA CLUB]

1950s

16mm	b/w	comopt	440ft		REF

p.c. ABC Television

Activities inside Community House, Glasgow, as seen by a visiting teenage couple. Dr. George MacLeod is interviewed, and the young couple are given a tour of the building and its facilities. Young people are seen dancing with a skiffle band.

2349 (RESTORATION OF IONA ABBEY)

1938-'59

16mm	col	silent	320ft		VIEW

[filmed by Dr. George MacLeod]

Amateur footage shot during 20 years of restoration work on the Abbey and buildings on Iona.

2350 PATTERN TO PENTECOST

1965

16mm	b/w	comopt	995ft		VIEW

p.c. BBC Television
p. Ronald Falconer

Narrated by Dr. George MacLeod, the film traces the beginnings of the Iona Community and the restoration of Iona Abbey, finishing with scenes of events on Iona at Pentecost 1965, when twenty nations' churchmen gathered for religious observance.

2351 IONA - WE SHALL REBUILD

1956*

16mm	b/w&col	silent	390ft		REF

sp. The Iona Community
filmed by the Scottish Religious Film Society

Progress of the construction work on Iona Abbey is seen through the eyes of Hector Ross, a young minister and John Kane, a carpenter.

2352 (AFRICAN VISITORS TO IONA)

1956*

16mm	col	silent	32ft		REF

[filmed by Dr. George MacLeod]

A party of visitors, possibly from Africa, being shown round the abbey site by a minister.

2353 RISE IN WAGES, A

1937c

16mm	b/w	silent	240ft		REF

sp. Sir German Sims Woodhead Memorial Trust

A temperance propaganda film using a fictional story of a man who gives up his beer to save money for dresses for his daughters so that they can go on a Sunday School picnic.

2354 EDINBURGH TEMPERANCE DAY

1938

16mm	b/w	silent	198ft		VIEW

A procession through Edinburgh by temperance groups, Band of Hope, etc. Footage of communal hymn singing on the Meadows and the crowning ceremony of the Temperance King and Queen.

191

2355 (TEMPERANCE DAYS AND ORGANISATIONS 1936)

1936

16mm	b/w	silent	450ft		REF

Footage of Temperance Days in Edinburgh, Dundee and Kilsyth. Members of the Scottish Temperance Alliance and National Order of Good Templars, Edinburgh, in regalia.

2356 (TEMPERANCE EVENTS. EDINBURGH 1939)

1939

16mm	b/w	silent	420ft		REF

Various events at the Edinburgh Temperance Day. The film also shows footage of the Edinburgh Royal Infirmary Pageant and the British Women's Temperance Association at the Highland and Agriculture Show, Edinburgh.

2357 (TEMPERANCE DAYS. EDINBURGH 1936-'37)

1936

16mm	b/w	silent	420ft		REF

filmed by the Scottish Temperance Film Association (Edinburgh)

Edinburgh Temperance Day celebrations, showing the Edinburgh Royal Infirmary Pageant and the crowning ceremonies of the Temperance King and Queen.

2358 MARGARET BAKER IN LECTURES AND STORIES

1937*

16mm	b/w	silent	320ft		REF

sp. Sir German Sims Woodhead Memorial Trust

An open-air lecture by Margaret Baker telling the story about the dangers of drink, and propounding the benefits of drinking milk.

Dundee Courier, 1911. Compositors at supper. Ref. 1604
With kind permission of The Courier, Dundee.

2359   HOWER
1937

16mm	b/w	silent	396ft		REF

filmed by William Kirkness

Amateur footage of the excavation of a prehistoric site on Papa Westray, Orkney.

2360   ROWIEGAR
1937c

16mm	b/w	silent	260ft		REF

filmed by William Kirkness

The excavation of a long stalled, chambered cairn on Rousay, Orkney.

2361   MIDHOWE BROCH
1932

16mm	b/w	silent	380ft		REF

filmed by William Kirkness

Shots of a broch at Mousa, Shetland, and general views of the site of the Midhowe Broch, Rousay, Orkney.

2362   (HAWICK C1913)
1913c

35mm	b/w	silent	800ft		VIEW

Local events in Hawick; workers leaving Eastfield Mill, schoolgirls dancing round a maypole, a children's procession, a scout parade and Baden-Powell receiving the Freedom of the Burgh.

2363   FLOOD IN DUMFRIES
1936*

35mm	b/w	silent	90ft		VIEW

[filmed as a local topical for the Regal Cinema, Dumfries]

Flood waters breaking over the banks of the River Nith in Dumfries town centre. People are seen standing in doorways and wading through the water.

2364   CASTING "THE BRUCE" AT CHELTENHAM
1963/'64

16mm	b/w	silent	500ft		REF

The various stages of the casting process of the statue of Robert the Bruce, erected at Bannockburn.

2365   PERCHANCE TO SAIL
1946

16mm	b/w	comopt	1200ft		REF

p.c. Elder Dalrymple Productions
ph. & d. J. Blake Dalrymple

Drama concerning the yacht voyage by J. Stirling Gillespie from the West Coast of Scotland to Germany and Poland in 1936. The film includes actuality footage of both countries shot by Elder-Dalrymple Films at that time.

2366   FOLLOWING THE RIVER NO. 2: THE MIDDLE STRETCH
1955c

16mm	col	silent	350ft		VIEW

p.c. GB Instructional
p. J.C. Elder

From the Falls of Clyde, two children follow the river into the wider Clyde valley visiting fruit farms and passing the Carron Grain Mills, a power station and the Popinjay Hotel.

2367   [ON THE ISLAND]
1950c

16mm	b/w	silent	320ft		REF

[p.c. Elder Films]

Three Scottish children spend a holiday at the croft of their grandmother. They see a sheep being shorn, butter being churned, and wool being spun.

2368   (NCB STAFF BUS OUTINGS)
1955

16mm	b/w&col	silent	390ft		REF

Possibly footage of various excursions for Coal Board staff where places visited includes Burns country, the Trossachs, Stirling, Moffat and Largs.

2369   LORD ROBENS INTERVIEW
1968

16mm	b/w	comopt	290ft		REF

[p.c. Scottish Television]

Lord Robens is interviewed about the relationship between the Coal Board and the electricity and steel industries and the outlook for the future of the coal industry.

2370   FARMER'S BOY, THE
1938

16mm	b/w	silent	348ft		VIEW

p.c. Elder-Dalrymple Productions

Prospects for a young boy in farming are illustrated by activities on a farm throughout the year.

2371   OBAN CELTIC MEET NEWTONMORE (REPLAY)
1937

35mm	b/w	comopt	428ft		VIEW

sp. Playhouse, Oban
p.c. Scottish Films

The final at Inverness of the Camanachd Association Shinty Cup between Oban Celtic and Newtonmore.

193

2372 ARBROATH'S NEW SWIMMING POOL

1935

35mm	b/w	comopt	460ft	VIEW

The official opening ceremony of Arbroath's new swimming pool by the Earl of Strathmore.

2373 [DUNDEE'S SCREEN SNAPSHOTS] SERIES

1932-'35c

35mm	b/w	silent	1100ft	VIEW

Compilation of various events in Dundee, including bottling at James Robertson's factory, Harry Lauder leaving for an afternoon out, unemployed hikers arriving home after a holiday at Belmont, and unloading jute at Dundee harbour.

2374 ANNAN. RIDING OF THE MARCHES 1925

1925

35mm	b/w	silent	610ft	VIEW

p.c. Pathe Gazette

The 1925 annual festival of the Riding of the Marches at Annan, Dumfriesshire.

2375 ANNAN RIDING OF THE MARCHES 1938

1938

35mm	b/w	silent	770ft	VIEW

The 400th Anniversary celebrations of the annual festival of the Riding of the Marches in Annan, Dumfriesshire.

2376 ANNAN. RIDING OF THE MARCHES 1930

1930

35mm	b/w	silent	700ft	VIEW

Events at the annual Riding of the Marches festival in Annan, Dumfriesshire.

2377 ANNAN RIDING OF THE MARCHES 1935

1935

35mm	b/w	silent	700ft	VIEW

Events at the annual festival in Annan, Dumfriesshire.

2378 GREAT BRIDGE OVER THE FORTH

1936

35mm	b/w	comopt	210ft	VIEW

p.c. Gaumont British News

Opening ceremony of the Kincardine Bridge in 1936.

2381 HEWERS OF COAL

1939

16mm	b/w	silent	684ft	VIEW

p.c. Elder-Dalrymple Production
d. J.C. Elder

A group of boys intending to be mineworkers are given a short course of instruction explaining the elementary principles of coal mining and simple geology.

2382 [AERIALS OF THE CLYDE AND DUMBARTON]

1956-'58

16mm	col	silent	340ft	REF

p.c. Elder Films

Aerial views of Glasgow, Clyde shipyards and Loch Lomond.

2383 (HOLIDAY IN SCOTLAND 1964)

1964

std.8mm	col	silent	300ft	REF

[filmed by C. Pashley]

The lochs, glens and mountains of Ross-shire and Inverness-shire.

2384 HOW TO MAKE YOUR OWN TEMPLETON CARPETS

1973

16mm	col	comopt	935ft	VIEW

sp. Templeton's Carpets
p.c. Martin Benson Films, St. Albans

A tour inside the Templeton carpet factory in Glasgow showing all aspects of the production processes.

2385 MV "KIRRIEMOOR"

1959*

16mm	col	silent	380ft	REF

The naming ceremony and launch of the Moor Line ship MV "Kirriemoor" at the Hebburn shipbuilding yard.

2386 ["COURLAND" AT KARLSHAMM]

1964

16mm	col	silent	164ft	REF

Shots of the Currie Line vessel the "Courland" being loaded with timber at Karlshamm docks.

2387 [CURRIE LINE FILMS 1 & 2]

1963*

16mm	col	silent	200ft	REF

[sp. The Currie Line]
[filmed by R. McVey]

Shots of the Currie Line's vessels the "Courland" and the "Pentland" at Grangemouth docks.

194

2388	BONNIE SCOTLAND				
1949					
16mm	b/w	silent	106ft		REF

[filmed by R.E. Seaton]

An amateur film made during a holiday to Edinburgh, showing the Castle and Princes Street, the river Forth with the ferry and Rail Bridge.

2389	(BOXING MATCHES. SCOTLAND V ENGLAND)				
1954*					
16mm	b/w	silent	200ft		VIEW

p.c. Elder Films

A boxing contest between Scotland and England in the Kelvin Hall, Glasgow.

2390	(ARRIVAL AT NEW YORK)				
1931					
16mm	b/w	silent	225ft		REF

Taken from the deck of a vessel arriving at New York with shots of the Manhattan skyline. The end of the film shows the river Clyde with the liner the "Queen Mary" on stocks.

2391	(IRVINE MEADOW V FAULDHOUSE UNITED)				
1958					
16mm	b/w	silent	270ft		REF

sp. Scottish Television
p.c. Elder Films

A football match in progress between Irvine Meadow and Fauldhouse United in 1958.

2392	LOMOND MC/SKI-ING				
1939					
9.5mm	b/w	silent	800ft		REF

[filmed by Sam Drysdale]

Camping week-ends in the Highlands with the Lomond Mountaineer Club, one of several workers' "weekender" groups.

2393	(GUY FAMILY FILM)				
1930					
9.5mm	b/w	silent	400ft		REF

[filmed by John L. Guy]

The Guy family sailing on the west coast of Scotland with shots of yachts and steamers.

2394	(PRESTON FAMILY FILM 1962)				
1962					
std.8mm	col	silent	100ft		REF

[filmed by Robert Preston]

The Preston family at home on the west coast of Scotland with footage of the steam vessel the "Comet" and of the last Tram Cavalcade in Glasgow.

2395	CHURCH ACTIVITIES. ST. MARTIN'S. EDINBURGH				
1959-'68					
9.5mm	b/w&col	silent	830ft		REF

[filmed by William Reid]

The various activities and clubs associated with St. Martin's Church in Edinburgh during the years 1959-1968.

2396	SCOTLAND THROUGH THE LENS				
1963-'65					
std.8mm	col	silent	650ft		REF

[filmed by C. Pashley]

Taken by film-maker when he and his wife toured Scotland in their Hillman Imp. Sights include Loch Lomond, Eilean Donan Castle, Strome and Ballachulish ferries, the Falls of Dochart and Dunvegan Castle.

2397	(PEACE DEMONSTRATION. CLYDEBANK)				
1952					
16mm	b/w	silent	550ft		REF

[filmed by a member of the Dawn Cine Group]

The Youth Festival in Clydebank on 28th September 1952; crowds gather for a demonstration and groups carry banners for "World Youth Friendship and Peace" and "Ban the Atom Bomb".

195

2398	FITNESS FOR WOMEN				
1953*					
16mm	b/w	silent	452ft		VIEW

sp. National Fitness Council for Scotland
p.c. Campbell Harper Films, Edinburgh

A demonstration of how women can keep fit and healthy through exercise, keep fit classes and dancing. The Margaret Morris dance technique is included.

2399	FITNESS FOR BOYS				
1953*					
16mm	b/w	silent	399ft		VIEW

sp. National Fitness Council for Scotland
p.c. Campbell Harper Films, Edinburgh

Aimed at boys of school-leaving age, the film promotes a healthy way of life involving regular exercise and sports.

2400   FITNESS FOR GIRLS

1953*

| 16mm | b/w | silent | 404ft | | REF |

sp. National Fitness Council for Scotland
p.c. Campbell Harper Films, Edinburgh

Aimed at girls about to leave school, the film shows how to live a healthy life including keeping fit, dancing, sports and the Girl Guides.

2401   [HALFWAY TO PARADISE: GI BLUES]

1989

| 16mm | col | sep mag | 227ft | | REF |

sp. Channel 4 Television
p.c. Big Star in a Wee Picture
series p. Don Coutts and Stuart Cosgrove

The impact of the presence of American GIs on the Holy Loch, Argyll, as seen from the GI's point of view and that of the local people.

2402   [HALFWAY TO PARADISE: VENTRILOQUIST]

1989

| 16mm | col | sep mag | 354ft | | REF |

sp. Channel 4 Television
p.c. Big Star in a Wee Picture
series p. Don Coutts and Stuart Cosgrove

A profile of the ventriloquist Harry Kydd and his life on stage with his dummy Jimmy.

2403   [HALFWAY TO PARADISE: TARTAN]

1989

| 16mm | col | sep mag | 148ft | | REF |

sp. Channel 4 Television
p.c. Big Star in a Wee Picture
series p. Don Coutts and Stuart Cosgrove

The Scottish musician Jesse Rae talks about his philosophy on wearing tartan, and Michael Stewart of Albany talks about the authenticity of his genealogy claims to Charles Edward Stewart.

2404   [HALFWAY TO PARADISE: POLL TAX]

1989

| 16mm | col | sep mag | 227ft | | REF |

sp. Channel 4 Television
p.c. Big Star in a Wee Picture
series p. Don Coutts and Stuart Cosgrove

An irreverent look at the Poll Tax and how not to pay it.

2405   [HALFWAY TO PARADISE: HEN PARTY]

1989

| 16mm | col | sep mag | 261ft | | REF |

sp. Channel 4 Television
p.c. Big Star in a Wee Picture
series p. Don Coutts and Stuart Cosgrove

Glasgow brides-to-be give their views on marriage and the traditional Scottish "hen party".

2406   [HALFWAY TO PARADISE: JOCKY WILSON]

1989

| 16mm | col | sep mag | 189ft | | REF |

sp. Channel 4 Television
p.c. Big Star in a Wee Picture
series p. Don Coutts and Stuart Cosgrove

A profile of the Fife darts player Jocky Wilson who talks about his early life in Kirkcaldy and his success as World Title holder in 1982.

2407   BIRDS OF THE ORKNEY ISLANDS

1952*

| 16mm | b/w | silent | 335ft | | VIEW |

p.c. Royal Society for the Protection of Birds
d. Gwen Davies

Close up shots of the different varieties of birds inhabiting the Orkney islands.

2408   PROPERTY IN THE COUNTRY, A

1977*

| 16mm | col | comopt | 502ft | | VIEW |

p.c. Royal Society for Protection of Birds
d. Hugh Miles

Ian Prescott, Director of the RSPB introduces the concept of the need to provide 'houses' for birds showing bird reserves in Sussex, Norfolk and Suffolk and on the moorlands of the Orkney Islands.

2409   PUFFINS COME HOME

1969*

| 16mm | col | comopt | 868ft | | VIEW |

p.c. RSPB Film Unit
d. Sarah Quests

A study of the puffin colony on Skokholm Island, south west Wales.

2410   BEYOND A TANGLED SHORE

1977*

| 16mm | col | comopt | 1999ft | | VIEW |

p.c. Royal Society for Protection of Birds Film Unit
d. Alan McGregor

The story of the crofters who live on the Hebridean island of North Uist narrated by islander, Finlay J. Macdonald.

2411   OSPREY

1979*

| 16mm | col | comopt | 1895ft | | VIEW |

p.c. Royal Society for Protection of Birds Film Unit
d. Hugh Miles

Robert Powell tells the story of the osprey which returns to Scotland from Africa every spring.

2412 HIGHLAND BIRDS
1958*

16mm	col	comopt	1938ft	VIEW

p.c. Royal Society for Protection of Birds
d. George Waterston

Close-up footage of the different species of birds found in the Highlands of Scotland, including whooper swans, woodcock, capercaillie, goldcrest, oyster catchers and ring ouzels.

2413 BENMORE HOUSE AND ESTATE
1934*

16mm	b/w	silent	475ft	REF

Views of Benmore House and Estate, gifted by H.G. Younger as a forestry and botany demonstration area.

2414 (FORESTRY TECHNIQUES)
1931*

16mm	b/w	silent	370ft	REF

The preparations for the transplanting of nursery seedlings and their various stages of growth.

2415 OLD ROTHESAY
1937-'68*

16mm	b/w&col silent	2160ft	REF

A compilation of amateur films about the town of Rothesay on the Isle of Bute.

2416 STALLION SHOW AT SCOTSTOUN
1920

35mm	b/w	silent	60ft	VIEW

p.c. Gaumont Graphic

Excerpt from a newsreel showing Scotstoun showground in Glasgow as horses are paraded in front of spectators.

2417 [SERVICE OF THANKSGIVING IN ST. GILES' CATHEDRAL]
1960

16mm	b/w	comopt	2500ft	REF

p.c. BBC Television
p. Revd. Dr. Ronald Falconer

One of a series of telerecordings of the live transmission of events celebrating the 4th Centenary of the Scottish Reformation, 11th-12th October 1960. [See also refs. 2418-2421.]

2418 [HER MAJESTY THE QUEEN AT GENERAL ASSEMBLY]
1960

16mm	b/w	comopt	2500ft	REF

p.c. BBC Television
p. Revd. Dr. Ronald Falconer

HM Queen Elizabeth and the Duke of Edinburgh attend the service in the Assembly Hall, Edinburgh. [See also refs. 2417-2421.]

2419 [HOLY COMMUNION SERVICE. ST. GILES']
1960

16mm	b/w	comopt	2160ft	REF

p.c. BBC Television
p. Revd. Dr. Ronald Falconer

Holy Communion service in St. Giles' Cathedral, Edinburgh. [See also refs. 2417-2421]

2420 [RE-AFFIRMATION OF PRINCIPLES]
1960

16mm	b/w	comopt	2900ft	REF

p.c. BBC Television
p. Revd. Dr. Ronald Falconer

The General Assembly of the Church of Scotland during the reaffirmation of principles with the Moderator, the Right Revd. J. H. S. Burleigh. [See also refs. 2417-2421.]

2421 [CLOSING OF THE GENERAL ASSEMBLY]
1960

16mm	b/w	comopt	4000ft	REF

p.c. BBC Television
p. Revd. Dr. Ronald Falconer

The closing of the General Assembly led by the Moderator of the Church of Scotland, the Right Revd. J. H. S. Burleigh. [See also refs. 2417-2420.]

2422 GLENDOLL
1951c

16mm	b/w	silent	480ft	REF

[filmed by a member of the Dawn Cine Group]

Skiers on the slopes of Glendoll, Angus, possibly members of the Ski-ing and Outdoor Club of Glasgow.

2423 INCHMURRIN 1950
1950

9.5mm	b/w	silent	c300ft	REF

filmed by Charlie Bukelis

Members of the Glasgow Ski-ing and Outdoor Club at a campsite and walking near Ben Lomond.

2424	NEWS MAGAZINE: DAILY WORKER OUTING			
1951-'56				
16mm	b/w&col	silent	350ft	VIEW

[filmed by Charlie Bukelis]

A compilation reel of protest marches in Glasgow including the Gorbals Tenants Rents Protest and mass deputation to Edinburgh. Marches by various political groups including the Labour Party and Communist Party.

2425	(VISIT TO SOVIET UNION)			
1959-'60				
16mm	b/w	silent	200ft	VIEW

[attributed to Charlie Bukelis, Dawn Cine Group]

A visit to the Soviet Union by a group of British delegates (possibly trade unionists), including a display of a national dance and the laying of flowers on a memorial.

2426	[LITHUANIA 1960]			
1960				
16mm	col	silent	360ft	REF

Scenes in Lithuania, including a display of dancing and a religious procession.

2427	[WICK SCENES]			
1946c				
9.5mm	b/w	silent	c600ft	REF

Scenes of life in Wick; a pony and cart carrying hay, a steam train on the Wick line and men rolling barrels at the Glenmorangie distillers.

2428	ROYAL NORTHERN YACHT CLUB:NOSES HOMEWARD			
1934				
16mm	b/w	silent	398ft	REF

[filmed by E.F.L. Mucklow]

Yachts and boats on the west coast of Scotland, by the Kyle of Lochalsh, round Ardnamurchan, Loch Linnhe and back to Rhu by the canal.

2429	ROYAL NORTHERN YACHT CLUB SAILING FILMS 1934-1935			
1934/'35				
16mm	b/w	silent	284ft	REF

[filmed by E.F.L. Mucklow]

Yachting on the west coast of Scotland, including the Royal Western Yacht Club Tighnabruaich Race.

2430	ROYAL NORTHERN YACHT CLUB CADETS AT LOCH LOMOND			
1938/'39				
16mm	col	silent	145ft	REF

[filmed by E.F.L. Mucklow]

Cadets sailing dinghies on Loch Lomond with shots of battleships in background.

2431	[LAUNCH OF "OTTER", SUBMARINE]			
1961				
16mm	b/w	mute	88ft	REF

p.c. BBC and Scottish Television news

Launch of the submarine "Otter" at Scott-Lithgow's shipyard on the 15th May 1961.

2432	[LAUNCH OF "RESOURCE"]			
1965*				
16mm	col	silent	102ft	REF

Launch of the vessel "Resource" in Scott-Lithgow's shipyard.

2433	[CLYDESIDE - 1ST BRITISH OIL DRILLING SHIP]			
1977				
16mm	col	comopt	97ft	REF

p.c. BBC news

Shots of the off-shore oil drilling rig the "Ben Ocean Lancer" and the rig "Pacnorse I" under construction in Scott-Lithgow's shipyard.

2434	[RAM-BOW TANKER]			
1964				
16mm	col	comopt	220ft	VIEW

sp. [Trident Tankers Ltd.] Scott-Lithgow's
p.c. Moore Todd Associates Ltd.

Construction and fitting of the new style ram bow to Trident Tankers Ltd's vessel ORISSA.

2435	[LAUNCH OF "KALDFONN"]			
1955				
16mm	col	mute	576ft	REF

sp. Scott-Lithgow Ltd.
p.c. Elder Film Productions

Launch of the Anchor Line vessel "Kaldfonn" at Scott-Lithgow's shipyard in Greenock.

2436	SCOTT-LITHGOW GROUP, THE			
1964-'68				
16mm	col	comopt	400ft	REF

sp. Scott-Lithgow Ltd.
p.c. Templar Films

General views of the Scott-Lithgow shipyard and construction methods used. The launching of the tanker "Orissa", the ferry "Sound of Islay", and the container vessel "Sugar Producer" at the company's shipyards.

2437	(DUKE OF EDINBURGH VISITS SCOTT-LITHGOW)			
1961c				
16mm	b/w	mute	257ft	REF

sp. Scott-Lithgow Ltd.

Two versions of the filming of a visit by the Duke of Edinburgh to Scott-Lithgow's shipyard.

2438	LAUNCH OF HMS "GALATEA"			
1934				
16mm	b/w	silent	65ft	REF

p.c. Pathe Gazette

The launch of the cruiser HMS "Galatea" at the Scott-Lithgow shipyard, Greenock.

2439	[LAUNCHING "THE IRON HORSE"]			
1960				
16mm	b/w	silent	80ft	REF

p.c. Scottish Television

The launch party for the vessel "The Iron Horse" at Scott-Lithgow Shipyard.

2440	MV "CRYSTAL CUBE"			
1974*				
16mm	col	silent	288ft	REF

sp. Scott-Lithgow
p.c. Templar Films

Mrs. I.D. Lyle launches the first bulk sugar carrier for Sugarline Ltd., MV "Crystal Cube" at the Scott-Lithgow shipyard.

2441	[LAUNCH OF SUBMARINE 'WALRUS']			
1959				
16mm	b/w	silent	85ft	REF

The launch of the submarine "Walrus" at Scott-Lithgow shipyard.

2442	[LAUNCH OF "QUILOA"]			
1959				
16mm	b/w	silent	40ft	REF

The launch of the vessel "Quiloa" from Scott-Lithgow's shipyard at Greenock.

2443	[LAUNCH MT "MORAR"]			
1958				
16mm	b/w	comopt	190ft	REF

Launch of the ship MT "Morar" at Scott-Lithgow's shipyard with a voice-over explaining the advantages of this, the first British free-piston powered ship.

2444	ESV "IOLAIR"			
1982				
16mm	col	silent	600ft	REF

sp. Scott-Lithgow Ltd
p.c. Danish Ship Research Laboratory

The testing of the vessel ESV "Iolair" by means of a model in a test tank, carried out for Scott-Lithgow Shipbuilders at the Danish Ship Research Laboratory.

2445	(TEST FOR LAUNCH OF TANKER IN TWO HALVES)			
n.d.				
16mm	col	silent	200ft	REF

A model of both halves of a large tanker, built at the Scott-Lithgow shipyard, being tested for its launch.

2446	SYSTEMS BEHAVIOUR - SHIPBUILDING 1			
1973*				
16mm	col	mute	324ft	REF

p.c. BBC Open University

A narrator in Scott-Lithgow shipyard explains some of the processes as the tanker "Naess Scotsman" is seen under construction.

2447	[RIVER CLYDE STORY]			
1970*				
16mm	col	comopt	271ft	REF

p.c. BBC

A television reporter in the Scott-Lithgow shipyard on the upper reaches of the Clyde. The fitting-out basin, gantries, welders at work and assembly sheds are all featured.

2448	(CONSTRUCTION OF TANKER "NORDIC CLANSMAN")			
1971*-'79				
16mm	col	commag	3100ft	VIEW

The construction of a tanker in two halves at the Scott-Lithgow shipyard.

2449	BEETLING AT AVONBANK			
1981				
16mm	col	sep opt	576ft	REF

p.c. University of Strachclyde Audio-Visual Unit

The beetling manufacturing process which gives cloth the texture required for making window roller blinds. Shot at Avonbank in Lanarkshire where the last beetling machines to operate in Britain were still working in 1981.

2450   [CENTURY OF CIVIL ENGINEERING, A]
1984

16mm	col	sep mag	c2000ft	REF

sp. University of Strathclyde
p.c. University of Strathclyde Audio-Visual Services

Original slates showing the Tay and Forth road and rail bridges, and Pitlochry and Torness power stations.

2451   ETNA BRICKWORKS
1985

16mm	col	sepopt	348ft	VIEW

sp. University of Strathclyde, Dept. of History
p.c. University of Strathclyde - Audio Visual Services
d. Gordon Thomson

Shot at the premises of Armadale Brick in West Lothian, showing the manufacture of building bricks from crushing to firing. [The kilns shown in use were demolished shortly after filming.]

2452   HAMPDEN PARK
1974

16mm	col	mute	c700ft	REF

p.c. University of Strathclyde Audio-Visual Unit

Football League Cup Final between Celtic and Partick Thistle.

2453   [GLASGOW WEEK IN HAMBURG]
1974

16mm	col	sep mag	612ft	REF

Events during the official visit by Glasgow city officials to Hamburg during the week 4th to 9th March 1974.

2454   STEAM POWERED WEAVING MILL
1979

16mm	col	sep opt	650ft	REF

p.c. University of Strathclyde Audio-Visual Dept.

The Glenruthven weaving mill showing how its steam power was transferred to the hand looms in operation. [This mill was the last Scottish factory of any kind to be driven by steam.]

2455   WOOL PIECING MACHINE
1979

16mm	col	sep opt	166ft	REF

sp. University of Strathclyde, Dept. of History
p.c. University of Strathclyde, Audio-Visual Services

Shot at Bridgend, Islay, showing the last wool piecing machine in operation in the UK.

2456   QUESTION OF BALANCE, A
1975

16mm	col	sep opt	960ft	VIEW

sp. University of Strathclyde
p.c. University of Strathclyde Audio-Visual Services

A lecturer from Strathclyde University records the measures taken to make safe a partially collapsed tower crane at Queen Street Station, Glasgow and then investigates the cause of the accident.

2457   STUDENT DEMONSTRATION
1981

16mm	col	sep mag	100ft	REF

p.c. University of Strathclyde Audio-Visual Services

A student demonstration during NUS Week of Action against cuts in grants.

2458   PEDESTRIANISATION
1972

16mm	b/w	mute	c2000ft	VIEW

p.c. University of Strathclyde

Shots of Glasgow streets after their pedestrianisation: Sauchiehall Street, Argyle Street and Buchanan Street.

2459   [LANGUAGE INSERTS]
1974c

16mm	b/w	sep mag	460ft	VIEW

p.c. University of Strathclyde Audio-Visual Services

Shots of different images including shipyards and shipping on the Clyde, ferries, the Clyde Tunnel and Prestwick Airport. [The soundtrack commentary is not linked specifically to these images, but is to do with language teaching.]

2460   LORD HIGH COMMISSIONER IN GLASGOW
1956-'57

16mm	b/w	mute	280ft	REF

p.c. Movietone News

Sir Walter Elliot, Lord High Commissioner to the General Assembly lays a wreath at the War Memorial in Glasgow and visits the Royal Infirmary. In Edinburgh he inspects the Guard of Honour at the opening of the General Assembly.

2461   BUDAPEST LA REINE DU DANUBE
1935c

16mm	b/w	silent	345ft	VIEW

[filmed by John Gray]

Scenes in and around Budapest including a street market, traditional dancing and horses on the Puszta.

200

2462	AUTUMN IN SCOTLAND				

1960c

16mm	col	silent	282ft	VIEW

sp. SEFA and SFC
p.c. Templar Film Studios

The autumn harvesting of potatoes and turnips.

2463	ANNUAL ART COMPETITION				

1955c

16mm	col	silent	240ft	VIEW

sp. Schools Museums Service, Corporation of Glasgow
filmed by Louise Annand

Schoolchildren taking part in the annual art competition held in the Glasgow Art Gallery and Museum.

2464	AT THE MUSEUM				

1954c

16mm	b/w	silent	175ft	REF

sp. Schools Museum Service, Glasgow
filmed by Louise Annand

Exhibits in the Glasgow Art Gallery and Museum.

2465A	ARMS AND ARMOUR PART I				

1955

16mm	col	silent	372ft	REF

sp. Schools Museum Service, Glasgow Education Department
filmed by Louise Annand

A prize-winning film at the Scottish Amateur Film Festival demonstrating how different hand weapons would originally have been used.

2465B	ARMS AND ARMOUR PART II				

1955

16mm	col	silent	306ft	REF

p.c. Glasgow Schools Museum Service

A variety of fire arms are described and demonstrated including matchlock, wheel-lock and flint-lock guns, muskets and breech-loader rifles.

2466	PREPARING A WAX RESIN RE-LINING				

1955/'56

16mm	b/w	silent	290ft	REF

sp. Schools Museums Service, Glasgow
filmed and edited by Louise Annand

A demonstration of the stages and processes in relining a picture.

2467	AUTOLITHOGRAPHY				

n.d.

16mm	col	silent	450ft	REF

filmed by Henry Aston Clinton for the Glasgow SEFA Production Group

A demonstration of each stage in the making of a lithograph. [Made by a student at the Glasgow School of Art in lieu of a thesis for his DA.]

2468	HISTORY OF LIGHTING				

1959

16mm	col	silent	334ft	VIEW

sp. Schools Museums Service, Glasgow
filmed by Louise Annand for Glasgow SEFA Production Group

A history of different sources of lighting showing the earliest examples of flame torches to oil lamps, gas light and to modern day electric lighting.

2469	MISSILE WEAPONS				

1960c

16mm	col	silent	86ft	REF

sp. Schools Museums Service, Glasgow Education Department
filmed by Louise Annand

Demonstrations of how a bow and arrow and a crossbow would have been used, illustrated from the Scott and Martini collections at the Glasgow Art Gallery and Museum.

2470	[MODEL INDIANS]				

1960c

16mm	col	silent	352ft	REF

sp. Schools Museum Service, Glasgow Corporation
[filmed by Louise Annand]

Hand made models of American Indians in traditional costume are shown by Thomas Lindsay, a teacher with the Glasgow Schools Museum Service who made the models himself and would supply his own spoken commentary at his demonstrations.

2471	GORBALS OLD GORBALS NEW - ONE WOMAN'S STORY				

1966c

16mm	b/w	commag	c360ft	REF

p.c. Thomson Foundation Television College
d. Rada Radosevic

Footage of the demolition of the old Gorbals and the construction of the new, including an interview with a resident who had lived in the Gorbals before its reconstruction.

2472	LONDON LINE				

1966

16mm	b/w	comopt	526ft	REF

p.c. Thomson Foundation Television College

A training film for television production, showing the work of the Thomson Foundation Television College in Glasgow.

2473	DISCOVERY OF TELEVISION				

1966

16mm	b/w	comopt	1760ft	REF

sp. Mullard Limited in assoc. with BBC TV
p.c. J.B.M. production
d. John Lloyd

The story of the men involved in the discovery of television.

201

2474	WALES V SCOTLAND				
1958*					
35mm	b/w	comopt	180ft		REF

Highlights of a football match between Wales and Scotland at Ninian Park, Cardiff. Wales (0) Scotland (3) - goals scored by Leggatt and Bobby Collins.

2475	PEARL AND DEAN ADVERTISEMENTS				
1960s,c					
35mm	col	comopt	460ft		REF

Miscellaneous adverts for local businesses in Annan, Dumfries and district. Also ads for cigarettes, Borzoi Vodka and Breaker Malt Liquor.

2476A	APPLICATION OF EXPERIMENTS PART I				
1962					
16mm	col	mute	279ft		VIEW

sp. Joint Production Committee
filmed by SEFA Production Group Glasgow

An educational film to show how to control burning by excluding air/oxygen.

2476B	APPLICATION OF EXPERIMENTS PART II				
1962c					
16mm	col	mute	355ft		VIEW

sp. Joint Production Committee
filmed by SEFA Production Group Glasgow

An educational film demonstrating how to increase burning by lighting open hearths and stoves.

2476C	APPLICATION OF EXPERIMENTS PART III				
1962c					
16mm	col	mute	414ft		VIEW

sp. Joint Production Committee
filmed by SEFA Production Group Glasgow

An educational film giving demonstrations of bunsen burners, paraffin and gas blow-lamps, a diesel engine and automatic coal-burning furnace.

2477	PRESENT FOR THE GROOM, A				
1956					
16mm	b/w	silent	290ft		VIEW

filmed by SAAC

The misfortunes of newly-weds at the outset of their honeymoon. [Made by members of the Scottish Association of Amateur Cinematographers during a week-end at Crieff Hydro.]

2478	SPRING IN SCOTLAND				
1960c					
16mm	col	silent	1012ft		VIEW

sp. Joint Production Committee of SEFA and SFC
p.c. Templar Film Studios

One of a series of films introducing aspects of the four seasons in Scotland, made for use in primary schools. [See also ref. 2479.]

2479	WINTER IN SCOTLAND				
1960c					
16mm	col	silent	558ft		VIEW

sp. Joint Production Committee of the SEFA and the SFC
p.c. Templar Film Studios

One of a series of films introducing aspects of the four seasons in Scotland, made specially for use in primary schools. [See also ref. 2478.]

2480	GORBALS STOCK SHOTS				
1956-'57					
16mm	b/w	mute	330ft		VIEW

p.c. BBC Television

Material used in the television documentary "Glasgow by the Way" and stock shot material for a "Panorama" programme on the Gorbals. Shots of the Princess (now Citizens) Theatre, the Mosque, shops and closes, children playing in back courts and women going to the "Steamie" with a pramful of washing.

2481	(GLASGOW PUBS)				
1960c					
16mm	col	sep mag	36ft		VIEW

p.c. Movietone News

Movietone News footage used in television documentary series "Look at Life" including shots of Glasgow pubs and crowds entering Hampden Park football.

2482	WOMEN'S PROHIBITION DEMO				
1914					
16mm	b/w	silent	27ft		REF

p.c. Pathe Gazette

A women's demonstration in favour of prohibition of alcohol.

2483	(QUEEN OPENS GORBALS "HUTCHIE E")				
1961					
16mm	b/w	sep mag	70ft		VIEW

p.c. Movietone News

Footage of HM the Queen opening the Huchesontown housing estate in the Gorbals Glasgow, and of the demolition of the old Gorbals tenements.

2484	(PAUL ROBESON AT GLASGOW MAY DAY)			
1960				
16mm	b/w	mute	160ft	VIEW

p.c. Pathe News

Paul Robeson taking part in the May Day parade in Glasgow, from George Square to Glasgow Green where the crowds listen to him making a speech.

2485	[WORKERS TOPICAL NEWS NO. II]			
1930				
16mm	b/w	silent	144ft	VIEW

p.c. Atlas Film Co.

A Scottish contingent on a hunger march, passing through Bolton.

2486	(BROWN FAMILY FILM)			
1934-'38				
9.5mm	b/w	silent	750ft	REF

[filmed by George D. Brown]

An infant on holiday at Portobello, being bathed in a tin tub in front of the fire and playing on her tricycle in the garden.

2487	CRYSTAL CASE, THE			
1938				
9.5mm	b/w	silent	c4000ft	REF

filmed by George D. Brown

A science fiction story filmed by an amateur film-maker over a period of three years. The film was premiered in a church hall in Perth where it ran for a week to a full house.

2488	[IRON AND STEEL]			
1931*				
16mm	b/w	silent	1100ft	REF

sp. Dorman Long Ltd.

Iron and steel making processes at use in Dorman Long's Middlesborough works, with sites at Lakenby and Redcar.

2489	FABRICATION			
1937*				
16mm	b/w	silent	800ft	REF

sp. Redpath Brown Ltd.

Steel manufacturing processes at Westburn Works, of Redpath Brown, Cambuslang, Lanarkshire.

2490	NEW TYNE BRIDGE, THE			
1928				
16mm	b/w	silent	1200ft	VIEW

sp. Dorman Long Ltd.

A record of the construction of the Tyne Bridge, Newcastle, from virgin site to opening day.

2491	[GOVERNMENT OFFICES. CALTON HILL EDINBURGH]			
1937				
16mm	b/w	silent	230ft	REF

[sp. Redpath Brown]

The ceremony of the laying of the foundation stone for St. Andrews House, Edinburgh, attended by HRH the Duke of Gloucester.

2492	[MCVITIE'S AND CUMBERLAND HOTEL COLUMNS FABRICATION]			
1931*				
16mm	b/w	silent	220 ft	REF

sp. Redpath Brown or Dorman Long

The assembly of steel plates into columns.

2493	[CINEMA TRAILERS III]			
1970s				
35mm	col	comopt	c500 ft	VIEW

Miscellaneous cinema trailers and adverts.

2494	LOCH LOMOND - WATER SCENE			
1973				
16mm	col	mute	c360ft	REF

sp. Educational Films of Scotland
[p.c. Park Film Studios]

A technical record of the building of the water scheme at Loch Lomond.

203

2495	[DUMFRIES GUID NYCHBURRIS DAY 1947]			
1947				
16mm	b/w	silent	170 ft	VIEW

Gymkhana events and the Queen of the South floats procession at Dumfries Guid Nychburris Day Festival.

2496	(GUGA HUNTERS)			
1957c				
16mm	col	silent	140ft	VIEW

[filmed by John Morrison]

The first film made by John Morrison, it shows guga hunters (a guga is a young gannet) being landed on Sula Sgier for the annual 2-3 week season.

2497	[HIGHLAND CROFTERS' FAREWELL]			
1924				
16mm	b/w	silent	45ft.	REF

[p.c. Gaumont British News]

Footage of people setting out to emigrate to Canada from the islands of St. Kilda and Barra.

2498	[UNICA, GLASGOW 1951]				
1951					
16mm	b/w&col	silent	500 ft		REF

[sp. SAAC]
[filmed by SAAC]

Delegates of the UNICA conference at the Scottish Film Council offices Glasgow, on organised trips to the Hiram Walker whisky distillery in Dunblane, to Gleneagles Hotel and on a cruise "doon the water" on the paddle steamer the "Waverley".

2499	[CRIEFF HYDRO WEEKEND]				
1949*					
16mm	b/w	silent	325 ft		REF

[filmed by SAAC]

Made during the SAAC's annual film-making weekend at Crieff Hydro, the film shows a family enjoying a holiday at the hotel.

2500	YEARS AGO IN COWDENBEATH				
1920-'24					
35mm	b/w	silent	1486ft		VIEW

filmed by E. Kay and J.W. Brown

A compilation of events in Cowdenbeath, including the children's procession for the Co-operative Gala of 1923 and a 1st division football match between Cowdenbeath and Hearts at Central Park, Cowdenbeath.

2501	CITIZENS THEATRE				
1989					
16mm	col	sep mag	1080ft		REF

p.c. Reality Productions
d. Diane Tammes

Rushes from a documentary on the construction of the extension to the Citizens' Theatre in the Gorbals, Glasgow.

2502	(SHEARER FAMILY FILM ONE)				
1932*					
16mm	col	silent	45ft		REF

A family on the beach. [Shot on Kodacolor.]

2503	(SHEARER FAMILY FILM TWO)				
1928*					
16mm	col	silent	54ft		REF

A family taking tea in the garden. [Shot on Kodacolor.]

2504	CONSECRATION OF MONSEIGNEUR WARD OF ST. MARY'S CALTON				
1960					
16mm	b/w	silent	211ft		REF

Consecration ceremony of Monseigneur Ward of St. Mary's Calton, Glasgow.

204

2505	(SEAWEED)				
1954*					
16mm	col	silent	190ft		REF

Men on a fishing boat collecting seaweed, measuring and weighing it.

2506	(MCQUILKEN FILM ONE)				
1973-'75					
8mm	col	silent	c120ft		REF

[filmed by William McQuilken]

Footage of demonstrations and marches in Edinburgh and Glasgow including the OAPs "Beat the Cold"; UCS rally; miners in Edinburgh; an anti-polaris march to Faslane. [The late William McQuilken was Paisley District Secretary of the AEU and an active member of the Communist Party.] [See also ref. 2507.]

2507	(MCQUILKEN FILM TWO)				
1960c					
8mm	col	silent	c120ft		REF

[filmed by William McQuilken]

Footage of strikes in the early 1960s: mill strike; apprentices' strike; Rolls Royce; the Pressed Steel industry. [See also ref. 2506.]

2508	(WILLIE GALLACHER AND FUNERAL)				
1961-'65					
8mm	col	silent	c120ft		REF

[filmed by William McQuilken]

Footage of the 80th birthday celebrations of Willie Gallacher in St. Andrew's Halls, Glasgow with speeches and the presentation of a bronze bust. Shots of the funeral procession for Willie Gallacher with the coffin draped in the Communist Party Central Committee banner. [See also ref. 1912.]

2509	ARCTIC SETTLEMENT, AN				
1975c					
16mm	col	sep opt	560ft		REF

sp. BBC
d. Jenny Gilbertson

Made for the BBC series "People of Many Lands", the film details the life of an Inuit settlement.

2510	JENNY'S DOG TEAM JOURNEY				
1975+					
16mm	col	sep opt	900ft		REF

d. Jenny Gilbertson

A dog team journey made from Igloolik to Repulse Bay, 300 miles by sea ice and over the hills of the Melville Peninsula, with four adults and a three months old baby. The journey took two weeks, sleeping in an igloo every night. [BBC purchased British rights and the film was shown on March 2nd, 1978. A re-edited version was made in 1982.]

2511	APPROACH TO API				
1954*					
16mm	col	silent	366ft		REF

filmed by John Tyson

Footage of the villages in the foothills of the mountain of Api in North-West Nepal and of a climbing team with sherpas setting up camp. [Highly commended at the SAAC 1953 Festival.]

2512	AYRSHIRE DAIRY FARMER				
1967c					
16mm	col	mute	430ft		VIEW

p.c. Educational Films of Scotland

Life on Hapland Dairy Farm near Dunlop, Aryshire. The day-to-day and season-to-season cycle of work of a dairy farmer.

2513	(MACFARLANE FAMILY 1938)				
1938					
16mm	b/w&col silent		373ft		REF

filmed by Jack Macfarlane

The Macfarlane family [of Macfarlane & Lang Biscuit manufacturers] on holiday near Aviemore and footage of scenes of the Clyde. [See also refs. 2514-2524.]

2514	(MACFARLANE FAMILY 1939)				
1939					
16mm	b/w&col silent		370ft		REF

[filmed by Jack Macfarlane]

Jack and Robert Macfarlane cruising on the Clyde in their motor yacht, "Yvaldal". [See also refs. 2513-2524.]

2515	(MACFARLANE FAMILY - WEDDING)				
1939c					
16mm	col	silent	365ft		REF

[filmed by Jack Macfarlane]

A "society" wedding in Glasgow Cathedral. [See also refs. 2513-2524.]

2516	(MACFARLANE FAMILY 1930-1931)				
1930-'31					
16mm	b/w	silent	300ft		REF

[filmed by Jack Macfarlane]

The Macfarlane family on holiday at Loch Insh. [See also refs. 2513-2524.]

2517	(MACFARLANE FAMILY 1937)				
1937					
16mm	b/w&col silent		374ft		REF

[filmed by Jack Macfarlane]

The Macfarlane family at their home in Helensburgh and scenes of the Clyde. [See also refs. 2513-2524.]

2518	(MACFARLANE FAMILY - CLYDE CRUISE 1934)				
1934					
16mm	b/w&col silent		467ft		REF

[filmed by Jack Macfarlane]

Scenes of the Clyde taken from the Macfarlane family's motor cruiser. [See also refs. 2513-2524.]

2519	(GLASGOW FLOODS 1936)				
1936					
16mm	b/w	silent	387ft		REF

[filmed by Jack Macfarlane]

Holiday shots in the Lake District and York and footage of the Glasgow floods in 1936. [See also refs. 2513-2524.]

2520	(MACFARLANE FAMILY 1932)				
1932					
16mm	b/w	silent	365ft		REF

[filmed by Jack Macfarlane]

Sir James and Lady Katherine Macfarlane at the turf cutting ceremony to mark the start of work on Canniesburn Hospital, Glasgow and footage of scenes on the Clyde. [See also refs. 2513-2524.]

2521	(NAMING OF THE LIFEBOAT "JOHN AND FRANCES MACFARLANE")				
1958					
16mm	col	silent	111ft		REF

[filmed by Jack Macfarlane]

The launching of the lifeboat "John and Frances Macfarlane" at Aith, Shetland in 1958. [See also refs. 2513-2524.]

2522	(MACFARLANE FAMILY 1930)				
1930-'32					
16mm	b/w	silent	247ft		REF

[filmed by Jack Macfarlane]

The Macfarlane family on holiday. [See also refs. 2513-2524.]

2523	(LAUNCH OF "QUEEN MARY" - MACFARLANE FILM)				
1933-'34					
16mm	b/w	silent	355ft		REF

The launching of the liner "The Queen Mary" at John Brown's shipyard and footage of the launch of Jack Macfarlane's motor cruiser on the Clyde. [See also refs. 2513-2524.]

205

2524   (MACFARLANE FAMILY 1931-1932)

1931

16mm	b/w	silent	399ft		REF

[filmed by Jack Macfarlane]

The Macfarlane family on holiday and footage of scenes of the Clyde. [See also refs. 2513-2524.]

2525   [STAFF PICNIC 1937]

1936*

16mm	b/w	silent	86ft		REF

Employees of the Aberdeen department store, Isaac Benzie Ltd. on a works' outing. [See also refs. 2152, 2526-2536.]

2526   [PICNIC TO BALLATER, NO. 2]

1935*

16mm	b/w	silent	48ft		REF

Employees of the Aberdeen department store Isaac Benzie Ltd. on a works' outing to Ballater. [See also refs. 2152, 2525-2536.]

2527   [KING GEORGE V AT BALLATER]

1935

16mm	b/w	silent	95ft		REF

King George V inspecting the Guard of Honour at Ballater station. [Part of the film collection relating to the Isaac Benzie family of Aberdeen.] [See also refs. 2152, 2525-2536.]

2528   [STAFF PICNIC. GOLF AND WILLIE ELDER]

1932*

16mm	b/w	silent	91ft		REF

Employees of the Aberdeen department store, Isaac Benzie Ltd. on a works' golf outing. [See also refs. 2152, 2525-2536.]

2529   [SHOP PICNIC, CARNOUSTIE]

1937*

16mm	b/w	silent	96ft		REF

Employees of the Aberdeen department store Isaac Benzie Ltd. on a works' outing to Carnoustie. [See also refs. 2152, 2525-2536.]

2530   [STAFF PICNIC]

1935*

16mm	b/w	silent	45ft		REF

Employees of the Aberdeen department store, Isaac Benzie Ltd. on a works' outing. [See also refs. 2152, 2525-2536.]

2531   [SHOP PICNIC. FARLAIR SWIMMING POOL]

1937*

16mm	b/w	silent	94ft		REF

Employees of the Aberdeen department store Isaac Benzie Ltd. on a works' outing to an open-air swimming pool. [See also refs. 2152, 2525-2536.]

2532   [CORONATION PARADE WITH FLOATS, 1953?]

1946*/'57

16mm	b/w	silent	99ft		REF

Coronation Parade in Aberdeen. [See also refs. 2152, 2525-2536.]

2533   (BENZIE'S WORKS OUTING)

1932*

16mm	b/w	silent	183ft		REF

Employees of the Aberdeen department store, Isaac Benzie Ltd. on a works' outing. [See also refs. 2152, 2525-2536.]

2534   [STAFF PICNIC 1930?]

1931*

16mm	b/w	silent	85ft		REF

Employees of the Aberdeen department store Isaac Benzie Ltd. on their works' outing. [See also refs. 2152, 2525-2536.]

2535   BENCOF OUTING AT ABOYNE. SEASON 1931

1931

16mm	b/w	silent	270ft		REF

Employees of the Aberdeen department store Isaac Benzie Ltd. on their works' outing. [See also refs. 2152, 2525-2536.]

2536   (BENCOF OUTING)

1932c

16mm	b/w	silent	387ft		REF

Employees of the Aberdeen department store Isaac Benzie Ltd. on their works' outing. [See also refs. 2152, 2525-2535.]

2537   CONSEQUENCES

c1970

16mm	col	comopt	864ft		VIEW

sp. The Scottish Police
p.c. IFA (Scotland) Ltd.
d. Charles Leigh Bennett

The dramatised account of how a teenager gets into trouble with the police, ending up in a young offender's court.

2538	**IT'S MORE THAN A JOB**			
1971				
16mm	col	comopt	684ft	REF

sp. Scottish Police Authorities
p.c. Cairngorm Films Ltd.

A look at the Scottish Police Training College at Tulliallan and the varied roles of policemen and women both on and off duty.

2539	**ARE YOU NEXT?**			
c1970				
16mm	col	comopt	790ft	VIEW

sp. Central Office of Information for the Scottish Office
p.c. Clyde Film Service

Highlighting the dangers of lack of careful security in your home and business.

2540	**IT WASN'T ME MISTER**			
1974c				
16mm	col	comopt	925ft	REF

sp. Educational Films of Scotland
p.c. Pelicula Films Ltd.
d. Michael Alexander

A dramatic description of a youngster taken on his first shoplifting spree by an older boy and both ending up in trouble with the police.

2541	**(HONOLULU AND CHARLIE CHAPLIN)**			
1935*				
16mm	b/w&col silent		396ft	REF

[filmed by W.C. Honeyman]

A cruise to Honolulu by Mr. and Mrs. Honeyman where Mrs Honeyman is seen talking to Charlie Chaplin. [Part of a collection of films taken by the late W. C. Honeyman, former Glasgow shipowner.] [See also refs. 2542-2559.]

2542	**(BATTLESHIPS ON THE CLYDE)**			
1935				
16mm	b/w&col silent		138ft	REF

[filmed by W.C. Honeyman]

Battleships sailing in the Clyde. [Part of a collection of films taken by the late W.C. Honeyman, former Glasgow shipowner.] [See also refs. 2541-2559.]

2543	**(ST. MORITZ 1946, I)**			
1946				
16mm	col	silent	197ft	REF

[filmed by W.C. Honeyman]

A holiday in St. Moritz showing the town's streets, horse-drawn sleighs, skiers and outdoor skating. [See also refs. 2541-2559.]

2544	**(ST. MORITZ 1946, II)**			
1946*				
16mm	col	silent	360ft	REF

[filmed by W.C. Honeyman]

A holiday in St. Moritz, showing skiing, a bob-sleighing competition, skaters and horse-drawn sleighs. [See also refs. 2541-2559.]

2545	**(ST. MORITZ 1946, III)**			
1946				
16mm	b/w&col silent		298ft	REF

[filmed by W.C. Honeyman]

A holiday taken in St. Moritz, showing skaters on the Grand Hotel ice rink including the world pairs champions, Maxi Herber and Ernst Baier, and the English champion, Patsy Sheridan. [See also refs. 2541-2559.]

2546	**(DORNOCH HOLIDAY)**			
1935*				
16mm	b/w	silent	220ft	REF

[filmed by W.C. Honeyman]

A holiday in Dornoch with country walks, picnics and fishing. [See also refs. 2541-2559.]

2547	**(COWAL GAMES, DUNOON 1933)**			
1933				
16mm	b/w&col silent		396ft	REF

[filmed by W.C. Honeyman]

Highland dancing, tossing the caber, and pipe bands at the Cowal Games, and a holiday at Gairloch, Ross-shire. [See also refs. 2541-2559.]

2548	**(ST. MORITZ 1932)**			
1932				
16mm	b/w	silent	360ft	REF

[filmed by W.C. Honeyman]

The streets of St. Moritz with people on toboggans and skis, an ice hockey game, skating, a horse race on a snow-laden track and horse-drawn sleighs. [See also refs. 2541-2559.]

2549	**(CRUISE ON "IBERIA", I)**			
1934*				
16mm	b/w	silent	382ft	REF

[filmed by W.C. Honeyman]

A cruise to South Africa and Bali. Footage includes street scenes in Durban, a visit to an African village, a local market and traditional dance. [See also refs. 2541-2559.]

207

2550   (CRUISE ON "IBERIA", II)
1934

| 16mm | b/w | silent | 360ft | | REF |

[filmed by W.C. Honeyman]

Continuation of the cruise to South Africa and the Far East, taken by Mr. and Mrs. Honeyman. The film shows local scenes in Java and deck games on board the liner. [See also refs. 2541-2559.]

2551   (CRUISE ON "IBERIA", III)
1934

| 16mm | b/w | silent | 390ft | | REF |

[filmed by W.C. Honeyman]

The Honeymans on their cruise to the Far East showing the Raffles Hotel, Singapore and street scenes in Ceylon. [See also refs. 2541-2559.]

2552   (CRUISE ON "IBERIA", IV)
1934

| 16mm | b/w | silent | 360ft | | REF |

[filmed by W.C. Honeyman]

The final stage of the Far East cruise taken by Mr. and Mrs. Honeyman showing the port at Aden, the railway station of Port Tewfik, and the pyramids at Cairo. The end of the film shows the couple returning to their Glasgow home. [See also refs. 2541-2559.]

2553   (CRUISE TO SOUTH AMERICA, I)
1956

| 16mm | col | silent | 324ft | | REF |

[filmed by W.C. Honeyman]

A cruise to South America, taking in Chile, the Panama Canal, and Venezuela. [See also refs. 2541-2559.]

2554   (CRUISE TO SOUTH AMERICA, II)
1953*

| 16mm | col | silent | 331ft | | REF |

[filmed by W.C. Honeyman]

The return journey of a cruise to South America by Mr. and Mrs. Honeyman; crowds on the dockside at Callao, street scenes in Balboa, the Panama Canal and the streets of Corunna. [See also refs. 2541-2559.]

2555   (PANTOMIME 1937)
1937

| 16mm | b/w | silent | 90ft | | REF |

[filmed by W.C. Honeyman]

Scenes from a local pantomime in the north of Scotland [location unidentified.] [See also refs. 2541-2559.]

2556   (CRUISE TO CANADA, I)
1950

| 16mm | col | silent | 324ft | | REF |

[filmed by W.C. Honeyman]

A cruise to Canada on the "Empress of Scotland", with shots of the liner at Greenock before setting out. [See also refs. 2541-2559.]

2557   (CRUISE TO CANADA, II)
1950*

| 16mm | col | silent | 350ft | | REF |

[filmed by W.C. Honeyman]

The second half of the Honeyman's cruise to Canada. [See also refs. 2541-2559.]

2558   (BERMUDA HOLIDAY)
1947*

| 16mm | col | silent | 360ft | | REF |

[filmed by W.C. Honeyman]

A holiday in Bermuda and New Jersey showing Riddells Bay Golf Course, people fishing for turtles, and Mr. and Mrs. Honeyman boarding a BOAC plane for New Jersey. [See also refs. 2541-2559.]

2559   (HONEYMAN FAMILY HOME)
1946c

| 16mm | col | silent | 298ft | | REF |

[filmed by W.C. Honeyman]

Shots of the Glasgow home of Mr. and Mrs. Honeyman showing the garden with its flowerbeds, the greenhouse, apple trees and orchids. [See also refs. 2541-2559.]

2560   (LAUNCH SS "DUNDEE" AND MV "ARBROATH")
1933-'35

| 16mm | b/w | silent | 320ft | | REF |

[filmed by H.M. Plenderleith]

Launching of SS "Dundee" at Caledon shipyard, Dundee, Dec. 1933 and the start of her maiden voyage in Feb. 1934. Launching ceremonies of the MV "Arbroath", Aug. 1935 and the lifeboat "Mona", Sept. 1935.

2561   (CRUISE AND HOLIDAYS)
1934*-'39

| 16mm | col | silent | 280ft | | REF |

filmed by H.M. Plenderleith

A cruise on the SS "Perth" in 1936 and a holiday during the Dundee Holiday Week in 1934 to London and the Highlands.

2562	[SPITHEAD REVIEW 1937]				
1936*					
16mm	b/w&col	silent	435ft		REF

[filmed by H.M. Plenderleith

A tour of the vessel "Highlander" with passengers playing deck games and views of naval and civilian shipping.

2563	(CARGO LOADING AT DOCKS)				
1956*					
16mm	b/w	silent	400ft		REF

Vessels loading and unloading at London docks.

2564	(CRUISE ON SS "PERTH")				
1934*-'35					
16mm	b/w&col	silent	380ft		REF

[filmed by H. M. Plenderleith]

Deck games and dancing during a cruise on the SS "Perth" in 1934 and a flight in an Imperial Airways bi-plane.

2565	MV "GLAMIS"				
1936					
16mm	b/w	silent	154ft		REF

[filmed by H.M. Plenderleith]

The launching of M V "Glamis" at the Caledon Shipyard, Dundee on the 2nd September 1936.

2566	SS "ABOYNE"				
1936					
16mm	b/w	silent	140ft		REF

[filmed by H. M. Plenderleith]

The launching of SS "Aboyne" at the Caledon Shipyard, Dundee on 28th December 1936.

2567	[LAUNCH "DUNDEE" AT BURNTISLAND]				
1953					
16mm	b/w	silent	100ft		REF

[filmed by H. M. Plenderleith]

The launching of the vessel "Dundee" at Burntisland, Fife.

2568	(SHIPPING JUTE TO LONDON)				
1954					
16mm	b/w	silent	365ft		REF

Shots of jute manufacturing processes at the Caldrum Works, Dundee and of jute being loaded onto a vessel in Dundee and unloaded in London.

2569	(PLEASANCE TRUST BOYS' CLUB 1955-1962)				
1955-'62					
16mm	b/w&col	silent	259ft		REF

A jumble sale, concert, picnic and a camp with the Pleasance Trust Boys' Club of Edinburgh. [See also ref. 2570.]

2570	(PLEASANCE TRUST BOYS' CLUB 1967-1969)				
1967-'69					
16mm	col	silent	686ft		REF

An outing for handicapped children, a class at nursery school and a camp with the Pleasance Trust Boys' Club of Edinburgh. [See also ref. 2569.]

2571	(ALKA-SELTZER ADVERTS)				
n.d.					
16mm	b/w&col	comopt	252ft		REF

A series of animated adverts for Alka-Seltzer.

2572	DUNARA CRUISE 1937				
1937					
9.5mm	b/w	silent	c400ft		REF

filmed by James Marshall

A cruise taken by the film-maker to the island of St. Kilda on the "Dunara Castle", sailing from Glasgow. [Part of a collection of films taken by James Marshall of the Glasgow family-owned firm "Marshall's Semolina".] [See also refs. 2573-2577.]

209

2573	ROAD TO LEWIS 1936, THE				
1936					
9.5mm	b/w	silent	c400ft		VIEW

filmed by James Marshall

A family trip to Lewis via the West Highland Line, setting out from Glasgow Queen Street Station. [See also refs. 2572-2577.]

2574	CLYDE STEAMERS 1931-1939				
1931-'39					
9.5mm	b/w	silent	c400ft		REF

filmed by James Marshall

Shots of the numerous steamers sailing up and down the Clyde during the years 1931-1939. [See also refs. 2572-2577.]

2575	UIST HOLIDAY 1937				
1937					
9.5mm	b/w	silent	c400ft		REF

filmed by James Marshall

A family holiday to the Hebridean island of Uist. [See also refs. 2572-2577.]

2576	HOLIDAYS 1933				
1933					
9.5mm	b/w	silent	c400ft		REF

filmed by James Marshall

Holiday scenes of the Marshall family taken at their home in Bridge of Weir, Renfrewshire and of picnics near Tomintoul. [See refs. 2572-2577.]

2577A	FAMILY FILMS 1931-1938				
1931-'38					
9.5mm	b/w	silent	c400ft		REF

filmed by James Marshall

Films of the Marshall family taken over the years 1931-1938. [See also refs. 2572-2576.]

2577B	LORETTO SCHOOL				
1933c					
9.5mm	b/w	silent	c400ft		REF

[filmed by James Marshall]

Sports day at Loretto School, Midlothian. [See also refs. 2572-2576.]

2578	WEDDING AT NORTH BERWICK				
1934					
35mm	b/w	mute	c900ft		VIEW

p.c. Universal, British Movietone, British Paramount News, Pathe Gazette

Newsreel footage of the wedding of Col. Walter Elliot to Miss Katharine Tennant, 2nd April 1934.

2579	EVACUATION DIFFICULTIES				
1940*					
35mm	b/w	comopt	130ft		VIEW

p.c. Pathe Gazette

Walter Elliot, Minister of Agriculture talks to a group of evacuee children from London and thanks the Scottish women who took the children in.

2580	ROARING GAME, THE				
1925*-'28					
35mm	b/w	silent	630ft		VIEW

p.c. Pathe Super Gazette, Gaumont Graphic, Paramount

"The Roarin' Game" - the curling contest for the Queenshill Cup on Carlingwark Loch, Castle Douglas.

2581	BUY YOUR OWN CHERRIES				
1904					
35mm	b/w	silent	298ft		VIEW

p.c. R.W. Paul

Possibly made for the Grand Lodge of England to promote temperance, showing how drink can lead to ruin, and temperance to a happy family life.

2582	HOST, THE				
1988					
16mm	col	sep mag	480ft		VIEW

sp. Scottish Film Training Trust
p.c. Last Supper Productions
p. Andrea Calderwood

A trainee film produced by young people during their year on the Scottish Film Training Trust Programme. A drama based on the short story "Supper on the Wall" by Hugh McBain. [The film toured the Scottish Regional Film Theatres and was entered for the Celtic Film Festival 1989.]

2583	RETURN OF THE INTERNED				
1918					
35mm	b/w	silent	334ft		VIEW

p.c. Green's Film Service/ Scottish Moving Picture News

Taken at Leith in 1918, the film shows the arrival by ship of internees returning from Europe, with the request "watch the picture carefully, and see if you can identify anyone".

2584	HARTHILL SERVICES				
1984-'85					
16mm	col	sep mag	6012ft		REF

p.c. University of Strathclyde Audio-Visual Services

Rushes from an unfinished documentary on the re-building and expansion of Harthill Services on the M8 motorway.

2585	DEMOLITION OF CHIMNEYS				
1984					
16mm	col	mute	441ft		VIEW

p.c. University of Strathclyde Audio-Visual Services

Part of an unfinished documentary on the demolition of power station chimneys in the Dundee area.

2586	(JEWISH WEDDING, A)				
1949					
16mm	b/w&col silent		324ft		REF

A wedding ceremony in Pollokshields Synagogue, 22nd March 1949.

2587	ISLE OF RHUM				
1970					
16mm	col	comopt	1050ft		VIEW

sp. Films of Scotland
p.c. Ogam Films Ltd. [Kinloch Castle sequences]
d. Christopher Mylne

A study of the animal and plantlife on the island of Rhum, and a history of the island's Kinloch Castle.

BAFTA
SCOTLAND

The Academy Award is based on a design by Mitzi Cunliffe

Do please call our office for further information on 0141-357 4317 or fax us on 0141-337 1432. We look forward to hearing from you.

BAFTA Scotland, 74 Victoria Crescent Road, Glasgow G12 9JN.

Established in 1986, BAFTA Scotland Membership is growing every year, membership is open to people residing in Scotland and working in film/television and associate industries. Student and Corporate memberships are available and BAFTA Scotland would be happy to meet with business partners to discuss sponsorship opportunities.

Among our activities throughout the year are, Premiers, Screenings (free to members), Discussions, Celebrity Lectures, Special Events, Monthly Newsletters and not forgetting our bi-annual Awards Ceremony the next of which is being televised by Grampian in 1995.

Picture: Delighted Winners at the Second BAFTA Scotland Awards, held at the Moathouse International, Glasgow in collaboration with BBC Scotland.

211

2588   PARKHILL SCHOOL 1937
1937

9.5mm	b/w	silent	c400ft	REF

Amateur footage of children playing games in a school playground, and at a school's sports day.

2589   [CORONATION DECORATIONS 1937]
1937

9.5mm	b/w	silent	c200ft	REF

Huntly, Rhynie, Stonehaven and Laurencekirk streets and buildings decorated with bunting and banners celebrating the Coronation.

2590   (PRIESTLY COLLECTION)
1935-'38

9.5mm	b/w	silent	c400ft	REF

filmed by Charles F. Priestly

Various farming processes used in the 1930s including horse-harrowing, cattle grazing, Fordson ploughing, reaping and binding.

2591   FAIR RIVER, THE
1945*

16mm	b/w	comopt	c610ft	REF

filmed by C. J. Cayley

A tour of the countryside on the banks of the River Tweed from the Forest of Ettrick, through Kelso, Coldstream and finally to Berwick.

2592   ISLES OF THE WEST
1939c

16mm	b/w	comopt	586ft	VIEW

filmed by C. J. Cayley

Life in the Outer Hebrides including footage of Stornoway and its harbour, herring fishing and gutting, a fish auction, tweed-making on Harris, cockle gathering on Barra and Barra Highland Games.

2593   MISTY ISLE
1945*

16mm	b/w	comopt	576ft	VIEW

filmed by C. J. Cayley

Life on the isle of Skye.

2594	[OPENING OF NEW CO-OP HYPERMARKET, MORRISON ST., GLASGOW]

1977

16mm	col	mute	75ft		REF

p.c. Scottish Television

The Lord Provost of Glasgow attends the opening of a new Co-op hypermarket.

2595	ARE SALES LOST ON SATURDAYS?

1958

16mm	b/w	silent	555ft		REF

[sp. SCWS]

Made by Glasgow South Co-operative Society giving an overview of shopping habits to try to establish if shutting Co-op shops on Saturday meant loss of sales.

2596	[SCWS CREAMERY AT WISHAW]

1954*

16mm	b/w	silent	450ft		REF

sp. SCWS
p.c. Peak Film Production
d. J. Jackson

The machinery and processes at the SCWS Creamery in Wishaw, Lanarkshire.

2597	(GLASGOW CO-OP SHOPS)

1959*

16mm	b/w	silent	99ft		REF

sp. SCWS

Exterior shots of two shops belonging to the Glasgow South Co-operative Society with pedestrians and traffic passing by.

2598	(CO-OP ADVERTISING STILLS)

n.d.

16mm	b/w	silent	30ft		REF

"Remember the Dividend" and "Co-op for Value" adverts for the Co-op.

2599	(PRINCESS MARGARET VISITS GLASGOW)

n.d.

16mm	b/w	silent	40ft		REF

Princess Margaret waves to cheering crowds, gives a speech and tours an exhibition in Glasgow.

2600	(CO-OP ADVERTISING FILMS)

1960c

16mm	b/w	comopt	216ft		REF

A variety of adverts for Co-op goods including Lofty Peak flour, Orchid Margarine and Triona and Morven shoes.

2601	DIVIDED WE STAND

1968

16mm	b/w	comopt	1224ft		REF

p.c. Scottish Television
d. Ted Williamson

A history of the SCWS movement to mark the centenary of its founding.

2602	DYING OF THIRST

1975

16mm	col	comopt	792ft		REF

d. Sarah Erulkar

An educational film aimed at teenagers to highlight the dangers of alcohol abuse.

2603	ROYAL OCCASION, A

1964

16mm	col	silent	360ft		REF

filmed by Stan. Munro, J.E. Henderson, Aberdeen

The opening of the Scottish North Eastern Counties Police Force Headquarters by her majesty the Queen Mother on 14th May 1964.

2604	(REPORT ON NORTH AYRSHIRE TOWNS)

1962

16mm	b/w	comopt	550ft		REF

p.c. Scottish Television

A programme made to highlight the level of unemployment in Ayrshire created by industrial recession.

2605	(HOLIDAY SCOTLAND)

1949

16mm	col	silent	852ft		REF

[filmed by Frank Bealing]

The city of Edinburgh and its castle, Burns' country, and the Highlands.

2606	MINING REVIEW NO. 3

1951

16mm	b/w	comopt	387ft		REF

sp. National Coal Board
p.c. Data Production

Barge transport of coal to London's power stations; mine shaft maintenance at night; Welsh miner Willie Pierce competing in the World Amateur Billiards competition; shots of the residential training centre for future miners at Dungavel House, Lanarkshire. [See also refs. 2607-2608.]

212

2607 [DUNGAVEL OPEN DAY]

1963*

16mm	col	mute	442ft		REF

The open day at the NCB Dungavel Residential Training Centre for young miners. [See also refs. 2606, 2608.]

2608 FIRE AT DUNGAVEL TRAINING CENTRE

1964

16mm	b/w	mute	115ft		REF

p.c. Scottish Television and BBC

Two newsreel items on the fire at the NCB's Dungavel Training Centre for young miners on 12th. November, 1964. [See also refs. 2606-2607.]

2609 OPENING OF THE NEW QUEEN'S BRIDGE, PERTH

1960

35mm	b/w	mute	432ft		VIEW

filmed by James S. Nairn

The opening ceremony of the New Queen's Bridge, Perth, by Her Majesty Queen Elizabeth II, 10th October, 1960.

2610 RESTORATION OF THE CHURCH OF THE HOLY RUDE

1936-'37

16mm	b/w	silent	c1008ft		REF

sp. Home Board of the Church of Scotland
filmed by James S. Nairn

Work in progress on the restoration of the Church of the Holy Rude, Stirling. HM Queen Mary visits the progress of work.

2611 BOYS' BRIGADE - 1956 REVIEW OF THE GLASGOW BATTALION

1956

16mm	col	silent	396ft		REF

[filmed by Mr. Beveridge]

Footage of the 1956 Boys' Brigade Review held at Queen's Park, Glasgow, 5th May.

2612 BRIGADE PARADE 1948

1948

16mm	col	silent	335ft		REF

[filmed by Mr. Beveridge]

The Glasgow Boys' Brigade battalions at their 1948 parade; demonstrations include a tent-pitching competition, cycling, sword dancing, bugle and drum tattoo, and games in fancy dress.

2613 ROYAL SALUTE

1952

16mm	col	silent	396ft		VIEW

[filmed by Mr. Beveridge]

HRH Prince Bernhard of the Netherlands taking the "Royal Salute" at Ibrox Stadium, Glasgow. The Boys' Brigade put on demonstrations of various sports, and Scottish country dancing.

2614 CARING PROFESSION, THE

1971

16mm	col	comopt	900ft		VIEW

sp. Scottish Home and Health Department
p.c. Cairngorm Films Ltd.
d. Peter Hopkinson

A promotional film for the nursing profession presented by Andrew Cruickshank.

2615 SETTLED OUT OF COURT

1970

16mm	col	comopt	1480ft		REF

sp. Central Office of Information for the Scottish Office
p.c. IFA (Scotland) Ltd.
d. Laurence Henson

A look at the system of Children's Hearings set up to deal with juvenile offenders.

2616 LOOK TO THE SEA

1970c

16mm	col	comopt	936ft		VIEW

sp. Central Office of Information for the Scottish Office
p.c. IFA (Scotland) Ltd.
d. Laurence Henson

A review of the work of the Marine Laboratory, Aberdeen.

2617 SKETCH PLAN OF THE EMPIRE EXHIBITION

1938

16mm	col	silent	185ft		REF

The architect Thomas S. Tait at work on the plans for the Empire Exhibition.

2618A DAY OUT AT CARNBOOTH, A

1932

16mm	b/w	silent	252ft		REF

A day out to "Carnbooth" house for the residents of Balmanno Old Folks' Home. [See also refs. 2618B-2620.]

213

2618B ROUND THE THREE LOCHS AND VISIT TO CARNBOOTH

1939-'40

16mm	col	silent	468ft	REF

Outings by the residents of Balmanno Old Folks' Home to Loch Lomond, Loch Long and Loch Goil and an afternoon spent at "Carnbooth" house. [See also refs. 2618A-2620.]

2619 (BALMANNO HOUSE NEW YEAR'S DAY)

1940

16mm	b/w	silent	396ft	REF

New Year's Day festivities at Balmanno Old Folks' Home, Glasgow. [See also refs. 2618A-2620.]

2620 VIEWS OF MILNCROFT AND CROFTCROIGHN

1939

16mm	b/w&col silent	360ft	REF

Residents from Balmanno old folks' home leaving church and enjoying a day out at Croftcroighn house. [See also refs. 2618A-2619.]

2621 (GAME OF BOWLS, A)

1939

16mm	b/w&col silent	108ft	REF

A game of bowls at the Whitevale and Kingswood Bowling Clubs, Glasgow.

2622 ISLAND OF THE BIG CLOTH

1971

35mm	col	comopt	792ft	VIEW

sp. Films of Scotland

The story of Harris tweed and of the lives of the islanders who produce it.

2623 [RODONO FACTORY HISTORY]

1959

16mm	b/w&col silent	390ft	REF

[filmed by Ernest E. Tait]

A history of Pringle's Rodono factory, Hawick including the demolition of the old factory and construction of the new one. [See also refs. 2624-2626.]

2624 [PRINGLE'S PLANT]

1961c

16mm	b/w	mute	20ft	REF

p.c. BBC

Delivery of new weaving machines at Pringle's factory, Hawick. [See also refs. 2623-2626.]

2625 ANNUAL PICNIC, PRINGLE'S 1950

1950

16mm	b/w&col silent	288ft	REF

[filmed by Ernest E. Tait]

Pringle's staff outing to Bewlie House, Lilliesleaf, Roxburghshire. [See also refs. 2623-2626.]

2626 CLYDE TRIP MAY 1960

1960

16mm	col	silent	245ft	REF

[filmed by Ernest E. Tait]

Pringle's staff outing from Hawick to Glasgow for a trip on the Clyde steamer "Queen Mary II". [See also refs. 2623-2625.]

2627 ORANGEMEN ON PARADE 1951

1951

16mm	col	silent	18ft	REF

[filmed by Ernest E. Tait]

Orange March along Princes Street, Edinburgh.

2628 BORDER FESTIVALS OF 1956

1956

16mm	b/w&col silent	685ft	REF

[filmed by Ernest E. Tait]

Footage of various Border festivals including Selkirk, Langholm, and Lauder Common Riding and the Flodden Cavalcade at Coldstream.

2629 OLD FOLKS TRIP 1950

1950

16mm	b/w&col silent	236ft	REF

[filmed by Ernest E. Tait]

Hawick pensioners' outing to St. Mary's Loch and Eyemouth.

2630 (CARAVAN HOLIDAYS)

1957-'58

16mm	col	silent	360ft	REF

[filmed by Ernest E. Tait]

A family holiday by car and caravan through Scotland.

2631 HOLIDAY SCOTLAND

1966

35mm	col	comopt	3690ft	VIEW

sp. Films of Scotland
p.c. Campbell Harper Films Ltd.

A scenic tour of Scotland taking in the Borders, Edinburgh, Glasgow, Stirling, Perth, Pitlochry, Aberdeen and the west coast by way of Ullapool and the Hebrides.

2632	LORD ROBERTS VISIT TO ABERDEEN				
1913					
16mm	b/w	silent	72ft		REF

Lord Roberts presents the Colours to the 4th Battalion of the Gordon Highlanders.

2633	GOLFING AT THE JODHPUR CLUB				
1944*					
16mm	col	silent	108ft		REF

Amateur footage of the Jodhpur Club, India, showing members playing golf and relaxing at the club.

2634	(INDIAN OXYGEN COMPANY)				
1946*					
16mm	b/w	silent	139ft		REF

The offices of the Indian Oxygen Company and a manufacturer's exhibition of engineering equipment.

2635	TRIP TO BHUTAN				
1946c					
16mm	b/w&col	silent	252ft		REF

Amateur footage of a trip to Bhutan including a journey by rail, an elephant safari and scenes of village life.

2636	DURISDEER COTTAGE AND FARMING				
1946*					
16mm	b/w	silent	180ft		REF

A family cottage in Ayrshire and shots of harvesting on a local farm.

2637	HADDOCK FISHING				
1941					
16mm	b/w	silent	144ft		REF

p.c. Craft Studio, Edinburgh
Line-fishing for haddock from cobble fishing boats. [Commended at the Scottish Amateur Film Festival 1941.]

2638	TALES FROM THE NORTH				
1958					
16mm	b/w	silent	279ft		REF

[filmed by SAAC]
A whimsical look at human foibles. [Made at the SAAC's annual film-making weekend at Crieff.]

2639	BRAEMAR GATHERING				
1940					
16mm	col	silent	440ft		REF

[filmed by Alan Stott]
The Highland Games at Braemar. King George VI, Queen Elizabeth and the two Princesses are among the spectators. [Highly commended at the SAAC 1941.]

2640	CHRISTMAS IN LIGHT				
1965					
16mm	col	silent	210ft		VIEW

filmed by Alan Stott
The "switching on" ceremony of the Christmas illuminations in Union Street, Aberdeen.

2641	DEESIDE INDUSTRY, A				
1965*					
16mm	col	comopt	125ft		VIEW

filmed by Kay Gordon
The processing and distillation of lavender water at the Banchory lavender growers, Ingasetter Ltd.

2642	JOHNSTONE GARDENS, ABERDEEN				
1973*					
16mm	col	silent	275ft		REF

filmed by Ronald Macmillan
Views of the flowers and trees in Aberdeen's Johnston Gardens.

2643	CLANSMAN AT WORK				
1965*					
16mm	b/w	comopt	145ft		VIEW

[filmed by Clansman Films]
A humorous look at how a film is conceived and made [Filmed by Clansman amateur filmmakers.]

215

2644	STRATHDEE STABLE, THE				
1963c					
16mm	col	commag	380ft		VIEW

filmed by Clansman Films
Veteran cars at the Kildrummy Rally and the restoration of a "Humberette".

2645	HORN CARVING				
1963*					
16mm	b/w	sep mag	140ft		VIEW

filmed by Clansman Films
The craftsman Hamish Robson at work in his workshop in Braemar.

2646	LINEN WEAVING				
1963*					
16mm	b/w	mute	135ft		VIEW

filmed by Kay Gordon
A linen weaver in the Angus village of Luthermuir setting up and working at his loom. [The last linen weaver in Scotland to weave by hand.]

2647	TRAWLER TOWN				
1963c					
16mm	b/w	mute		360ft	VIEW

filmed by Ron Miller

Trawlers unload their catch at Aberdeen harbour and the fish auction gets underway.

2648	FAREWELL TO STEAM				
1965c					
16mm	col	commag	470ft		VIEW

filmed by Clansman Films

Steam trains at Aberdeen and Ballater stations, watched by enthusiasts. The trains include "Sir Nigel Gresley", "Union of South Africa" and "City of Aberdeen".

2649	GANG SHOW, THE				
1967					
16mm	b/w&col	commag	1100ft		VIEW

filmed by Clansman Films

Rehearsals and shots of the final performance of "The Gang Show" at Her Majesty's Theatre in Aberdeen.

2650	HIGHLAND LINE				
1962*					
16mm	col	mute		1260ft	REF

The stations and scenery along the "Highland Line" from Inverness to Kyle of Lochalsh.

2651	PORTSOY GIRL GUIDES DEDICATION OF THEIR NEW COLOURS				
1950					
16mm	b/w	silent		70ft	REF

[filmed by William Davidson]

A youth organisations parade in Banffshire. [See also refs. 2652-2666.]

2652	CROWNING OF PORTSOY GALA QUEEN				
1947-'53					
16mm	b/w	silent		75ft	REF

[filmed by William Davidson]

The crowning of Portsoy Gala Queen and festival parade. [See also refs. 2651-2666.]

2653	[BB RELAY RACE]				
1947-'53					
16mm	b/w	silent		40ft	REF

[filmed by William Davidson]

A Boys' Brigade relay race at Portsoy, Banffshire. [See also refs. 2651-2666.]

2654	[PORTSOY SUNDAY SCHOOL PICNIC]				
1947*					
16mm	b/w	silent		40ft	REF

[filmed by William Davidson]

Children eating ice cream on a Sunday School picnic. [See also refs. 2651-2666.]

2655	PORTSOY ARMISTICE PARADE/ CULLEN GALA				
1949*					
16mm	b/w	silent		75ft	REF

[filmed by William Davidson]

The Armistice Parade and Service at Portsoy War Memorial and the Cullen Gala Week fancy dress parade. [See also refs. 2651-2666.]

2656	[PORTSOY SUNDAY SCHOOL PICNIC]				
1946*					
16mm	b/w	silent		73ft	REF

[filmed by William Davidson]

Picnicers boarding a bus and children playing on swings. [See also refs. 2651-2666.]

2657	[FANCY DRESS PARADE, BUCKIE]				
1947-'53					
16mm	b/w	silent		105ft	REF

[filmed by William Davidson]

Gala floats and a fancy dress parade in Buckie, Banffshire. [See also refs. 2651-2666.]

2658	KEITH SHOW 1948				
1948					
16mm	b/w&col	silent		124ft	REF

[filmed by William Davidson]

Horse racing, a tug of war, a donkey race and highland dancing at the Keith Show. [See also refs. 2651-2666.]

2659	[PORTSOY SUNDAY SCHOOL PICNIC]				
1947-'53					
16mm	b/w	silent		120ft	REF

[filmed by William Davidson]

A Sunday School picnic with a tug of war, a mothers' race and children eating ice cream. The picnicers are seen disembarking from the train at Portsoy station. [See also refs. 2651-2666.]

2660	FOOTBALL MATCH MARRIED V SINGLE LADIES				
1948					
16mm	b/w	silent		72ft	REF

[filmed by William Davidson]

A women's football match at Portsoy in July 1948. [See also refs. 2651-2666.]

2661	CROWNING OF PORTSOY'S GALA QUEEN 1948

1948

| 16mm | b/w | silent | 82ft | | REF |

[filmed by William Davidson]

The crowning of the Gala Queen at Portsoy's Town Hall, followed by the fancy dress parade. [See also refs. 2651-2666.]

2662	ABERCHIRDER AND PORTSOY FANCY DRESS

1947-'53

| 16mm | b/w | silent | 100ft | | REF |

[filmed by William Davidson]

Fancy dress parades at Aberchirder and Portsoy in Banffshire. [See also refs. 2651-2666.]

2663	ABERCHIRDER BRITISH LEGION PARADE

1946*

| 16mm | b/w | silent | 130ft | | REF |

[filmed by William Davidson]

Parade of war veterans and youth organisations to dedicate the war memorial at Marnoch Church, Aberchirder. [See also refs. 2651-2666.]

2664	MARNOCH SPORTS BARREL BOXING

1947*

| 16mm | b/w | silent | 20ft | | REF |

[filmed by William Davidson]

Two boys barrel boxing at the Marnoch Sports, Banffshire. [See also refs. 2651-2666.]

2665	[PETER FAIR]

1947-'53

| 16mm | b/w | silent | 85ft | | REF |

[filmed by William Davidson]

A funfair and the launching ceremony of a lifeboat at Buckie, Banffshire. [See also refs. 2651-2666.]

2666	(GALES AT SEATOWN, CULLEN)

1953

| 16mm | b/w | silent | 72ft | | REF |

[filmed by William Davidson]

The seafront at Cullen, Banffshire, lashed by heavy seas during January gales. [See also refs. 2651-2665.]

2667	SCOTLAND'S ISLE OF SEALS

1958*

| 16mm | col | silent | 232ft | | VIEW |

sp. JPC
filmed by EFS

A study of the seal colony on the island of Shillay, in the Outer Hebrides.

2668	SKIMSTERS, THE

1959

| 16mm | col | comopt | 395ft | | VIEW |

filmed by Harry Birrell

Waterskiers on Loch Earn, practising and taking part in Loch Earn Water Skiing championships. [Winner of the Marshall Quaich award at the 1959 SAFF.]

2670	TABLE D/HOLT

1953

| 16mm | b/w | comopt | 238ft | | REF |

filmed by Harry Birrell

Short comedy of an announcement of an engagement at a dinner party.

2671	HIGHLANDS OF SCOTLAND

1952

| 16mm | col | silent | 382ft | | REF |

filmed by Harry Birrell

The landscape of the Highlands and Islands, including Glencoe, Rannoch Moor, Mallaig and the island of Arran.

2672	OFFICER CADET TRAINING UNIT 165

1940

| 16mm | b/w&col | silent | 792ft | | REF |

filmed by Harry Birrell

Military cadets at training camp in Dunbar; on parade, at bayonet practice, and taking part in various sports.

2673	KELVINGROVE PARK

1978

| 16mm | col | commag | 271ft | | REF |

filmed by Harry Birrell

Skateboarders in Kelvingrove Park, Glasgow.

2674	NORTH AND WEST OF THE GREAT GLEN

1952

| 16mm | col | comopt | 376ft | | REF |

filmed by Harry Birrell

The lochs and mountains of the Highlands.

2675	EMPIRE EXHIBITION

1938

| 16mm | col | silent | 147ft | | REF |

[filmed by Harry Birrell]

Shots taken at night of the 1938 Empire Exhibition in Glasgow, showing the buildings, statues, and fountains lit up by neon lights.

217

2676   OLD TIME MOVIES
1948

16mm	col	silent	364ft		REF

filmed by Harry Birrell

Winter holiday scenes at Pitlochry and in Paris.

2677   SCOTTISH SNOWGROUNDS, THE
1951

16mm	col	comopt	708ft		REF

filmed by Harry Birrell

Scenes of skiers from the Scottish Ski Club and Dundee Ski Club on the slopes of Ben Lawers.

2678   [ONE FINE DAY]
1956-'57

16mm	b/w&col	silent	700ft		REF

[sp. Dumfries Academy]
[filmed by a teacher in Dumfries Academy]

One of a series of films made about life in Dumfries Academy 1955-1978, featuring the school's academic year 1956-'57. [See also refs. 2679-2680.]

2679   [DUMFRIES ACADEMY 1969-'70]
1969-'70

16mm	b/w	silent	360ft		REF

[sp. Dumfries Academy]
[filmed by pupils of Dumfries Academy]

Filmed by Dumfries Academy pupils in the academic year 1969-1970, with several "in-jokes". [See also refs. 2678-2680.]

2680   DAY IN THE LIFE OF DUMFRIES ACADEMY, A
1978

16mm	col	mute	700ft		REF

[sp. Dumfries Academy]
[filmed by R.D. Fraser]

As well as scenes of daily school life in Dumfries Academy, the film includes footage of the flooding of the river Nith on 31st October 1977. [See also refs. 2678-2679.]

2681   HERE AND THERE / WINTER IN WICK
1945-'46*

16mm	col	silent	110ft		REF

[filmed by Alex Johnston]

Peat cutting near Wick, winter scenes and shots of a family of 'tinkers' on a country road.

2682   BENNO SCHOTZ
1973

16mm	col	sep opt	659ft		REF

sp. Educational Films of Scotland
p.c. IFA (Scotland)

The sculptor Benno Schotz at work in his studio in Glasgow.

2683   (DUFFTOWN SCENES)
1938-'55*

16mm	b/w&col silent	504ft		REF

[filmed by William Watt]

A royal motorcade in Aberdeen, sheep shearing, harvesting, and a local fete in the countryside around Dufftown in Banffshire. [See also refs. 2684-2685.]

2684   (WATT FAMILY FILM)
1946*

16mm	col	silent	100ft		REF

[filmed by William Watt]

Amateur footage of a family holiday in Banffshire. [See also refs. 2683-2685.]

2685   (PROCLAMATION OF KING EDWARD VIII)
1936*

16mm	b/w&col silent	72ft		REF

[filmed by William Watt]

Provost Spence of Dufftown reads the proclamation of King Edward VIII to onlooking crowds. [See also refs. 2683-2684.]

2686   STILL LIFE WITH HONESTY
1970

16mm	col	comopt	748ft		VIEW

sp. Films of Scotland and the Scottish Arts Council
p.c. Ogam Films
d. Bill Forsyth, Martin Singleton

The late Sir William Gillies, R.S.A., speaks of his life's work while the camera lingers on his paintings.

2698   HIGHLAND HOLIDAY
1972

16mm	col	comopt	576ft		VIEW

sp. Films of Scotland Committee
p.c. Ogam Films
d. Oscar Marzaroli

An impression of some of the holiday attractions offered by the Highlands, from sand yachting at Dunnet Bay, to skiing on the Cairngorms.

2700   29 SECONDS TO ZERO

1978

| 16mm | col | sep opt | c360ft | REF |

filmed by Ian Rintoul

A dramatic reconstruction of the Japanese attack on Pearl Harbour. Made entirely with home-built models and special effects, the film won the 1979 'Ten Best' award from 'Movie Maker' magazine. [Shown in its entirety on BBC 2 in 1980.]

2701   LOCH NESS MONSTER MOVIE, THE

1984

| 16mm | col | commag | 630ft | REF |

filmed by Ian Rintoul

A comedy about the "escape" of the Loch Ness Monster into the Firth of Forth and subsequent terrorisation of the city of Edinburgh.

2702   WINFIELD 1950

1950

| 16mm | b/w&col | silent | 358ft | REF |

filmed by Andrew Clarke

Motor racing at Winfield Aerodrome, Galashiels, and the Gala Harriers interclub run with the Teviotdale Harriers.

2703   MAN AND HIS KILT, A

1954*

| 16mm | col | silent | 360ft | VIEW |

sp. Scottish Film Council
filmed by SEFA - Edinburgh branch

The weaving of a tartan and making of a kilt.

2704   GALA 25 MILE CYCLE RACE 1951

1952

| 16mm | b/w | silent | 61ft | REF |

filmed by Andrew Clarke

The Galashiels Cycling Club's confined 25 mile race.

2705   FISHERS ALL

1951

| 16mm | col | silent | 435ft | REF |

filmed by Bill Dobson

A small boy sneaks off to go fishing instead of going to church. [Highly commended at the Scottish Association of Cinematographers' 1952 Festival.]

2706   BUSY AFTERNOON, A

1950

| 16mm | col | silent | 260ft | REF |

filmed by Iain Dunnachie

A small girl playing in her back garden building sand pies and bathing her doll. [Highly commended at the first Festival of the Scottish Association of Amateur Cinematographers 1950.]

2707   KNIFE GRINDER AT FERNIEHURST / GALA HOTSPURS GAME

1961

| 16mm | col | silent | 102ft | REF |

filmed by Andrew Clarke

A travelling knife grinder demonstrates his machine by the side of a rural road in the Borders. The film also contains footage of a Gala Hotspurs football match.

2708   PEEBLES BELTANE QUEEN GAMES

1954

| 16mm | b/w | silent | 446ft | REF |

filmed by Andrew Clarke

Track racing at Peebles Beltane Highland Games.

2709   GALA HARRIERS 1951

1951

| 16mm | b/w&col | silent | 360ft | REF |

filmed by Andrew Clarke

Junior and Senior races of the Gala Harriers and the presentation of cups and prizes.

2710   JEDBURGH AND HAWICK AMATEUR SPORTS

1951

| 16mm | b/w | silent | 390ft | REF |

filmed by Andrew Clarke

Men's track races, the women's sprint race and cycle racing at the Jedburgh and Hawick amateur sports, August 1951.

2711   POWDERHALL

1955

| 16mm | b/w | silent | 87ft | REF |

filmed by Andrew Clarke

Track runners racing the no. 3 heats of the one-mile handicaps at Powderhall race track, Edinburgh.

2712   ST. RONAN'S GAMES

1954c

| 16mm | b/w | silent | 82ft | REF |

filmed by Andrew Clarke

The men's track races at St. Ronan's Games, Selkirk Common Riding Festival.

2713   OPENING OF THE REHABILITATION CLINIC

1940

| 16mm | b/w | silent | 150ft | REF |

Opening ceremony of Glasgow Royal Infirmary Out-Patient Department and Rehabilitation Clinic, 14th June 1940.

The cast of the variety show at the Pavilion Cinema, Johnstone, welcomes Julian the Tank on a fund raising exercise, c1917. Ref. 1238

2714   (HISTORY OF THE X-RAY)

1954

16mm	b/w	silent	270ft	REF

A history of the x-ray, including footage from Dr. Macintyre's early cinematograph film of 1897. [See also refs. 0520 and 0838.]

2715   ROYAL INFIRMARY FOUNDATION STONE CEREMONY

1974

16mm	col	silent	522ft	REF

[sp. Glasgow Royal Infirmary]
p.c. University of Strathclyde Audio-Visual Aids Film Unit
d. Jim Harold

Foundation stone ceremony for part of Phase I of the new building of the Glasgow Royal Infirmary, 29th March, 1974.

2716   THANK YOU LORD LISTER

1965

16mm	b/w	commag	1440ft	REF

p.c. STV
d. Geoff Rimmer

A television documentary made to mark the centenary of Lister's first putting into practice his discovery of antiseptics for use in surgery.

2717   DRESSINGS TECHNIQUE

1970c

16mm	col	commag	736ft	REF

sp. Glasgow Royal Infirmary and Associated Hospitals
p. Alan McIlroy

Nurses demonstrate the preparations necessary for the replacement of a patient's dressing.

2718   APPLE A DAY, AN

1941

16mm	b/w	silent	364ft	VIEW

[filmed by Frank Marshall]

A prize-winning film at the 8th Scottish Amateur Film Festival, it tells the story of two children who become ill from eating too much stolen fruit.

2719   SCHOOL IN THE TROSSACHS

1960c

| 16mm | col | comopt | 790ft | REF |

sp. Clackmannan County Council Education Committee
filmed by Brian Benson

Activities at a school camp near Gartocharn in Dunbartonshire; a visit to a farm, the production of the camp newspaper, and pupils dancing "the twist".

2720   [BRAEMAR GAMES. TWEED MAKING AND EDINBURGH]

1950

| 16mm | col | silent | 144ft | REF |

sp. Joint Production Committee, SEFA
p.c. SEFA

Scenes at the Braemar Highland Games, the spinning and weaving of tweed and street scenes in Edinburgh.

2721   SPRING IN GALLOWAY

1930s,c

| 16mm | b/w | silent | 360ft | VIEW |

[filmed by John Gray]

Spring in Galloway; a ploughman brings his horse to the village blacksmith, trees are felled and logs delivered to the sawmill, men gather mussels on the beach and fishermen mend their nets.

2722   (GEORGE SQUARE REDEVELOPMENT)

1968

| 16mm | b/w | comopt | 150ft | REF |

[p.c. Scottish Television]

A film insert for a news programme looking at the completion of the first phase of Edinburgh University's redevelopment in George Square. Hamish Henderson talks about the architecture of the Square.

2723   (NIMBLE TV COMMERCIALS)

1970

| 35mm | col | comopt | c1000ft | REF |

Two television commercials for 'Nimble' sliced bread - "only 35 calories a slice!"

2724   MARIAN YEAR, THE

1954

| 16mm | col | silent | 666ft | REF |

[sp. Scottish Catholic Film Institute]
[attributed to L.A. Russell & B. Mocogni]

Celebrations in Celtic Park, Glasgow on 30th May 1954 when Archbishop Campbell gives the Pontifical Mass.

2725   LOURDES CENTENARY CELEBRATION

1958

| 16mm | col | silent | 820ft | REF |

sp. Scottish Catholic Film Institute
filmed by L.A. Russell and Bert Mocogni

Celebration in Celtic Park, Glasgow, to mark the centenary of the first apparition of Our Lady of Lourdes.

2726   (CATHOLIC YOUNG MEN'S SOCIETY CENTENARY CELEBRATIONS, GLASGOW)

1949

| 16mm | col | silent | 380ft | REF |

[sp. Catholic Young Men's Society]
[filmed by Dr. Banciewcz]

Archbishop Campbell celebrates Holy Mass in Celtic Park, Glasgow.

2727   KIRKCALDY MOTOR CYCLE ROAD RACES

1949

| 16mm | col | silent | 756ft | REF |

[filmed by Dr. Swanson]

Footage of the 1949 motor cycle road meeting at Beveridge Park, Kirkcaldy, Fife, featuring the heats and finals of the 250cc and 350cc road races.

2728   HIGHWAY OVER THE CLYDE

1967

| 16mm | col | comopt | 1152ft | REF |

p.c. Templar Film Studios

The various stages in the construction of the Kingston Road Bridge Glasgow, and the opening ceremony by HM Queen Elizabeth, the Queen Mother.

2729   (J. H. JOHNSON COLLECTION)

1932-'33c

| 9.5mm | b/w | silent | c1500ft | REF |

[filmed by John Harold Johnson]

Scenes in Shetland including fishing boats in the harbour, fish being gutted and packed, and the burning of the "Viking" boat at the Up Helly Aa Festival.

2730   (J.H. JOHNSON - SEQUENCES)

1930s,c

| 9.5mm | b/w | silent | c300ft | REF |

[attributed to John Harold Johnson]

A football match at Lerwick, HMS "Rodney" at Lerwick, and the laying of the GPO cable track on Shetland.

221

Dalkeith wedding, 1929. The wedding procession of Major Thomas Sturrock and Miss Isabelle Paxton. Ref. 2819

2731   (GREAT NORTH OF SCOTLAND RAILWAY FILMS)

1961*-'63

16mm	col	silent	730ft	REF

[filmed by David Gordon, Marquis of Aberdeen and Temair]

Footage of various steam locomotives, diesel engines and railway related activities. [Filmed by railway enthusiast, the Marquis of Aberdeen and Temair.] [See also ref. 2732.]

2732   (MARQUIS OF ABERDEEN'S RAILWAY FILMS)

1953*-'67

16mm	col	silent	1080ft	REF

[filmed by David Gordon, Marquis of Aberdeen and Temair]

Footage of various steam locomotives and diesel trains. [See also ref. 2731.]

2733   (NORTH EAST AND THE HIGHLANDS: CELEBRATIONS AND EVENTS)

1949*-'53

16mm	b/w&col silent	972ft	REF

Aberdeen streets decorated in bunting for the Coronation celebrations, queues for the Aberdeen 'C & A' opening sale, and motor racing on the Rest-and-Be-Thankful course.

2734   (FAMILY WEDDING AND LIFE AT "SHANZIE")

1947*-'48

16mm	b/w&col silent	1404ft	REF

Life on the Herd family farm "Shanzie" and family wedding celebrations. [The family owned the Aberdeen Herd's Corner House Cafe.] [See also refs. 2735-2736.]

2735   (HERD'S CAFE AND FAMILY FARM)

1940*-'67

| 16mm | b/w&col | silent | 1692ft | REF |

Interiors of the Aberdeen Herd's Corner House Cafe, packed with diners and waitresses at work and shots of the Herd family at their farm. [See also refs. 2734-2736.]

2736   (HERD FAMILY FILM)

1947-'53*

| 16mm | col | silent | 1690ft | REF |

Work on the farm, the Herd family at home, and wedding celebrations. [See also refs. 2734-2736.]

2737   GATHERING OF THE BRAEMAR ROYAL HIGHLAND SOCIETY, THE

1951

| 16mm | col | silent | 540ft | REF |

sp. J.E. Henderson Ltd.
filmed by J. Macdougal, J.B. Macdonald

The 1951 Braemar Highland Games attended by HM Queen Elizabeth and King George VI.

2738   ORIENTEERING

1970c

| 16mm | col | comopt | 1714 ft | REF |

sp. William Younger
pc. Jordanhill College Film Unit
d. Norman Shannon

A series of four instructional films on orienteering skills, teaching map reading, how to use a compass, and navigation.

2739   OFFICIAL BRITISH SKI INSTRUCTIONAL FILM, THE

1970c

| 16mm | col | commag | 684ft | REF |

p.c. Morgren Studios and Egeline Films

A training film for British ski instructors.

2741   (KATE KENNEDY PROCESSION AND KIRKCALDY RIFLE RANGE)

1957-'60

| 16mm | col | silent | 324ft | REF |

The Kate Kennedy Procession at St. Andrews University in 1957, a family wedding and target practice at Kirkcaldy Rifle Range.

2742   MEETING POINT: THE IONA COMMUNITY AT WORK AND WORSHIP

1959

| 16mm | b/w | comopt | 918ft | REF |

p.c. BBC
p. Bill Northwood

Maurice Lindsay interviews Dr. George Macleod and fellow members of the Iona Community about the origins of the Community, their work and aims. [See also ref. 2344.]

2743   (CONSTRUCTION WORK AT IONA ABBEY)

1938-'52

| 16mm | col | silent | 400ft | REF |

[filmed by Dr. George McLeod]

Construction work on Iona Abbey during the years 1938-1951, and the ceremony to mark the completion of a rock garden by Iona community campers in 1952.

2744   AYRSHIRE EARLY POTATOES

1948

| 16mm | col | silent | 500ft | REF |

The sowing and harvesting of Ayrshire potatoes and "tattie howkers" at work.

2745   DAY ON THE SANDS, A

1949c

| 16mm | col | silent | 200ft | VIEW |

p.c. GB Instructional Ltd.
p. John C. Elder

Two boys playing on the beach at Oban where they build a sandcastle, find a starfish and go out in a fisherman's boat to catch lobsters.

2746   TROSSACHS, THE

1935c

| 16mm | b/w | silent | 360ft | REF |

filmed by James S. Nairn and James Atterson

The lochs, mountains and castles in the Trossachs.

2747   AMONG THE HIGHLANDS AND ISLANDS

1948c

| 16mm | col | silent | 300ft | REF |

p.c. GB Instructional Ltd.
p. John C. Elder

Kittiwakes, guillemots, cormorants, puffins and razorbills are some of the seabirds featured in this educational film.

223

2748   AT THE CATTLE MARKET
1948c

16mm	col	silent	298ft		REF

p.c. GB Instructional Ltd.
p. John C. Elder

Two young boys watch cattle and pigs being auctioned at a livestock market.

2749   HERRING PACKING
1952/'53

16mm	b/w&col	sep opt	275ft		REF

p.c. Crosse & Blackwell Ltd. Peterhead

A training film for Crosse & Blackwell employees, showing a trawler unloading its herring catch at Peterhead harbour and being transferred to the Crosse & Blackwell packing factory where the herring are weighed and packed into cans.

2750   SUMMER IN SCOTLAND
1950c

16mm	col	silent	258ft		VIEW

sp. JPC of SEFA
p.c. Templar Film Studios

A small girl enjoys a summers day on the farm where she watches a shepherd and his border collie rounding up a flock of blackface sheep which are shorn and dipped.

2751   HUMPTY DUMPTY
1950c

16mm	col	silent	168ft		REF

filmed by SEFA Glasgow Group Production

An animated film to help children read and spell.

2752   GLASGOW UNIVERSITY GATES
1951*

16mm	col	silent	61ft		REF

The opening ceremony of the Glasgow University's gates gifted by the Graduates' Association to mark the second part of the University's quincentenary celebrations.

2753   FARM BABIES
1953*

16mm	col	silent	161ft		REF

filmed by SEFA Lanarkshire Production Group

Children at a farm with piglets, chickens, Shetland ponies, lambs and calves.

2754   PRIME TIME: MEDIA WEEK IN STENHOUSEMUIR PRIMARY SCHOOL
1988

16mm	col	mute	c1080ft		REF

sp. Scottish Film Council
p.c. Jordanhill College Television Unit

A project made with the assistance of members of the film workshop of Edinburgh, the film shows the activities of children at Stenhousemuir Primary School during a 'media' week: the making of animations to tell stories, developing photographs and working with computers.

2755   CIRCLE OF CARE
1980

16mm	col	sep opt	1080ft		REF

sp. Church of Scotland
p. Ian Gall

The work of the department of social responsibility of the Church of Scotland including interviews with staff in charge of hostels and homes throughout Scotland.

2756   HIGHLANDS, THE
1971

35mm	col	comopt	2785ft		VIEW

sp. HIDB in assoc. with Films of Scotland
p.c. Ogam Films
d. & ph. Oscar Marzaroli

The industries of the Highlands: the Invergordon Smelter, Ben Cruachan and Dounreay Power Stations, the glass works at Wick, a sheep market at Lairg, felling timber at Rattigan Forest and the leisure facilities at Aviemore.

2757   SPINNING
1955*

16mm	col	mute	270ft		REF

p.c. Glasgow Schools Museum Service

A demonstration of carding and spinning wool.

2758   EXTINGUISHERS
1979c

16mm	col	sep opt	250ft		VIEW

p.c. Glasgow School Museum Service

A demonstration of how and when to use three types of fire extinguishers; Water-Gas, CO_2 and Dry Powder.

2759   EASTER REVOLUTION
1960/'61

16mm	b/w	mute	144ft		REF

filmed by David Middleton

An award winner at the International Scout Film Festival for "most felicitous film", it tells the humorous story of a group of scouts who rebel against their ogre of a scout master.

2760 SUMMER CAMP 1960

1960/'61

16mm	b/w	mute	432ft		REF

filmed by David Middleton

52nd Glasgow Scouts' camp at Killin.

2761 PAISLEY PATTERNS

1957-'60

16mm	col	comopt	540ft		REF

sp. Paisley Town Council
[p.c. Elder Films]
d. John C. Elder

A promotional film on the re-development of Paisley and the new housing schemes under the Town and Country Planning (Scotland) Act.

2762 SECOND CASE, THE

1950*

16mm	b/w	silent	176ft		REF

filmed by SAAC

Made during the SAAC's annual weekend at Crieff Hydro, the film tells the humorous story of a mix up over swopped ladies' and gents' suitcases at the hotel.

2763 ZOO BABIES

1953*

16mm	col	silent	164ft		REF

sp. Joint Production Committee
filmed by Glasgow SEFA Production Group

A variety of baby animals filmed at Edinburgh Zoo, Calderpark Zoo and Wilson's Zoo in Glasgow.

2764 SEABIRDS OF THE FORTH

1953*

16mm	col	silent	388ft		REF

filmed by H.B. (Frank) Marshall

A look at the wide variety of birds living in the nature reserve on the Isle of May in the Firth of Forth.

2765 ESKIMO LIFE IN GREENLAND

1950c

16mm	col	silent	336ft		REF

filmed by St. Andrews University

Filmed by members of St. Andrews' University while on an expedition to Greenland, showing daily life, a local sports event and Eskimo traditional craftwork.

2766 DOMESTIC SCIENCE AS A CAREER

1936-'38c

16mm	b/w	silent	580ft		REF

p.c. Elder-Dalrymple Production
d. J.C. Elder

Students at work on the various courses available at the Glasgow and West of Scotland College of Domestic Science.

2767 KINTYRE

1955c

16mm	col	sep opt	360ft		REF

filmed by Iain Dunnachie

Scenes of life on the Mull of Kintytre including shots of holiday makers and local inhabitants. Shots of farming, fishing and mining at the Argyle Colliery and general views of Campbeltown.

2768 (GEORGE MAY FAMILY FILM)

1932-'35*

16mm	b/w	silent	810ft		REF

[filmed by George May]

Holiday activities of the Cargill family of Arbroath, owners of Cargill's Hairdressing Salon.

2769 ARP: A REMINDER FOR PEACE

1939-'40

16mm	b/w	silent	565ft		REF

[filmed by Frank Marshall]

Commended at the 7th Scottish Amateur Film Festival in 1940, illustrating a household preparing for the black-out and using an air-raid shelter.

2770 MAKING A SCRAPBOOK

1952*

16mm	col	silent	380ft		VIEW

sp. Scottish JPC
filmed by SEFA Dumbartonshire Production Group

A short educational film explaining how to make a scrapbook.

2771 MARY GETS READY FOR SCHOOL

1951*

16mm	col	silent	230ft		VIEW

sp. SEFA
p.c. Elder Film Productions Ltd., Glasgow

A small girl gets ready for school.

2772 MARY'S GARDEN

1947*

16mm	col	silent	110 ft		REF

filmed by SEFA Glasgow Group

An animated film illustrating a nursery rhyme to help young children read out loud. [Awarded a principal prize in the 1948 Scottish Amateur Film Festival.]

2773 ZOO'S BIG FIVE, THE

1953*

16mm	col	silent	178ft		REF

filmed by SEFA Lanarkshire Production Group

Zebras, a camel, yak, bison and elephant at Calder Park Zoo, Glasgow.

225

2774   THISTLE, THE
1942*

16mm	b/w	silent	360ft		REF

sp. Gaumont British Instructional

An educational film showing how the thistle grows and is pollenated by bees.

2775   (DUNDEE ARCHITECTURE)
1967-'69c

16mm	b/w	silent	c1500ft		REF

[d. Fred Smith and Jimmy Howie]

Rushes from a film made to record aspects of Dundee city life including shots of tenements, housing estates, crowds at Tannadice football ground and street scenes.

2777   SECRETARY OF STATE (FOR SCOTLAND)
1964c

16mm	b/w	comopt	1112ft		VIEW

pc. BBC TV Scotland
p. Finlay J. Macdonald

Through a series of interviews with former Secretaries of State, the film traces the development of this ministerial position describing the responsibilities of the Minister and his relationship with both local and central government.

2778   SEAS AROUND US, THE: GREAT BRITISH FOOD
1979

16mm	col	comopt	972ft		VIEW

sp. British Gas and White Fish Authority
p.c. Viscom Production
w. & d . David Gowring

A look at the fishing industry and the efforts of the White Fish Authority to improve the design of fishing boats.

2779   SERVING A CHANGING INDUSTRY
1979c

16mm	col	comopt	864ft		REF

sp. White Fish Authority
p.c. G. & R.
p . Ted Bullock

A film about the research and development work of the fishing industry in Britain, including how the White Fish Authority exports its techniques to the Middle East.

2780   [HADDO ESTATE OPERATIONS 1955]
1955

16mm	b/w&col silent	800ft		REF

[filmed by David Gordon, Marquis of Aberdeen and Temair]

A record of various activities involved in the running of Haddo Estate, Aberdeenshire, including the maintenance of Haddo House, its outbuildings and the agricultural activities on the estate farmlands throughout the year. [See also refs. 2781-2786.]

226

Glasgow May Day, 1937. Ref. 1722

2781 [HADDO ESTATE OPERATIONS 1961]
1961

16mm	col	silent	700ft		REF

[filmed by David Gordon, Marquis of Aberdeen and Temair]

Activities at Haddo Estate, Aberdeenshire, including the maintenance of Haddo House, its outbuildings and agricultural activities on the estate farmlands throughout the year. [See also refs. 2780-2786.]

2782 [HADDO ESTATE OPERATIONS 1962]
1962

16mm	b/w&col	silent	360ft		REF

[filmed by David Gordon, Marquis of Aberdeen and Temair]

Activities at Haddo Estate, Aberdeenshire, including the maintenance of Haddo House, its outbuildings and agricultural activities on the estate farmlands throughout the year. [See also refs. 2780-2786.]

2783 [HADDO ESTATE OPERATIONS 1966-'67]
1966-'67

16mm	col	silent	326ft		REF

[filmed by David Gordon, Marquis of Aberdeen and Temair]

Activities at Haddo Estate, Aberdeenshire, including the maintenance of Haddo House, its outbuildings and agricultural activities on the estate farmlands throughout the year. [See also refs. 2780-2786.]

2784 (HADDO EVENTS)
1949-'50

16mm	b/w&col	silent	380ft		REF

[filmed by David Gordon, Marquis of Aberdeen and Temair]

The Gordon family at home, a scout camp at Haddo House, Aberdeenshire, and Lord Aberdeen greeting King George VI and royal family at Ballater station. [See also refs. 2780-2786.]

2785 ORDER OF ST. JOHN, THE
1971

16mm	col	comopt	250ft		REF

[p.c. Campbell Harper Films]

The official opening of the chancery of St. John, Priory of Scotland, Edinburgh by HRH Princess Anne. The royal party is greeted by Lord Haddo. [See also refs. 2780-2786.]

2786 (QUEEN MOTHER'S VISIT TO HADDO)
1957

16mm	col	silent	180ft		REF

[filmed by David Gordon, Marquis of Aberdeen and Temair]

HM Queen Elizabeth, the Queen Mother visits Lord and Lady Aberdeen at Haddo House, Aberdeenshire. [See also refs. 2780-2785.]

2787 SINGLE SPINDLE APPLICATIONS
1974*

16mm	col	comopt	372ft		REF

p.c. Wickman Film Unit Production

The Wickman single spindle machine at work. [This machine manufactured at Wickman Lang Ltd., Johnstone.] [See also ref. 2788.]

2788 WICKMAN SINGLE SPINDLE AUTOMATIC, THE
1974*

16mm	col	comopt	360ft		REF

p.c. Wickman Film Unit Production

The single spindle automatic machine at work. [This machine manufactured at Wickman Lang Ltd., Johnstone.] [See also ref. 2787.]

2790 CRUACHAN
1966

35mm	col	comopt	2790ft		VIEW

sp. Films of Scotland
p.c. Templar Film Studios

A detailed description of the civil and electrical engineering work involved during the building of the pumped-storage hydro-electric scheme at Loch Awe, Argyll. [See also ref. 2214 for alternative version.]

2791 [GOLDEN THISTLE AWARD]
1970

35mm	col	mute	95ft		REF

sp. Films of Scotland Committee

Close up shots of the Golden Thistle award with its inscription"Edinburgh Film Festival 1970. Golden Thistle Award for outstanding achievement in the Art of Cinematography, Darryl F. Zanuck. Presented by Films of Scotland Committee".

2792 AYR FROM THE AULD BRIG
1961

35mm	col	comopt	1091ft		VIEW

sp. Films of Scotland Committee
p.c. Thames & Clyde Film Co. Ltd.
d. Stanley Russell

The story of the town of Ayr and its links with Robert Burns.

2793 EDINBURGH ON PARADE
1970

35mm	col	comopt	1293ft		VIEW

sp. Films of Scotland
p.c. IFA (Scotland) Ltd.
d. & ph. Mark Littlewood

The streets of Edinburgh at Festival time and the opening Parade along Princes Street.

227

2794 CASHMERE STORY, THE
1960

35mm	col	comopt	1262ft	REF

sp. Pringle of Scotland and Films of Scotland
p.c. Associated British Pathe

Cashmere wool is transported from the Himalayas to the Borders of Scotland where, in the Pringle woollen mill it is treated, knitted and finely crafted into Pringle sweaters.

2795 STORY OF TORMORE, THE
1963

35mm	col	comopt	1695ft	VIEW

sp. Films of Scotland Committee
p.c. Campbell Harper Films Ltd.
d. Alan Harper

The construction of the Tormore Distillery, and the distilling processes.

2796 ZOO YEAR
1965

35mm	col	comopt	1800ft	VIEW

sp. Films of Scotland
p.c. Campbell Harper Films Ltd.
d. Henry Cooper

The animals at the Scottish National Zoological Park, Edinburgh.

2797 WINSTON CHURCHILL VISITS ABERDEEN
1947

35mm	b/w	silent	360ft	VIEW

[attributed to Ernest Bromberg]

Winston Churchill, accompanied by his wife and daughter, plant a tree in the home of Sir Thomas and Lady Jaffrey and the University of Aberdeen confers on him the Honorary Degree of LLD.

2798 HAWICK COMMON RIDING
1937

35mm	b/w	silent	360ft	VIEW

The parade of riders through the streets of Hawick, watched by onlooking crowds at the Common Riding festival.

2799 (FUNERAL OF ALEXANDER BUIST)
1901

35mm	b/w	silent	150ft	VIEW

The funeral procession of Alexander Buist, proprietor of Ward Jute Mills, Dundee, one of the first mill owners to supply a creche and school for children of his mill workers.

2800 ABERDEEN SCHOOL SPORTS
1925

35mm	b/w	silent	45ft	VIEW

p.c. Pathe Super Gazette

HRH the Duke of York attends an Aberdeen school sports day at Pittodrie Park.

2801 (SCENES OF ORKNEY)
1935-'37

16mm	b/w	silent	288ft	REF

[filmed by John Stout]

Farm workers on Orkney, St. Magnus Cathedral, a local fete, and footage of a motor launch bearing the German Swastika bringing passengers to Kirkwall harbour.

2802 NORMAN MACCAIG: A MAN IN MY POSITION
1977

16mm	col	comopt	1080ft	REF

sp. Scottish Arts Council in assoc. with Films of Scotland
p.c. Pelicula Films
d. Michael Alexander

The poet Norman MacCaig talks about his work to Magnus Magnusson and John MacInnes.

2803 WHISPER AND I SHALL HEAR
1913-'14

35mm	b/w	mute	180ft	VIEW

[p.c. attributed to Edison]

Originally screened with a separate source of soundtrack, the film shows a couple in a garden dressed in Regency Costume singing a duet. [Original tinted nitrate preserved by the National Film Archive.]

2804 AS LONG AS YOU'RE YOUNG
1962

35mm	col	comopt	1996ft	VIEW

sp. Films of Scotland
p.c. Glasgow Films Ltd.
d. Edward McConnell

Leisure pursuits in Scotland; hikers enjoying walking by Loch Lomond, skiers in Glen Coe, cyclists in the Borders, yachting on the Clyde and people of all nationalities strolling in Edinburgh's Princes Street Gardens.

2805 PLEASURE ISLAND
1960

35mm	col	comopt	921ft	REF

sp. Films of Scotland Committee
p.c. Glasgow Films Ltd.
d. David Welsh

The holiday island of Bute and the pleasures of Rothesay and Ettrick Bay.

2806   ELGIN CITY AND BOYS' BRIGADE
1935c

35mm	b/w	silent	118ft	VIEW

[filmed by James S. Nairn]

A football match between Elgin City and an unidentified team, and the Inspection and Presentation of Colours of the Boys' Brigade.

2807   PROSPECT FOR A CITY
1967

35mm	col	comopt	2167ft	VIEW

sp. Films of Scotland
p.c. Campbell Harper Films Ltd.
d. Henry Cooper

Produced to commemorate the bi-centenary of Craig's Plan for the first New Town of Edinburgh, 1767, the film shows the Town's buildings, gardens and monuments.

2808   AROUND DUNDEE IN THE 1930'S
1935-'47c

16mm	b/w&col silent	760ft	VIEW

[filmed by John Stout]

Places and events in and around Dundee in the 1930s; ships in the city's docks, a parade in Baxter Park, boxing matches at Forfar, skating at Claypotts, Dundee FC playing at Dens Park, and the flight of the Maia and Mercury aircraft.

2809   SPRING FLOWERS IN A SCOTTISH WOOD
1980

16mm	col	sep opt	300ft	REF

filmed by Charles E. Palmar

Shots of various woodland spring flowers.

2810   HIGHLAND HERONRY
1961

16mm	col	sep opt	1000ft	REF

filmed by Charles E. Palmar

Herons seen in their natural habitat in the highlands of Scotland. [Joint winner of BBC/ Nature Conservancy film competition for amateurs, 1963.]

2811   HIGHLAND EAGLE
1970

16mm	b/w	mute	700ft	VIEW

filmed by Charles E. Palmar

The Golden Eagle filmed in its natural habitat.

2812   COMMEMORATION DAY. GLENALMOND AND YACHTING
1932

16mm	b/w	silent	90ft	REF

[filmed by Dr. A.W.M. Battersby]

Commemoration Day at Glenalmond School, Perthshire and yachting on the Clyde. [See also refs. 2813.]

2813   COMMEMORATION DAY GLENALMOND
1932

16mm	b/w	silent	90ft	REF

[filmed by Dr. A.W.M. Battersby]

Commemoration Day ceremonies at Glenalmond School, Perthshire. [See also ref. 2812.]

2814   BOTANIC GARDENS AND OLD GLASGOW
1930*

16mm	b/w	silent	90ft	REF

[filmed by Dr. A.W.M. Battersby]

Amateur footage of people in Glasgow's Botanic Gardens, traffic on Great Western Road and street scenes in the city.

2815   AYR PAGEANT
1934

16mm	b/w	silent	90ft	REF

[filmed by Dr. A.W.M. Battersby]

Scenes at the Ayr Pageant on 23rd June 1934.

2816   (RANGOON HOSPITAL AND SCENES FROM THE EAST)
1930*

16mm	b/w	silent	360ft	REF

[filmed by Dr. A.W.M. Battersby]

Made by Dr. Alexander Battersby during the time he worked as ship's surgeon with the British Steam Navigation Co., the film shows street scenes in Ceylon, the hospital in Rangoon, shipping, and the docks and streets of Dublin and Hamburg.

2817   (BADMINTON IN THE GARDEN)
1932

16mm	b/w	silent	72 ft	REF

[filmed by Mr. Martin]

A family game of badminton in the garden.

229

2818	BARS OF SILVER				
1956					
16mm	b/w	comopt	660ft		VIEW

p.c. Editorial Films

The fish auction at Billingsgate, London; landing fish at Hull and Buckie; the smoking of haddock and fishmongers at work.

2819	(DALKEITH WEDDING)			
1929				
35mm	b/w	silent	135ft	

[filmed as a local topical for the Picture Palace Dalkeith]

The wedding procession of Major Thomas Sturrock and Miss Isabelle Paxton in Dalkeith, Midlothian showing the newly wedded couple being driven through Dalkeith in a gun-carriage drawn by Scots Greys. 28th March 1929.

2820	(CRICHTON COLLECTION)			
1950/'60s				
std.8mm	b/w&col silent	200ft		REF

[filmed by W.G. Crichton]

Amateur footage of various scenes and events including the demolition of No. 24 Queen Street, Glasgow, road construction beside Loch Cluanie, the Strome ferry, RAC Veteran car rally, the seafront at Anstruther and boats on the Crinan canal.

230

2821	(MONTGOMERY FAMILY OUTINGS)			
1930*				
16mm	b/w	silent	195ft	REF

[filmed by Frances Hedges Montgomery]

Picnics and a snowball fight. [Made by Frances Montgomery of Fife, burgh councillor of St. Andrews c1929.] [See also refs. 2822-2832.]

2822	[CART HORSE SHOW]			
1928*				
16mm	b/w	silent	180ft	VIEW

[filmed by Frances Hedges Montgomery]

Tossing the caber, wrestling and the parading of horses in the showground at the Royal Highland Show in Perth. [See also refs. 2821-2832.]

2823	AMATEUR GOLF CHAMPIONSHIP ST. ANDREWS			
1930				
16mm	col	silent	210ft	VIEW

[filmed by Frances Hedges Montgomery]

Footage of an amateur golf championship at St. Andrews in May 1930. [See also refs. 2821-2832.]

2824	[GOLF AT LADYBANK]			
1930				
16mm	b/w	silent	108ft	REF

[filmed by Frances Hedges Montgomery]

A family game of golf at Ladybank in Fife. [See also refs. 2821-2832.]

2825	(MONTGOMERY FAMILY HOLIDAYS)			
1928-'30*				
16mm	b/w	silent	210ft	REF

[filmed by Frances Hedges Montgomery]

The Montgomery family on the beach at St. Andrews and at the grandfather's home 'Penniwells' at Elstree, London. [See also refs. 2821-2832.]

2826	(MONTGOMERY FAMILY - NEW HOUSE)			
1934*				
16mm	b/w	silent	207ft	REF

[filmed by Frances Hedges Montgomery]

A new garden being laid at the Montgomery family home, the family in the car and the children horse riding. [See also refs. 2821-2832.]

2827	[KATE KENNEDY PARADE NO. 1]			
1929*				
16mm	b/w	silent	200ft	VIEW

[filmed by Frances Hedges Montgomery]

University students taking part in the Kate Kennedy procession in St. Andrews.[See also refs. 2821-2832.]

2828	[KATE KENNEDY PARADE NO. 2]			
1928*				
16mm	b/w	silent	200ft	VIEW

[filmed by Frances Hedges Montgomery]

The University of St. Andrews' Kate Kennedy Parade and the town's harbour where fishermen unload their catch. [See also refs. 2821-2832]

2829	[CLAY PIGEON SHOOTING]			
1934*				
16mm	b/w	silent	132ft	VIEW

[filmed by Frances Hedges Montgomery]

The building of a new conservatory at the Montgomery family home, clay pigeon shooting and Mrs. Montgomery driving the family Rolls Royce.[See also refs. 2821-2832]

2830	[PENNIWELLS AND ST. ANDREWS]			
1929*				
16mm	b/w	silent	432ft	VIEW

[filmed by Frances Hedges Montgomery]

A flight in a 'Pleasure Flying Services' aeroplane, a fire fighting demonstration, the launching of a lifeboat and a boxing match. [See also refs. 2821-2832]

2831 [DUCHESS OF YORK IN ST. ANDREWS]

1928*/'29

| 16mm | b/w | silent | 432ft | REF |

[filmed by Frances Hedges Montgomery]

The visit to St. Andrews by the Duke and Duchess of York. The Duke is seen playing golf and the Duchess attends the opening ceremony of the Younger Graduation Hall. Stanley Baldwin also attends the graduation ceremony. [See also refs. 2821-2832]

2832 [TOWN COUNCIL ELECTION DAY]

1928-'29*

| 16mm | b/w | silent | 470ft | VIEW |

[filmed by Frances Hedges Montgomery]

Footage taken during the campaign for the election of Mrs Frances Montgomery onto the town council of St. Andrews. [See also refs. 2821-2831.]

2833 WEDDING OF JOHN GLAISTER AND ISOBEL LINDSAY

1918

| 35mm | b/w | silent | 50ft | VIEW |

p.c. Scottish Moving Picture News/ Green's Film Service

The wedding of Captain John Glaister and Isobel Lindsay at Glasgow Cathedral, 25th May, 1918. [See also ref. 1659.]

2834 PRIDE OF PENGUINS, A

1970c

| 35mm | col | comopt | 1854ft | VIEW |

sp. Films of Scotland
d. & cam. Christopher Mylne

The rearing of penguins at Edinburgh Zoo.

2835 [LANIMER DAYS 1946/'47]

1946-'49

| 16mm | col | silent | 286ft | REF |

[filmed by Prentice]

The procession of floats and children in fancy dress at the Lanark Lanimer Day celebrations. Unveiling of the War Memorial.

2836 LANIMER DAY, LANARK 1948

1948

| 16mm | col | silent | 227ft | REF |

[filmed by Prentice]

A pageant with horse-drawn floats, children in fancy dress and a march by of different youth organisations at the Lanark Lanimer Day celebrations.

2837 LANARK LANIMER DAY 1949 AND 1952

1949/'52

| 16mm | col | silent | 310ft | REF |

[filmed by Prentice]

The processions of floats and bands at Lanark Lanimer Days, 1949 and 1952.

2838 (PRENTICE FAMILY EVENTS)

1951-'55

| 16mm | col | silent | 282ft | REF |

[filmed by Prentice]

Glasgow University graduation ceremony 1951, a family party Christmas 1952, the Royal Highland Show in Alloa 1955, and the visit to Lanark of HM the Queen and Duke of Edinburgh, 1953.

2839 FAMILY SCRAPBOOK NO. 1

1931-'36

| 9.5mm | b/w | silent | c400ft | REF |

[filmed by Prentice]

Family holidays at Prestwick, Ayrshire.

2840 FAMILY SCRAPBOOK NO. 2

1937-'39

| 9.5mm | b/w | silent | c350ft | REF |

[filmed by Prentice]

A visit to London, holidays in Ayrshire and the Lanimer Day festivals of 1938 and 1939.

2841 FAMILY SCRAPBOOK NO. 3

1940

| 9.5mm | b/w | silent | c350ft | REF |

[filmed by Prentice]

A snowstorm, a garden party, a concert in aid of charity, a holiday at Ayr and winter sports.

2842 FAMILY SCRAPBOOK NO. 4

1941-'42

| 9.5mm | b/w | silent | c350ft | REF |

[filmed by Prentice]

Family holidays at Ayr, a naval convoy and shots of ARP duty.

2843 FAMILY SCRAPBOOK NO. 5

1943-'45

| 9.5mm | b/w | silent | c350ft | REF |

[filmed by Prentice]

Golfing, school sports and Girl Guide camp.

231

232

Dumbarton, 1944-1946. "Bonny Baby Contest" VE Day. Ref. 1871

2844	VARIOUS PARADES 1940-1945			
1943-'45				
9.5mm	b/w	silent	c400ft	REF

[filmed by Prentice]

Footage of various parades and festivals including an ATC church parade, a "Wings for Victory" parade, an ARP practice at Dunglass Castle, Lanimer Day of 1942 [curtailed due to the war] and Sir Harry Lauder opening an NFS fete in Lanark.

2845	VARIOUS PARADES 1943-1945			
1943-'45				
9.5mm	b/w	silent	c400ft	REF

[filmed by Prentice]

A Home Guard anniversary parade and various youth parades. Lanimer Day 1943 and a Red Cross fete opened by Lord Dunglass.

2846	(PRENTICE WARTIME FILM)			
1942				
9.5mm	col	silent	c50ft	REF

[filmed by Prentice]

Cinderella pantomime at Stanmore House, Lanark 1942 in aid of charity.

2847	[PORT ELPHINSTONE SCHOOL PICNIC]			
1952				
16mm	b/w	silent	320ft	REF

[sp. Hall & Welfare Committee, Port Elphinstone]
[filmed by 'squeaker' Smith]

A school picnic with a fancy dress parade and games at the fair.

2850 [MOVING THE UNICORN]
1962

std.8mm	col	silent	150ft	REF

[filmed by Alan D. McLagan]

Moving the training sailing ship "Unicorn" to enable preparation work for the building of the Tay Road Bridge.

2851 [DEMISE OF THE "HEADWAY"]
1970-'72c

std.8mm	col	silent	c50ft	REF

Shots of the fishing vessel the "Headway" keeled over against the quay at Aberdeen harbour.

2852 [GLASGOW TAXI DRIVERS OUTING]
1957

16mm	b/w	mute	c300ft	REF

[d. Eddie McConnell]

Children on their annual outing from Glasgow to Troon, transported by Glasgow taxi-drivers in fancy dress. Jimmy Logan is seen talking to the children. [Footage used by John Grierson in "This Wonderful World".]

2853 GREY METROPOLIS, THE
1952

16mm	b/w	sep opt	540ft	VIEW

[filmed by J. T. Ritchie, N. McIsaac, R.Townsend]

Made by teachers at Norton Park School, Edinburgh, the film shows the city through the thoughts and songs of R.L. Stevenson. [Winner of the Lizars Cup, Scottish Amateur Film Festival 1953.]

2855 TAY BRIDGE DISASTER
1968

16mm	b/w	commag	250ft	REF

filmed by Ian Rintoul

Reconstruction of the events leading up to, and re-enactment of the Tay Bridge disaster December 1879.

2856 HOUR OF THE EAGLE
1976

16mm	col	commag	720ft	VIEW

filmed by Ian Rintoul

Dramatised account of the Luftwaffe bombing raid on Edinburgh on 16th October, 1939 told from the viewpoint of both sides of the combat. [Awarded in 1976 Movie Maker's Ten Best Winner and Best Editing and Best Soundtrack Trophy.]

2857 BRITISH CARNIVOROUS PLANTS
1942

16mm	col	silent	290ft	VIEW

p.c. Natural History Film Production Soc.
d. C. Eric Palmar

An instructional film using diagrams and close-ups of three types of carnivorous plants grown in Britain - Butterwort, Sundew and Bladderwort.

2858 [OUTER HEBRIDES - HUMAN ACTIVITIES]
1968*

16mm	col	silent	610ft	REF

[filmed by Charles E. Palmar]

Crofting in the Outer Hebrides with footage of spinning and carding of wool, collecting seaweed and lobster fishing.

2859 MORE THAN YOU THINK
1974c

16mm	col	comopt	850ft	VIEW

sp. Scottish Society for the Mentally Handicapped
p.c. Ogam Films
ph. & d. Martin Singleton

The experience of parenting and caring for mentally handicapped children.

2860 [GOLF BALL FACTORY]
1961

16mm	b/w	mute	31ft	REF

p.c. BBC Scotland

Brief interior shot taken inside a golf ball factory.

2861 NIGHT AT THE HAP, A
1962-'67

16mm	b/w&col	silent	576ft	VIEW

filmed by Ciano Soave

Teenagers spending an evening at the Haparanda Cafe, Dundee. [Filmed by the owner of the Cafe - a popular haunt for local teenagers in the '60s. The Cafe has now been demolished.] [See also ref. 2862.]

2862 HAP DANCES, THE
1962-'65

16mm	b/w&col	silent	576ft	VIEW

filmed by Ciano Soave

'The Paladians', 'Erle Blue Stars' and 'Prohibition Pete' playing to crowded dance floors where the "twist" and other '60s dances are in evidence at 'The Hap Dances' organised by the owner of the Haparanda Cafe in Dundee. [See also ref. 2861.]

233

2864   [TRIP ABOARD TRAINING KETCH "FALCON"]

1950s

16mm	b/w	silent	420ft		REF

[filmed by Don Sawkins]

A trip aboard Fleck's training ketch the "Falcon", based at Rhu, Gareloch. The trainee crew are seen working on board and in the galley.

2865   (SAWKINS NO. 7)

1959*

16mm	col	mute	320ft		REF

[attributed to Don Sawkins]

Leaving Glasgow by steamer and cruising to Dunoon, Oban, Iona and Fingal's Cave on Staffa.

2866   (HUNTERS QUAY TEACHERS YACHT)

1950s,c

16mm	col	silent	415ft		REF

[filmed by Don Sawkins]

A yacht race filmed by local cinematographer from Dunoon.

2867   [AMERICAS CUP CHALLENGERS]

1950s,c

16mm	col	silent	360ft		REF

[filmed by Don Sawkins]

Americas Cup challengers "Sceptre" and "Sovereign" racing on the Clyde.

2868 (SAWKINS NO. 11)
1950s,c

| 16mm | b/w | silent | 270ft | REF |

[filmed by Don Sawkins]

Footage of the West Highland Pottery showroom in Dunoon with shots of the glazing and firing of pots and of customers in the Pottery's tearoom.

2869 [COWAL HIGHLAND GATHERING]
1959*

| 16mm | col | silent | 432ft | REF |

[filmed by Don Sawkins]

Footage of the Cowal Highland Gathering with shots of the pipe band marching through the streets of Dunoon, a dancing competition, the presentation of trophies and a fireworks display.

2870 DUNOON - THE GEM OF THE CLYDE
1950s

| 16mm | col | silent | 800ft | REF |

[filmed by Don Sawkins]

Holidaymakers enjoying the beach and various sporting activities at Dunoon. Shots of a stalking party on a hillside.

2871 HOLIDAY DUNOON
1950s

| 16mm | col | mute | 720ft | REF |

sp. Dunoon Development Association
p.c. Radiant Film Production
cam. Don Sawkins

A promotional film for the holiday resort of Dunoon and the Clyde coast showing holidaymakers on steamers arriving at Dunoon and Rothesay, Iona and Staffa. Ballroom dancing, a ceilidh in the Pavilion Theatre Rothsay and the Cowal Highland Games.

2872 [DUNOON OCCASIONS]
1958/'66

| 16mm | col | silent | 860ft | REF |

[filmed by Don Sawkins]

Various events in Dunoon shot by local cinematographer. Footage includes a visit by HM the Queen on the Royal Yacht "Britannia", a gala day, a yacht race, a vintage car rally, a fete and a ceilidh.

2873 DUNOON - HOLIDAYS UNDER SAIL
1950s

| 16mm | col | mute | 560ft | REF |

filmed by Don Sawkins

A young couple enjoying the leisure facilities of the holiday resort of Dunoon.

2874 SAILING FOR SPORT
1961

| 16mm | col | comopt | 590ft | VIEW |

sp. Educational Films of Scotland
filmed by Don Sawkins

Yachts racing at the regattas during "Clyde Week".

2875 [BERVIE PARISH CHURCH JUMBLE SALE]
1965

| 16mm | b/w | silent | 56ft | VIEW |

[filmed by Sandy Couper]

An open air jumble sale at Bervie Parish Church.

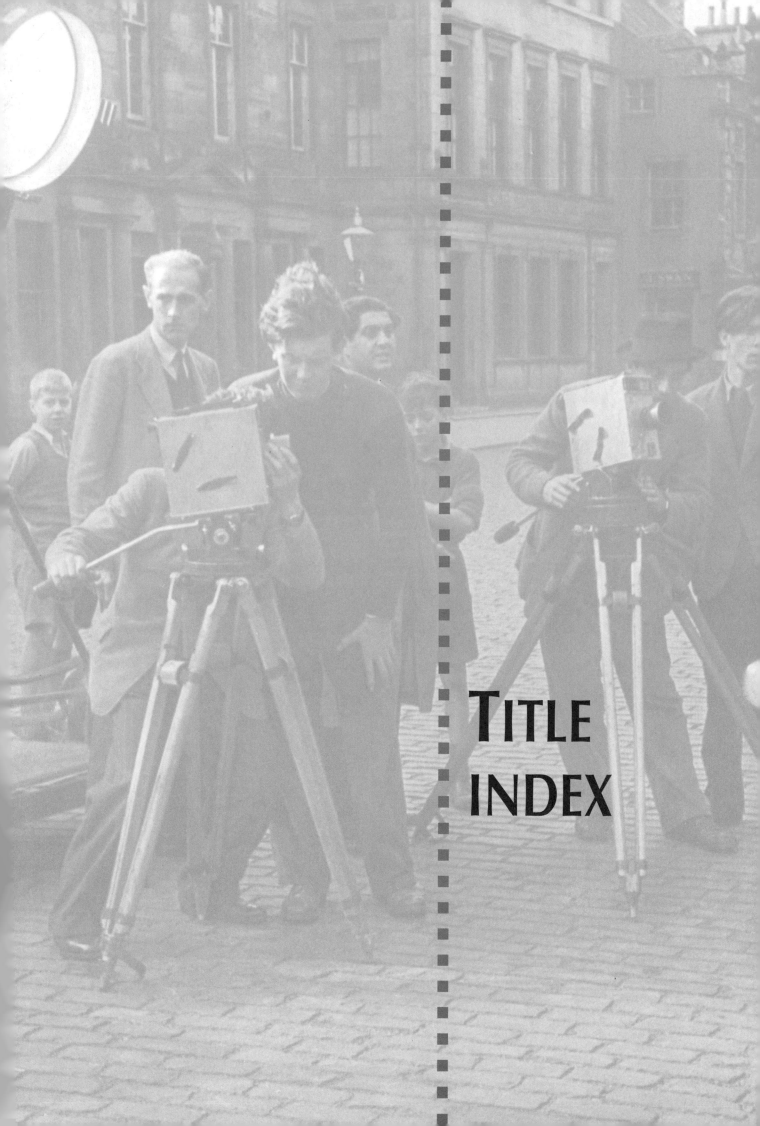

TITLE
INDEX

240

C

241

247

249

251

252

N

254

256

257

SEA CITY GREENOCK	2236
(SEA OF GALILEE MISSION HOSPITAL, TIBERIAS)	0346
(SEA OF GALILEE MISSION HOSPITAL, TIBERIAS)	0347
SEA SCOUTS PART II	0295
SEABIRDS IN SCOTLAND	1830
SEABIRDS IN THE SHETLAND ISLANDS	1128
SEABIRDS OF THE FORTH	2764
SEAFOOD	1060
SEALING WAX AND WAFERS	2312
SEAS AROUND US, THE: GREAT BRITISH FOOD	2778
SEAWARDS THE GREAT SHIPS	2230
(SEAWEED)	2505
SECOND CASE, THE	2762
SECOND FOLLIES, THE	1188
SECRETARY OF STATE (FOR SCOTLAND)	2777
SECTIONS FROM "CURRENT ACCOUNT" WAVERLEY PROGRAMME	0165
[SEE CANADA THIS SUMMER]	1220
SEEDS OF PROSPERITY	0495
SEEING IS BELIEVING	0437
SEINE NET	0276
SERMON IN STONE, A	0473
SERVICE COMMEMORATING 750TH ANNIVERSARY/OPENING OF QUEENS' BRIDGE	1953
SERVICE NOT SELF	0455
SERVICE OF THANKSGIVING	2092
[SERVICE OF THANKSGIVING IN ST. GILES' CATHEDRAL]	2417
SERVING A CHANGING INDUSTRY	2779
SETTING UP THE BOLEX S-221 (PROJECTOR)	1289
SETTLED OUT OF COURT	2615
SEVEN TILL FIVE	1100
SHARK FISHING	1984
(SHAWLANDS CROSS)	1024
(SHEARER FAMILY FILM ONE)	2502
(SHEARER FAMILY FILM TWO)	2503
(SHEEP DIPPING)	0667
SHEPHERD AND HIS DOG, THE	2164
[SHETLAND - A FEW ASPECTS]	1616
(SHETLAND AND FAIR ISLE SCENES)	1617
SHETLAND, PEOPLE OF MANY LANDS	1286
SHETLAND PONY	1130
(SHETLAND SCENES)	1615
[SHIELDHALL COFFEE]	0994
SHIELDHALL FURNITURE - MARCH OF PROGRESS	0742
(SHIELDHALL PART TWO)	0857
SHIELDHALL SHOES	1032
SHINTY IN THE HIGHLANDS	1972
(SHIP GAMES)	1223
(SHIPPING JUTE TO LONDON)	2568
[SHOP PICNIC, CARNOUSTIE]	2529
[SHOP PICNIC, FARLAIR SWIMMING POOL]	2531
SHORENESTING BIRDS OF SCOTLAND	1831
SHOSTAKOVITCH AND HUGH MACDIARMID	0537
[SHOTS OF EDINBURGH]	0380
SHOTTS FARMERS' ANNUAL BALL 1951	1861
SHOTTS FESTIVAL 1951	1967
SHOTTS HIGHLAND GAMES	1628
SILVER CITY, THE	2225
SILVER TRUMPET, THE	1160

[SIMON SQUARE EXHIBITION]	2016
(SIMPSON FAMILY FILM)	1989
SINBAD THE SAILOR/ BABES IN THE WOOD	2180
[SINGER SPORTS AND GALA 1954]	1585
[SINGER SPORTS AND GALA 1957]	1586
SINGER SPORTS GALA 1952	1584
[SINGER] SPORTS GALA 1961	1587
[SINGER'S FOUNDRY]	1502
SINGING STREET, THE	0799
SINGLE SPINDLE APPLICATIONS	2787
SIR DAVID ROBERTSON, MP, OPENS NEW BRICK WORKS	0597B
(SIR HENRY FOWLER)	0854
SIR PATRICK SPENS	0312
SIR WILLIAM BRUCE	1832
SKETCH PLAN OF THE EMPIRE EXHIBITION	2617
[SKI-ING IN SCOTLAND]	2149
SKI-ING IN SCOTLAND	2121
(SKI-ING ON BEN LAWERS)	2147
SKIMSTERS, THE	2668
SKYE	0027
SKYWAY AMBULANCE	1269
SLAUGHTER ON THE AVENUE (SEARCHLIGHT)	1213
[SLEEPING BEAUTY 1940, THE]	1145
SMART BOY WANTED	1171
SMITHS IN SCOTLAND, THE	2231
SMOCKING	1413
SMOKIES	1781
SNAPPY SNAPS OF RUTHERGLEN	1975
SNATCHES FROM THE FORTY THIEVES PANTOMIME	2179
(SNOW)	0852
SNOW PLOUGH, THE	1637
SO MANY PARTINGS	0806
SOAP MAKING	2169
(SOC CLUB RACES)	2096
SOLDIER COMES HOME, A	0433
SOLWAY COUNTIES, THE	1792
SOME BEAUTY SPOTS IN NORTH SCOTLAND	1577B
SOME EVENTS IN GLASGOW 1937	1068
SONG FOR PRINCE CHARLIE, A	2256
SONG OF THE CLYDE	0460
SONGS OF SCOTLAND	2235
SOUTH RONA EXPEDITION: THE DESCENT TO THE CAVE	0748
SOUTHERN SCOTLAND	0914
SOUTHERN SCOTLAND	1132
SOUTHERN UPLANDS	0630B
SOVEREIGN "SCOTCH", THE	1932
SPINNING	2757
SPIRIT OF THE GAMES, THE	0472
[SPITHEAD REVIEW 1937]	2562
SPORT IN SCOTLAND	0314
SPORTS AT WEST OF SCOTLAND SCHOOLS OTC CAMP	1439
SPORTS CARNIVAL AT HAMPDEN	1660
[SPOT THE LIKENESS]	1025
(SPOT THE SPOT)	0863C
SPRING FLOWERS IN A SCOTTISH WOOD	2809
SPRING IN GALLOWAY	2721
SPRING IN SCOTLAND	2478
SPRING IN THE FIELDS	2161

259

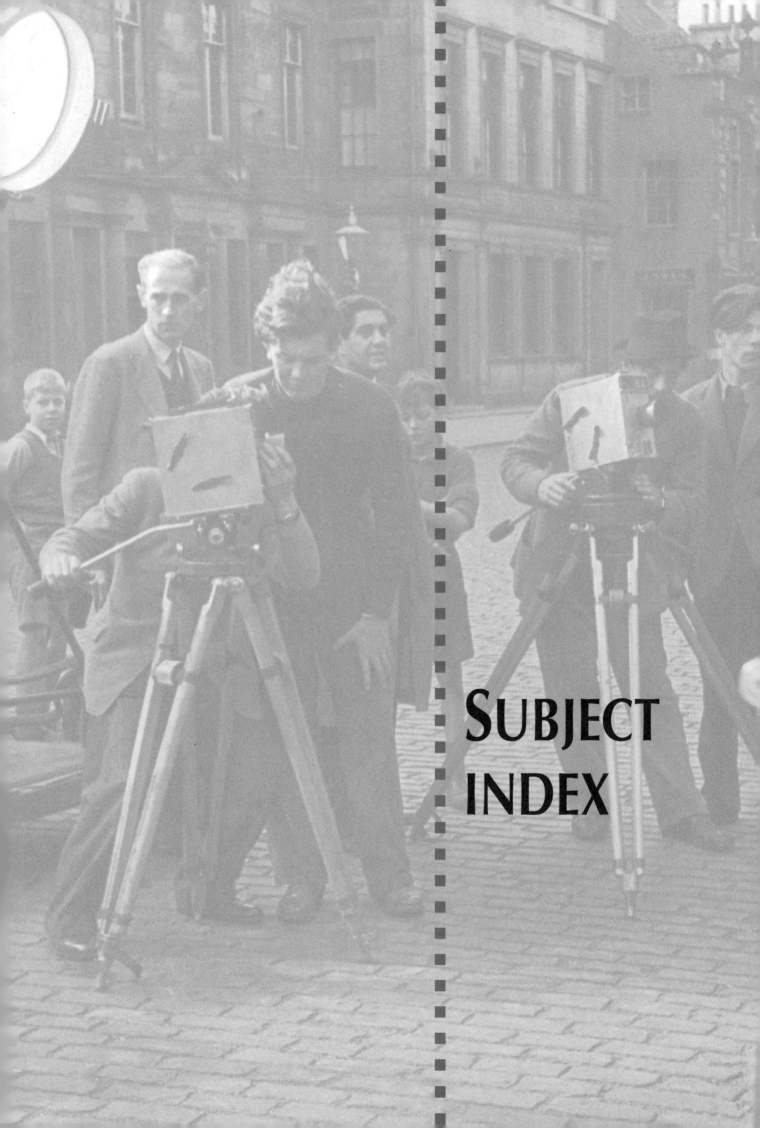

SUBJECT
INDEX

ABBEYS

See MONASTIC BUILDINGS

ABERDEEN and ABERDEENSHIRE

0010	ABERDEEN UNIVERSITY QUATER CENTENARY CELEBRATIONS
0023A/D	ROYAL TOUR OF SCOTLAND
0042	ABERDEEN 1906
0164	ABERDEEN
0188	ROYAL OCCASIONS OF SCOTLAND
0233	GATHERING OF BRAEMAR ROYAL HIGHLAND SOCIETY
0234	GORDON HIGHLANDERS' PRESENTATION OF THE FREEDOM OF THE CITY OF ABERDEEN
0235	PRESENTATION OF NEW COLOURS TO GORDON HIGHLANDERS
0237	FLICKS OF ABERDEEN'S TERRITORIAL WEEK
0238	(ABERDEEN'S "BLACK FRIDAY")
0239	ABERDEEN CELEBRATES THE CORONATION
0241	CINEMA NEWS, ABERDEEN
0242	THEIR MAJESTIES ATTEND DIVINE SERVICE
0244	NEWSREEL
0245A	BRITISH MEDICAL CONFERENCE
0245B	SCHOOL SPORTS
0246A	ARP
0246B	QUEEN ELIZABETH (QUEEN MOTHER)
0247	LAYING FOUNDATION STONE OF THE BISHOP SEABURY MEMORIAL
0249	(MILITARY PARADE IN ABERDEEN)
0277	ABERDEEN ANGUS
0281	NORTH EAST CORNER
0302	LAND O' CLANS
0305	[GASKIN REPORT, THE]
0362	HIGHLAND HOSPITALITY
0385	SCOTTISH UNIVERSITIES
0448	(SCENES AT BALMORAL)
0449	GORDON HIGHLANDERS LEAVE FOR THE BOER WAR
0499	SCOTTISH COASTS
0501	ROUTES AND CENTRES
0506	ABERDEEN AND ITS INDUSTRIES
0523	HER MAJESTY THE QUEEN PAYS INFORMAL VISIT TO ABERDEEN
0525	(VISIT OF DUCHESS OF GLOUCESTER)
0529A	BRITISH LEGION CONFERENCE IN ABERDEEN
0529B	(OPENING OF NEW BRIDGE OVER DEE BY KING GEORGE AND QUEEN ELIZABETH)
0529C	(DAMAGED HOTEL)
0529D	(OPENING OF NEW BATHS, ABERDEEN)
0554	(SUMMER SEASON IN ABERDEENSHIRE)
0586	DEE VALLEY
0607	GET IT AT THE CO-OP
0631	NORTHERN SCOTLAND
0694	WELLS OF MONTROSE, THE
0804	GREAT SCOT - MARY SLESSOR
0845	(RONNIE JAY WITH KING GEORGE VI)
0873A	ABERDEEN HIGH SCHOOL FOR GIRLS PRIMARY SPORTS
0873B	(HIGHLAND GAMES, ABERDEEN)
0873D	(WAITING CROWDS)
0875A	(SALVATION ARMY)
0875B	FLICKS ROYAL HIGHLAND GATHERING AT BRAEMAR
0875D	(MEN CLEARING ROAD)
0920	(BUS TOUR, THE)
0982	ABERDEEN INFIRMARY, OPENING CEREMONY

1060	SEAFOOD
1080A	ABERDEEN AWA' AUGUST 1949
1151	[BEACH PAVILION, ABERDEEN AND FAMILY C1926]
1152	BEACH PAVILION, ABERDEEN AND VARIETY
1236	(GREEN'S 1917 FILM SERVICE)
1238A/B	SCOTTISH MOVING PICTURE NEWS NO. 32
1335	REMEMBRANCE DAY
1336	BOYS' BRIGADE RALLY IN ABERDEEN
1337	ROYAL VISIT TO ABERDEEN
1338	[FAMILY HOLIDAYS 1936/38]
1371	ABERDEEN BY SEASIDE AND DEESIDE
1373	HUNTLY GALA DAY
1381B	FERGUSLIE THREAD WORKS OUTING TO BRAEMAR
1501	BEYOND THE GRAMPIANS
1577B	SOME BEAUTY SPOTS IN NORTH SCOTLAND
1613	OVER THE CAPEL TO BIRKHALL
1696	ROYAL SCOTLAND
1704	(SCOTTISH WEDDING, A)
1705	HIGHLAND TOUR, CROOKSTON STREET SCHOOL
1727	[AT THE SMIDDY/THE ROAD TO BRAEMAR]
1760	KIPPERS
1761	FAIR RENT
1836	KING IN SCOTLAND
1880	UPPER DEESIDE
1966	HUNTLY GALA QUEEN
2051	ABERDEEN
2124	BUCHAN CLUB AT FYVIE CASTLE, THE
2125	JUBILEE CELEBRATIONS OF THE BUCHAN CLUB
2152	OUT FOR VALUE
2221	QUEEN IN SCOTLAND, THE
2225	SILVER CITY, THE
2245	WEAVE ME A RAINBOW
2280	RESTORATION OF PROVOST SKENE'S HOUSE
2320	ABERDEEN
2522	[MACFARLANE FAMILY 1930]
2525	[STAFF PICNIC 1937]
2526	[PICNIC TO BALLATER, NO. 2]
2527	[KING GEORGE V AT BALLATER]
2528	[STAFF PICNIC. GOLF AND WILLIE ELDER]
2530	[STAFF PICNIC]
2531	[SHOP PICNIC, FARLAIR SWIMMING POOL]
2534	[STAFF PICNIC 1930?]
2589	[CORONATION DECORATIONS 1937]
2639	BRAEMAR GATHERING
2644	STRATHDEE STABLE, THE
2645	HORN CARVING
2648	FAREWELL TO STEAM
2720	[BRAEMAR GAMES, TWEED MAKING AND EDINBURGH]
2731	(GREAT NORTH OF SCOTLAND RAILWAY FILMS)
2734	(FAMILY WEDDING AND LIFE AT "SHANZIE")
2737	GATHERING OF THE BRAEMAR ROYAL HIGHLAND SOCIETY, THE
2749	HERRING PACKING
2755	CIRCLE OF CARE
2778	SEAS AROUND US, THE; GREAT BRITISH FOOD
2780-2784	[HADDO ESTATE OPERATIONS]
2786	(QUEEN MOTHER'S VISIT TO HADDO)
2818	BARS OF SILVER
2847	[PORT ELPHINSTONE SCHOOL PICNIC]

2851	[DEMISE OF THE "HEADWAY"]

ACROBATS and ACROBATICS
See CIRCUSES and CARNIVALS

ACTORS and ACTRESSES
See ENTERTAINERS and ENTERTAINMENT

ADVERTISING

0105	AMATEUR CINEMATOGRAPHY
0111	WORLD OF STEEL
0184	LYCEUM CINEMA TRAILERS AND ADVERTISEMENTS
0194A	MINISTRY OF FOOD FLASHES
0194B	CHRISTMAS 1943
0195A	MERRY CHRISTMAS AND A HAPPY NEW YEAR
0391	[HAPPY IN THE MORNING]
0423	STORY OF A SHABBY SUIT, THE
0424	[NEW FRANCO BARBE HAT SHAPES]
0425	HOW SCWS CIGARETTES AND TOBACCO ARE MADE
0428	LAND O' BURNS BAKERIES
0430	CASTLEBANK FOR COLLARS
0434	(IS WASHDAY WORTHWHILE?)
0435	MESSAGE OF THE DRUM, THE
0436	(DOUGLAS FRASER JUTE MACHINERY)
0437	SEEING IS BELIEVING
0438	BRUNTON'S WIRE AND ROPE WORKS, MUSSELBURGH
0439	SCOTLAND'S BRIGHTEST INDUSTRY
0440	PIGS IN CLOVER
0442	BRIEF BEEF BIOGRAPHY, A
0443	OVER THE HILLS AND FAR AWAY
0445	JERSEY WATER LILIES
0447	HANDLING "TEE-PAK" CASINGS
0451	THOUSAND HAPPY DAYS, A
0510	BEAUTIFUL DRIMA
0535	BISCUIT MAKING IN 1928
0571	PURE NEW WOOL - AND SCOTTISH
0578	CASHMERE IS SCOTTISH
0579	WORLD OF CASHMERE
0581	VARIETY MOMENTS
0607	GET IT AT THE CO-OP
0612	YOUR SILENT SALESMAN
0642	VOTE FOR HARRY KEMP
0647	TREASURE ISLAND
0655	[HENDRY'S DOUBLE TOP AMERICAN COLA]
0656	[LOFTY PEAK CAKE MIXES]
0657	[COME CO-OPERATIVE SHOPPING]
0658	[COME CO-OPERATIVE SHOPPING]
0659	[SAVE IN 1969]
0660	COME CO-OPERATIVE SHOPPING
0674	(SCWS LOFTY PEAK XMAS CAKE ADVERTISEMENT)
0675-0676	(SCWS LEMON CURD ADVERTISEMENT)
0677	(SCWS CREAMERY BUTTER ADVERTISEMENT)
0678-0679	(SCWS MARMALADE ADVERTISEMENT)
0680	(SCWS COFFEE ESSENCE ADVERTISEMENT)
0681	(SCWS MARGARINE ADVERTISEMENT)
0682	(SCWS MARGARINE ADVERTISEMENT)
0683	(SCWS SPECIAL OFFERS)
0684	(SCWS MARMALADE ADVERTISEMENT)
0685-0686	(SCWS MARGARINE ADVERTISEMENT)
0687	(COGENT CIGARETTES ADVERTISEMENT)
0688	(CO-OP ROCKY MOUNT CIGARETTES ADVERT)
0689	(MONTRIL ORANGE DRINK)
0690	[1968 CO-OP PRESENTATION FILM]
0701	(SCWS MARGARINE ADVERTISEMENT)
0723	[CO-OP ADVERTISEMENTS STRATHCLYDE SCHOOLWEAR]
0736	(CO-OP ADVERTISEMENT)
0737	(CO-OP ADVERTS)
0774	(CONSTRUCTION OF THE RITZ CINEMA, EDINBURGH 1929)
0785	HEART IS HIGHLAND, THE
0802	WILL YE NO' COME BACK AGAIN
0828	(CAPTIONS AND ADVERTS)
0832	(CINEMA SALES KIOSK)
0863B	(AIR CIRCUS CAPTION)
0863C	(SPOT THE SPOT)
0865	(ALLOA ADVERTS)
0876	(HOW BLUEBELL MARGARINE IS MADE)
0881	(CINEMA ADVERTISEMENTS)
0904	(TEAZIE WEAZIE)
0907	(GEORGE YOUNG AD.)
0917	GLASGOW - MASS ASSAULT ON TB
0944	(ADVERT FOR "THE MAGGIE")
0949-0950	STONEHOUSE - CENTRE FOR SUCCESS
0956	(DUMFRIES CINEMA ADVERTS)
0960C	CROWNING OF LOCHGELLY'S FIRST "QUEEN" BY THE COUNTESS OF ELGIN
0961B	HOSPITAL/FUND RAISING PAGEANT, LOCHGELLY
0971	(BLUEBELL BAKING MARGARINE)
0974	GLASGOW 1980
0975	GLENROTHES
0993	[AUSTRALIAN WEEK]
0994	[SHIELDHALL COFFEE]
0995	[COME CO-OP SHOPPING]
0996	[BLUEBELL MARGARINE]
0998	[LOFTY PEAK FLOUR]
0999	[ORCHID MARGARINE]
1000	[LOFTY PEAK FLOUR]
1001	[LOFTY PEAK SCRAPER OFFER]
1002	[COME CO-OP SHOPPING AT CHRISTMAS]
1003	[COPEX COOKING FAT]
1004	[MONTRIL PARTY]
1005	[GOLDEN BALL MARMALADE]
1006	[COME CO-OP SHOPPING]
1007	[CO-OP SUGAR]
1008	[CHEDDAR CHEESE]
1009	[PINEAPPLE AND RICE]
1010	[CWS CENTENARY EXHIBITION]
1011	[SPRING SALE]
1012	[SAUCES]
1013-1014	[COME CO-OP SHOPPING]
1015	[MARGARINE CARTOON]
1016	[LOFTY PEAK CAKE MIX]
1017	[STAFF RECRUITMENT FILM]
1018	[LEMON CURD]
1019	[STRAWBERRY JAM]
1020	[GOLDEN BALL MARMALADE]
1021	[ORCHID BUTTER]
1022	[JELLY CRYSTALS]
1023	[CO-OP CARTOON]
1025	[SPOT THE LIKENESS]
1027	CLAN HAS ARRIVED, THE

268

1028	HOMES IN BRITAIN
1029	UNITAS OATS
1030	KNITWEAR WITHOUT TEARS
1031	CO-OP SHOPPING
1032	SHIELDHALL SHOES
1033	[99 TEA]
1034	[ORCHID MARGARINE]
1035	[COGENT CIGARETTES]
1044	OBEDIENT FLAME, THE
1047	GOOD OLD DAYS, THE
1053	CHEMICAL SUNDRIES DEPARTMENT
1054	(CO-OP DIVIDENDS)
1055	(CO-OP BUTTER)
1056	(OUT OF SYNC. DIVIDENDS)
1083	(WARTIME DUMBARTON)
1087	(HOLIDAY AT ARROCHAR)
1103	CINEMA ADVERTS
1107	(DRINK AND DRIVE COMMERCIALS)
1247	IT'S ABOUT TIME
1256-1257	[CO-OP ADVERTS]
1260-1261	[CO-OP ADVERTS]
1263	[SCWS WHEATSHEAF BREAD ADVERTISEMENT]
1285	(CINEMA TRAILERS II)
1288C	YOU AND YOUR MONEY
1438	[NATIONAL SAVINGS TRAILER]
1462	CHRISTMAS 1943
1495	[SAVING OF A SHABBY COAT]
1537	IN THE CLEAR
1559	(CINEMA ADVERTS)
1560	[RED CROSS APPEAL/ LOCAL ADS]
1590	TULLIS OF CLYDEBANK
1630	BELL'S TRAILER
1785	GREEN'S PLAYHOUSE BALLROOM
1868	BANK FOR SCOTLAND
1869	BUSINESSWISE
1870	MONEYWISE
1901	WEE DRAM, A
1909	FROM THE PROJECTION BOX
1932	SOVEREIGN "SCOTCH", THE
1954	KING GEORGE VI
1978	(CINEMA ADVERTS)
1980	TIME OUT OF SCOTLAND
1997	FALKIRK
2006	CAMERON IRON WORKS
2016	[SIMON SQUARE EXHIBITION]
2026	QUEST, THE (GIRLS' GUILDRY)
2056	(ABBOTT'S WHISKY COMMERCIAL)
2063	(HILLFOOT PICTURE HOUSE ADVERTS, ETC.)
2065	(MISCELLANEOUS CINEMA ANNOUNCEMENTS)
2086	(CINEMA ADVERTS)
2089	("QUIET WEDDING" TRAILER NO. 1)
2090	("QUIET WEDDING" TRAILER NO. 2)
2129	OUR HIGHLAND HERITAGE
2141	[TV COMMERCIALS]
2152	OUT FOR VALUE
2493	[CINEMA TRAILERS III]
2571	(ALKA-SELTZER ADVERTS)
2598	(CO-OP ADVERTISING FILMS)
2600	(CO-OP ADVERTISING FILMS)
2723	(NIMBLE TV COMMERCIALS)

AFRICA

0060	NEWS PARADE 1939
0082	MODERN MECHANICAL MINING IN A SOUTH AFRICAN COALMINE
0143	JERASH AND BAALBEK
0145	TREETOPS
0147	AFRICAN ANIMALS
0150	ROYAL SOUTH AFRICAN TOUR
0152	AFRICAN ANECDOTES
0153	KENYA TO DURBAN
0163	EAST OF SUEZ
0354	(CONTINENTAL HOLIDAYS)
0356	(VARIOUS - NO. 1)
0358	(VARIOUS - NO. 2)
0359	(VARIOUS - NO. 3)
0426	[YEAR OF DESTINY]
0435	MESSAGE OF THE DRUM, THE
0804	GREAT SCOT - MARY SLESSOR
0818	PRIME MINISTER IN SCOTLAND
1109	1959 SCOTTISH INDUSTRIES EXHIBITION
1276	NORTH BRITISH
1671	LIVINGSTONE
1958	IN THE FOOTSTEPS OF DAVID LIVINGSTONE
2175	LAND OF THE WHITE RHINO
2176-2177	(CAPE TO CAIRO)
2183	(CAPE TO CAIRO - WILDLIFE AND NATIVE SCENES)
2239	METAL IN HARMONY
2411	OSPREY
2549-2550	(CRUISE ON "IBERIA")
2552	(CRUISE ON "IBERIA", IV)

AGRICULTURAL SHOWS

0196	ROAD THROUGH THE SUNSET ISLES
0199	WINDSOR
0201	HIGHLAND HORSE SHOW, ALLOA
0242	THEIR MAJESTIES ATTEND DIVINE SERVICE
0882	RIVER TWEED
0898	(AGRICULTURAL SHOW, ISLAY?)
1441	[KEITH SHOW, 14TH AUGUST, 1951]
1557	(AGRICULTURAL SHOW, GHILLIE)
1854	(PROVOST FLETT COLLECTION)
1873	THORNHILL SHOW
1879	VILLAGE VARIETIES
2123	(FFORDE COLLECTION)
2143	ABERFELDY AGRICULTURAL SHOW 1952
2145	(STRANRAER LOCAL EVENTS)
2213	HIGHLAND CAPITAL
2356	(TEMPERANCE EVENTS, EDINBURGH 1939)
2658	KEITH SHOW 1948
2782	[HADDO ESTATE OPERATIONS 1962]
2792	AYR FROM THE AULD BRIG
2808	AROUND DUNDEE IN THE 1930'S
2838	(PRENTICE FAMILY EVENTS)

AGRICULTURE (gen.)

See also CROFTS and CROFTING/ DAIRY and RELATED TECHNOLOGIES

0027	SKYE
0028	WESTERN ISLES

269

2024	FORTH - POWERHOUSE FOR INDUSTRY
2050	[FARM IN SOUTHERN SCOTLAND, A]
2088	FAIR COUNTY OF AYR
2110	(VIOLET ANDERSON FILM)
2123	(FFORDE COLLECTION)
2137-2138	(MACNEILL TRACTORS DEMONSTRATION FILMS)
2139	PLOUGHING DEMONSTRATION
2143	ABERFELDY AGRICULTURAL SHOW 1952
2145	(STRANRAER LOCAL EVENTS)
2161	SPRING IN THE FIELDS
2172	GRAIN HARVEST
2201	DRAM LIKE THIS, A
2203	CHAMPIONS IN THE SUN
2204	COUNTY OF THE CLYDE
2205	COUNTY ON THE MOVE
2211	GOOD SERVANT, THE
2212	HEBRIDEAN HIGHWAY
2213	HIGHLAND CAPITAL
2215	IN GOOD HEART
2223	BORDERS, THE
2237	ONE DAY IN IRVINE
2243	TAY ROAD BRIDGE
2253	WATER, WATER EVERYWHERE
2258	LOTHIAN LANDSCAPE
2259	PRIDE OF ISLANDS
2293	(WARTIME IN TAYPORT)
2356	(TEMPERANCE EVENTS, EDINBURGH 1939)
2370	FARMER'S BOY, THE
2462	AUTUMN IN SCOTLAND
2478	SPRING IN SCOTLAND
2512	AYRSHIRE DAIRY FARMER
2514	(MACFARLANE FAMILY 1939)
2516	(MACFARLANE FAMILY 1930-1931)
2522	(MACFARLANE FAMILY 1930)
2524	(MACFARLANE FAMILY 1931-1932)
2587	ISLE OF RHUM
2590	(PRIESTLY COLLECTION)
2592	ISLES OF THE WEST
2593	MISTY ISLE
2636	DURISDEER COTTAGE AND FARMING
2637	HADDOCK FISHING
2658	KEITH SHOW 1948
2683	(DUFFTOWN SCENES)
2721	SPRING IN GALLOWAY
2734	(FAMILY WEDDING AND LIFE AT "SHANZIE")
2735	(HERD'S CAFE AND FAMILY FILM)
2736	(HERD FAMILY FILM)
2744	AYRSHIRE EARLY POTATOES
2750	SUMMER IN SCOTLAND
2780-2781	[HADDO ESTATE OPERATIONS 1955/ 1961]
2783	[HADDO ESTATE OPERATIONS 1966-'67]
2791	[HADDO ESTATE OPERATIONS 1961]
2792	AYR FROM THE AULD BRIG
2808	AROUND DUNDEE IN THE 1930S

AIRCRAFT

See also HELICOPTERS

0013	GOVAN FAIR 1947
0033	HIGHLAND DOCTOR

0034	FACE OF SCOTLAND
0044	GLASGOW AND THE CLYDE COAST
0060	NEWS PARADE 1939
0108	GRAND UNION CANAL
0113	HOSPITAL TEAM
0152	AFRICAN ANECDOTES
0153	KENYA TO DURBAN
0163	EAST OF SUEZ
0170	DUMFRIES GUID NYCHBURRIS DAY
0247	LAYING FOUNDATION STONE OF THE BISHOP SEABURY MEMORIAL
0271	GOOD HEALTH TO SCOTLAND
0296	SCOTLAND AND THE NEW WORLD
0305	[GASKIN REPORT, THE]
0310	[RAF LEUCHARS RECEIVE FREEDOM OF THE CITY OF ST. ANDREWS]
0366	STEP AHEAD, A
0384	[ISLE OF BARRA]
0426	(YEAR OF DESTINY)
0462	NEWS SPOTLIGHT
0487	AN EYE TO THE FUTURE
0534	KOSB FREEDOM OF ENTRY INTO THE BURGH
0559	PATHE REVIEW OF THE YEAR
0584	[SCOTTISH FLYING CLUB PAGEANT, RENFREW]
0591	LOOKING BACK
0622	PRIDE AND PROGRESS
0633	STORY OF ALFRED NOBEL, THE
0646A	INAUGURATION OF INVERNESS AIRPORT
0646B	INAUGURATION OF FIRST HIGHLAND AIR SERVICE
0653B	[AIR SHOW]
0694	WELLS OF MONTROSE, THE
0750	ROMANCE OF ENGINEERING, A
0773	NORTHERN OUTPOST
0781	(ARMY BOX WORK)
0782	(TO SHOW WAR)
0784	("EMPRESS OF BRITAIN")
0802	WILL YE NO' COME BACK AGAIN
0840B	VISIT OF HER ROYAL HIGHNESS THE PRINCESS ROYAL TO WICK
0851	TINY WINGS
0856	OPENING INVERNESS MUNICIPAL AIRPORT BY HIS GRACE THE DUKE OF SUTHERLAND
0863B	(AIR CIRCUS CAPTION)
0864	(R101 AIRSHIP)
0889	IMMORTAL MEMORY OF ROBERT BURNS
0915	GLASGOW
0955	WHY SCOTLAND, WHY EAST KILBRIDE
0974	GLASGOW 1980
0981	CROFTER'S LIFE IN SHETLAND, A
1061	DUNDEE
1133	[HALF PAST EIGHT SHOW]
1148	[HARRY GORDON VISITS NEW YORK AND PANTOMIMES]
1236	(GREEN'S 1917 FILM SERVICE)
1249	IT COMES FROM COAL
1269	SKYWAY AMBULANCE
1272	FLYING ABOVE THE CLOUDS
1322	(TO IRELAND BY AIR)
1338	(FAMILY HOLIDAYS 1936/'38)
1400	(SUTHERLAND)
1405	(UNIDENTIFIED STEAMER ON CLYDE COAST)

272

2355	(TEMPERANCE DAYS AND ORGANISATIONS 1936)
2356	(TEMPERANCE EVENTS, EDINBURGH 1939)
2357	(TEMPERANCE DAYS, EDINBURGH 1936-'37)
2358	MARGARET BAKER IN LECTURES AND STORIES
2482	WOMEN'S PROHIBITION DEMO
2581	BUY YOUR OWN CHERRIES
2602	DYING OF THIRST
2862	HAP DANCES, THE

ALGAE (e.g. seaweed)

1342	(ROCKET RANGE, BENBECULA)
1943	ENCHANTED ISLES
2009	LIFE IN THE ORKNEYS
2046	MAGIC KEY, THE
2505	(SEAWEED)

AMATEUR FILM

See CINEMATOGRAPHY

AMBULANCES

0033	HIGHLAND DOCTOR
0271	GOOD HEALTH TO SCOTLAND
0539A	RED CROSS WORK AT SALONIKA
0826A	AT YOUR SERVICE - DUMFRIES AND GALLOWAY ROYAL INFIRMARY
1269	SKYWAY AMBULANCE
1580	ON THE SPOT WITH FIRST AID

AMERICA

See NORTH AMERICA and SOUTH AMERICA

ANGLERS and ANGLING

0504	TAY VALLEY
0882	RIVER TWEED
1501	BEYOND THE GRAMPIANS
1943	ENCHANTED ISLES
2366	FOLLOWING THE RIVER NO. 2: THE MIDDLE STRETCH
2870	DUNOON - THE GEM OF THE CLYDE

ANGUS

0160	JUTE MANUFACTURE
0302	LAND O' CLANS
0641	GLIMPSE OF THE LIFEBOAT SERVICE
0785	HEART IS HIGHLAND, THE
0902	[DAILY RECORD GARDEN CHAMPIONSHIP 1958]
1251	LIFEBOAT DRILL
1265	LIFEBOAT COMING
1612	CONSTRUCTION OF THE BACKWATER DAM
1697	[ARBROATH HISTORICAL PAGEANT 1947]
1698	[ARBROATH HIGH SCHOOL SPORTS AND OPENING OF BATHING POOL]
1707	DUCHESS OF YORK NAMES NEW LIFEBOAT
1708	ARBROATH HISTORICAL PAGEANT/ THE STONE RETURNS
1720	[NAMING CEREMONY, THE "DUKE OF MONTROSE"]
1781	SMOKIES
1856	(DIXINE MISCELLANY)
2215	IN GOOD HEART
2257	TAYSIDE
2372	ARBROATH'S NEW SWIMMING POOL
2422	GLENDOLL
2423	INCHMURRIN 1950
2768	(GEORGE MAY FAMILY FILM)
2808	AROUND DUNDEE IN THE 1930'S

ANIMALS (misc.)

See also CATS/ CATTLE/ DOGS/ HORSES/ SHEEP/ ZOOS

0775	(LANARK RACECOURSE AND RENFREWSHIRE HUNT)
0781	(ARMY BOX WORK)
0785	HEART IS HIGHLAND, THE
0786	(RACE MEETING)
0822	(OTTER HUNTING AND PROCESSION)
0911	ST. KILDA - THE LONELY ISLANDS
0916	PADDY'S MILESTONE
0933	BY BORDER BYWAYS
0961B	HOSPITAL/FUND RAISING PAGEANT, LOCHGELLY
1063	THEY MADE THE LAND
1617	(SHETLAND AND FAIR ISLE SCENES)
1675	STRATHNETHY IN SPRING
1822	INTRODUCING MAMMALS
1827	RED DEER
1845	POLECATS, WEASELS AND STOATS
1847	WATER SHREW, RATS AND VOLES
1848	RED SQUIRREL
1849	LOCH LOMOND NATURE RESERVE
1852	FOXES, THE
1856	(DIXINE MISCELLANY)
1943	ENCHANTED ISLES
1989	(SIMPSON FAMILY FILM)
2003	[ST. CUTHBERT'S NINETIETH BIRTHDAY]
2036	RAIN ON THE ROOF
2037	ST. KILDA - JULY 1956
2113	TRAPPED
2175	LAND OF THE WHITE RHINO
2176	(CAPE TO CAIRO - ANIMALS)
2260	LINE TO SKYE, THE
2270	[GLASGOW UNIVERSITY NORTH RONA EXPEDITION]
2370	FARMER'S BOY, THE
2478	SPRING IN SCOTLAND
2516	(MACFARLANE FAMILY 1930-1931)
2522	(MACFARLANE FAMILY 1930)
2587	ISLE OF RHUM
2667	SCOTLAND'S ISLE OF SEALS
2780	[HADDO ESTATE OPERATIONS 1955]

ANIMATION

0166	THIS FILM IS DANGEROUS
0635	ADVENTURES OF WEE ROB ROY, THE
0650	STARS AND STRIPES
0651	LITTLE PHANTASY, A
0680	(SCWS COFFEE ESSENCE ADVERTISEMENT)
0686	(SCWS MARGARINE ADVERTISEMENT)
0892	ONCE BEFORE NOON
0956	(DUMFRIES CINEMA ADVERTS)
1015	[MARGARINE CARTOON]
1044	OBEDIENT FLAME, THE
1058	[POTATO PICKING TRAILER]
1098	CAMERA MAKES WHOOPEE
1203	TO YOUR HEALTH
1457	HOPPITY HOP
1937	BRIDE AND GROOM
1994	[WITCH CRAFT]
2108	JUNGLE JINKS, ETC.

273

274

2053	[OBAN, IONA, STAFFA AND HARRIS]
2119-2120	REST-AND-BE-THANKFUL HILL CLIMB 1949/1950
2129	OUR HIGHLAND HERITAGE
2192	[MAKING A SPINNING WHEEL AT PORTSONACHAN]
2212	HEBRIDEAN HIGHWAY
2214	HOLLOW MOUNTAIN, THE
2217	LAND LIVED IN, A
2218	LEATHERNECK AMBASSADORS
2273	MAILLEY FAMILY FILM
2282	[STONES]
2314	QUEEN IN OBAN, THE
2333	(DUNOON AND ROTHESAY PIER)
2392	LOMOND MC/SKI-ING
2396	SCOTLAND THROUGH THE LENS
2401	[HALFWAY TO PARADISE: GI BLUES]
2428	ROYAL NORTHERN YACHT CLUB: NOSES HOMEWARD
2547	(COWAL GAMES, DUNOON 1933)
2555	[PANTOMIME 1937]
2601	DIVIDED WE STAND
2674	NORTH AND WEST OF THE GREAT GLEN
2733	(NORTH EAST AND THE HIGHLANDS: CELEBRATIONS AND EVENTS)
2745	DAY ON THE SANDS, A
2755	CIRCLE OF CARE
2767	KINTYRE
2790	CRUACHAN
2804	AS LONG AS YOU'RE YOUNG
2820	(CRICHTON COLLECTION)
2863	(SAWKINS NO. 2)
2865	(SAWKINS NO. 7)
2868-2874	[DON SAWKINS COLLECTION]

ARMY

See MILITARY

ART and ARTISTS

0007	SCOTS OF TOMORROW
0090	CHARLES RENNIE MACKINTOSH
0282	CITY SIDELIGHTS - SECTIONS
0306	HAPPY WEEKEND
0328	CITY SIDELIGHTS NO. 3
0458	TAM O' SHANTER
0651	LITTLE PHANTASY, A
0763	OPENING OF OLD GALA HOUSE
0803	(DANCE SEQUENCES)
0804	GREAT SCOT - MARY SLESSOR
0952	STONEHOUSE - CENTRE FOR SUCCESS (NO. 4)
0954	LAUREL BANK SCHOOL FILM
0974	GLASGOW 1980
1100	SEVEN TILL FIVE
1493	FESTIVAL IN EDINBURGH
1744	(TEN GLASGOW ARTISTS EXHIBITION)
2003	[ST. CUTHBERT'S NINETIETH BIRTHDAY]
2007	KING AND THE WHISKY, THE
2009	LIFE IN THE ORKNEYS
2011	EPSTEIN IN EDINBURGH
2067	TECHNIQUES OF ETCHING
2226	MACKINTOSH
2231	SMITHS IN SCOTLAND, THE
2263	THREE SCOTTISH PAINTERS
2463	ANNUAL ART COMPETITION
2466	PREPARING A WAX RESIN RE-LINING
2467	AUTOLITHOGRAPHY
2682	BENNO SCHOTZ

ART GALLERIES

See also MUSEUMS

0397	OUR ART GALLERIES
0417	MEN AND WOMEN OF TOMORROW
0459	EDINBURGH FESTIVAL, THE
0557	MARCH OF THE MOVIES, THE
1073B	(DUKE AND DUCHESS OF YORK IN PERTH)
1494	HOLIDAYS AT HOME 1942-'44
2720	[BRAEMAR GAMES, TWEED MAKING AND EDINBURGH]
2793	EDINBURGH ON PARADE
2807	PROSPECT FOR A CITY

ASIA, the FAR EAST, the ORIENT

0060	NEWS PARADE 1939
0070	LOGGING IN THE SUNDARABANS, EAST PAKISTAN
0127	PACIFIC PANORAMA
0134	HIMALAYAN HOLIDAY
0140	IDLING IN INDIA
0146	CEYLON CALLING
0198	CHINA
0299	LUDHIANA MADE THE DIFFERENCE
0390	RADAR
0441	KING, GOD BLESS HIM, THE
0559	PATHE REVIEW OF THE YEAR
0578	CASHMERE IS SCOTTISH
0579	WORLD OF CASHMERE
0601	(GREEN FAMILY IN INDIA, THE)
0610	HELPING HAND - SCWS BRUSH MAKING, A
0614	EASTERN ROSE
0624	ROSE OF THE ORIENT
0649	GRASS
0664	(BOWLS IN HONG KONG)
0666	MISCELLANEOUS SEA-GOING VESSELS
0668	(IVORY CARVING)
0669	(SCENES IN THE MIDDLE EAST)
0829	BIRTHDAY GREETINGS TO QUEEN MARY
1394	OIL FROM IRAN
1395	IN THE LAND OF THE SHAH
1715	[ST. LEONARD'S EXPEDITION TO SIKKIM]
1796	GB NEWS REVIEW 1948
1835	2ND BATTALION BLACK WATCH SAYS FAREWELL TO PAKISTAN
1855	REVIEW OF THE YEAR 1950
2000A	BENS, THE
2511	APPROACH TO API
2549-2552	(CRUISE ON "IBERIA")
2633	GOLFING AT THE JODHPUR CLUB
2634	(INDIAN OXYGEN COMPANY)
2635	TRIP TO BHUTAN
2794	CASHMERE STORY, THE
2816	(RANGOON HOSPITAL AND SCENES FROM THE EAST)

ASTRONOMY and ALLIED SCIENCES

0796	DUMFRIESSHIRE JOURNEY

ATHLETICS

0008	GLASGOW UNIVERSITY CELEBRATES

275

278

BANKS and BANKING
See FINANCE and FINANCIAL INSTITUTIONS

BARGES
See CANALS

BEACH SCENES

0043	(LARGS SUMMER SEASON 1936)
0044	GLASGOW AND THE CLYDE COAST
0444	RIVALLING THE RAINBOW
0445	JERSEY WATER LILIES
0499	SCOTTISH COASTS
0528	ALL ON A SUMMER'S DAY
0554	(SUMMER SEASON IN ABERDEENSHIRE)
0705	SADNESS AND GLADNESS
0718	(HOLIDAY FILM)
0797	COASTS OF CLYDE, THE
0946	NETHERTON'S CORONATION DAY PROCESSION
1066	(PENNYCOOK FAMILY FILM)
1314	(SUMMER SEASON IN DUNOON)
1318	CLYDE RESORT: AN INTRODUCTION TO GIRVAN
1321	AYR
1328	BEAUTY SPOTS IN GREAT BRITAIN
1371	ABERDEEN BY SEASIDE AND DEESIDE
1456	[CAMBUSLANG ORPHANED CHILDREN'S EXCURSION]
1520	HOME AND AWAY NO. 10
1581	(HOLIDAY SCOTLAND)
1655	BARRA
1764	LOTHIANS PART I, THE
1766	[SCOTT FAMILY FILM]
1780	OBAN
1808	(ALLAN FAMILY HOLIDAYS)
1853	DIXINE NEWS
1989	(SIMPSON FAMILY FILM)
2075	(STEIN FAMILY HOLIDAYS)
2225	SILVER CITY, THE
2247	ST. ANDREWS BY THE NORTHERN SEA
2253	WATER, WATER EVERYWHERE
2258	LOTHIAN LANDSCAPE
2273	MAILLEY FAMILY FILM
2276	[JOYCE AND IRENE ON THE CLYDE, SUMMER 1955]
2288	ALLAN GLEN'S SCHOOL CAMP
2307	IN SEARCH OF TAYPORT
2320	ABERDEEN
2334	HOLIDAY SCENES AT ROTHESAY
2339	(LADY LAUDER IN ROTHESAY)
2383	(HOLIDAY IN SCOTLAND 1964)
2395	CHURCH ACTIVITIES, ST. MARTIN'S, EDINBURGH
2486	(BROWN FAMILY FILM)
2502	(SHEARER FAMILY FILM ONE)
2529	[SHOP PICNIC, CARNOUSTIE]
2538	IT'S MORE THAN A JOB
2547	(COWAL GAMES, DUNOON 1933)
2631	HOLIDAY SCOTLAND
2672	OFFICER CADET TRAINING UNIT 165
2674	NORTH AND WEST OF THE GREAT GLEN
2745	DAY ON THE SANDS, A
2767	KINTYRE
2768	(GEORGE MAY FAMILY FILM)

2784	(HADDO EVENTS)
2792	AYR FROM THE AULD BRIG
2801	(SCENES FROM ORKNEY)
2805	PLEASURE ISLAND
2825	(MONTGOMERY FAMILY HOLIDAYS)
2828	[KATE KENNEDY PARADE NO. 2]
2852	[GLASGOW TAXI DRIVERS OUTING]
2870	DUNOON - THE GEM OF THE CLYDE
2873	DUNOON - HOLIDAYS UNDER SAIL

BEER
See BREWED and MALTED BEVERAGES

BERWICKSHIRE

0622	PRIDE AND PROGRESS
0882	RIVER TWEED
0914	SOUTHERN SCOTLAND
1244	(COASTAL SCENES)
1766	[SCOTT FAMILY FILM]
1868	BANK FOR SCOTLAND
1989	(SIMPSON FAMILY FILM)
2223	BORDERS, THE
2246	HAND OF ADAM
2591	FAIR RIVER, THE
2629	OLD FOLKS TRIP 1950
2834	PRIDE OF PENGUINS, A

BICYCLES

0157	(ANTI-GAS PRECAUTIONS IN GLASGOW)
0231	SCOTLAND FOR FITNESS
0244	NEWSREEL
0385	SCOTTISH UNIVERSITIES
0494	COUNTRY POLICEMAN
0512	STIRLING: GATEWAY TO THE HIGHLANDS
0540	[CHALLENGE TO FASCISM]
0608	ACHIEVEMENT
0653A	[BOYS' BRIGADE]
0736	(CO-OP ADVERTISEMENT)
0791-0792	[BORDERS LOCAL NEWSREELS]
0796	DUMFRIESSHIRE JOURNEY
0823	(FAIR FESTIVAL)
0826A	AT YOUR SERVICE - DUMFRIES AND GALLOWAY ROYAL INFIRMARY
0891	(EAST KILBRIDE DEVELOPMENT CORPORATION TRIMS 1947/'54)
0935	CRIEFF HIGHLAND GATHERING
1062	WEALTH OF A NATION
1090	FORUM FROLICS
1107	(DRINK AND DRIVE COMMERCIALS)
1315	ST. ANDREWS 1916
1494	HOLIDAYS AT HOME 1942-'44
1685	THREE MUST-GET-THERE'S, THE
1854	(PROVOST FLETT COLLECTION)
1886	SCHOOLBOY HOSTELLERS
2054	EVERYTHING BY DESIGN
2683	(DUFFTOWN SCENES)
2704	GALA 25 MILE CYCLE RACE 1951
2710	JEDBURGH AND HAWICK AMATEUR SPORTS
2804	AS LONG AS YOU'RE YOUNG

BIOLOGY

0744	BIOLOGICAL EXPEDITION, ISLAND OF RAASAY

0745	(BIOLOGICAL EXPEDITION, RONA)
0746	MARINE BIOLOGY
0747	(EXPEDITION TO RONA)
0748	SOUTH RONA EXPEDITION: THE DESCENT TO THE CAVE
2046	MAGIC KEY, THE
2505	(SEAWEED)

BIRDS

0392	LIFE ON THE FAROE ISLANDS
0418	ST. KILDA - BRITAIN'S LONELIEST ISLE
0632	ANTARCTIC WHALE HUNT
0728	[KINGS IN EXILE]
0773	NORTHERN OUTPOST
0775	(LANARK RACECOURSE AND RENFREWSHIRE HUNT)
0776	AILSA CRAIG - A SEABIRDS' ISLAND
0777	(MISCELLANEOUS SCENES, RENFREWSHIRE)
0783	(FEEDING BIRDS)
0785	HEART IS HIGHLAND, THE
0789	(BIRDS AND HORSE JUMPING)
0800	[CAITHNESS, ORKNEY, KIRKWALL]
0846	PORTRAIT D'UN OISEAU
0911	ST. KILDA - THE LONELY ISLANDS
0912	HEART OF SCOTLAND, THE
0916	PADDY'S MILESTONE
0927	BASS ROCK AND TANTALLON CASTLE
0933	BY BORDER BYWAYS
0978	ISLAND OF ST. KILDA, THE
0988	ST. KILDA. ITS PEOPLE AND BIRDS
0990	YOUNG GANNET, A
1128	SEABIRDS IN THE SHETLAND ISLANDS
1286	SHETLAND, PEOPLE OF MANY LANDS
1618	FAIR ISLE, THE
1619	GANNETS AT LERWICK
1654	GOLDEN EAGLE, THE
1675	STRATHNETHY IN SPRING
1795	TASK FORCE
1830	SEABIRDS IN SCOTLAND
1831	SHORENESTING BIRDS OF SCOTLAND
1850	HIGHLAND BUZZARD
2053	[OBAN, IONA, STAFFA AND HARRIS]
2258	LOTHIAN LANDSCAPE
2260	LINE TO SKYE, THE
2270	[GLASGOW UNIVERSITY NORTH RONA EXPEDITION]
2407	BIRDS OF THE ORKNEY ISLANDS
2408	PROPERTY IN THE COUNTRY, A
2409	PUFFINS COME HOME
2410	BEYOND A TANGLED SHORE
2411	OSPREY
2412	HIGHLAND BIRDS
2496	(GUGA HUNTERS)
2587	ISLE OF RHUM
2592	ISLES OF THE WEST
2631	HOLIDAY SCOTLAND
2721	SPRING IN GALLOWAY
2747	AMONG THE HIGHLANDS AND ISLANDS
2764	SEABIRDS OF THE FORTH
2811	HIGHLAND EAGLE
2834	PRIDE OF PENGUINS, A

280

BLOOD

0189	BLOOD TRANSFUSION IN BATHGATE
0365	BLOOD CAN WORK MIRACLES
0757	TO SAVE A LIFE
0758	BLOOD IS LIFE
1703	BLOOD TRANSFUSION SERVICE
1927	GEORGE THE BLOOD DONOR
2716	THANK YOU LORD LISTER

BOATS and BOATING

0354	(CONTINENTAL HOLIDAYS)
0384	[ISLE OF BARRA]
0426	[YEAR OF DESTINY]
0603	(HUGH MCLEAN & SONS LTD. BOATBUILDERS)
0631	NORTHERN SCOTLAND
0773	NORTHERN OUTPOST
0785	HEART IS HIGHLAND, THE
0806	SO MANY PARTINGS
0820	[ARGYLLSHIRE PIERS]
0885	FIFE
0911	ST. KILDA - THE LONELY ISLANDS
0912	HEART OF SCOTLAND, THE
0916	PADDY'S MILESTONE
0969	HOLIDAY IN THE HIGHLANDS
0986	GLASGOW
0991	RUGGED ISLAND
1061	DUNDEE
1069	KIRKINTILLOCH
1070	BLIZZARD, FEBRUARY 1947
1077	VOYAGEUR TRAILS
1078	SAGA OF THE SILVER HORDE
1096	WAY THE MONEY GOES, THE
1104	(GLASGOW PARKS 1941)
1618	FAIR ISLE, THE
1780	OBAN
1783	RIVER TAY
2022	SCOTTISH MINERS GALA DAY
2037	ST. KILDA - JULY 1956
2254	ERSKINE BRIDGE, THE
2278	[HIGHLAND FUND IN ACTION, HIGHLAND INITIATIVE]
2429	ROYAL NORTHERN YACHT CLUB SAILING FILMS 1934-1935
2718	APPLE A DAY, AN
2736	(HERD FAMILY FILM)
2767	KINTYRE
2801	(SCENES OF ORKNEY)
2805	PLEASURE ISLAND
2808	AROUND DUNDEE IN THE 1930s

BOOKS and the BOOK INDUSTRY

0124	MAKING OF THE HOLY BIBLE
0907	(GEORGE YOUNG AD.)
0909	MIRROR FROM THE EAST
1083	(WARTIME DUMBARTON)
2324	[HALFWAY TO PARADISE: JAMES KELMAN]

BOTANY (gardens etc.)

See also PARKS

0001	(GLASGOW TRAMS AND BOTANIC GARDENS)
0012	GLASGOW'S YESTERDAYS
0275	SCOTLAND'S GARDENS AND ALLOTMENTS
0300	OUR PUBLIC PARKS

BOXERS and BOXING

BOY SCOUTS/ BOYS' BRIGADE

See YOUTH ORGANISATIONS

BREWED and MALTED BEVERAGES

BRIDGES

2826	(MONTGOMERY FAMILY - NEW HOUSE)
2855	TAY BRIDGE DISASTER

BUSES

0001	(GLASGOW TRAMS AND BOTANIC GARDENS)
0004	INTO THE MISTS
0005	PASSING OF THE TRAMCAR, THE
0032	SCOTLAND'S WATER SUPPLY
0057	OUR TRANSPORT SERVICES
0126	(GLASGOW TRAMS - TRIMS)
0255A	CAMPING WE WILL GO, A
0255B	LETTER FROM JOHNNY
0255C	CAMPING IS FUN
0262	ROAD SAFETY
0345	BUSMAN'S HOLIDAY
0379	CITY SIDELIGHTS NO. 1
0497	DUMFRIES - A MARKET TOWN
0580	RIVER CLYDE
0610	HELPING HAND - SCWS BRUSH MAKING, A
0785	HEART IS HIGHLAND, THE
0795	(ARRIVAL AT WHITEHART HOTEL, CAMPBELTOWN)
0875C	(BUS OUTING, ABERDEENSHIRE)
0875D	(MEN CLEARING ROAD)
0914	SOUTHERN SCOTLAND
0920	(BUS TOUR, THE)
0960A	LOCHGELLY OLD AGE PENSIONERS DRIVE TO CROOK O' DEVON
0969	HOLIDAY IN THE HIGHLANDS
0975	GLENROTHES
1024	(SHAWLANDS CROSS)
1049	GLASGOW, NO MEAN CITY
1075	PREVENTION IS BETTER
1091	(TRAMS IN EDINBURGH AND BRUSSELS)
1096	WAY THE MONEY GOES, THE
1104	(GLASGOW PARKS 1941)
1232	[GLASGOW TRAMWAYS AND CLARKSTON TROLLEY BUSES]
1383	WOMEN'S GUILD OF EMPIRE C1933
1497	[GLASGOW'S PROGRESS]
1517	[HOME AND AWAY NO. 2]
1641	ISLES OF YOUTH, THE
1769	SCOTTISH TRANSPORT
1798	FENWICK EVENTS OF 1931
1875	CHILDREN'S EXCURSION 1952
2368	(NCB STAFF BUS OUTINGS)
2526	[PICNIC TO BALLATER, NO. 2]
2530	[STAFF PICNIC]
2533	(BENZIE'S WORKS OUTING)
2534	[STAFF PICNIC 1930?]
2621	(GAME OF BOWLS, A)
2629	OLD FOLKS TRIP 1950
2730	(J.H. JOHNSON - SEQUENCES)
2805	PLEASURE ISLAND
2814	BOTANIC GARDENS AND OLD GLASGOW

BUTCHERS

0437	SEEING IS BELIEVING
0440	PIGS IN CLOVER
0442	BRIEF BEEF BIOGRAPHY, A
0443	OVER THE HILLS AND FAR AWAY
0956	(DUMFRIES CINEMA ADVERTS)
0961B	HOSPITAL/ FUND RAISING PAGEANT, LOCHGELLY

1096	WAY THE MONEY GOES, THE
1234	DALMELLINGTON FANCY DRESS PARADE
2223	BORDERS, THE

BUTE

0044	GLASGOW AND THE CLYDE COAST
0253	TAM TRAUCHLE'S TROUBLES
0398	RIVER CLYDE, THE
0568	NOBEL'S TRIP TO ROTHESAY
0788	(MARQUIS OF BUTE/BUTE MOUNT STEWART)
0797	COASTS OF CLYDE, THE
0820	[ARGYLLSHIRE PIERS]
0954	LAUREL BANK SCHOOL FILM
0959	(ROTHESAY ENTERTAINERS' TRAILER 1918)
1120	SAIL TO INVERARAY
1228	HOLIDAYS AT ROTHESAY
1322	(TO IRELAND BY AIR)
1452	(CLYDE COAST STEAMERS)
1481	CLYDESCOPE
1578	(MAVOR FAMILY FILM)
1581	(HOLIDAY SCOTLAND)
1624	SCOTS HONOUR THE PRINCE
1629	AULDHOUSE CINEMAGAZINE
1787	[CLYDE RIVER]
1805	FENWICK EVENTS OF 1933
1963	THRU' THE KYLES
2075	(STEIN FAMILY HOLIDAYS)
2083	JUBILEE CELEBRATION
2085	FIRE AT ROTHESAY PIER
2123	(FFORDE COLLECTION)
2184	[ISLE OF BUTE CARNIVAL]
2332	ROTHESAY ACADEMY, CHRISTMAS 1928
2333	(DUNOON AND ROTHESAY PIER)
2334	HOLIDAY SCENES AT ROTHESAY
2335	ROTHESAY FANCY DRESS PARADE
2336	ROTHESAY PEACE CELEBRATIONS
2337	(MACEWAN'S FREEDOM OF ROTHESAY)
2338	(ROTHESAY 1918)
2339	(LADY LAUDER IN ROTHESAY)
2415	OLD ROTHESAY
2631	HOLIDAY SCOTLAND
2671	HIGHLANDS OF SCOTLAND
2805	PLEASURE ISLAND
2871	HOLIDAY DUNOON

CAITHNESS

0274	HIGHLAND LADDIE
0450	AROUND WICK HARBOUR
0800	[CAITHNESS, ORKNEY, KIRKWALL]
0801	[CAITHNESS, ORKNEY]
0805	[KIRKWALL, WICK, DOUNREAY]
0840A	PROVOST JOHN SINCLAIR SHOWS ORKNEY GUIDES AROUND THE HARBOUR AT THURSO
1096	WAY THE MONEY GOES, THE
1288A	WICK SHOPPING WEEK - PRIMARY SCHOOL SPORTS
1288B	CARNIVAL PROCESSION AND CROWNING OF HERRING QUEEN
1338	(FAMILY HOLIDAYS 1936/'38)
1514	[THURSO HIGH SCHOOL OPENING]
1725	[LOST TREASURES]
2253	WATER, WATER EVERYWHERE
2427	[WICK SCENES]

284

0395	Scottish shipbuilding
0418	St. Kilda - britain's loneliest isle
0419	Sailing 1000 miles up the amazon
0450	Around wick harbour
0460	Song of the clyde
0463	Gateway of the east, the
0467	Port of leith
0474	Gateway of the west, the
0480	Dundee
0481	Down to the sea
0504	Tay valley
0506	Aberdeen and its industries
0526	Our city - today and tomorrow
0559	Pathe review of the year
0580	River clyde
0587	Central scotland
0621	Piece of cake, a
0624	Rose of the orient
0773	Northern outpost
0912	Heart of scotland, the
0915	Glasgow
0938	Glasgow's docklands
1318	Clyde resort: an introduction to girvan
1517	[home and away no. 2]
1521	Home and away no. 11
1524	Home and away no. 14
1540	Steamer journey
1638	Wire lines
1653	Edinburgh
1676	Bridge town, the
1691	Greenock plans ahead
1694	Industrial clydesdale
1745	Port health authority
1765	Lothians part ii, the
1766	[scott family film]
1956	Industrial stirlingshire
2000a	Bens, the
2009	Life in the orkneys
2024	Forth powerhouse for industry
2046	Magic key, the
2954	Everything by design
2110	(violet anderson film)
2216	Invergordon smelter, the
2225	Silver city, the
2239	Metal in harmony
2243	Tay road bridge
2373	[dundee screen snapshots] series

CARNIVALS

See CIRCUSES and CARNIVALS

CARRIAGES and CARTS

0010	Aberdeen university quater centenary celebrations
0042	Aberdeen 1906
0044	Glasgow and the clyde coast
0114	Waverley steps
0536	(neil armstrong in langholm)
0571	Pure new wool - and scottish
0625	Wishaw co-op gala day
0662	Textiles

0751	(border country)
0771	Glimpse of the camperdown works, a
0791-0792	[borders local newsreels]
0794	(glasgow trams c1902)
0795	(arrival at whitehart hotel, campbeltown)
0810a/b	(tain carnival 1935/ 1936)
0819	Royal visit to scotland
0833	Miss violet hopson visits dundee fire station
0879	(kirkcaldy pageant week 1951)
1258	(honeymoon carriage ride)
1603	Paddy black memorial mission district trip
1604	[dundee courier 1911]
1641	Isles of youth, the
1676	Bridge town, the
1684	New lives
1691	Greenock plans ahead
2210	George iv's edinburgh
2427	[wick scenes]

CARS

See AUTOMOBILES

CARTOONS

See ANIMATION

CASTLES

0034	Face of scotland
0098	Lieder der volker (songs of the people)
0114	Waverley steps
0182	Edinburgh
0196	Road through the sunset isles
0199	Windsor
0235	Presentation of new colours to gordon highlanders
0244	Newsreel
0251	Introducing scotland
0256	Eilean an fhraoich [isle of lewis]
0260	Honeymoon cruise no. 2
0281	North east corner
0296	Scotland and the new world
0302	Land o' clans
0332	[ensign ewart]
0345	Busman's holiday
0354	(continental holidays)
0362	Highland hospitality
0363	Over the sea to skye
0364	Perthshire panorama
0380	[shots of edinburgh]
0384	[isle of barra]
0415	Honeymoon cruise no. 1
0416	Learning for living
0418	St. Kilda - britain's loneliest isle
0431	Cruise to st. Kilda and the western isles
0448	(scenes at balmoral)
0455	Service not self
0459	Edinburgh festival, the
0492	Stan and ollie
0501	Routes and centres
0512	Stirling: gateway to the highlands
0530	Scottish shale industry
0550	Stornoway
0586	Dee valley

2246	HAND OF ADAM
2256	SONG FOR PRINCE CHARLIE, A
2258	LOTHIAN LANDSCAPE
2262	CASTLE AND CAPITAL
2264	PRACTICAL ROMANTIC, SIR WALTER SCOTT
2309	STEALING AWAY TO STORNOWAY
2334	HOLIDAY SCENES AT ROTHESAY
2337	(MACEWAN'S FREEDOM OF ROTHESAY)
2383	(HOLIDAY IN SCOTLAND 1964)
2388	BONNIE SCOTLAND
2396	SCOTLAND THROUGH THE LENS
2415	OLD ROTHESAY
2587	ISLE OF RHUM
2591	FAIR RIVER, THE
2592	ISLES OF THE WEST
2593	MISTY ISLE
2605	(HOLIDAY SCOTLAND)
2610	RESTORATION OF THE CHURCH OF THE HOLY RUDE
2631	HOLIDAY SCOTLAND
2674	NORTH AND WEST OF THE GREAT GLEN
2720	[BRAEMAR GAMES, TWEED MAKING AND EDINBURGH]
2734	(FAMILY WEDDING AND LIFE AT "SHANZIE")
2746	TROSSACHS, THE
2794	CASHMERE STORY, THE
2805	PLEASURE ISLAND
2807	PROSPECT FOR A CITY
2844	VARIOUS PARADES 1940-1945
2863	(SAWKINS NO. 2)

CATHEDRAL CHURCHES

See also CHURCHES

0051	QUEEN IN SCOTLAND, THE
0054	ROYAL VISIT OF GEORGE VI
0064	QUEEN ELIZABETH RECEIVES THE HONOURS OF SCOTLAND
0106	GLASGOW'S POLICE
0114	WAVERLEY STEPS
0142	ROYAL VISIT TO SCOTLAND
0149	ITALIAN INTERLUDE
0186	ROYAL VISIT TO SCOTLAND
0247	LAYING FOUNDATION STONE OF THE BISHOP SEABURY MEMORIAL
0303	FUTURE OF SCOTLAND
0305	[GASKIN REPORT, THE]
0354	(CONTINENTAL HOLIDAYS)
0362	HIGHLAND HOSPITALITY
0364	PERTHSHIRE PANORAMA
0380	[SHOTS OF EDINBURGH]
0459	EDINBURGH FESTIVAL, THE
0504	TAY VALLEY
0526	OUR CITY - TODAY AND TOMORROW
0530	SCOTTISH SHALE INDUSTRY
0546	GLASGOW
0552	QUEEN MOTHER IN SCOTLAND, THE
0587	CENTRAL SCOTLAND
0631	NORTHERN SCOTLAND
0665	(HOLIDAY IN LONDON)
0704	HANDBA' AT KIRKWALL, ORKNEY
0713	REVIEW OF THE YEAR 1940
0715	CORONATION OF KING GEORGE VI AND QUEEN ELIZABETH
0722	BILLY GRAHAM IN GLASGOW

0819	ROYAL VISIT TO SCOTLAND
0915	GLASGOW
0968	ROYAL MILE EDINBURGH, THE
0986	GLASGOW
1112	STATE ENTRY INTO EDINBURGH
1113	HONOURS OF SCOTLAND
1231	EDINBURGH
1241	ROYAL MILE
1276	NORTH BRITISH
1324	FILM OF GLASGOW, A
1340	BRITAIN WELCOMES THE KING OF NORWAY IN EDINBURGH
1343	HISTORIC EDINBURGH
1371	ABERDEEN BY SEASIDE AND DEESIDE
1431	ST. ANDREWS
1487	EDINBURGH
1515	FORTROSE CELEBRATES ITS 500TH ANNIVERSARY
1572	CARPETS OF DISTINCTION
1577B	SOME BEAUTY SPOTS IN NORTH SCOTLAND
1653	EDINBURGH
1659	WEDDING OF ALYS COUPER AND DOUGLAS LINDSAY
1669	ST. ANDREWS
1705	HIGHLAND TOUR, CROOKSTON STREET SCHOOL
1766	[SCOTT FAMILY FILM]
1769	SCOTTISH TRANSPORT
1783	RIVER TAY
1854	(PROVOST FLETT COLLECTION)
1939	LOWLANDS OF SCOTLAND
2009	LIFE IN THE ORKNEYS
2022	SCOTTISH MINERS GALA DAY
2040	FIBRE WEB, THE
2209	FROM GLASGOW GREEN TO BENDIGO
2221	QUEEN IN SCOTLAND, THE
2247	ST. ANDREWS BY THE NORTHERN SEA
2320	ABERDEEN
2417	[SERVICE OF THANKSGIVING IN ST. GILES' CATHEDRAL]
2419	[HOLY COMMUNION SERVICE, ST. GILES']
2460	LORD HIGH COMMISSIONER IN GLASGOW
2515	(MACFARLANE FAMILY - WEDDING)
2605	(HOLIDAY SCOTLAND)
2833	WEDDING OF JOHN GLAISTER AND ISOBEL LINDSAY

CATTLE

0251	INTRODUCING SCOTLAND
0256	EILEAN AN FHRAOICH [ISLE OF LEWIS]
0264	QUEEN OF THE MILKY WAY
0274	HIGHLAND LADDIE
0277	ABERDEEN ANGUS
0278	AYRSHIRE CATTLE
0281	NORTH EAST CORNER
0303	FUTURE OF SCOTLAND
0331	OUR HEALTH SERVICES
0364	PERTHSHIRE PANORAMA
0380	[SHOTS OF EDINBURGH]
0442	BRIEF BEEF BIOGRAPHY, A
0474	GATEWAY OF THE WEST, THE
0481	DOWN TO THE SEA
0490	FARM IS RECLAIMED, A
0497	DUMFRIES - A MARKET TOWN
0501	ROUTES AND CENTRES
0504	TAY VALLEY

287

288

CELTIC CROSSES

See RELIGIOUS MONUMENTS

CEMETERIES

See DEATH

CERAMIC INDUSTRIES

CEREMONIES

289

CHARITIES, FUND-RAISING

CHEMICAL and RELATED TECHNOLOGY

CHILDBIRTH

CHILDREN and INFANTS

See also SCHOOLS

290

2102	MUNGO'S MEDALS
2103	(SCENIC PICTURE HOUSE CLOSURE)
2204	COUNTY OF THE CLYDE
2205	COUNTY ON THE MOVE
2231	SMITHS IN SCOTLAND, THE
2235	SONGS OF SCOTLAND
2241	HEALTH OF A CITY
2253	WATER, WATER EVERYWHERE
2281	WHEELS OF CHANCE
2290	JUBILEE DAY IN TAYPORT, 6TH MAY 1935
2303	(CHURCH HUT, TAYPORT)
2370	FARMER'S BOY, THE
2381	HEWERS OF COAL
2395	CHURCH ACTIVITIES, ST. MARTIN'S, EDINBURGH
2399	FITNESS FOR BOYS
2400	FITNESS FOR GIRLS
2471	GORBALS OLD GORBALS NEW - ONE WOMAN'S STORY
2478	SPRING IN SCOTLAND
2479	WINTER IN SCOTLAND
2480	GORBALS STOCK SHOTS
2486	(BROWN FAMILY FILM)
2497	[HIGHLAND CROFTERS' FAREWELL]
2500	YEARS AGO IN COWDENBEATH
2533	(BENZIE'S WORKS OUTING)
2537	CONSEQUENCES
2540	IT WASN'T ME MISTER
2546	(DORNOCH HOLIDAY)
2569-2570	(PLEASANCE TRUST BOYS' CLUB)
2577A	FAMILY FILMS 1931-1938
2579	EVACUATION DIFFICULTIES
2591	FAIR RIVER, A
2615	SETTLED OUT OF COURT
2654	[PORTSOY SUNDAY SCHOOL PICNIC]
2656	[PORTSOY SUNDAY SCHOOL PICNIC]
2659	[PORTSOY SUNDAY SCHOOL PICNIC]
2674	NORTH AND WEST OF THE GREAT GLEN
2705	FISHERS ALL
2706	BUSY AFTERNOON, A
2718	APPLE A DAY, AN
2731	(GREAT NORTH OF SCOTLAND RAILWAY FILMS)
2735	(HERD'S CAFE AND FAMILY FARM)
2736	(HERD FAMILY FILM)
2745	DAY ON THE SANDS, A
2750	SUMMER IN SCOTLAND
2751	HUMPTY DUMPTY
2753	FARM BABIES
2755	CIRCLE OF CARE
2767	KINTYRE
2768	(GEORGE MAY FAMILY FILM)
2771	MARY GETS READY FOR SCHOOL
2776	(CHILDREN'S PANEL AT WORK)
2784	(HADDO EVENTS)
2801	(SCENES OF ORKNEY)
2805	PLEASURE ISLAND
2825-2826	(MONTGOMERY FAMILY FILMS)
2832	[TOWN COUNCIL ELECTION DAY]
2835-2837	LANARK LANIMER DAYS 1946-1949/1952
2852	[GLASGOW TAXI DRIVERS OUTING]
2859	MORE THAN YOU THINK

292

CHRISTMAS
See also NEW YEAR

0024	CHRISTMAS 1937
0194A	MINISTRY OF FOOD FLASHES
0194B	CHRISTMAS 1943
0195B	GUID NYCHBURRIS DAY
0320	STORY OF HILLINGTON, THE
0379	CITY SIDELIGHTS NO. 1
0590	(CHRISTMAS STREET DECORATIONS IN GLASGOW)
1002	[COME CO-OP SHOPPING AT CHRISTMAS]
1103	CINEMA ADVERTS
1143	(PANTOMIME AND CHRISTMAS PARTY)
1307	(NOTRE DAME COLLEGE GRADUATES AND WEDDING)
1462	CHRISTMAS 1943
1485	(GUILD OF AID ANNUAL TREATS)
1497	[GLASGOW'S PROGRESS]
1668	CHRISTMAS
1743	FAMILY PARTIES
1989	(SIMPSON FAMILY FILM)
2187	XMAS LIGHTS
2640	CHRISTMAS IN LIGHT
2768	(GEORGE MAY FAMILY FILM)
2838	(PRENTICE FAMILY EVENTS)

CHURCHES
See also CATHEDRAL CHURCHES

0009	FIFTH CENTENARY OF THE UNIVERSITY OF GLASGOW
0019	GREAT WESTERN ROAD 1914
0034	FACE OF SCOTLAND
0051	QUEEN IN SCOTLAND, THE
0090	CHARLES RENNIE MACKINTOSH
0099	SUBSIDENCE
0114	WAVERLEY STEPS
0236	PORTHLETHEN CHURCH
0242	THEIR MAJESTIES ATTEND DIVINE SERVICE
0249	(MILITARY PARADE IN ABERDEEN)
0284	CRAIGMOUNT SCHOOL FILMS
0292	LIFE OF BURNS, THE
0303	FUTURE OF SCOTLAND
0307	NEW DAY
0323	TWO SISTERS
0362	HIGHLAND HOSPITALITY
0364	PERTHSHIRE PANORAMA
0416	LEARNING FOR LIVING
0431	CRUISE TO ST. KILDA AND THE WESTERN ISLES
0473	SERMON IN STONE, A
0483	GOOD NEIGHBOURS
0512	STIRLING: GATEWAY TO THE HIGHLANDS
0536	(NEIL ARMSTRONG IN LANGHOLM)
0553	FUNERAL OF MISS JEAN ARMOUR BURNS BROWN
0586	DEE VALLEY
0598	[YOUTH SERVICES PARADE]
0600	[REMEMBRANCE DAY 1956]
0640	FUNERAL OF THE LATE MAJOR GENERAL LORD LOVAT
0744	BIOLOGICAL EXPEDITION, ISLAND OF RAASAY
0752	CRIEFF - OUR TOWN
0796	DUMFRIESSHIRE JOURNEY
0800	[CAITHNESS, ORKNEY, KIRKWALL]
0802	WILL YE NO' COME BACK AGAIN

0821	(BOY SCOUTS PARADE, SCOTLAND)
0863C	(SPOT THE SPOT)
0920	(BUS TOUR, THE)
0922	PROGRESS REPORT NO. 2
0963	ST. PATRICK'S CHURCH, LOCHGELLY
0964	CLOSE OF JUBILEE YEAR PROCESSION
0966	LOCHGELLY WAR MEMORIAL
0967	LOCHGELLY AT WORK AND PLAY
0968	ROYAL MILE EDINBURGH, THE
0974	GLASGOW 1980
0981	CROFTER'S LIFE IN SHETLAND, A
1095	(UNIDENTIFIED RURAL TOWN TRIMS)
1105	(FOUNDATION STONE)
1112	STATE ENTRY INTO EDINBURGH
1118	SCHERZO
1120	SAIL TO INVERARAY
1208	NO VACANT CHAIRS
1245	NEWMILNS CIVIC WEEK
1252	FOCUS ON BRIDGETON
1315	ST. ANDREWS 1916
1321	AYR
1324	FILM OF GLASGOW, A
1374	LAYING FOUNDATION STONE, KIRKINTILLOCH PARISH CHURCH
1431	ST. ANDREWS
1455	(9TH HIGHLAND LIGHT INFANTRY)
1481	CLYDESCOPE
1487	EDINBURGH
1494	HOLIDAYS AT HOME 1942-'44
1538	LOCH LOMOND
1554	INVERNESS THANKSGIVING PARADE TO EAST CHURCH
1564	(FERRARI FAMILY FILM)
1567	(WEDDING FILM NO. 2)
1641	ISLES OF YOUTH, THE
1661	PROMINENT PAISLEY WEDDING
1669	ST. ANDREWS
1704	(SCOTTISH WEDDING, A)
1705	HIGHLAND TOUR, CROOKSTON STREET SCHOOL
1733	GREAT GLASGOW FIRES
1786	(FIRST COMMUNION CEREMONY)
1854	(PROVOST FLETT COLLECTION)
1874	[FILM OF MONIAIVE 1950-1955]
1894	CRUISE TO SCOTTISH GARDENS, A
1939	LOWLANDS OF SCOTLAND
1943	ENCHANTED ISLES
1969	CAER-PEN-TULACH
1987	(HOME GUARD, "A" COY., 1ST BATTN)
1997	FALKIRK
2007	KING AND THE WHISKY, THE
2009	LIFE IN THE ORKNEYS
2018	IN THY HANDS
2025	GATEWAY TO SECURITY
2026	QUEST, THE (GIRLS' GUILDRY)
2054	EVERYTHING BY DESIGN
2098	CARRICK KNOWE - CHURCH OF SCOTLAND
2112	WEDDING DAY 1936
2204	COUNTY OF THE CLYDE
2210	GEORGE IV'S EDINBURGH
2212	HEBRIDEAN HIGHWAY
2213	HIGHLAND CAPITAL

2215	IN GOOD HEART
2219	LIVINGSTON - A TOWN FOR THE LOTHIANS
2226	MACKINTOSH
2228	PLAN FOR LIVING, A
2246	HAND OF ADAM
2258	LOTHIAN LANDSCAPE
2262	CASTLE AND CAPITAL
2289	(TAYPORT PARISH CHURCH SALES OF WORK)
2303	(CHURCH HUT, TAYPORT)
2304	CORONATION YEAR 1953
2320	ABERDEEN
2343	IONA COMMUNITY YOUTH GROUP, THE
2347	ALF GOES TO WORK
2395	CHURCH ACTIVITIES, ST. MARTIN'S, EDINBURGH
2419	[HOLY COMMUNION SERVICE, ST. GILES']
2460	LORD HIGH COMMISSIONER IN GLASGOW
2504	CONSECRATION OF MONSEIGNEUR WARD OF ST. MARY'S CALTON
2517	(MACFARLANE FAMILY 1937)
2519	(GLASGOW FLOODS 1936)
2572	DUNARA CRUISE 1937
2592	ISLES OF THE WEST
2605	(HOLIDAY SCOTLAND)
2610	RESTORATION OF THE CHURCH OF THE HOLY RUDE
2620	VIEWS OF MILNCROFT AND CROFTCROIGHN
2631	HOLIDAY SCOTLAND
2676	OLD TIME MOVIES
2705	FISHERS ALL
2721	SPRING IN GALLOWAY
2755	CIRCLE OF CARE
2785	ORDER OF ST. JOHN, THE
2792	AYR FROM THE AULD BRIG

CINEMAS

0013	GOVAN FAIR 1947
0044	GLASGOW AND THE CLYDE COAST
0175	DUMFRIES 1959 - GUID NYCHBURRIS CELEBRATIONS
0181	DUMFRIES 1955 GUID NYCHBURRIS FESTIVAL
0184	LYCEUM CINEMA TRAILERS AND ADVERTISEMENTS
0194B	CHRISTMAS 1943
0195A	MERRY CHRISTMAS AND A HAPPY NEW YEAR
0239	ABERDEEN CELEBRATES THE CORONATION
0329	(X-RAY UNIT IN DUMFRIES)
0337	BO'NESS CHILDREN'S FAIR FESTIVAL
0376A	WHERE EVERYBODY GOES
0379	CITY SIDELIGHTS NO. 1
0404A	BO'NESS PUBLIC SCHOOL: QUEEN KATHLEEN JAMIESON
0404B	ST. MARY'S RC SCHOOL: QUEEN MARY MERKIE
0404C	BO'NESS ACADEMY 1932: QUEEN HELEN BURNETT
0404D	BORROWSTOUN SCHOOL 1933: QUEEN MARGARET MCMAHON
0404E	KINNEIL PUBLIC SCHOOL: QUEEN HELEN YOUNG
0413	BO'NESS FAIR FESTIVAL 1952
0460	SONG OF THE CLYDE
0492	STAN AND OLLIE
0561A	EXCLUSIVE PICTURES OF ROYAL VISIT TO PAISLEY
0561C	WOMEN'S GUILD OF EMPIRE LEAVE FOR TOUR OF CANADA
0561D	IT HAPPENED IN PAISLEY
0561E	EXCLUSIVE TO LA SCALA...FUNERAL OF FIREMASTER ALEX GIRDWOOD

CINEMATOGRAPHY (equipment etc.)

CIRCUSES and CARNIVALS
See also FAIRS and FAIRGROUNDS

0164	ABERDEEN
0241	CINEMA NEWS, ABERDEEN
0344	BO'NESS CHILDREN'S FAIR FESTIVAL
0380	[SHOTS OF EDINBURGH]
0573	GREEN OF GLASGOW, THE
0863B	(AIR CIRCUS CAPTION)
1068	SOME EVENTS IN GLASGOW 1937

CITY PLANNING

0268	PROGRESS REPORT
0307	NEW DAY
0386	MONEY PROGRAMME, THE
0526	OUR CITY - TODAY AND TOMORROW
0891	(EAST KILBRIDE DEVELOPMENT CORPORATION TRIMS 1947/'54)
0915	GLASGOW
0949-0950	STONEHOUSE - CENTRE FOR SUCCESS
0952-0953	STONEHOUSE - CENTRE FOR SUCCESS
0974	GLASGOW 1980
0975	GLENROTHES
1076	(EAST KILBRIDE TRIMS)
1497	[GLASGOW'S PROGRESS]
1691	GREENOCK PLANS AHEAD
1821	GEOGRAPHER AT WORK
1825	NEW SCOTLAND
1826	NEW TOWNS
2024	FORTH - POWERHOUSE FOR INDUSTRY
2102	MUNGO'S MEDALS
2204	COUNTY OF THE CLYDE
2205	COUNTY ON THE MOVE
2208	FORTH ROAD BRIDGE, THE
2219	LIVINGSTON - A TOWN FOR THE LOTHIANS
2227	CUMBERNAULD, TOWN FOR TOMORROW
2228	PLAN FOR LIVING, A
2237	ONE DAY IN IRVINE
2458	PEDESTRIANISATION
2807	PROSPECT FOR A CITY

CIVIL DEFENCE

0031	ARP SCHOOLS
0156	CIVIL DEFENCE IN GLASGOW
0157	(ANTI-GAS PRECAUTIONS IN GLASGOW)
0158	CIVIL DEFENCE
0238	(ABERDEEN'S "BLACK FRIDAY")
0246A	ARP
0266	CROWNING OF THE MERCHANT NAVY QUEEN, THE
0271	GOOD HEALTH TO SCOTLAND
0524	(HOME GUARD ON MANOEUVRES)
0538	(BOMBING OF THE CLYDE)
0561F	REVIEW OF PAISLEY'S CIVIL DEFENCE
0713	REVIEW OF THE YEAR 1940
1082	FIRE FIGHTING
1084	BOMB FELL, A
1085	CROWD GATHERS, A
1386	TENEMENT WARDEN
1396	MESSAGE MUST GET THROUGH, THE
1445	MOBILE CIVIL DEFENCE SURGICAL UNIT
1446	GLASGOW CASUALTY SERVICE

1464	(ARP DISPLAY)
1545	QUEEN'S OWN CAMERON HIGHLANDERS 50TH ANNIVERSARY
1625	TRIBUTE TO WARTIME PRODUCTION
2769	ARP: A REMINDER FOR PEACE
2842	FAMILY SCRAPBOOK NO. 4
2843	FAMILY SCRAPBOOK NO. 5
2844-2845	VARIOUS PARADES 1940-1945

CIVIL ENGINEERING

0153	KENYA TO DURBAN
0279	POWER FOR THE HIGHLANDS
0296	SCOTLAND AND THE NEW WORLD
0364	PERTHSHIRE PANORAMA
0507	NORTH OF THE GREAT GLEN
0631	NORTHERN SCOTLAND
0785	HEART IS HIGHLAND, THE
1062	WEALTH OF A NATION
1132	SOUTHERN SCOTLAND
1325	CRUACHAN HYDRO-ELECTRIC, ROYAL OPENING
1535	[LOCAL EVENTS, INVERNESS AREA]
1612	CONSTRUCTION OF THE BACKWATER DAM
1768	JOB FOR THE FUTURE, A
2214	HOLLOW MOUNTAIN, THE
2240	RIVERS AT WORK

CLACKMANNANSHIRE

0581	VARIETY MOMENTS
0605	LESSONS THROUGH THE LETTERBOX
1350	RIVER FORTH
1853	DIXINE NEWS
2217	LAND LIVED IN, A
2838	(PRENTICE FAMILY EVENTS)

CLANS and THE CLAN SYSTEM

0785	HEART IS HIGHLAND, THE
1784	HIGHLAND CASTLES
1882	WESTERN PERTHSHIRE
1883	[ROAD TO CARBISDALE, THE]
2213	HIGHLAND CAPITAL

CLAY INDUSTRY

0597B	SIR DAVID ROBERTSON, MP, OPENS NEW BRICK WORKS
0948	OCHILTREE TILE WORKS
1956	INDUSTRIAL STIRLINGSHIRE
2070	(CASTLECARY EVENTS)
2071	(BRICKMAKING)
2072	[WALLHOUSE - MINING CLAY]
2182	POTTERY, THE
2205	COUNTY ON THE MOVE
2451	ETNA BRICKWORKS

CLIMBING and MOUNTAINEERING

0134	HIMALAYAN HOLIDAY
0144	CANADIAN CAMEOS NO. 2
0151	SWITZERLAND 1947
0231	SCOTLAND FOR FITNESS
0363	OVER THE SEA TO SKYE
0586	DEE VALLEY
0992	(YOUNG AND OLD PASTIMES)
1062	WEALTH OF A NATION
1086	CRAGSMAN'S DAY, A
1088	(MOUNTAIN RESCUE TRAINING)
1599	NORTH AMERICAN IMP

295

1643	Cairngorms, the
1651	To the top of Ben Nevis
1811	Climbers, the
1880	Upper Deeside
1881	Ratagan/torridon
1882	Western perthshire
1886	Schoolboy hostellers
1887	[glencoe and nevis]
2097	Camping and outdoor club
2150	In days of old
2151	Glenmore and the cairngorms
2155	Rhum and water/ lscc 50th anniversary
2186	Areas of scotland - highland
2214	Hollow mountain, the
2392	Lomond mc/ski-ing
2430	Royal northern yacht club cadets at loch lomond
2721	Spring in galloway
2842	Family scrapbook no. 4

CLOTHING (fashion etc.)

See also COSTUME/ TEXTILE INDUSTRY

0025	(history of the tailor and garment workers union)
0123	City sidelights no. 2
0197	Glenhar factory, hillington
0282	City sidelights - sections
0320	Story of hillington, the
0430	Castlebank for collars
0544	[from wool to wearer]
0578	Cashmere is scottish
0579	World of cashmere
0608	Achievement
0617	Tomorrow is yours
0636	Back to back
0772	(steam locomotives and scenes at lanark racecourse)
0775	(lanark racecourse and renfrewshire hunt)
0791	[borders local newsreels no. 1]
0858	Keeping step with the times
0904	(teazie weazie)
1254	(fashion show)
1257	[co-op adverts ii]
1261	[co-op adverts iv]
1495	[saving of a shabby coat]
2029	Mary's lamb
2046	Magic key, the
2137	(macneill tractors demonstration films)
2372	Arbroath's new swimming pool
2502-2503	(shearer family film)
2546	(dornoch holiday)
2559	(honeyman family home)
2605	(holiday scotland)
2612	Brigade parade 1948
2618b	Round the three lochs and visit to carnbooth
2639	Braemar gathering
2766	Domestic science as a career
2794	Cashmere story, the
2861	Night at the hap, a
2862	Hap dances, the

CLYDE RIVER

0030	It began on the clyde
0048	Port of glasgow
0062	Glasgow - our city
0077	Report on industrial scotland
0162	Views of the clyde and around
0165	Sections from "current account" waverley programme
0188	Royal occasions of scotland
0231	Scotland for fitness
0232	"queen mary" goes down to the sea
0251	Introducing scotland
0253	Tam trauchle's troubles
0257	Festival of fellowship
0286b	Lighters
0296	Scotland and the new world
0301	Land of invention
0314	Sport in scotland
0377	River clyde - a survey of scotland's greatest river
0395	Scottish shipbuilding
0398	River clyde, the
0456	Fighting fields
0460	Song of the clyde
0463	Gateway of the east, the
0473	Sermon in stone, a
0474	Gateway of the west, the
0481	Down to the sea
0487	An eye to the future
0500	Heavy industries
0505	County of dunbarton
0508	Scottish trade mission to canada
0515c	Trip down the clyde, a
0526	Our city - today and tomorrow
0530	Scottish shale industry
0531	(guild of aid work in the gorbals)
0538	(bombing of the clyde)
0546	Glasgow
0580	River clyde
0587	Central scotland
0591	Looking back
0622	Pride and progress
0666	Miscellaneous sea-going vessels
0670	(scenes on the clyde and edinburgh zoo)
0673	Scotland welcomes their majesties
0695	"queen mary" goes down to the sea/ wins blue riband
0703	Clyde, the
0749	(local film from kirkintilloch area)
0775	(lanark racecourse and renfrewshire hunt)
0784	("empress of britain")
0797	Coasts of clyde, the
0915	Glasgow
0938	Glasgow's docklands
0986	Glasgow
1049	Glasgow, no mean city
1062	Wealth of a nation
1068	Some events in glasgow 1937
1080b	River clyde
1214	Sunshine cruise to the mediterranean, a

296

1841	GUIDE THEM ON THEIR WAY
1956	INDUSTRIAL STIRLINGSHIRE
2022	SCOTTISH MINERS GALA DAY
2024	FORTH - POWERHOUSE FOR INDUSTRY
2088	FAIR COUNTY OF AYR
2204	COUNTY OF THE CLYDE
2205	COUNTY ON THE MOVE
2232	I REMEMBER, I REMEMBER
2369	LORD ROBENS INTERVIEW
2381	HEWERS OF COAL
2606	MINING REVIEW NO. 3
2767	KINTYRE
2814	BOTANIC GARDENS AND OLD GLASGOW

COCKLE GATHERING

See MOLLUSCS

COLLEGES

See also UNIVERSITIES

0090	CHARLES RENNIE MACKINTOSH
0249	(MILITARY PARADE IN ABERDEEN)
0282	CITY SIDELIGHTS - SECTIONS
0316	OUR SCHOOLS
0328	CITY SIDELIGHTS NO. 3
0330	CITY SIDELIGHTS NO. 4
0526	OUR CITY - TODAY AND TOMORROW
0712	[SAUCHIEHALL STREET ROOF TOPS]
0769	[KILMARNOCK]
0915	GLASGOW
0974	GLASGOW 1980
0986	GLASGOW
1080A	ABERDEEN AWA' AUGUST 1949
1098	CAMERA MAKES WHOOPEE
1100	SEVEN TILL FIVE
1273	(NOTRE DAME COLLEGE - MOVE TO BEARSDEN 1963-1970)
1307	(NOTRE DAME COLLEGE GRADUATES AND WEDDING)
1481	CLYDESCOPE
1497	[GLASGOW'S PROGRESS]
1501	BEYOND THE GRAMPIANS
1528	HOME AND AWAY NO. 19
1605	[EDWARD VII LAYS FOUNDATION STONE]
1653	EDINBURGH
1765	LOTHIANS PART II, THE
1862	HERIOT WATT COLLEGE, EDINBURGH
1955	STUDENTS AT LAWERS SCHOOL OF AGRICULTURE
1982	EFFECTS OF SURFACE TENSION
1983	LAND-SHIP, THE
1984	SHARK FISHING
2023	BETTER HAY
2032	PHYSICS FOR ALL (AN EXPERIMENTAL APPROACH)
2049	OUR THREE R'S
2077	STONES OF GLASGOW, THE
2110	(VIOLET ANDERSON FILM)
2140	(GSA KINECRAFT SOCIEY)
2223	BORDERS, THE
2226	MACKINTOSH
2231	SMITHS IN SCOTLAND, THE
2257	TAYSIDE
2320	ABERDEEN
2467	AUTOLITHOGRAPHY

298

2766	DOMESTIC SCIENCE AS A CAREER

COMEDY

0285	(ROADSIDE DRAMA)
0635	ADVENTURES OF WEE ROB ROY, THE
0719	BUYING A HORSE
1090	FORUM FROLICS
1121	CRABBIT GRANNY
1207	TONI
2022	SCOTTISH MINERS GALA DAY
2759	EASTER REVOLUTION

COMICS

See NEWSPAPERS and MAGAZINES

COMPUTERS

See ELECTRONICS

CONFECTIONERY

0379	CITY SIDELIGHTS NO. 1
0498	MAKING CHOCOLATES
0609	PRODUCTIVE GROCERY DEPARTMENT - SHIELDHALL FACTORY PRODUCTS
0655	[HENDRY'S DOUBLE TOP AMERICAN COLA]
0828	(CAPTIONS AND ADVERTS)
0832	(CINEMA SALES KIOSK)
0881	(CINEMA ADVERTISEMENTS)
1752	MAKING SWEETS
1909	FROM THE PROJECTION BOX
2063	(HILLFOOT PICTURE HOUSE ADVERTS, ETC.)
2141	[TV COMMERCIALS]
2329	[HALFWAY TO PARADISE: IRN BRU]
2493	[CINEMA TRAILERS III]
2830	[PENNIWELLS AND ST. ANDREWS]
2861	NIGHT AT THE HAP, A

CONFERENCES

0025	(HISTORY OF THE TAILOR AND GARMENT WORKERS UNION)
0052	SYHA CONFERENCE
0245A	BRITISH MEDICAL CONFERENCE
0634	(CWS CONGRESS IN GLASGOW)
0756	PIONEERS THEN AND NOW
1165	BFI SUMMER SCHOOL (BANGOR 1949)
1731	SRDA CONFERENCE, GLENEAGLES
1790	(CEA CONFERENCE, GLENEAGLES C1949)
2271	UNICA, BRUXELLES 1953)
2498	[UNICA, GLASGOW 1951]

CONSTRUCTION

See also HOUSING

0141	CONSTRUCTION OF THE KING GEORGE V BRIDGE, GLASGOW
0268	PROGRESS REPORT
0301	LAND OF INVENTION
0307	NEW DAY
0317	OUR HOMES
0386	MONEY PROGRAMME, THE
0387	BIG MILL, THE
0388	CALLER HERRIN
0505	COUNTY OF DUNBARTON
0550	STORNOWAY
0563	COUNCIL'S ENTERPRISE
0774	(CONSTRUCTION OF THE RITZ CINEMA, EDINBURGH 1929)
0800	[CAITHNESS, ORKNEY, KIRKWALL]

CONVENTS

See MONASTIC BUILDINGS

COOKERY

See FOODS and FOODSTUFFS

See also BAKING and BAKERIES/DOMESTIC ARTS

CORONATION CELEBRATIONS

COSTUME (e.g. Fancy dress / national)

0013	GOVAN FAIR 1947
0172	DUMFRIES 1936 - GUID NYCHBURRIS DAY
0179	DUMFRIES 1950 GUID NYCHBURRIS FESTIVAL
0210	SHEPHERDS AND HERDSMEN IN HUNGARY
0256	EILEAN AN FHRAOICH [ISLE OF LEWIS]
0284	CRAIGMOUNT SCHOOL FILMS
0325	(DUMFRIES)
0337	BO'NESS CHILDREN'S FAIR FESTIVAL
0339	BO'NESS CHILDREN'S FAIR FESTIVAL
0341	BO'NESS CHILDREN'S FAIR FESTIVAL
0343	BO'NESS CHILDREN'S FAIR FESTIVAL
0400-0409	[BO'NESS CHILDREN'S FAIR FESTIVALS]
0411-0413	BO'NESS CHILDREN'S FESTIVAL
0444	RIVALLING THE RAINBOW
0449	GORDON HIGHLANDERS LEAVE FOR THE BOER WAR
0491	(WILL FYFFE)
0516	(UNIVERSITY NEWS)
0521	STIRLING CHARITIES DAY
0555	(PANTOMIME IN SUMMER)
0599	HIGHLAND GATHERING
0638	GLENFINNAN AND THE '45
0760	GALASHIELS HISTORICAL PEACE PAGEANT
0761	[CHILDREN'S PROCESSION GALASHIELS]
0792	[BORDERS LOCAL NEWSREELS NO. 2]
0795	(ARRIVAL AT WHITEHART HOTEL, CAMPBELTOWN)
0803	(DANCE SEQUENCES)
0810A/B	(TAIN CARNIVAL 1935/ 1936)
0811	LOCHGELLY EQUITABLE CO-OPERATIVE SOCIETY'S SHOPPING WEEK
0813	KIRKCALDY HOSPITAL PAGEANT
0823	(FAIR FESTIVAL)
0862	GIRLS' CLUBS APPEAL
0878	(GUID NYCHBURRIS CELEBRATIONS)
0931	AROUND INVERNESS
0934	CROFTING IN SKYE
0958	MAKING A SPORRAN IN LEATHER
1291	BROXBURN GALA DAY AND CROWNING OF QUEEN
1293	BROXBURN HIGH SCHOOL SPORTS
1388	4TH CAMERON HIGHLANDERS AT BEDFORD
1455	(9TH HIGHLAND LIGHT INFANTRY)
1474	[INVERNESS FESTIVAL YEAR 1951]
1784	HIGHLAND CASTLES
2425	(VISIT TO SOVIET UNION)
2461	BUDAPEST LA REINE DU DANUBE
2541	(HONOLULU AND CHARLIE CHAPLIN)
2549	(CRUISE ON "IBERIA", I)
2612	BRIGADE PARADE 1948
2613	ROYAL SALUTE
2703	MAN AND HIS KILT, A
2803	WHISPER AND I SHALL HEAR
2825	(MONTGOMERY FAMILY HOLIDAYS)
2835-2837	LANARK LANIMER DAY 1946-1949/1952
2847	[PORT ELPHINSTONE SCHOOL PICNIC]
2852	[GLASGOW TAXI DRIVERS OUTING]

COURTS

See LAW

CRAFTS (traditional)

See also CERAMIC INDUSTRIES/ GLASS and GLASS BLOWING/ TEXTILE CRAFTS

0007	SCOTS OF TOMORROW
0017	DAY IN THE HOME, A
0028	WESTERN ISLES
0114	WAVERLEY STEPS
0123	CITY SIDELIGHTS NO. 2
0124	MAKING OF THE HOLY BIBLE
0302	LAND O' CLANS
0388	CALLER HERRIN
0394	COOPERAGE
0431	CRUISE TO ST. KILDA AND THE WESTERN ISLES
0482	BORDER WEAVE
0494	COUNTRY POLICEMAN
0505	COUNTY OF DUNBARTON
0593	VILLAGE BLACKSMITH
0668	(IVORY CARVING)
0707	SCOTLAND
0777	(MISCELLANEOUS SCENES, RENFREWSHIRE)
0778	(SCENES AT RENFREWSHIRE HUNT)
0814	QUEEN LAUDS SCOTTISH EXHIBITION, GLASGOW
0862	GIRLS' CLUBS APPEAL
0911	ST. KILDA - THE LONELY ISLANDS
0958	MAKING A SPORRAN IN LEATHER
0981	CROFTER'S LIFE IN SHETLAND, A
0983	[PEOPLE OF MANY LANDS - THE ESKIMOS]
1030	KNITWEAR WITHOUT TEARS
1087	(HOLIDAY AT ARROCHAR)
1127	DA MAKKIN O' A KESHIE
1153	WHEELWRIGHT, THE
1286	SHETLAND, PEOPLE OF MANY LANDS
1342	(ROCKET RANGE, BENBECULA)
1413	SMOCKING
1502	[SINGER'S FOUNDRY]
1522	HOME AND AWAY NO. 12
1530	WELDING IN BOILER MANUFACTURE
1547	CROWNING OF THE DARVEL LACE QUEEN 1952
1570	[RUSSELL'S LIBRARY FOOTAGE]
1591	INDUSTRY ON PARADE - THE DEFENDING CHAMPION
1592	BIRTH OF A SEWING MACHINE
1596	GRANITE
1615	(SHETLAND SCENES)
1641	ISLES OF YOUTH, THE
1691	GREENOCK PLANS AHEAD
1727	[AT THE SMIDDY/ THE ROAD TO BRAEMAR]
1754	LACE MAKING
1766	[SCOTT FAMILY FILM]
1779	WITH CAR AND CAMERA THROUGH THE LAKE DISTRICT TO SOUTHERN SCOTLAND
1793	(CONSTRUCTION OF DUNFERMLINE'S WAR MEMORIAL)
1916	VILLAGE BLACKSMITH
1928	TRIP TO SKYE, ORKNEY AND SHETLAND
1935	FORGE, THE
2022	SCOTTISH MINERS GALA DAY
2026	QUEST, THE (GIRLS' GUILDRY)

2106	GLASGOW JUNIOR INSTRUCTION CENTRE, A
2108	JUNGLE JINKS, ETC.
2165	BLIND BASKET MAKER, THE
2171	WOODCRAFT
2192	[MAKING A SPINNING WHEEL AT PORTSONACHAN]
2201	DRAM LIKE THIS, A
2203	CHAMPIONS IN THE SUN
2211	GOOD SERVANT, THE
2226	MACKINTOSH
2254	ERSKINE BRIDGE, THE
2258	LOTHIAN LANDSCAPE
2259	PRIDE OF ISLANDS, A
2294	(TAYPORT EVENTS 1946-'49)
2296	INDUSTRIES OF TAYPORT, THE
2311	HEATH VISITS THE WEAVERS
2346	CAN THESE STONES LIVE?
2610	RESTORATION OF THE CHURCH OF THE HOLY RUDE
2635	TRIP TO BHUTAN
2645	HORN CARVING
2721	SPRING IN GALLOWAY
2766	DOMESTIC SCIENCE AS A CAREER
2858	[OUTER HEBRIDES - HUMAN ACTIVITIES]

CRANES

0377	RIVER CLYDE - A SURVEY OF SCOTLAND'S GREATEST RIVER
0387	BIG MILL, THE
0580	RIVER CLYDE
1248	STEEL GOES TO SEA
1270	VISIT TO A SHIPBUILDING YARD
1480	YOUNG IN HEART
1518	HOME AND AWAY NO. 4
1521	HOME AND AWAY NO. 11
1525	HOME AND AWAY NO. 16
1526	HOME AND AWAY NO. 17
1528	HOME AND AWAY NO. 19
1581	(HOLIDAY SCOTLAND)
1597	(SCENES ON THE RIVER CLYDE)
1638	WIRE LINES
1691	GREENOCK PLANS AHEAD
1694	INDUSTRIAL CLYDESDALE
1997	FALKIRK
2024	FORTH - POWERHOUSE FOR INDUSTRY
2134	GLASGOW'S SUNDAY 1963
2159	WIRE ROPE-MAKING
2459	[LANGUAGE INSERTS]

CRICKET

0441	KING, GOD BLESS HIM, THE
0515A	CRICKET MATCH, CARLTON CLUB GROUND
0559	PATHE REVIEW OF THE YEAR
0796	DUMFRIESSHIRE JOURNEY
1243	(LEISURE TIME)
1372	NEWMILLS, TORRYBURN AND CROMBIE GALA
1389	(GROSVENOR TOPICALS NO. 2)
1414	CRICKET LOOPS
1796	GB NEWS REVIEW 1948
1802	PRINCESS STREET CHURCH SNAPSHOTS OF 1939
2207	FETTES
2733	(NORTH EAST AND THE HIGHLANDS: CELEBRATIONS AND EVENTS)
2736	(HERD FAMILY FILM)

2784	(HADDO EVENTS)

CROFTS and CROFTING

0028	WESTERN ISLES
0034	FACE OF SCOTLAND
0112	CROFTER BOY
0120	CROFTERS, THE
0155	WEST OF INVERNESS
0231	SCOTLAND FOR FITNESS
0251	INTRODUCING SCOTLAND
0256	EILEAN AN FHRAOICH [ISLE OF LEWIS]
0274	HIGHLAND LADDIE
0280	HILL SHEEP FARM
0303	FUTURE OF SCOTLAND
0345	BUSMAN'S HOLIDAY
0362	HIGHLAND HOSPITALITY
0384	[ISLE OF BARRA]
0418	ST. KILDA - BRITAIN'S LONELIEST ISLE
0456	FIGHTING FIELDS
0504	TAY VALLEY
0507	NORTH OF THE GREAT GLEN
0514	PRINCE WITH HIS FUSILIERS, THE
0549	ISLE OF LEWIS
0589	NEIL GUNN - LIGHT IN THE NORTH
0631	NORTHERN SCOTLAND
0773	NORTHERN OUTPOST
0928	LIFE IN THE HIGHLANDS
0932	ARDNAMURCHAN
0934	CROFTING IN SKYE
0936	CROFTERS OF WESTER ROSS
0980	SCENES FROM A SHETLAND CROFT LIFE
0981	CROFTER'S LIFE IN SHETLAND, A
0991	RUGGED ISLAND
1063	THEY MADE THE LAND
1096	WAY THE MONEY GOES, THE
1127	DA MAKKIN O' A KESHIE
1129	IN SHEEP'S CLOTHING
1130	SHETLAND PONY
1269	SKYWAY AMBULANCE
1286	SHETLAND, PEOPLE OF MANY LANDS
1342	(ROCKET RANGE, BENBECULA)
1436	ORKNEY - SCENES AROUND SHAPINSAY
1440	THATCHED CROFT
1451	LIFE IN THE HIGHLANDS
1641	ISLES OF YOUTH, THE
1655	BARRA
1701	ERISKAY - A POEM OF REMOTE LIVES
1943	ENCHANTED ISLES
2202	BY LOCHABER I WILL GO
2242	IN GREAT WATERS
2278	[HIGHLAND FUND IN ACTION, HIGHLAND INITIATIVE]
2318	LIFE IN THE SCOTTISH HIGHLANDS
2367	[ON THE ISLAND]
2410	BEYOND A TANGLED SHORE
2497	[HIGHLAND CROFTERS' FAREWELL]
2547	(COWAL GAMES, DUNOON 1933)
2592	ISLES OF THE WEST
2593	MISTY ISLE
2858	[OUTER HEBRIDES - HUMAN ACTIVITIES]

301

CURLING

0114	WAVERLEY STEPS
0454A	QUEENSHILL CUP AT CASTLE DOUGLAS, THE
0591	LOOKING BACK
0916	PADDY'S MILESTONE
1805	FENWICK EVENTS OF 1933
2123	(FFORDE COLLECTION)
2130	AIR CANADA SILVER BROOM 1969
2131	AIR CANADA SILVER BROOM 1975
2544	(ST. MORITZ 1946, II)
2580	ROARING GAME, THE
2698	HIGHLAND HOLIDAY
2831	[DUCHESS OF YORK IN ST. ANDREWS]

CYCLING

See BICYCLES

DAIRY and RELATED PRODUCTS

0251	INTRODUCING SCOTLAND
0264	QUEEN OF THE MILKY WAY
0278	AYRSHIRE CATTLE
0322	(HILLINGTON INDUSTRIAL ESTATE EXHIBITION)
0467	PORT OF LEITH
0571	PURE NEW WOOL - AND SCOTTISH
0607	GET IT AT THE CO-OP
0615	BLADNOCH CREAMERY
0637	ANIMAL HUSBANDRY
0676	(SCWS CREAMERY BUTTER ADVERTISEMENT)
0681-0682	(SCWS MARGARINE ADVERTISEMENT)
0686	(SCWS MARGARINE ADVERTISEMENT)
0701	(SCWS MARGARINE ADVERTISEMENT)
0727	GALLONS OF GOODNESS
0859	HOW GUILD MARGARINE IS MADE
0876	(HOW BLUEBELL MARGARINE IS MADE)
0996	[BLUEBELL MARGARINE]
0998	[LOFTY PEAK FLOUR]
0999	[ORCHID MARGARINE]
1000	[CHEDDAR CHEESE]
1015	[MARGARINE CARTOON]
1021	[ORCHID BUTTER]
1034	[ORCHID MARGARINE]
1055	(CO-OP BUTTER)
1132	SOUTHERN SCOTLAND
1256	[CO-OP ADVERTS I]
1261	[CO-OP ADVERTS IV]
1267	(STATION FAREWELLS)
1344	PASTEURISED MILK
1348	CITY'S FARMS, THE
1451	LIFE IN THE HIGHLANDS
1764	LOTHIANS PART I, THE
1792	SOLWAY COUNTIES, THE
1854	(PROVOST FLETT COLLECTION)
2009	LIFE IN THE ORKNEYS
2088	FAIR COUNTY OF AYR
2166	MILK AT THE CREAMERY
2203	CHAMPIONS IN THE SUN
2215	IN GOOD HEART
2241	HEALTH OF A CITY
2278	[HIGHLAND FUND IN ACTION, HIGHLAND INITIATIVE]
2367	[ON THE ISLAND]

302

2370	FARMER'S BOY, THE
2512	AYRSHIRE DAIRY FARMER
2596	[SCWS CREAMERY AT WISHAW]
2721	SPRING IN GALLOWAY
2735	(HERD'S CAFE AND FAMILY FARM)
2767	KINTYRE
2858	[OUTER HEBRIDES - HUMAN ACTIVITIES]

DAMS

See CIVIL ENGINEERING/ WATER

DANCES and DANCING

0052	SYHA CONFERENCE
0098	LIEDER DER VOLKER (SONGS OF THE PEOPLE)
0114	WAVERLEY STEPS
0237	FLICKS OF ABERDEEN'S TERRITORIAL WEEK
0239	ABERDEEN CELEBRATES THE CORONATION
0249	(MILITARY PARADE IN ABERDEEN)
0288	CALLY HOUSE
0291	CHILDREN OF THE CITY
0313	RAKES OF GLASGOW
0316	OUR SCHOOLS
0385	SCOTTISH UNIVERSITIES
0400	BO'NESS PUBLIC SCHOOL: QUEEN MARY SMITH
0412A/B	[BO'NESS FAIR]
0412C	GRANGE PUBLIC SCHOOL: QUEEN ANDREA WALKER
0414	[BO'NESS FAIR C1911-1913]
0459	EDINBURGH FESTIVAL, THE
0460	SONG OF THE CLYDE
0483	GOOD NEIGHBOURS
0528	ALL ON A SUMMER'S DAY
0531	(GUILD OF AID WORK IN THE GORBALS)
0572	(INVERBERVIE PAGEANT)
0586	DEE VALLEY
0599	HIGHLAND GATHERING
0639B	FERGUSLIE MILLS IN INVERNESS
0712	[SAUCHIEHALL STREET ROOF TOPS]
0720	[HIGHLAND SHOW, DUNDEE]
0738	EATING AT WORK
0754	MUSIC FROM THE MOVIES
0756	PIONEERS THEN AND NOW
0761	[CHILDREN'S PROCESSION GALASHIELS]
0797	COASTS OF CLYDE, THE
0802	WILL YE NO' COME BACK AGAIN
0803	(DANCE SEQUENCES)
0804	GREAT SCOT - MARY SLESSOR
0810B	(TAIN CARNIVAL 1936)
0815	(GAUMONT SOUND MIRROR, 1927-1931)
0823	(FAIR FESTIVAL)
0848	L'ANNIVERSAIRE
0850	RIVER CREE, THE
0862	GIRLS' CLUBS APPEAL
0873B	(HIGHLAND GAMES, ABERDEEN)
0879	(KIRKCALDY PAGEANT WEEK 1951)
0880	GLENROTHES FESTIVAL WEEK
0896	(PRE MATCH DISPLAY, HAMPDEN STADIUM)
0899	HAMPDEN STORY, THE
0904	(TEAZIE WEAZIE)
0935	CRIEFF HIGHLAND GATHERING
0939	GLASGOW WELCOMES THE QUEEN

0943	(JOURNEY THROUGH BARRHEAD AND REVIEW OF THE FESTIVAL YEAR 1951)
0945	(SATURDAY MORNING MATINEE)
0951	STONEHOUSE NEW TOWN FESTIVAL
0953	STONEHOUSE TRIMS
0974	GLASGOW 1980
0986	GLASGOW
1049	GLASGOW, NO MEAN CITY
1073A	NIGHT SWORD DANCE
1087	(HOLIDAY AT ARROCHAR)
1092	MRS. MCLEOD
1098	CAMERA MAKES WHOOPEE
1101	("RIVER CREE" ENTERTAINS THE QUEEN, THE)
1103	CINEMA ADVERTS
1133	[HALF PAST EIGHT SHOW]
1134	[ROBINSON CRUSOE]
1140	(VARIOUS ARTISTS c1948)
1158	MASQUERADE
1188	SECOND FOLLIES, THE
1211	HIGHLAND GATHERING, A
1252	FOCUS ON BRIDGETON
1268	[YOKER SCHOOL FILM]
1284	UPHALL CHILDREN'S GALA ETC
1294	UPHALL STATION CHILDREN'S GALA
1301	(UNIDENTIFIED GALA AND SPORTS DAY, BROXBURN AREA NO. 1)
1302	(UNIDENTIFIED SPORTS DAY, BROXBURN AREA)
1368	PENICUIK CHILDREN'S GALA DAY 1953
1376	(MAY DAY PARADE, BO'NESS)
1441	[KEITH SHOW, 14TH AUGUST, 1951]
1457	HOPPITY HOP
1471	(ELGIN GALA DAY NO. 1)
1474	[INVERNESS FESTIVAL YEAR 1951]
1486	EDINBURGH FESTIVAL - PATHE
1493	FESTIVAL IN EDINBURGH
1494	HOLIDAYS AT HOME 1942-'44
1515	FORTROSE CELEBRATES ITS 500TH ANNIVERSARY
1521	HOME AND AWAY NO. 11
1526	HOME AND AWAY NO. 17
1589	CLYDEBANK BURGH JUBILEE 1936
1603	PADDY BLACK MEMORIAL MISSION DISTRICT TRIP
1634	(MIDSUMMER QUEEN GALA)
1641	ISLES OF YOUTH, THE
1784	HIGHLAND CASTLES
1785	GREEN'S PLAYHOUSE BALLROOM
1815	DUNBAR - THE A1 RESORT
1861	SHOTTS FARMERS' ANNUAL BALL 1951
1874	[FILM OF MONIAIVE 1950-1955]
1876	NEW GALLOWAY GALA WEEK
1889	LOCH LOMOND AND THE TROSSACHS
1921	WEST PILTON GALA DAY 1952
1923	CHILDREN'S GALA DAY 6TH JUNE 1954
1929	[CUMNOCK CLEBRATION, JUNE 1951]
1933	DUNDEE POLICE SPORTS
2002	COUNTRY OF THE BLIND
2007	KING AND THE WHISKY, THE
2026	QUEST, THE (GIRLS' GUILDRY)
2027	DIAMOND JUBILEE BRISBANE QUEEN, LARGS
2099	(JOSEPH HISLOP COLLECTION)

2129	OUR HIGHLAND HERITAGE
2142	GLASGOW AND DISTRICT CO-OPERATIVE ASSOCIATION
2143	ABERFELDY AGRICULTURAL SHOW 1952
2148	SCOTTISH SKI CLUB DINNER
2177	(CAPE TO CAIRO-NATIVE LIFE)
2206	EDINBURGH TATTOO, THE
2210	GEORGE IV'S EDINBURGH
2224	SCOTLAND DANCES
2225	SILVER CITY, THE
2228	PLAN FOR LIVING, A
2231	SMITHS IN SCOTLAND, THE
2241	HEALTH OF A CITY
2289	(TAYPORT PARISH CHURCH SALES OF WORK)
2291	CORONATION DAY, TAYPORT, 12TH MAY 1937
2348	[IONA CLUB]
2397	(PEACE DEMONSTRATION, CLYDEBANK)
2398	FITNESS FOR WOMEN
2425	(VISIT TO SOVIET UNION)
2426	[LITHUANIA 1960]
2461	BUDAPEST LA REINE DU DANUBE
2498	[UNICA, GLASGOW 1951]
2541	(HONOLULU AND CHARLIE CHAPLIN)
2546	(DORNOCH HOLIDAY)
2547	(COWAL GAMES, DUNOON 1933)
2549	(CRUISE ON "IBERIA", I)
2551	(CRUISE ON "IBERIA", III)
2564	(CRUISE ON SS "PERTH")
2605	(HOLIDAY SCOTLAND)
2612	BRIGADE PARADE 1948
2613	ROYAL SALUTE
2619	(BALMANNO HOUSE NEW YEAR'S DAY)
2631	HOLIDAY SCOTLAND
2639	BRAEMAR GATHERING
2649	GANG SHOW, THE
2658	KEITH SHOW 1948
2676	OLD TIME MOVIES
2698	HIGHLAND HOLIDAY
2719	SCHOOL IN THE TROSSACHS
2735	(HERD'S CAFE AND FAMILY FARM)
2737	GATHERING OF THE BRAEMAR ROYAL HIGHLAND SOCIETY, THE
2783	[HADDO ESTATE OPERATIONS 1966-'67]
2795	STORY OF TORMORE, THE
2805	PLEASURE ISLAND
2861	NIGHT AT THE HAP, A
2862	HAP DANCES, THE
2869	[COWAL HIGHLAND GATHERING]
2871-2873	[DON SAWKINS COLLECTION]

DEAFNESS
See HANDICAP
DEATH
See also WAR MEMORIALS

0119	DAY OF REMEMBRANCE MEMORIAL AT THE GLASGOW CENOTAPH
0188	ROYAL OCCASIONS OF SCOTLAND
0249	(MILITARY PARADE IN ABERDEEN)
0319	UNVEILING CEREMONY OF THE CAMERONIANS "SCOTTISH RIFLES"
0364	PERTHSHIRE PANORAMA

303

0497	DUMFRIES - A MARKET TOWN
0529c	(DAMAGED HOTEL)
0569	SALTCOATS FLOODED
0591	LOOKING BACK
0864	(R101 AIRSHIP)
1061	DUNDEE
1108	INCIDENT AT LONGNIDDRY
1238A	SCOTTISH MOVING PICTURE NEWS NO. 32
1353	FIRES IN TENEMENT BUILDINGS
1607	THEATRE FIRE IN EDINBURGH
1633	DESTRUCTION BY FIRE OF THE TOWN HALL, ELGIN
1699	SCOTTISH NATIONAL EXHIBITION
1721	LET GLASGOW FLOURISH
1733	GREAT GLASGOW FIRES
1738	[FIRE AT PAPER MILL, LINWOOD]
1797	MOVIES GREATEST HEADLINES
1855	REVIEW OF THE YEAR 1950
2066	ACTION FOR DISASTER
2085	FIRE AT ROTHESAY PIER
2110	(VIOLET ANDERSON FILM)
2205	COUNTY ON THE MOVE
2363	FLOOD IN DUMFRIES
2456	QUESTION OF BALANCE, A
2519	(GLASGOW FLOODS 1936)
2608	FIRE AT DUNGAVEL TRAINING CENTRE
2680	DAY IN THE LIFE OF DUMFRIES ACADEMY, A
2780	[HADDO ESTATE OPERATIONS 1955]
2855	TAY BRIDGE DISASTER

DISEASE

0346	(SEA OF GALILEE MISSION HOSPITAL, TIBERIAS)
0347	(SEA OF GALILEE MISSION HOSPITAL, TIBERIAS)
0917	GLASGOW - MASS ASSAULT ON TB
1075	PREVENTION IS BETTER
1349	CHILD WELFARE
1449	PERSONAL EPISODE
1537	IN THE CLEAR
1631	THIS LITTLE WORLD
1965	[SCOTTISH MISSION HOSPITAL, TIBERIAS]
2816	(RANGOON HOSPITAL AND SCENES FROM THE EAST)

DISTILLED LIQUORS

See also ALCOHOL/ PUBLIC HOUSES

0190	YOUR GLASS OF SHERRY
0281	NORTH EAST CORNER
0296	SCOTLAND AND THE NEW WORLD
0303	FUTURE OF SCOTLAND
0367	BANK AHEAD
0504	TAY VALLEY
0785	HEART IS HIGHLAND, THE
0814	QUEEN LAUDS SCOTTISH EXHIBITION, GLASGOW
1062	WEALTH OF A NATION
1497	[GLASGOW'S PROGRESS]
1573	PROUD SPIRIT, THE
1630	BELL'S TRAILER
1653	EDINBURGH
1901	WEE DRAM, A
1902	TIME WAS THE BEGINNING
1903c	ACCIDENTALLY YOURS
1932	SOVEREIGN "SCOTCH", THE

2007	KING AND THE WHISKY, THE
2009	LIFE IN THE ORKNEYS
2012	"PROJECT EAST MAINS"
2046	MAGIC KEY, THE
2056	(ABBOT'S WHISKY COMMERCIAL)
2088	FAIR COUNTY OF AYR
2201	DRAM LIKE THIS, A
2213	HIGHLAND CAPITAL
2231	SMITHS IN SCOTLAND, THE
2251	WATER OF LIFE, THE
2253	WATER, WATER EVERYWHERE
2254	ERSKINE BRIDGE, THE
2256	SONG FOR PRINCE CHARLIE, A
2257	TAYSIDE
2427	[WICK SCENES]
2498	[UNICA, GLASGOW 1951]
2638	TALES FROM THE NORTH
2795	STORY OF TORMORE, THE

DOCKS

0020	JAMES WATT
0048	PORT OF GLASGOW
0056	TRAM ROUTES IN GLASGOW AND STEAM RAILWAYS
0108	GRAND UNION CANAL
0114	WAVERLEY STEPS
0146	CEYLON CALLING
0162	VIEWS OF THE CLYDE AND AROUND
0163	EAST OF SUEZ
0182	EDINBURGH
0251	INTRODUCING SCOTLAND
0255A	CAMPING WE WILL GO, A
0284	CRAIGMOUNT SCHOOL FILMS
0296	SCOTLAND AND THE NEW WORLD
0377	RIVER CLYDE - A SURVEY OF SCOTLAND'S GREATEST RIVER
0380	[SHOTS OF EDINBURGH]
0395	SCOTTISH SHIPBUILDING
0398	RIVER CLYDE, THE
0417	MEN AND WOMEN OF TOMORROW
0418	ST. KILDA - BRITAIN'S LONELIEST ISLE
0441	KING, GOD BLESS HIM, THE
0456	FIGHTING FIELDS
0460	SONG OF THE CLYDE
0463	GATEWAY OF THE EAST, THE
0467	PORT OF LEITH
0474	GATEWAY OF THE WEST, THE
0480	DUNDEE
0501	ROUTES AND CENTRES
0504	TAY VALLEY
0506	ABERDEEN AND ITS INDUSTRIES
0508	SCOTTISH TRADE MISSION TO CANADA
0526	OUR CITY - TODAY AND TOMORROW
0580	RIVER CLYDE
0587	CENTRAL SCOTLAND
0608	ACHIEVEMENT
0619	BEYOND THE SUNSET
0662	TEXTILES
0669	(SCENES IN THE MIDDLE EAST)
0673	SCOTLAND WELCOMES THEIR MAJESTIES

DOGS

DOMESTIC ARTS and SCIENCES

EDUCATION (gen.)

See also COLLEGES/ SCHOOLS/ UNIVERSITIES

ELECTIONS

ELECTRICITY (apparatus & equipment)

0502	RAW MATERIALS
0956	(DUMFRIES CINEMA ADVERTS)
1068	SOME EVENTS IN GLASGOW 1937
1114	IN THE SHADOW
1122	CAPRICCIO
1604	[DUNDEE COURIER 1911]
2046	MAGIC KEY, THE
2294	(TAYPORT EVENTS 1946-'49)
2735	(HERD'S CAFE AND FAMILY FARM)
2790	CRUACHAN

ELECTRONICS

0296	SCOTLAND AND THE NEW WORLD
0307	NEW DAY
0366	STEP AHEAD, A
0975	GLENROTHES
1523	HOME AND AWAY NO. 13
1768	JOB FOR THE FUTURE, A
2253	WATER, WATER EVERYWHERE
2754	PRIME TIME: MEDIA WEEK IN STENHOUSEMUIR PRIMARY SCHOOL

EMIGRATION and IMMIGRATION

0038	FRASERS' RETURN
0303	FUTURE OF SCOTLAND
0800	[CAITHNESS, ORKNEY, KIRKWALL]
0801	[CAITHNESS, ORKNEY]
0802	WILL YE NO' COME BACK AGAIN
0806	SO MANY PARTINGS
1694	INDUSTRIAL CLYDESDALE
2497	[HIGHLAND CROFTERS' FAREWELL]

EMPLOYMENT and EMPLOYEES

See also LABOUR ECONOMICS/ UNEMPLOYMENT

0025	(HISTORY OF THE TAILOR AND GARMENT WORKERS UNION)
0034	FACE OF SCOTLAND
0040	NEW LEASE OF LIFE
0114	WAVERLEY STEPS
0298	THIS IS YOUR LIFE
0317	OUR HOMES
0373	THINGS THAT HAPPEN NO. 1
0387	BIG MILL, THE
0395	SCOTTISH SHIPBUILDING
0428	LAND O' BURNS BAKERIES
0473	SERMON IN STONE, A
0492	STAN AND OLLIE
0535	BISCUIT MAKING IN 1928
0605	LESSONS THROUGH THE LETTERBOX
0606	COUNTER COURTESY
0722	BILLY GRAHAM IN GLASGOW
0756	PIONEERS THEN AND NOW
0774	(CONSTRUCTION OF THE RITZ CINEMA, EDINBURGH 1929)
0797	COASTS OF CLYDE, THE
0800	[CAITHNESS, ORKNEY, KIRKWALL]
0801	[CAITHNESS, ORKNEY]
0835	RAILWAY JOURNEY
0837	ENOUGH TO EAT? - THE NUTRITION FILM
0889	IMMORTAL MEMORY OF ROBERT BURNS
0913	WHAT ABOUT THE WORKERS
0917	GLASGOW - MASS ASSAULT ON TB

0957	MINISTRY OF INFORMATION TRAILERS
0970	(EAST NEUK OF FIFE STEAM RAILWAY)
1017	[STAFF RECRUITMENT FILM]
1062	WEALTH OF A NATION
1351	COUNTY CLERK
1522	HOME AND AWAY NO. 12
1570	[RUSSELL'S LIBRARY FOOTAGE]
1691	GREENOCK PLANS AHEAD
1863	SCHOOL WITHOUT WALLS
1903	ACCIDENTALLY YOURS
1979	VITAL STATISTICS
2025	GATEWAY TO SECURITY
2046	MAGIC KEY, THE
2106	GLASGOW JUNIOR INSTRUCTION CENTRE, A
2157	[DENNY CLOSURE]
2223	BORDERS, THE
2257	TAYSIDE
2260	LINE TO SKYE, THE
2347	ALF GOES TO WORK
2373	[DUNDEE'S SCREEN SNAPSHOTS] SERIES
2485	[WORKERS TOPICAL NEWS NO. 11]
2546	(DORNOCH HOLIDAY)
2547	(COWAL GAMES, DUNOON 1933)
2552	(CRUISE ON "IBERIA", IV)
2554	(CRUISE TO SOUTH AMERICA, II)
2556	(CRUISE TO CANADA, I)
2559	(HONEYMAN FAMILY HOME)
2576	HOLIDAYS 1933
2577A	FAMILY FILMS 1931-1938
2601	DIVIDED WE STAND
2604	(REPORT ON NORTH AYRSHIRE TOWNS)
2707	KNIFE GRINDER AT FERNIEHURST/ GALA HOTSPURS GAME
2735	(HERD'S CAFE AND FAMILY FARM)
2768	(GEORGE MAY FAMILY FILM)
2780-2783	[HADDO ESTATE OPERATIONS]
2786	(QUEEN MOTHER'S VISIT TO HADDO)
2826	(MONTGOMERY FAMILY - NEW HOUSE)
2829	[CLAY PIGEON SHOOTING]
2830	[PENNIWELLS AND ST. ANDREWS]

ENGINEERING

0020	JAMES 2WATT
0029	HARNESSING THE HILLS
0034	FACE OF SCOTLAND
0072	VISIT TO MAVOR AND COULSON, A
0154	STEEL AND ENGINEERING
0182	EDINBURGH
0251	INTRODUCING SCOTLAND
0297	NEW MINE, THE
0303	FUTURE OF SCOTLAND
0305	[GASKIN REPORT, THE]
0395	SCOTTISH SHIPBUILDING
0481	DOWN TO THE SEA
0487	AN EYE TO THE FUTURE
0500	HEAVY INDUSTRIES
0505	COUNTY OF DUNBARTON
0506	ABERDEEN AND ITS INDUSTRIES
0580	RIVER CLYDE
0587	CENTRAL SCOTLAND

ENGLAND

ENTERTAINERS and ENTERTAINMENT

1138	[ALADDIN 1938]
1139	[KING AND] QUEEN OF HEARTS 1945
1140	(VARIOUS ARTISTS C1948)
1141	[KING AND QUEEN OF HEARTS]
1142	[RED RIDING HOOD 1943]
1143	(PANTOMIME AND CHRISTMAS PARTY)
1144	[HALF PAST EIGHT SHOW 1945 AND ROBINSON CRUSOE 1944]
1145	[SLEEPING BEAUTY 1940, THE]
1146	BABES IN THE WOOD
1147	[HUMPTY DUMPTY]
1148	[HARRY GORDON VISITS NEW YORK AND PANTOMIMES]
1149	DICK WHITTINGTON (1941)
1150	[PANTOMIME, SHOW PICNIC, AND VARIETY]
1151	[BEACH PAVILION, ABERDEEN AND FAMILY C1926]
1152	[BEACH PAVILION, ABERDEEN AND VARIETY C1925]
1222	PRESBYTERIAN TOUR OF CANADA
1287	GLASGOW CINEMA CLUB, 50TH ANNIVERSARY
1314	(SUMMER SEASON IN DUNOON)
1368	PENICUIK CHILDREN'S GALA DAY 1953
1486	EDINBURGH FESTIVAL - PATHE
1493	FESTIVAL IN EDINBURGH
1494	HOLIDAYS AT HOME 1942 - '44
1682	NURSERY SCHOOLDAYS
1853	DIXINE NEWS
2089	("QUIET WEDDING" TRAILER NO. 1)
2090	("QUIET WEDDING" TRAILER NO. 2)
2178	FORTY THIEVES PANTOMIME, THE
2179	SNATCHES FROM THE FORTY THIEVES PANTOMIME
2180	SINBAD THE SAILOR/ BABES IN THE WOOD
2181	QUEEN OF HEARTS PANTOMIME, THE
2325	[HALFWAY TO PARADISE: AL JOLSON]
2330	[HALFWAY TO PARADISE: CHIC MURRAY]
2373	[DUNDEE'S SCREEN SNAPSHOTS] SERIES
2402	[HALFWAY TO PARADISE: VENTRILOQUIST]
2403	[HALFWAY TO PARADISE: TARTAN]
2484	(PAUL ROBESON AT GLASGOW MAY DAY)
2555	(PANTOMIME 1937)
2569	(PLEASANCE TRUST BOYS' CLUB 1955 - 1962)
2649	GANG SHOW, THE
2805	PLEASURE ISLAND
2846	(PRENTICE WARTIME FILM)
2852	[GLASGOW TAXI DRIVERS OUTING]
2871	HOLIDAY DUNOON
2872	[DUNOON OCCASIONS]

EQUESTRIAN SPORTS

0169	DUMFRIES 1933 - GUID NYCHBURRIS DAY
0170	DUMFRIES GUID NYCHBURRIS DAY
0324	MONEY TO BURN
0364	PERTHSHIRE PANORAMA
0426	[YEAR OF DESTINY]
0441	KING, GOD BLESS HIM, THE
0576	(SCOTTISH GRAND NATIONAL)
0772	(STEAM LOCOMOTIVES AND SCENES AT LANARK RACECOURSE)
0775	(LANARK RACECOURSE AND RENFREWSHIRE HUNT)
0784	("EMPRESS OF BRITAIN")
0786	(RACE MEETING)
0789	(BIRDS AND HORSE JUMPING)

0792	[BORDERS LOCAL NEWSREELS NO. 2]
0819	ROYAL VISIT TO SCOTLAND
0827	(INVERNESS COMPILATION)
0829	BIRTHDAY GREETINGS TO QUEEN MARY
0831	(RACING)
0863A	(FRED ARCHER)
1109	1959 SCOTTISH INDUSTRIES EXHIBITION, THE
1134	[ROBINSON CRUSOE]
1140	(VARIOUS ARTISTS C1948)
1152	[BEACH PAVILION, ABERDEEN AND VARIETY C1925]
1321	AYR
1323	STEAM LOCOMOTIVES IN SCOTLAND
1401	(HONEST LAD AND LASS 1939)
1441	[KEITH SHOW, 14TH AUGUST, 1951]
1644	HAWICK COMMON RIDING
1764	LOTHIANS PART I, THE
1796	GB NEWS REVIEW 1948
1815	DUNBAR - THE A1 RESORT
1855	REVIEW OF THE YEAR 1950
1957	LANARK
2123	(FFORDE COLLECTION)
2189	[SCENES AROUND HALFWAY AND DISTRICT]
2237	ONE DAY IN IRVINE
2294	(TAYPORT EVENTS 1946-'49)
2307	IN SEARCH OF TAYPORT
2495	[DUMFRIES GUID NYCHBURRIS DAY 1947]
2548	(ST. MORITZ 1932)
2558	KEITH SHOW 1948
2792	AYR FROM THE AULD BRIG
2872	[DUNOON OCCASIONS]

EUROPE

See also EASTERN EUROPE

0035	SCOTTISH WOMEN'S HOSPITALS
0036	ATROCITIES, THE
0047	(GERMAN TRAINING FILM)
0060	NEWS PARADE 1939
0095	TISCHLEIN DECK DICH
0131	CROSSING NORTHERN LATITUDES
0133	MAJORCAN MEDLEY
0148	SARDINIA
0149	ITALIAN INTERLUDE
0151	SWITZERLAND 1947
0190	YOUR GLASS OF SHERRY
0284	CRAIGMOUNT SCHOOL FILMS
0333	DIABOLICAL LIBERTY, A
0354	(CONTINENTAL HOLIDAYS)
0360	HOMEWARD BOUND 1939
0392	LIFE ON THE FAROE ISLANDS
0462	NEWS SPOTLIGHT
0467	PORT OF LEITH
0539A	RED CROSS WORK AT SALONIKA
0540	[CHALLENGE TO FASCISM]
0559	PATHE REVIEW OF THE YEAR
0633	STORY OF ALFRED NOBLE, THE
0645	FROM TUNGSTEN ORE TO LUNA FILAMENT
0713	REVIEW OF THE YEAR 1940
0718	(HOLIDAY FILM)
0792	[BORDERS LOCAL NEWSREELS NO. 2]

FAIRS and FAIRGROUNDS

FANCY DRESS

See COSTUME

FARMYARDS and FARM BUILDINGS

0053	GOVAN FAIR 1952
0087-0089	LANARK LANIMER DAY
0168-0173	DUMFRIES GUID NYCHBURRIS DAY
0175-0176	DUMFRIES GUID NYCHBURRIS CELEBRATIONS
0178-0181	DUMFRIES GUID NYCHBURRIS DAY
0182	EDINBURGH
0195B	GUID NYCHBURRIS DAY
0296	SCOTLAND AND THE NEW WORLD
0303	FUTURE OF SCOTLAND
0325	(DUMFRIES)
0336-0344	BO'NESS CHILDREN'S FAIR FESTIVAL
0380	[SHOTS OF EDINBURGH]
0400-0414	[BO'NESS CHILDREN'S FAIR FESTIVALS]
0444	RIVALLING THE RAINBOW
0454B	(DUMFRIES - GUID NYCHBURRIS DAY)
0459	EDINBURGH FESTIVAL, THE
0466	(KING VIDOR AT EDINBURGH FILM FESTIVAL)
0469	(OPENING OF INDUSTRIAL POWER EXHIBITION)
0493	QUEEN OF THE BORDER
0522	SAY IT WITH FLOWERS
0527	JOHN NEWLAND'S DAY, 1950, BATHGATE
0542	[LANGHOLM COMMON RIDING]
0625	WISHAW CO-OP GALA DAY
0644	SALTCOATS QUATER CENTENARY CELEBRATIONS
0704	HANDBA' AT KIRKWALL, ORKNEY
0760	GALASHIELS HISTORICAL PEACE PAGEANT
0761	[CHILDREN'S PROCESSION GALASHIELS]
0764	CROSSING THE TWEED
0765	PICTURESQUE SCENES - 4TH ANNUAL BRAW LADS GATHERING
0766	GALASHIELS AND BRAW LADS GATHERING
0767	BRAW LADS GATHERING
0770	[PEACE DAY CELEBRATION, KILMARNOCK 1919]
0791-0792	[BORDERS LOCAL NEWSREELS]
0810A/B	[TAIN CARNIVAL]
0813	KIRKCALDY HOSPITAL PAGEANT
0822	(OTTER HUNTING AND PROCESSION)
0823	(FAIR FESTIVAL)
0825	[TAIN CARNIVAL AND ELGIN GALA WEEK]
0834	[EUROPEAN COD FESTIVAL, GOUROCK]
0878	(GUID NYCHBURRIS CELEBRATIONS)
0879	(KIRKCALDY PAGEANT WEEK 1951)
0880	GLENROTHES FESTIVAL WEEK
0882	RIVER TWEED
0883-0884	[TAIN CARNIVAL]
0942	(BARRHEAD FESTIVAL AND OLD FOLKS' OUTING)
0943	(JOURNEY THROUGH BARRHEAD AND REVIEW OF THE FESTIVAL YEAR 1951)
0951	STONEHOUSE NEW TOWN FESTIVAL
0953	STONEHOUSE TRIMS
0960-0962	LOCHGELLY CHILDREN'S GALA DAY
0965	CHILDREN'S GALA AT LOCHGELLY
0967	LOCHGELLY AT WORK AND PLAY
0976	(NATIONAL MOD TRIMS)
0981	CROFTER'S LIFE IN SHETLAND, A
1131	PROCESSION AND CROWNING OF THE QUEEN OF THE BONNIE LASSIES
1234	DALMELLINGTON FANCY DRESS PARADE
1239	MARYMASS PARADE, IRVINE

1244	(COASTAL SCENES)
1245	NEWMILNS CIVIC WEEK
1281	[FERRY FAIR]
1282	WINCHBURGH CHILDREN'S GALA DAY
1283	STEWARTFIELD GALA DAY, BROXBURN
1284	UPHALL CHILDREN'S GALA ETC
1288A	WICK SHOPPING WEEK - PRIMARY SCHOOL SPORTS
1290	(ARRAN FARMERS SOCIETY ANNUAL FAIR 1951)
1291	BROXBURN GALA DAY AND CROWNING OF QUEEN
1294	UPHALL STATION CHILDREN'S GALA
1295	FERRY FAIR 1955
1296	KIRKLISTON CHILDREN'S GALA AND CROWNING OF QUEEN
1297	FERRY FAIR OF 1954
1298	GALA DAY AND CROWNING CEREMONY AT BROXBURN
1300	BROXBURN AND DISTRICT CHILDREN'S GALA DAY AND CROWNING CEREMONY
1301	(UNIDENTIFIED GALA AND SPORTS DAY, BROXBURN AREA NO. 1)
1303	(BROXBURN GALA DAY 1953)
1309	UP HELLY AA FESTIVAL 1949
1316	[BO'NESS FAIR 1912]
1319-1320	[PAGEANT OF AYR]
1343	HISTORIC EDINBURGH
1357-1358	SALTCOATS QUEEN OF THE SEAS
1360	DUNFERMLINE CHILDREN'S GALA 1932
1362-1367	DUNFERMLINE CHILDREN'S GALA
1368	PENICUIK CHILDREN'S GALA DAY 1953
1372	NEWMILLS, TORRYBURN AND CROMBIE GALA
1373	HUNTLY GALA DAY
1375	PERTH HISTORICAL PAGEANT
1377	INVERKEITHING LAMMAS FAIR AND GAMES 1951
1401-1403	(HONEST LAD AND LASS)
1404	(FISHERMAN'S WALK 1933)
1441	[KEITH SHOW, 14TH AUGUST, 1951]
1459	JEDBURGH HANDBA'
1466-1467	ELGIN CHARCITY DAY
1468	ELGIN GALA WEEK 1950
1471-1472	(ELGIN GALA DAY)
1474	[INVERNESS FESTIVAL YEAR 1951]
1476	[PEEBLES BELTANE FESTIVALS 1920/'22]
1477	PEEBLES MARCH RIDING AND BELTANE FESTIVAL 1949
1483	EDINBURGH FESTIVAL OPENING CEREMONY
1486	EDINBURGH FESTIVAL - PATHE
1487	EDINBURGH
1491	ROYAL JUBILEE CELEBRATIONS
1493	FESTIVAL IN EDINBURGH
1510	[CROWNING OF QUEEN OF THE BONNIE LASSIES, AYR]
1545	QUEEN'S OWN CAMERON HIGHLANDERS 50TH ANNIVERSARY
1547-1548	CROWNING OF THE DARVEL LACE QUEEN
1555	INVERNESS GALA QUEEN 1950
1562	DALKEITH GALAS 1926, 1933/ LAUREL AND HARDY VISIT EDINBURGH
1584-1587	SINGER SPORTS GALA
1588	(CLYDEBANK, ARMISTICE DAY AND SINGER GALA)
1589	CLYDEBANK BURGH JUBILEE 1936
1606	(DALYELL FAMILY FILM)
1616	[SHETLAND - A FEW ASPECTS]
1634	(MIDSUMMER QUEEN GALA)
1644	HAWICK COMMON RIDING

1645	CORONATION PAGEANT PARADE AND CROWNING OF PAISLEY'S THREAD QUEEN
1646	DUNFERMLINE CHILDREN'S GALA 1952
1647	BO'NESS CHILDREN'S FAIR FESTIVAL 1957
1648	KIRKCALDY YOUTH PAGEANT 1952
1697	[ARBROATH HISTORICAL PAGEANT 1947]
1717	LANIMER DAY, LANARK 1968
1755-1757	BROXBURN CHILDREN'S GALA
1799	PRINCESS STREET CHURCH [PORT GLASGOW]
1854	(PROVOST FLETT COLLECTION)
1873	THORNHILL SHOW
1876	NEW GALLOWAY GALA WEEK
1920-1925	CHILDREN'S DAY [WEST PILTON]
1929	[CUMNOCK CELEBRATION, JUNE 1951]
1948	JOHN NEWLAND'S DAY, BATHGATE
1952	BATHGATE FESTIVAL WEEK 1951
1957	LANARK
1966	HUNTLY GALA QUEEN
1967	SHOTTS FESTIVAL 1951
2011	EPSTEIN IN EDINBURGH
2022	SCOTTISH MINERS GALA DAY
2102	MUNGO'S MEDALS
2105	HEIL OSTERREICH
2108	JUNGLE JINKS, ETC.
2184	[ISLE OF BUTE CARNIVAL]
2196	[RIDING OF THE MARCHES, ANNAN]
2206	EDINBURGH TATTOO, THE
2218	LEATHERNECK AMBASSADORS
2237	ONE DAY IN IRVINE
2247	ST. ANDREWS BY THE NORTHERN SEA
2315	[MELROSE FESTIVALS 1956-'61]
2335	ROTHESAY FANCY DRESS PARADE
2338	(ROTHESAY 1918)
2374-2377	ANNAN RIDING OF THE MARCHES
2395	CHURCH ACTIVITIES, ST. MARTIN'S, EDINBURGH
2495	[DUMFRIES GUID NYCHBURRIS DAY 1947]
2628	BORDER FESTIVALS OF 1956
2652	CROWNING OF PORTSOY GALA QUEEN
2655	PORTSOY ARMISTICE PARADE/ CULLEN GALA
2657	[FANCY DRESS PARADE, BUCKIE]
2661	CROWNING OF PORTSOY'S GALA QUEEN 1948
2662	ABERCHIRDER AND PORTSOY FANCY DRESS
2708	PEEBLES BELTANE QUEEN GAMES
2712	ST. RONAN'S GAMES
2729	(J.H. JOHNSON COLLECTION)
2793	EDINBURGH ON PARADE
2798	HAWICK COMMON RIDING
2835-2837	LANARK LANIMER DAYS 1946-1949/1952
2840	FAMILY SCRAPBOOK NO. 2
2844	VARIOUS PARADES 1940-1945
2872	[DUNOON OCCASIONS]

FETES and GARDEN PARTIES

0517A	BIGGAR AND DISTRICT JUNIOR IMPERIALIST UNION FETE
0788	(MARQUIS OF BUTE/ BUTE MOUNT STEWART)
0808	GORDONSTOUN SCHOOL GARDEN FETE
0823	(FAIR FESTIVAL)
1442	PLUSCARDEN PRIORY RESTORATION FETE
1728	UNVEILING OF KIRKCALDY WAR MEMORIAL
1777	NEILSTON REEL/ CATTLE SHOWS

1840	LOOK AROUND NORTH LANARK, SEVENTH DISTRICT
1854	(PROVOST FLETT COLLECTION)
1926	LOCAL COLOUR
2289	(TAYPORT PARISH CHURCH SALES OF WORK)
2683	(DUFFTOWN SCENES)
2801	(SCENES OF ORKNEY)
2841	FAMILY SCRAPBOOK NO. 3
2844	VARIOUS PARADES 1940-1945
2845	VARIOUS PARADES 1943-1945
2872	[DUNOON OCCASIONS]

FICTION

See also SCIENCE FICTION

0374	HAIR
0486	GLEN IS OURS, THE
0509	FICKLE FORTUNE
0528	ALL ON A SUMMER'S DAY
0812	MOWER MADNESS
0991	RUGGED ISLAND
1110	PETROL
1111	ROBOT THREE
1115	CAT, THE
1116	FERRY FLIRT
1117	CAMEO
1118	SCHERZO
1119	PLUGGERS' PICNIC
1123	BOTTLE, THE
1124	RIC HAS A BATH
1126	INCUBO
1155	PORPHYRIA
1156	BONGO BUBBLE
1159	AD INFERNUM BUDDY?
1160	SILVER TRUMPET, THE
1162	LIVING GHOST, THE
1170	FANTASMAGORIA
1171	SMART BOY WANTED
1172	WHITE LADY, THE
1173	CHICK'S DAY
1175	CAPPELLA OF ENCHANTMENT, THE
1176	TWILIGHT
1181	BEFORE TIME GAME
1182	NINE O'CLOCK
1183	CORKY
1226	FISHERMAN AND THE DJINN, THE
1331	MAIRI: THE ROMANCE OF A HIGHLAND MAIDEN
1658	WEEKEND QUARTET
1663	LITTLE GREATHEART
1702	ENCHANTED GLADE, THE
1859	RING, THE
1949	FOURTH IN HAND
2116	HAPPY THE MAN
2140	(GSA KINECRAFT SOCIETY)
2144	AULD TAM MCGUIRE
2229	DUNA BULL, THE
2365	PERCHANCE TO SAIL
2582	HOST, THE
2670	TABLE D/HOLT
2700	20 SECONDS TO ZERO
2701	LOCH NESS MONSTER MOVIE, THE

2832	[TOWN COUNCIL ELECTION DAY]

FINANCE and FINANCIAL SERVICES

See also TAXATION

0324	MONEY TO BURN
0333	DIABOLICAL LIBERTY, A
0334	RARE TEAR, A
0366	STEP AHEAD, A
0367	BANK AHEAD
0399	PROSPEROUS PATH
0915	GLASGOW
0957	MINISTRY OF INFORMATION TRAILERS
0974	GLASGOW 1980
1096	WAY THE MONEY GOES, THE
1378	SCHOOL BANK, GLASGOW
1438	[NATIONAL SAVINGS TRAILER]
1571	PARTNERS IN PROGRESS
1653	EDINBURGH
1706	DUNDEE WAR WEAPONS WEEK
1770	[WARTIME TRAILERS]
1868	BANK FOR SCOTLAND
1869	BUSINESSWISE
1870	MONEYWISE
1905	PORTRAIT OF THE ROYAL BANK
1906	ALL TO YOUR CREDIT
1950	QUEEN ELIZABETH'S VISIT TO POSB
2017	[NATIONAL COMMERCIAL BANK]
2025	GATEWAY TO SECURITY
2202	BY LOCHABER I WILL GO
2286	GOING TO MARKET
2313	BRIGHT FUTURE

FIRE SERVICE

0156	CIVIL DEFENCE IN GLASGOW
0166	THIS FILM IS DANGEROUS
0521	STIRLING CHARITIES DAY
0561E	EXCLUSIVE TO LA SCALA...FUNERAL OF FIREMASTER ALEX GIRDWOOD
0591	LOOKING BACK
0605	LESSONS THROUGH THE LETTERBOX
0673	SCOTLAND WELCOMES THEIR MAJESTIES
0769	[KILMARNOCK]
0792	[BORDERS LOCAL NEWSREELS NO. 2]
0833	MISS VIOLET HOPSON VISITS DUNDEE FIRE STATION
0937	DUMFRIES, QUEEN OF THE SOUTH
1071	INSPECTION OF PAISLEY FIRE BRIGADE BY PROVOST AND COUNCILLORS
1082	FIRE FIGHTING
1282	WINCHBURGH CHILDREN'S GALA DAY
1315	ST. ANDREWS 1916
1351	COUNTY CLERK
1353	FIRES IN TENEMENT BUILDINGS
1386	TENEMENT WARDEN
1464	(ARP DISPLAY)
1494	HOLIDAYS AT HOME 1942-'44
1607	THEATRE FIRE IN EDINBURGH
1633	DESTRUCTION BY FIRE OF THE TOWN HALL, ELGIN
1699	SCOTTISH NATIONAL EXHIBITION
1733	GREAT GLASGOW FIRES
1736	[WESTERN AREA FIRE STATIONS]

1737	WESTERN AREA FIRE BRIGADE (BARRHEAD)
1738	[FIRE AT PAPER MILL, LINWOOD]
1739	FIRE-FIRE-FIRE
1776	(REGAL CINEMA, DUNFERMLINE)
1997	FALKIRK
2085	FIRE AT ROTHESAY PIER
2110	(VIOLET ANDERSON FILM)
2608	FIRE AT DUNGAVEL TRAINING CENTRE
2758	EXTINGUISHERS
2830	[PENNIWELLS AND ST. ANDREWS]

FIREWORKS

0122	VICTORY PARADE
0239	ABERDEEN CELEBRATES THE CORONATION
1068	SOME EVENTS IN GLASGOW 1937
1245	NEWMILNS CIVIC WEEK
1373	HUNTLY GALA DAY
1491	ROYAL JUBILEE CELEBRATIONS
1516	[CORONATION DAY PARADE, INVERNESS]
1716	ST. LEONARD'S SCHOOL
1856	(DIXINE MISCELLANY)
1879	VILLAGE VARIETIES
1929	[CUMNOCK CELEBRATION, JUNE 1951]
2088	FAIR COUNTY OF AYR
2206	EDINBURGH TATTOO, THE
2291	CORONATION DAY, TAYPORT, 12TH MAY 1937
2869	[COWAL HIGHLAND GATHERING]
2871-2872	[DON SAWKINS COLLECTION]

FISH and FISHING

See also ANGLERS and ANGLING/ FISH GUTTING/ FISH MARKETS/ HERRING FISHING/ TRAWLERS

0027	SKYE
0028	WESTERN ISLES
0039	UPSTREAM
0112	CROFTER BOY
0136	HOLIDAYING IN HARRIS
0231	SCOTLAND FOR FITNESS
0251	INTRODUCING SCOTLAND
0256	EILEAN AN FHRAOICH [ISLE OF LEWIS]
0259	ARRIVAL OF THE MAIL STEAMER IN LERWICK
0274	HIGHLAND LADDIE
0276	SEINE NET
0279	POWER FOR THE HIGHLANDS
0281	NORTH EAST CORNER
0302	LAND O' CLANS
0303	FUTURE OF SCOTLAND
0305	[GASKIN REPORT, THE]
0307	NEW DAY
0364	PERTHSHIRE PANORAMA
0367	BANK AHEAD
0388	CALLER HERRIN
0418	ST. KILDA - BRITAIN'S LONELIEST ISLE
0431	CRUISE TO ST. KILDA AND THE WESTERN ISLES
0450	AROUND WICK HARBOUR
0452	[YARMOUTH FISH QUAY]
0453	SCOTS FISHER GIRLS AT YARMOUTH
0499	SCOTTISH COASTS
0503	BILLINGSGATE - THIS ART IS FISHY

323

F

FOOTBALL

325

GARDEN PARTIES

See FETES and GARDEN PARTIES

GAS

0301	LAND OF INVENTION
0391	[HAPPY IN THE MORNING]
0608	ACHIEVEMENT
0917	GLASGOW - MASS ASSAULT ON TB
1044	OBEDIENT FLAME, THE
1492	PSNS EXCURSION
1500	LAMPLIGHTER, THE
1527	HOME AND AWAY NO. 18
1732	SCOTTISH GAS BOARD, WESTFIELD WORKS
2775	(DUNDEE ARCHITECTURE)
2778	SEAS AROUND US, THE: GREAT BRITISH FOOD

GEOLOGY

0415	HONEYMOON CRUISE NO. 1
0508	SCOTTISH TRADE MISSION TO CANADA
0707	SCOTLAND
0745	(BIOLOGICAL EXPEDITION, RONA)
0748	SOUTH RONA EXPEDITION: THE DESCENT TO THE CAVE
0981	CROFTER'S LIFE IN SHETLAND, A
1542	(VISIT TO STAFFA)
1641	ISLES OF YOUTH, THE
2061	VOLCANOES
2069	LIVING SEDIMENTS

GIRL GUIDES

See YOUTH ORGANISATIONS

GLASGOW

0001	(GLASGOW TRAMS AND BOTANIC GARDENS)
0002	(TRAMS IN GLASGOW)
0005	PASSING OF THE TRAMCAR, THE
0008	GLASGOW UNIVERSITY CELEBRATES
0009	FIFTH CENTENARY OF THE UNIVERSITY OF GLASGOW
0012	GLASGOW'S YESTERDAYS
0015	STUDENTS' CHARITIES DAY GLASGOW
0019	GREAT WESTERN ROAD 1914
0022	MIDNIGHT MATINEE FOR THE REFUGEES
0030	IT BEGAN ON THE CLYDE
0031	ARP SCHOOLS
0044	GLASGOW AND THE CLYDE COAST
0045	EMPIRE EXHIBITION
0048	PORT OF GLASGOW
0051	QUEEN IN SCOTLAND, THE
0055	GLASGOW TRAMS, 21 MAY 1960
0056	TRAM ROUTES IN GLASGOW AND STEAM RAILWAYS
0057	OUR TRANSPORT SERVICES
0062	GLASGOW - OUR CITY
0065	EMPIRE EXHIBITION
0090	CHARLES RENNIE MACKINTOSH
0096	HER MAJESTY OPENS SCOTTISH INDUSTRIES EXHIBITION
0106	GLASGOW'S POLICE
0111	WORLD OF STEEL
0119	DAY OF REMEMBRANCE MEMORIAL AT THE GLASGOW CENOTAPH
0123	CITY SIDELIGHTS NO. 2
0126	(GLASGOW TRAMS - TRIMS)
0135	GLASGOW TAKES CARE OF ITS OLD FOLK

0141	CONSTRUCTION OF THE KING GEORGE V BRIDGE, GLASGOW
0142	ROYAL VISIT TO SCOTLAND
0156	CIVIL DEFENCE IN GLASGOW
0157	(ANTI-GAS PRECAUTIONS IN GLASGOW)
0158	CIVIL DEFENCE
0251	INTRODUCING SCOTLAND
0253	TAM TRAUCHLE'S TROUBLES
0258	VISIT OF HRH DUCHESS OF KENT TO WEST OF SCOTLAND
0268	PROGRESS REPORT
0282	CITY SIDELIGHTS - SECTIONS
0296	SCOTLAND AND THE NEW WORLD
0300	OUR PUBLIC PARKS
0303	FUTURE OF SCOTLAND
0315	HOW OUR CITY IS GOVERNED
0316	OUR SCHOOLS
0317	OUR HOMES
0328	CITY SIDELIGHTS NO. 3
0330	CITY SIDELIGHTS NO. 4
0377	RIVER CLYDE - A SURVEY OF SCOTLAND'S GREATEST RIVER
0379	CITY SIDELIGHTS NO. 1
0385	SCOTTISH UNIVERSITIES
0386	MONEY PROGRAMME, THE
0395	SCOTTISH SHIPBUILDING
0396	OUR WATER SUPPLY
0397	OUR ART GALLERIES
0398	RIVER CLYDE, THE
0420	KEEPING OUR CITY CLEAN
0421	GLASGOW SUBWAY
0460	SONG OF THE CLYDE
0463	GATEWAY OF THE EAST, THE
0469	(OPENING OF INDUSTRIAL POWER EXHIBITION)
0470	SCOTTISH INDUSTRIES EXHIBITION, GLASGOW
0471	RIGHT CHOICE, THE
0473	SERMON IN STONE, A
0474	GATEWAY OF THE WEST, THE
0478	YOUTH CENTRES
0479	PLAYS FOR THE PEOPLE
0516	(UNIVERSITY NEWS)
0519	(BAND CONCERT, KELVINGROVE PARK, 1928)
0522	SAY IT WITH FLOWERS
0526	OUR CITY - TODAY AND TOMORROW
0530	SCOTTISH SHALE INDUSTRY
0531	(GUILD OF AID WORK IN THE GORBALS)
0540	[CHALLENGE TO FASCISM]
0546	GLASGOW
0552	QUEEN MOTHER IN SCOTLAND, THE
0570	GREAT WESTERN ROAD 1922
0573	GREEN OF GLASGOW, THE
0580	RIVER CLYDE
0587	CENTRAL SCOTLAND
0590	(CHRISTMAS STREET DECORATIONS IN GLASGOW)
0591	LOOKING BACK
0608	ACHIEVEMENT
0617	TOMORROW IS YOURS
0634	(CWS CONGRESS IN GLASGOW)
0672	OUT OF THE BOX
0705	SADNESS AND GLADNESS
0712	[SAUCHIEHALL STREET ROOF TOPS]
0722	BILLY GRAHAM IN GLASGOW

329

GLASS and GLASS BLOWING

GOLF

GRAPHIC ART

See ART and ARTISTS

GYMNASTICS

GYPSIES, ROMANIES

HAIRDRESSING

See DOMESTIC ARTS and SCIENCES

HANDICAP, mental and physical

HARBOURS

0027	SKYE
0114	WAVERLEY STEPS
0136	HOLIDAYING IN HARRIS
0196	ROAD THROUGH THE SUNSET ISLES
0251	INTRODUCING SCOTLAND
0256	EILEAN AN FHRAOICH [ISLE OF LEWIS]
0259	ARRIVAL OF THE MAIL STEAMER IN LERWICK
0281	NORTH EAST CORNER
0295	SEA SCOUTS PART II
0302	LAND O' CLANS
0303	FUTURE OF SCOTLAND
0363	OVER THE SEA TO SKYE
0366	STEP AHEAD, A
0384	[ISLE OF BARRA]
0388	CALLER HERRIN
0415	HONEYMOON CRUISE NO. 1
0418	ST. KILDA - BRITAIN'S LONELIEST ISLE
0431	CRUISE TO ST. KILDA AND THE WESTERN ISLES
0450	AROUND WICK HARBOUR
0453	SCOTS FISHER GIRLS AT YARMOUTH
0481	DOWN TO THE SEA
0499	SCOTTISH COASTS
0506	ABERDEEN AND ITS INDUSTRIES
0512	STIRLING: GATEWAY TO THE HIGHLANDS
0545	ATLANTIC TRAWLER
0549	ISLE OF LEWIS
0550	STORNOWAY
0560	(ARDROSSAN SHIPYARD)
0563	COUNCIL'S ENTERPRISE
0586	DEE VALLEY
0619	BEYOND THE SUNSET
0631	NORTHERN SCOTLAND
0641	GLIMPSE OF THE LIFEBOAT SERVICE
0694	WELLS OF MONTROSE, THE
0704	HANDBA' AT KIRKWALL, ORKNEY
0747	(EXPEDITION TO RONA)
0773	NORTHERN OUTPOST
0785	HEART IS HIGHLAND, THE
0796	DUMFRIESSHIRE JOURNEY
0797	COASTS OF CLYDE, THE
0800	[CAITHNESS, ORKNEY, KIRKWALL]
0815	(GAUMONT SOUND MIRROR, 1927-1931)
0840A	PROVOST JOHN SINCLAIR SHOWS ORKNEY GUIDES AROUND THE HARBOUR AT THURSO
0882	RIVER TWEED
0885	FIFE
0914	SOUTHERN SCOTLAND
0916	PADDY'S MILESTONE
0931	AROUND INVERNESS
0934	CROFTING IN SKYE
0969	HOLIDAY IN THE HIGHLANDS
0981	CROFTER'S LIFE IN SHETLAND, A
0991	RUGGED ISLAND
1060	SEAFOOD
1078	SAGA OF THE SILVER HORDE
1080A	ABERDEEN AWA' AUGUST 1949
1096	WAY THE MONEY GOES, THE
1132	SOUTHERN SCOTLAND

1237	[SCENES OF LOCAL INTEREST]
1244	(COASTAL SCENES)
1265	LIFEBOAT COMING
1286	SHETLAND, PEOPLE OF MANY LANDS
1311	(BAXTER FAMILY FILMS)
1315	ST. ANDREWS 1916
1318	CLYDE RESORT: AN INTRODUCTION TO GIRVAN
1321	AYR
1328	BEAUTY SPOTS IN GREAT BRITAIN
1338	(FAMILY HOLIDAYS 1936/'38)
1342	(ROCKET RANGE, BENBECULA)
1371	ABERDEEN BY SEASIDE AND DEESIDE
1399	(SALMON FISHING AT BRORA)
1406	(TOBERMORY)
1430	WESTER ROSS
1431	ST. ANDREWS
1436	ORKNEY - SCENES AROUND SHAPINSAY
1443	LOSSIEMOUTH CORONATION TREE PLANTING
1501	BEYOND THE GRAMPIANS
1595	FISHING FLEET
1608	(LOCK GATES AT BOWLING)
1615	(SHETLAND SCENES)
1619	GANNETS AT LERWICK
1641	ISLES OF YOUTH, THE
1669	ST. ANDREWS
1704	(SCOTTISH WEDDING, A)
1705	HIGHLAND TOUR, CROOKSTON STREET SCHOOL
1707	DUCHESS OF YORK NAMES NEW LIFEBOAT
1720	[NAMING CEREMONY, THE "DUKE OF MONTROSE"]
1730	FINE FLOORS
1760	KIPPERS
1765	LOTHIANS PART II, THE
1780	OBAN
1815	DUNBAR - THE A1 RESORT
1853	DIXINE NEWS
1854	(PROVOST FLETT COLLECTION)
1928	TRIP TO SKYE, ORKNEY AND SHETLAND
1943	ENCHANTED ISLES
1993	(LAUNCH OF "BROUGHTY")
2000A	BENS, THE
2008	[LEITH DREDGER]
2009	LIFE IN THE ORKNEYS
2053	(OBAN, IONA, STAFFA AND HARRIS)
2188	RAINBOW TRAILS
2189	[SCENES AROUND HALFWAY AND DISTRICT]
2201	DRAM LIKE THIS, A
2202	BY LOCHABER I WILL GO
2212	HEBRIDEAN HIGHWAY
2221	QUEEN IN SCOTLAND, THE
2223	BORDERS, THE
2225	SILVER CITY, THE
2242	IN GREAT WATERS
2243	TAY ROAD BRIDGE
2257	TAYSIDE
2258	LOTHIAN LANDSCAPE
2259	PRIDE OF ISLANDS, A
2293	(WARTIME IN TAYPORT)
2307	IN SEARCH OF TAYPORT
2320	ABERDEEN

HEALTH

See PUBLIC HEALTH
See also DIET

HEBRIDEAN ISLANDS

See INNER HEBRIDES/ OUTER HEBRIDES

HELICOPTERS

HERRING and HERRING FISHING

HIGHLAND GAMES

HOUSES and HOUSING (gen.)

See also CONSTRUCTION/ DEMOLITION/ SLUMS/ TENEMENTS

HOUSES AND HOUSING (GEN.) (CONT.)

HOUSES AND HOUSING (GEN.) (CONT.)

HUNTING

ICE CREAM

See CONFECTIONERY

ICE SKATING

IMMIGRATION

See EMIGRATION

INDUSTRIAL ESTATES

338

INVENTIONS and INVENTORS

INVERNESS-SHIRE

341

343

"LOCH NESS MONSTER"

See LEGENDS and FOLKLORE

LOCHS

See also LAKES

0020	JAMES WATT
0029	HARNESSING THE HILLS
0129	HOLIDAY AT DORNOCH, A
0231	SCOTLAND FOR FITNESS
0251	INTRODUCING SCOTLAND
0260	HONEYMOON CRUISE NO. 2
0295	SEA SCOUTS PART II
0302	LAND O'CLANS
0314	SPORT IN SCOTLAND
0345	BUSMAN'S HOLIDAY
0362	HIGHLAND HOSPITALITY
0364	PERTHSHIRE PANORAMA
0373	THINGS THAT HAPPEN NO. 1
0396	OUR WATER SUPPLY
0454A	QUEENSHILL CUP AT CASTLE DOUGLAS, THE
0504	TAY VALLEY
0507	NORTH OF THE GREAT GLEN
0591	LOOKING BACK
0622	PRIDE AND PROGRESS
0634	(CWS CONGRESS IN GLASGOW)
0638	GLENFINNAN AND THE '45
0639B	FERGUSLIE MILLS IN INVERNESS
0707	SCOTLAND
0749	(LOCAL FILM FROM KIRKINTILLOCH AREA)
0751	(BORDER COUNTRY)
0752	CRIEFF - OUR TOWN
0785	HEART IS HIGHLAND, THE
0797	COASTS OF CLYDE, THE
0798	STRATHYRE TO BROADFORD, SKYE, BY TRAIN AND BOAT
0815	(GAUMONT SOUND MIRROR, 1927-1931)
0835	RAILWAY JOURNEY
0862	GIRLS' CLUBS APPEAL
0912	HEART OF SCOTLAND, THE
0914	SOUTHERN SCOTLAND
0931	AROUND INVERNESS
1028	HOMES IN BRITAIN
1049	GLASGOW, NO MEAN CITY
1096	WAY THE MONEY GOES, THE
1104	(GLASGOW PARKS 1941)
1120	SAIL TO INVERARAY
1227	CRUISING ON LOCH LOMOND
1314	(SUMMER SEASON IN DUNOON)
1333	TRIP TO IONA AND STAFFA, OBAN DISTRICT AND GLENCOE
1430	WESTER ROSS
1432	LOCH LOMOND
1453	LADY OF THE LAKE
1518	HOME AND AWAY NO. 4
1538	LOCH LOMOND
1539	(LOCH LOMOND PILOT FILM)
1581	(HOLIDAY SCOTLAND)
1582	DOON THE WATER
1680	[1938]
1686	CALEDONIAN CANAL, THE
1690	[FINNART OCEAN TERMINAL]
1779	WITH CAR AND CAMERA THROUGH THE LAKE DISTRICT TO SOUTHERN SCOTLAND
1783	RIVER TAY
1784	HIGHLAND CASTLES
1803	HONEYMOON TOUR
1833	(WILKIE FAMILY COLLECTION)
1849	LOCH LOMOND NATURE RESERVE
1881	RATAGAN/ TORRIDON
1883	[ROAD TO CARBISDALE, THE]
1885	[YOUTH GOES HOSTELLING]
1888	TOURING THE TROSSACHS
1889	LOCH LOMOND AND THE TROSSACHS
1890	(LOCH LOMOND, QUEEN OF SCOTTISH LOCHS)
1939	LOWLANDS OF SCOTLAND
2036	RAIN ON THE ROOF
2040	FIBRE WEB, THE
2046	MAGIC KEY, THE
2049	OUR THREE R'S
2097	CAMPING AND OUTDOOR CLUB
2129	OUR HIGHLAND HERITAGE
2188	RAINBOW TRAILS
2202	BY LOCHABER I WILL GO
2212	HEBRIDEAN HIGHWAY
2213	HIGHLAND CAPITAL
2219	LIVINGSTON - A TOWN FOR THE LOTHIANS
2220	PLAYING AWAY
2235	SONGS OF SCOTLAND
2241	HEALTH OF A CITY
2250	LOCH LOMOND
2253	WATER, WATER EVERYWHERE
2254	ERSKINE BRIDGE, THE
2257	TAYSIDE
2260	LINE TO SKYE, THE
2264	PRACTICAL ROMANTIC, SIR WALTER SCOTT
2382	[AERIALS OF THE CLYDE AND DUMBARTON]
2383	(HOLIDAY IN SCOTLAND 1964)
2393	(GUY FAMILY FILM)
2396	SCOTLAND THROUGH THE LENS
2401	[HALFWAY TO PARADISE: GI BLUES]
2428	ROYAL NORTHERN YACHT CLUB: NOSES HOMEWARD
2430	ROYAL NORTHERN YACHT CLUB CADETS AT LOCH LOMOND
2494	LOCH LOMOND - WATER SCENE
2516	(MACFARLANE FAMILY 1930-1931)
2573	ROAD TO LEWIS 1936, THE
2580	ROARING GAME, THE
2605	(HOLIDAY SCOTLAND)
2618B	ROUND THE THREE LOCHS AND VISIT TO CARNBOOTH
2629	OLD FOLKS TRIP 1950
2631	HOLIDAY SCOTLAND
2668	SKIMSTERS, THE
2674	NORTH AND WEST OF THE GREAT GLEN
2733	(NORTH EAST AND THE HIGHLANDS: CELEBRATIONS AND EVENTS)
2746	TROSSACHS, THE
2756	HIGHLANDS, THE
2804	AS LONG AS YOU'RE YOUNG
2820	(CRICHTON COLLECTION)

345

LOCOMOTIVES

See RAILWAYS and RAIL TRANSPORT/ STEAM TRAINS

LONDON

0011	HARRY LAUDER LEAVES FOR AMERICA
0020	JAMES WATT
0032	SCOTLAND'S WATER SUPPLY
0040	NEW LEASE OF LIFE
0122	VICTORY PARADE
0174	("SS BERENGARIA")
0192	DAVID LIVINGSTONE
0199	WINDSOR
0283	MARCH
0433	SOLDIER COMES HOME, A
0441	KING, GOD BLESS HIM, THE
0472	SPIRIT OF THE GAMES, THE
0503	BILLINGSGATE - THIS ART IS FISHY
0558	PATHE PICTORIAL NO. 2
0559	PATHE REVIEW OF THE YEAR
0665	(HOLIDAY IN LONDON)
0694	WELLS OF MONTROSE, THE
0713	REVIEW OF THE YEAR 1940
0715	CORONATION OF KING GEORGE VI AND QUEEN ELIZABETH
0716	(PATHESCOPE GAZETTE/ NEW EMPIRE NEWS)
0717	PRIME MINISTER AND PRESIDENT
0756	PIONEERS THEN AND NOW
0772	(STEAM LOCOMOTIVES AND SCENES AT LANARK RACECOURSE)
0815	(GAUMONT SOUND MIRROR, 1927-1931)
0818	PRIME MINISTER IN SCOTLAND
0829	BIRTHDAY GREETINGS TO QUEEN MARY
0888	HOMES FOR THE PEOPLE
0913	WHAT ABOUT THE WORKERS
0975	GLENROTHES
1068	SOME EVENTS IN GLASGOW 1937
1161	[LONDON 51]
1213	SLAUGHTER ON THE AVENUE (SEARCHLIGHT)
1240	CAMERON HIGHLANDERS IN LONDON
1328	BEAUTY SPOTS IN GREAT BRITAIN
1437	OUR PAPERS
1488	EXCURSION TO WEMBLEY
1506	PRINCESS MARGARET SEES IDEAL HOME
1519	HOME AND AWAY NO. 8
1526	HOME AND AWAY NO. 17
1572	CARPETS OF DISTINCTION
1671	LIVINGSTONE
1708	ARBROATH HISTORICAL PAGEANT/ THE STONE RETURNS
1791	WEDDING AT ALL SOULS
1796	GB NEWS REVIEW 1948
1868	BANK FOR SCOTLAND
1950	QUEEN ELIZABETH'S VISIT TO POSB
2040	FIBRE WEB, THE
2209	FROM GLASGOW GREEN TO BENDIGO
2342	(TOWERS FAMILY FILM PART 2)
2424	NEWS MAGAZINE: DAILY WORKER OUTING
2473	DISCOVERY OF TELEVISION
2516	(MACFARLANE FAMILY 1930-1931)
2522	(MACFARLANE FAMILY 1930)
2561	(CRUISE AND HOLIDAYS)
2563	(CARGO LOADING AT DOCKS)
2568	(SHIPPING JUTE TO LONDON)
2606	MINING REVIEW NO. 3
2732	(MARQUIS OF ABERDEEN'S RAILWAY FILMS)
2735	(HERD'S CAFE AND FAMILY FARM)
2777	SECRETARY OF STATE (FOR SCOTLAND)
2818	BARS OF SILVER
2825	(MONTGOMERY FAMILY HOLIDAYS)
2840	FAMILY SCRAPBOOK NO. 2

LOOMS

See TEXTILE ARTS/ TEXTILE INDUSTRY

MACHINERY (misc.)

0034	FACE OF SCOTLAND
0071	HESSIAN LOOM AND COP LOADER
0123	CITY SIDELIGHTS NO. 2
0124	MAKING OF THE HOLY BIBLE
0185	DUNDEE JUTE
0270	FROM FOREST TO FACTORY
0316	OUR SCHOOLS
0345	BUSMAN'S HOLIDAY
0383	TRUCK TO KEELSON
0428	LAND O' BURNS BAKERIES
0436	(DOUGLAS FRASER JUTE MACHINERY)
0487	AN EYE TO THE FUTURE
0901	(NEW PRINTING PLANT, DAILY RECORD)
0912	HEART OF SCOTLAND, THE
0914	SOUTHERN SCOTLAND
0950	STONEHOUSE - CENTRE FOR SUCCESS
0952	STONEHOUSE - CENTRE FOR SUCCESS (NO. 4)
0968	ROYAL MILE EDINBURGH, THE
0974	GLASGOW 1980
0975	GLENROTHES
1030	KNITWEAR WITHOUT TEARS
1061	DUNDEE
1079	BIG TIMBER
1108	INCIDENT AT LONGNIDDRY
1327	SCOTTISH DAILY NEWS
1354	STORY OF A STEEL WIRE ROPE
1437	OUR PAPERS
1504	(WARTIME PRODUCTION - H. MORRIS & CO.)
1509	WOOD GOES TO WAR
1533	AUTOMATIC FEEDING DEVICE FOR HORIZONTAL FORGING MACHINES
1534	CABLE BELT CONVEYOR, THE
1569	LAMBERTON COLD BILLET SHEAR, THE
1590	TULLIS OF CLYDEBANK
1592	BIRTH OF A SEWING MACHINE
1604	[DUNDEE COURIER 1911]
1747	(JUTE MACHINERY - TECHNICAL RECORDS)
1788	(BERTRAMS LTD.)
1860	PROGRESS OF A DUNDEE JUTE MILL
1997	FALKIRK
2023	BETTER HAY
2036	RAIN ON THE ROOF
2040	FIBRE WEB, THE
2046	MAGIC KEY, THE
2054	EVERYTHING BY DESIGN

2159	WIRE ROPE-MAKING
2204	COUNTY OF THE CLYDE
2208	FORTH ROAD BRIDGE, THE
2601	DIVIDED WE STAND
2683	(DUFFTOWN SCENES)
2707	KNIFE GRINDER AT FERNIEHURST/ GALA HOTSPURS GAME
2767	KINTYRE
2787	SINGLE SPINDLE APPLICATIONS
2788	WICKMAN SINGLE SPINDLE AUTOMATIC, THE

MAGAZINES
See NEWSPAPERS and MAGAZINES

MAIL SERVICE
See POSTAL SERVICES

MANUFACTURING (misc.)

0063	CLYDE FITTINGS
0097	BLACK AND DECKER LIMITED
0100	SCOTLAND'S FOREST FACTORIES
0251	INTRODUCING SCOTLAND
0296	SCOTLAND AND THE NEW WORLD
0314	SPORT IN SCOTLAND
0371	PRODUCING CRUDE RUBBER
0373	THINGS THAT HAPPEN NO. 1
0383	TRUCK TO KEELSON
0438	BRUNTON'S WIRE AND ROPE WORKS, MUSSELBURGH
0439	SCOTLAND'S BRIGHTEST INDUSTRY
0610	HELPING HAND - SCWS BRUSH MAKING, A
0673	SCOTLAND WELCOMES THEIR MAJESTIES
0733	VELCRO
0734	CARING FOR CARPETS
0742	SHIELDHALL FURNITURE - MARCH OF PROGRESS
0836	CONSIDER THE CARPET
0857	(SHIELDHALL PART TWO)
0877	(MAKING SOAP)
0915	GLASGOW
0916	PADDY'S MILESTONE
1026	PRODUCTIVE GROCERY DEPARTMENT
1053	CHEMICAL SUNDRIES DEPARTMENT
1060	SEAFOOD
1274	OTHER MAN'S JOB, THE
1354	STORY OF A STEEL WIRE ROPE
1480	YOUNG IN HEART
1504	(WARTIME PRODUCTION - H. MORRIS & CO.)
1505	(EXPERIMENTAL HELICOPTER AND AUTOGYRO BLADES)
1507	(GLASGOW'S WEDDING GIFT)
1508	(H. MORRIS FURNITURE FACTORY)
1509	WOOD GOES TO WAR
1590	TULLIS OF CLYDEBANK
1591	INDUSTRY ON PARADE - THE DEFENDING CHAMPION
1592	BIRTH OF A SEWING MACHINE
1593	NEEDLE BRUSHING MACHINE USED AT SINGER
1625	TRIBUTE TO WARTIME PRODUCTION
1626	TEMPLETON'S CARPETS
1638	WIRE LINES
1639	(MARTIN BLACK AND COMPANY - UNUSED MATERIAL)
1649	(BISCUIT FACTORY AND WEDDING)
1730	FINE FLOORS
1740	(CRAWFORD'S BISCUITS)
1752	MAKING SWEETS

1788	(BERTRAM'S LTD.)
1980	TIME OUT OF SCOTLAND
2044	DISTANCE NO OBJECT
2088	FAIR COUNTY OF AYR
2104	BUILDING THE NEW CHRYSLER
2159	WIRE ROPE-MAKING
2169	SOAP MAKING
2204	COUNTY OF THE CLYDE
2209	FROM GLASGOW GREEN TO BENDIGO
2231	SMITHS IN SCOTLAND, THE
2237	ONE DAY IN IRVINE
2248	CALTREX CALENDERING LINE
2253	WATER, WATER EVERYWHERE
2254	ERSKINE BRIDGE, THE
2312	SEALING WAX AND WAFERS
2329	[HALFWAY TO PARADISE: IRN BRU]
2449	BEETLING AT AVONBANK

MARKETS (livestock)
See also FISH MARKETS

2568	(SHIPPING JUTE TO LONDON)
2634	(INDIAN OXYGEN COMPANY)
2860	[GOLF BALL FACTORY]
0359	(VARIOUS - NO. 3)
0526	OUR CITY - TODAY AND TOMORROW
0637	ANIMAL HUSBANDRY
0661	MUTTON
0673	SCOTLAND WELCOMES THEIR MAJESTIES
0785	HEART IS HIGHLAND, THE
0800	[CAITHNESS, ORKNEY, KIRKWALL]
0863C	(SPOT THE SPOT)
0882	RIVER TWEED
0937	DUMFRIES, QUEEN OF THE SOUTH
0986	GLASGOW
1080A	ABERDEEN AWA' AUGUST 1949
1096	WAY THE MONEY GOES, THE
1497	[GLASGOW'S PROGRESS]
1764	LOTHIANS PART I, THE
2004	[CATTLE FROM THE UPLANDS]
2050	[FARM IN SOUTHERN SCOTLAND, A]
2088	FAIR COUNTY OF AYR
2204	COUNTY OF THE CLYDE
2213	HIGHLAND CAPITAL
2215	IN GOOD HEART
2259	PRIDE OF ISLANDS, A
2320	ABERDEEN
2721	SPRING IN GALLOWAY
2748	AT THE CATTLE MARKET
2756	HIGHLANDS, THE
2818	BARS OF SILVER

MARRIAGE

0024	CHRISTMAS 1937
0196	ROAD THROUGH THE SUNSET ISLES
0303	FUTURE OF SCOTLAND
0323	TWO SISTERS
0441	KING, GOD BLESS HIM, THE
0457	CAMPBELL TURNBULL WEDDING
0559	PATHE REVIEW OF THE YEAR
0751	(BORDER COUNTRY)

0768	(STANLEY L. RUSSELL'S WEDDING)
0777	(MISCELLANEOUS SCENES, RENFREWSHIRE)
0796	DUMFRIESSHIRE JOURNEY
0981	CROFTER'S LIFE IN SHETLAND, A
1179	[LOCAL WEDDINGS]
1185	FAMILY RECORDS
1258	(HONEYMOON CARRIAGE RIDE)
1307	(NOTRE DAME COLLEGE GRADUATES AND WEDDING)
1389	(GROSVENOR TOPICALS NO. 2)
1436	ORKNEY - SCENES AROUND SHAPINSAY
1566	(WEDDING FILM NO. 1)
1567	(WEDDING FILM NO. 2)
1571	PARTNERS IN PROGRESS
1606	(DALYELL FAMILY FILM)
1649	(BISCUIT FACTORY AND WEDDING)
1659	WEDDING OF ALYS COUPER AND DOUGLAS LINDSAY
1661	PROMINENT PAISLEY WEDDING
1680	[1938]
1704	(SCOTTISH WEDDING, A)
1766	[SCOTT FAMILY FILM]
1772	[BOAT OF GARTEN 1932]
1791	WEDDING AT ALL SOULS
1796	GB NEWS REVIEW 1948
1802	PRINCESS STREET CHURCH SNAPSHOTS OF 1939
1803	HONEYMOON TOUR
1855	REVIEW OF THE YEAR 1950
1900	(GREEN'S NEWSREEL)
1926	LOCAL COLOUR
1937	BRIDE AND GROOM
1984	SHARK FISHING
1989	(SIMPSON FAMILY FILM)
2002	COUNTRY OF THE BLIND
2112	WEDDING DAY 1936
2189	[SCENES AROUND HALFWAY AND DISTRICT]
2310	PRETTY DART, A
2342	(TOWERS FAMILY FILM PART 2)
2349	(RESTORATION OF IONA ABBEY)
2405	[HALFWAY TO PARADISE: HEN PARTY]
2477	PRESENT FOR THE GROOM, A
2515	(MACFARLANE FAMILY - WEDDING)
2578	WEDDING AT NORTH BERWICK
2586	(JEWISH WEDDING, A)
2670	TABLE D/HOLT
2734	(FAMILY WEDDING AND LIFE AT "SHANZIE")
2736	(HERD FAMILY FILM)
2741	(KATE KENNEDY PROCESSION AND KIRKCALDY RIFLE RANGE)
2819	(DALKEITH WEDDING)
2833	WEDDING OF JOHN GLAISTER AND ISOBEL LINDSAY

MEDICINE (practice)

See also HOSPITALS/ SURGERY and RELATED TOPICS

0030	IT BEGAN ON THE CLYDE
0033	HIGHLAND DOCTOR
0034	FACE OF SCOTLAND
0035	SCOTTISH WOMEN'S HOSPITALS
0040	NEW LEASE OF LIFE
0113	HOSPITAL TEAM
0135	GLASGOW TAKES CARE OF ITS OLD FOLK

0189	BLOOD TRANSFUSION IN BATHGATE
0253	TAM TRAUCHLE'S TROUBLES
0271	GOOD HEALTH TO SCOTLAND
0272	BIRTHDAY
0291	CHILDREN OF THE CITY
0294	START IN LIFE, A
0331	OUR HEALTH SERVICES
0346	(SEA OF GALILEE MISSION HOSPITAL, TIBERIAS)
0365	BLOOD CAN WORK MIRACLES
0484	OESOPHAGEAL SPEECH
0520	[DR. MACINTYRE'S X-RAY FILM]
0531	(GUILD OF AID WORK IN THE GORBALS)
0539A	RED CROSS WORK AT SALONIKA
0699	4 AND 20 FIT GIRLS
0755	VICTORY OVER PAIN
0826B	AT YOUR SERVICE
0917	GLASGOW - MASS ASSAULT ON TB
0930	HAND TRANSPORT OF THE INJURED
0974	GLASGOW 1980
1075	PREVENTION IS BETTER
1084	BOMB FELL, A
1085	CROWD GATHERS, A
1088	(MOUNTAIN RESCUE TRAINING)
1094	(WESTERN INFIRMARY)
1253	TWO GOOD FAIRIES
1346	BATHING THE BABY
1349	CHILD WELFARE
1631	THIS LITTLE WORLD
1691	GREENOCK PLANS AHEAD
1985	LIGHT IN OUR DARKNESS
1997	FALKIRK
2241	HEALTH OF A CITY
2283	IMAGE RECONSTRUCTION OF SEBACEOUS GLANDS
2716	THANK YOU LORD LISTER
2717	DRESSINGS TECHNIQUE
2718	APPLE A DAY AN

METALLURGY

0251	INTRODUCING SCOTLAND
0296	SCOTLAND AND THE NEW WORLD
0301	LAND OF INVENTION
0303	FUTURE OF SCOTLAND
0387	BIG MILL, THE
0500	HEAVY INDUSTRIES
0502	RAW MATERIALS
0560	(ARDROSSAN SHIPYARD)
0587	CENTRAL SCOTLAND
0750	ROMANCE OF ENGINEERING, A
0908	INDUSTRIAL BRITAIN
1036	[ETNA STEEL MILL]
1039	[COLVILLE'S PRODUCTION NO. OF 20]
1062	WEALTH OF A NATION
1249	IT COMES FROM COAL
1354	STORY OF A STEEL WIRE ROPE
1503	OPENING OF A NEW ALUMINIUM WORKS
1520	HOME AND AWAY NO. 10
1523	HOME AND AWAY NO. 13
1531	STEAM
2046	MAGIC KEY, THE

2204	COUNTY OF THE CLYDE
2216	INVERGORDON SMELTER, THE
2239	METAL IN HARMONY

MIDDLE EAST

0346-0347	(SEA OF GALILEE MISSION HOSPITAL, TIBERIAS)
0348	WILD FLOWERS OF PALESTINE
0349	JERUSALEM
0350	[LAKE GALILEE AND HOLY LAND]
0351	[ISRAEL AND JORDAN]
0352	FLORAL BEAUTY OF THE HOLY LAND
0353	SYRIA - INTRODUCING THE DRUZES
0355	[TIBERIAS 1935]
0357	[ARAB CUSTOMS]
0361	JULIA AND LYDIA
0649	GRASS
1224	[WAYSIDE SCENES IN PALESTINE]
1649	(BISCUIT FACTORY AND WEDDING)
1965	[SCOTTISH MISSION HOSPITAL, TIBERIAS]
2253	WATER, WATER EVERYWHERE
2779	SERVING A CHANGING INDUSTRY

MIDLOTHIAN

0380	[SHOTS OF EDINBURGH]
0587	CENTRAL SCOTLAND
0819	ROYAL VISIT TO SCOTLAND
1368	PENICUIK CHILDREN'S GALA DAY 1953
1401-1403	(HONEST LAD AND LASS)
1404	(FISHERMAN'S WALK 1933)
1544	OIL BLASTING IN SCOTLAND
1562	DALKEITH GALAS 1926, 1933/ LAUREL AND HARDY VISIT EDINBURGH
1674	UNDAUNTED: THE TREFOIL SCHOOL
1726	[BOYS' BRIGADE RECRUITING MARCHES, LEITH]
1764-1765	LOTHIANS PART I AND II
2002	COUNTRY OF THE BLIND
2024	FORTH - POWERHOUSE FOR INDUSTRY
2042	UNIROYAL LTD.
2205	COUNTY ON THE MOVE
2219	LIVINGSTON - A TOWN FOR THE LOTHIANS
2228	PLAN FOR LIVING, A
2577B	LORETTO SCHOOL
2819	DALKEITH WEDDING

MIGRATION (internal)

1694	INDUSTRIAL CLYDESDALE

MILITARY

See also PARACHUTES/ WAR MEMORIALS/ WEAPONRY

0012	GLASGOW'S YESTERDAYS
0034	FACE OF SCOTLAND
0035	SCOTTISH WOMEN'S HOSPITALS
0037	QUEEN'S OWN HIGHLANDERS
0042	ABERDEEN 1906
0047	(GERMAN TRAINING FILM)
0049A	ARMISTICE SERVICE VICTORIA PARK WHITEINCH
0060	NEWS PARADE 1939
0116	PRINCESS MARY PRESENTS NEW COLOURS TO ROYAL SCOTS
0117	CHURCH PARADE OF GLASGOW LOWLAND SIGNAL UNITS
0119	DAY OF REMEMBRANCE MEMORIAL AT THE GLASGOW CENOTAPH

0122	VICTORY PARADE
0164	ABERDEEN
0180	DUMFRIES 1953 GUID NYCHBURRIS FESTIVAL
0188	ROYAL OCCASIONS OF SCOTLAND
0199	WINDSOR
0201	HIGHLAND HORSE SHOW, ALLOA
0234	GORDON HIGHLANDERS' PRESENTATION OF THE FREEDOM OF THE CITY OF ABERDEEN
0235	PRESENTATION OF NEW COLOURS TO GORDON HIGHLANDERS
0237	FLICKS OF ABERDEEN'S TERRITORIAL WEEK
0239	ABERDEEN CELEBRATES THE CORONATION
0241	CINEMA NEWS, ABERDEEN
0244	NEWSREEL
0249	(MILITARY PARADE IN ABERDEEN)
0319	UNVEILING CEREMONY OF THE CAMERONIANS "SCOTTISH RIFLES"
0325	(DUMFRIES)
0326	KOSB - PRESENTATION OF COLOURS
0332	[ENSIGN EWART]
0376A	WHERE EVERYBODY GOES
0376B	ROUTE MARCH 1ST BATTALION LANARKSHIRE VOLUNTEER REGIMENT
0376C	[LANARKSHIRE REGIMENT]
0441	KING, GOD BLESS HIM, THE
0449	GORDON HIGHLANDERS LEAVE FOR THE BOER WAR
0459	EDINBURGH FESTIVAL, THE
0462	NEWS SPOTLIGHT
0480	DUNDEE
0514	PRINCE WITH HIS FUSILIERS, THE
0524	(HOME GUARD ON MANOEUVRES)
0559	PATHE REVIEW OF THE YEAR
0595	AT INVERNESS TERRITORIAL ARMY JUBILEE
0639A	TROOPING THE COLOUR
0781	(ARMY BOX WORK)
0790	(TRIMS)
0792	[BORDERS LOCAL NEWSREELS NO. 2]
0795	(ARRIVAL AT WHITEHART HOTEL, CAMPBELTOWN)
0824	TROOPING OF THE COLOUR, 1ST BATTALION KOSB...
0827	(INVERNESS COMPILATION)
0890	(ARMISTICE DAY MEMORIAL SERVICE)
0911	ST. KILDA - THE LONELY ISLANDS
0913	WHAT ABOUT THE WORKERS
0939	GLASGOW WELCOMES THE QUEEN
0968	ROYAL MILE EDINBURGH, THE
1073A	NIGHT SWORD DANCE
1073C	(KING GEORGE INSPECTS GUARD OF HONOUR, BLACK WATCH)
1073D	2ND BATTALION BLACK WATCH REHEARSE FOR THE NAVAL AND MILITARY TOURNAMENT
1083	(WARTIME DUMBARTON)
1112	STATE ENTRY INTO EDINBURGH
1113	HONOURS OF SCOTLAND
1237	[SCENES OF LOCAL INTEREST]
1240	CAMERON HIGHLANDERS IN LONDON
1304	(DUMFRIES - VISIT AND INSPECTION)
1317	[HOME GUARD, AYR - STAND DOWN]
1337	ROYAL VISIT TO ABERDEEN
1339	JUNIOR PIPERS AND BANDSMEN TRAINING IN EDINBURGH
1342	(ROCKET RANGE, BENBECULA)
1343	HISTORIC EDINBURGH

MILLS and MILL WORK

MINING

See also COAL MINES

2205	COUNTY ON THE MOVE
2239	METAL IN HARMONY

MOD, The

See GAELIC/ MUSIC

MOLLUSCS (cockles, mussels, pearl oysters)

1655	BARRA
1943	ENCHANTED ISLES
2631	HOLIDAY SCOTLAND
2721	SPRING IN GALLOWAY
2745	DAY ON THE SANDS, A

MONASTIC BUILDINGS

0191	STORY OF CULROSS, THE
0192	DAVID LIVINGSTONE
0296	SCOTLAND AND THE NEW WORLD
0345	BUSMAN'S HOLIDAY
0362	HIGHLAND HOSPITALITY
0415	HONEYMOON CRUISE NO. 1
0431	CRUISE TO ST. KILDA AND THE WESTERN ISLES
0457	CAMPBELL TURNBULL WEDDING
0473	SERMON IN STONE, A
0512	STIRLING: GATEWAY TO THE HIGHLANDS
0561A	EXCLUSIVE PICTURES OF ROYAL VISIT TO PAISLEY
0622	PRIDE AND PROGRESS
0630	SOUTHERN UPLANDS
0707	SCOTLAND
0751	(BORDER COUNTRY)
0882	RIVER TWEED
0914	SOUTHERN SCOTLAND
0968	ROYAL MILE EDINBURGH, THE
0969	HOLIDAY IN THE HIGHLANDS
1068	SOME EVENTS IN GLASGOW 1937
1328	BEAUTY SPOTS IN GREAT BRITAIN
1333	TRIP TO IONA AND STAFFA, OBAN DISTRICT AND GLENCOE
1381A	WOMEN'S GUILD OF EMPIRE 1934
1381B	FERGUSLIE THREAD WORKS OUTING TO BRAEMAR
1383	WOMEN'S GUILD OF EMPIRE C1933
1442	PLUSCARDEN PRIORY RESTORATION FETE
1478	SCOTS ACCLAIM ROYAL FAMILY
1487	EDINBURGH
1488	EXCURSION TO WEMBLEY
1528	HOME AND AWAY NO. 19
1542	(VISIT TO STAFFA)
1572	CARPETS OF DISTINCTION
1606	(DALYELL FAMILY FILM)
1671	LIVINGSTONE
1696	ROYAL SCOTLAND
1697	[ARBROATH HISTORICAL PAGEANT 1947]
1708	ARBROATH HISTORICAL PAGEANT/ THE STONE RETURNS
1884	BORDER RAID
1888	TOURING THE TROSSACHS
1943	ENCHANTED ISLES
1989	(SIMPSON FAMILY FILM)
2053	[OBAN, IONA, STAFFA AND HARRIS]
2212	HEBRIDEAN HIGHWAY
2213	HIGHLAND CAPITAL
2223	BORDERS, THE
2233	KEEP YOUR EYE ON PAISLEY

2243	TAY ROAD BRIDGE
2246	HAND OF ADAM
2264	PRACTICAL ROMANTIC, SIR WALTER SCOTT
2344	THAT SACRED ISLE IONA
2346	CAN THESE STONES LIVE?
2347	ALF GOES TO WORK
2349	(RESTORATION OF IONA ABBEY)
2350	PATTERN TO PENTECOST
2351	IONA - WE SHALL REBUILD
2352	(AFRICAN VISITORS TO IONA)
2591	FAIR RIVER, THE
2631	HOLIDAY SCOTLAND
2721	SPRING IN GALLOWAY
2742	MEETING POINT: THE IONA COMMUNITY AT WORK AND WORSHIP
2743	(CONSTRUCTION WORK AT IONA ABBEY)
2804	AS LONG AS YOU'RE YOUNG
2865	(SAWKINS NO. 7)

MONEY

See FINANCE and FINANCIAL INSTITUTIONS

MONUMENTS

See also STATUES/ WAR MEMORIALS

0192	DAVID LIVINGSTONE
0247	LAYING FOUNDATION STONE OF THE BISHOP SEABURY MEMORIAL
0256	EILEAN AN FHRAOICH [ISLE OF LEWIS]
0282	CITY SIDELIGHTS - SECTIONS
0345	BUSMAN'S HOLIDAY
0362	HIGHLAND HOSPITALITY
0377	RIVER CLYDE - A SURVEY OF SCOTLAND'S GREATEST RIVER
0380	[SHOTS OF EDINBURGH]
0417	MEN AND WOMEN OF TOMORROW
0431	CRUISE TO ST. KILDA AND THE WESTERN ISLES
0504	TAY VALLEY
0512	STIRLING: GATEWAY TO THE HIGHLANDS
0550	STORNOWAY
0587	CENTRAL SCOTLAND
0622	PRIDE AND PROGRESS
0638	GLENFINNAN AND THE '45
0639B	FERGUSLIE MILLS IN INVERNESS
0665	(HOLIDAY IN LONDON)
0707	SCOTLAND
0751	(BORDER COUNTRY)
0752	CRIEFF - OUR TOWN
0766	GALASHIELS AND BRAW LADS GATHERING
0767	BRAW LADS GATHERING
0773	NORTHERN OUTPOST
0777	(MISCELLANEOUS SCENES, RENFREWSHIRE)
0791	[BORDERS LOCAL NEWSREELS NO. 1]
0796	DUMFRIESSHIRE JOURNEY
0800	[CAITHNESS, ORKNEY, KIRKWALL]
0804	GREAT SCOT - MARY SLESSOR
0889	IMMORTAL MEMORY OF ROBERT BURNS
0920	(BUS TOUR, THE)
0931	AROUND INVERNESS
0952	STONEHOUSE - CENTRE FOR SUCCESS (NO. 4)
1049	GLASGOW, NO MEAN CITY
1091	(TRAMS IN EDINBURGH AND BRUSSELS)

351

1887	[GLENCOE AND NEVIS]
1889	LOCH LOMOND AND THE TROSSACHS
1890	(LOCH LOMOND, QUEEN OF SCOTTISH LOCHS)
1891	(HOSTEL SKI TRIP)
1894	CRUISE TO SCOTTISH GARDENS, A
1928	TRIP TO SKYE, ORKNEY AND SHETLAND
1943	ENCHANTED ISLES
2036	RAIN ON THE ROOF
2095	LET'S GO SKI-ING
2097	CAMPING AND OUTDOOR CLUB
2121	SKI-ING IN SCOTLAND
2146	KEEK AT THE HIGHLANDS, A
2147	(SKI-ING ON BEN LAWERS)
2188	RAINBOW TRAILS
2212	HEBRIDEAN HIGHWAY
2257	TAYSIDE
2383	(HOLIDAY IN SCOTLAND 1964)
2392	LOMOND MC/ SKI-ING
2396	SCOTLAND THROUGH THE LENS
2423	INCHMURRIN 1950
2511	APPROACH TO API
2593	MISTY ISLE
2631	HOLIDAY SCOTLAND
2674	NORTH AND WEST OF THE GREAT GLEN
2677	SCOTTISH SNOWGROUNDS, THE
2733	(NORTH EAST AND THE HIGHLANDS: CELEBRATIONS AND EVENTS)
2739	OFFICIAL BRITISH SKI INSTRUCTIONAL FILM, THE
2746	TROSSACHS, THE
2790	CRUACHAN

MUNICIPAL GOVERNMENT

See also PUBLIC REVENUE and TAXATION

0057	OUR TRANSPORT SERVICES
0062	GLASGOW - OUR CITY
0268	PROGRESS REPORT
0300	OUR PUBLIC PARKS
0316	OUR SCHOOLS
0317	OUR HOMES
0386	MONEY PROGRAMME, THE
0396	OUR WATER SUPPLY
0397	OUR ART GALLERIES
0420	KEEPING OUR CITY CLEAN
0526	OUR CITY - TODAY AND TOMORROW
0922	PROGRESS REPORT NO. 2
1610	EDUCATION AUTHORITY OF GLASGOW SPECIAL SERVICES
1721	LET GLASGOW FLOURISH
1745	PORT HEALTH AUTHORITY
1969	CAER-PEN-TULACH
1979	VITAL STATISTICS
2036	RAIN ON THE ROOF
2241	HEALTH OF A CITY

MUSEUMS

See also ART GALLERIES

0020	JAMES WATT
0123	CITY SIDELIGHTS NO. 2
0282	CITY SIDELIGHTS - SECTIONS
0292	LIFE OF BURNS, THE
0300	OUR PUBLIC PARKS

0315	HOW OUR CITY IS GOVERNED
0319	UNVEILING CEREMONY OF THE CAMERONIANS "SCOTTISH RIFLES"
0364	PERTHSHIRE PANORAMA
0380	[SHOTS OF EDINBURGH]
0397	OUR ART GALLERIES
0429	LAND O' BURNS BAKERIES - INTRODUCTION
0526	OUR CITY - TODAY AND TOMORROW
0546	GLASGOW
0557	MARCH OF THE MOVIES, THE
0573	GREEN OF GLASGOW, THE
0587	CENTRAL SCOTLAND
0622	PRIDE AND PROGRESS
0707	SCOTLAND
0712	[SAUCHIEHALL STREET ROOF TOPS]
0740	SECRETS OF LIFE - LIVING IN LONDON
0863C	(SPOT THE SPOT)
0889	IMMORTAL MEMORY OF ROBERT BURNS
0911	ST. KILDA - THE LONELY ISLANDS
0968	ROYAL MILE EDINBURGH, THE
0974	GLASGOW 1980
0986	GLASGOW
1049	GLASGOW, NO MEAN CITY
1080A	ABERDEEN AWA' AUGUST 1949
1104	(GLASGOW PARKS 1941)
1212	SCOTTISH HOLIDAY, A
1276	NORTH BRITISH
1321	AYR
1324	FILM OF GLASGOW, A
1481	CLYDESCOPE
1484	(GLASGOW "DISCARDS")
1572	CARPETS OF DISTINCTION
1653	EDINBURGH
1807	FENWICK EVENTS OF 1934
1854	(PROVOST FLETT COLLECTION)
1939	LOWLANDS OF SCOTLAND
2033	[PARAPLEGIC GAMES]
2046	MAGIC KEY, THE
2213	HIGHLAND CAPITAL
2237	ONE DAY IN IRVINE
2238	HIGHLAND FOLK
2463	ANNUAL ART COMPETITION
2464	AT THE MUSEUM
2465A/B	ARMS AND ARMOUR
2466	PREPARING A WAX RESIN RE-LINING
2469	MISSILE WEAPONS
2631	HOLIDAY SCOTLAND
2732	(MARQUIS OF ABERDEEN'S RAILWAY FILMS)
2792	AYR FROM THE AULD BRIG

MUSIC (gen.)

See also PIPE BANDS/ SONGS

0015	STUDENTS' CHARITIES DAY GLASGOW
0016	ORPHEUS CHOIR
0098	LIEDER DER VOLKER (SONGS OF THE PEOPLE)
0112	CROFTER BOY
0237	FLICKS OF ABERDEEN'S TERRITORIAL WEEK
0252	GAELIC MOD
0283	MARCH

353

0308	[BOWING PRINCIPLES FOR STRING PLAYERS]
0325	(DUMFRIES)
0332	[ENSIGN EWART]
0340-0344	BO'NESS CHILDREN'S FAIR FESTIVAL
0379	CITY SIDELIGHTS NO. 1
0380	[SHOTS OF EDINBURGH]
0391	[HAPPY IN THE MORNING]
0410	QUEEN JEANETTE MCGUIRE. ST. MARY'S SCHOOL 1948
0444	RIVALLING THE RAINBOW
0459	EDINBURGH FESTIVAL, THE
0519	(BAND CONCERT, KELVINGROVE PARK, 1928)
0528	ALL ON A SUMMER'S DAY
0537	(SHOSTAKOVITCH AND HUGH MACDIARMID)
0542	[LANGHOLM COMMON RIDING]
0574	ARDROSSAN AND SALTCOATS PLAYERS - WELCOME HOME
0581	VARIETY MOMENTS
0627	DEDICATION OF QUEEN'S PARK
0635	ADVENTURES OF WEE ROB ROY, THE
0644	SALTCOATS QUATER CENTENARY CELEBRATIONS
0691	MUSIC IN AMERICA
0739	WHEN DAY IS DONE - GLIMPSES OF MINERS WELFARE
0754	MUSIC FROM THE MOVIES
0756	PIONEERS THEN AND NOW
0785	HEART IS HIGHLAND, THE
0792	[BORDERS LOCAL NEWSREELS NO. 2]
0802	WILL YE NO' COME BACK AGAIN
0803	(DANCE SEQUENCES)
0804	GREAT SCOT - MARY SLESSOR
0813	KIRKCALDY HOSPITAL PAGEANT
0815	(GAUMONT SOUND MIRROR, 1927-1931)
0822	(OTTER HUNTING AND PROCESSION)
0827	(INVERNESS COMPILATION)
0849	SCOTTISH CUP FINAL. ABERDEEN V CELTIC AT HAMPDEN PARK 1937
0889	IMMORTAL MEMORY OF ROBERT BURNS
0896	(PRE MATCH DISPLAY, HAMPDEN STADIUM)
0942	(BARRHEAD FESTIVAL AND OLD FOLKS' OUTING)
0951	STONEHOUSE NEW TOWN FESTIVAL
0960B	LOCHGELLY CHILDREN'S GALA DAY
0960C	CROWNING OF LOCHGELLY'S FIRST "QUEEN"...
0961A	LOCHGELLY V CELTIC FIRST ROUND SCOTTISH CUP
0961B	HOSPITAL/ FUND RAISING PAGEANT, LOCHGELLY
0962	LOCHGELLY CORONATION YEAR CHILDREN'S GALA
0964	CLOSE OF JUBILEE YEAR PROCESSION
0965	CHILDREN'S GALA AT LOCHGELLY
0966	LOCHGELLY WAR MEMORIAL
0969	HOLIDAY IN THE HIGHLANDS
0976	(NATIONAL MOD TRIMS)
1098	CAMERA MAKES WHOOPEE
1206	ROCK OF AGES
1245	NEWMILNS CIVIC WEEK
1252	FOCUS ON BRIDGETON
1259	EMERSON MOUNTAINEERS, THE
1291	BROXBURN GALA DAY AND CROWNING OF QUEEN
1293	BROXBURN HIGH SCHOOL SPORTS
1295	FERRY FAIR 1955
1297	FERRY FAIR OF 1954
1300	BROXBURN AND DISTRICT CHILDREN'S GALA DAY AND CROWNING CEREMONY

1301	(UNIDENTIFIED GALA AND SPORTS DAY, BROXBURN AREA NO. 1)
1302	(UNIDENTIFIED SPORTS DAY, BROXBURN AREA)
1314	(SUMMER SEASON IN DUNOON)
1339	JUNIOR PIPERS AND BANDSMEN TRAINING IN EDINBURGH
1374	LAYING FOUNDATION STONE, KIRKINTILLOCH PARISH CHURCH
1379	LAYING FOUNDATION STONE, FREE GARDENERS' HALL
1385	(ANCIENT MARINER'S FILM)
1457	HOPPITY HOP
1483	EDINBURGH FESTIVAL OPENING CEREMONY
1486	EDINBURGH FESTIVAL - PATHE
1493	FESTIVAL IN EDINBURGH
1494	HOLIDAYS AT HOME 1942-'44
1501	BEYOND THE GRAMPIANS
1547	CROWNING OF THE DARVEL LACE QUEEN 1952
1548	[CROWNING OF LACE QUEEN, DARVEL 22ND AUG, 1953]
1642	GREAT WATERS MIGHTY ORGAN HARMONIES
1921	WEST PILTON GALA DAY 1952
1986	HIAWATHA
1988	(EDINBURGH OPERA COMPANY)
2009	LIFE IN THE ORKNEYS
2099	JOSEPH HISLOP COLLECTION
2218	LEATHERNECK AMBASSADORS
2224	SCOTLAND DANCES
2228	PLAN FOR LIVING, A
2254	ERSKINE BRIDGE, THE
2257	TAYSIDE
2403	[HALFWAY TO PARADISE: TARTAN]
2453	[GLASGOW WEEK IN HAMBURG]
2583	RETURN OF THE INTERNED
2587	ISLE OF RHUM
2601	DIVIDED WE STAND
2611	BOYS' BRIGADE - 1956 REVIEW OF THE GLASGOW BATTALION
2649	GANG SHOW, THE
2841	FAMILY SCRAPBOOK NO. 3
2861	NIGHT AT THE HAP, A
2862	HAP DANCES, THE

MUSSEL GATHERING

See MOLLUSCS

NAVY and NAVAL VESSELS

0023E	GREATEST BATTLESHIP LAUNCH
0028	WESTERN ISLES
0043	(LARGS SUMMER SEASON 1936)
0060	NEWS PARADE 1939
0296	SCOTLAND AND THE NEW WORLD
0441	KING, GOD BLESS HIM, THE
0462	NEWS SPOTLIGHT
0703	CLYDE, THE
0713	REVIEW OF THE YEAR 1940
0716	(PATHESCOPE GAZETTE/ NEW EMPIRE NEWS)
0717	PRIME MINISTER AND PRESIDENT
0773	NORTHERN OUTPOST
0792	[BORDERS LOCAL NEWSREELS NO. 2]
0800	[CAITHNESS, ORKNEY, KIRKWALL]
0801	[CAITHNESS, ORKNEY]
0818	PRIME MINISTER IN SCOTLAND
0819	ROYAL VISIT TO SCOTLAND

NEEDLE and HANDIWORK

See CRAFTS

NEW YEAR

NEW ZEALAND

See AUSTRALASIA

NEWSPAPERS and MAGAZINES

See also MACHINERY

NORTH AMERICA

NUCLEAR POWER

See POWER RESOURCES

NURSES and NURSING

0348	WILD FLOWERS OF PALESTINE
0353	SYRIA - INTRODUCING THE DRUZES
0357	[ARAB CUSTOMS]
0361	JULIA AND LYDIA
0365	BLOOD CAN WORK MIRACLES
0494	COUNTRY POLICEMAN
0522	SAY IT WITH FLOWERS
0523	HER MAJESTY THE QUEEN PAYS INFORMAL VISIT TO ABERDEEN
0826A	AT YOUR SERVICE - DUMFRIES AND GALLOWAY ROYAL INFIRMARY
0826B	AT YOUR SERVICE
1075	PREVENTION IS BETTER
1094	(WESTERN INFIRMARY)
1249	IT COMES FROM COAL
1349	CHILD WELFARE
1445	MOBILE CIVIL DEFENCE SURGICAL UNIT
1446	GLASGOW CASUALTY SERVICE
1449	PERSONAL EPISODE
1450	EVER OPEN DOOR, THE
1606	(DALYELL FAMILY FILM)
1631	THIS LITTLE WORLD
1693	OUR CITIZEN ARMY
1858	HOSPITALS FOR ALL
1965	[SCOTTISH MISSION HOSPITAL, TIBERIAS]
1979	VITAL STATISTICS
2577A	FAMILY FILMS 1931-1938
2614	CARING PROFESSION, THE
2717	DRESSINGS TECHNIQUE

NUTRITION and METABOLIC DISEASE
See DIET

OIL INDUSTRY
See PETROLEUM

OLD FOLKS HOMES
See INSTITUTIONAL CARE

ORCHARDS
See FRUIT

ORIENT, The
See ASIA

ORKNEY ISLANDS

0274	HIGHLAND LADDIE
0367	BANK AHEAD
0646B	INAUGURATION OF FIRST HIGHLAND AIR SERVICE
0704	HANDBA' AT KIRKWALL, ORKNEY
0800	[CAITHNESS, ORKNEY, KIRKWALL]
0801	[CAITHNESS, ORKNEY]
0805	(KIRKWALL, WICK, DOUNREAY)
0840A	PROVOST JOHN SINCLAIR SHOWS ORKNEY GUIDES AROUND THE HARBOUR AT THURSO
1311	(BAXTER FAMILY FILMS)
1436	ORKNEY - SCENES AROUND SHAPINSAY
1854	(PROVOST FLETT COLLECTION)
1928	TRIP TO SKYE, ORKNEY AND SHETLAND
2009	LIFE IN THE ORKNEYS
2118	FLYING SCOTSMEN
2221	QUEEN IN SCOTLAND, THE
2259	PRIDE OF ISLANDS, A

356

2359	HOWER
2360	ROWIEGAR
2361	MIDHOWE BROCH
2407	BIRDS OF THE ORKNEY ISLANDS
2408	PROPERTY IN THE COUNTRY, A
2801	(SCENES OF ORKNEY)

ORPHANAGES
See INSTITUTIONAL CARE

OUTER HEBRIDES

0028	WESTERN ISLES
0033	HIGHLAND DOCTOR
0136	HOLIDAYING IN HARRIS
0196	ROAD THROUGH THE SUNSET ISLES
0256	EILEAN AN FHRAOICH [ISLE OF LEWIS]
0274	HIGHLAND LADDIE
0384	[ISLE OF BARRA]
0418	ST. KILDA - BRITAIN'S LONELIEST ISLE
0431	CRUISE TO ST. KILDA AND THE WESTERN ISLES
0548	HARRIS
0549	ISLE OF LEWIS
0550	STORNOWAY
0631	NORTHERN SCOTLAND
0747	(EXPEDITION TO RONA)
0793	EVACUATION OF ST. KILDA
0940	ST. KILDA 1929
0978	ISLAND OF ST. KILDA, THE
0988	ST. KILDA. ITS PEOPLE AND BIRDS
1269	SKYWAY AMBULANCE
1342	(ROCKET RANGE, BENBECULA)
1606	(DALYELL FAMILY FILM)
1641	ISLES OF YOUTH, THE
1655	BARRA
1701	ERISKAY - A POEM OF REMOTE LIVES
1766	[SCOTT FAMILY FILM]
1881	RATAGAN/ TORRIDON
1896	ST. KILDA
1943	ENCHANTED ISLES
2037	ST. KILDA - JULY 1956
2053	[OBAN, IONA, STAFFA AND HARRIS]
2118	FLYING SCOTSMEN
2190	DEEP SEA DAYS
2202	BY LOCHABER I WILL GO
2212	HEBRIDEAN HIGHWAY
2231	SMITHS IN SCOTLAND, THE
2235	SONGS OF SCOTLAND
2242	IN GREAT WATERS
2259	PRIDE OF ISLANDS, A
2270	[GLASGOW UNIVERSITY NORTH RONA EXPEDITION]
2279	AMONG THE ISLES
2309	STEALING AWAY TO STORNOWAY
2310	PRETTY DART, A
2311	HEATH VISITS THE WEAVERS
2410	BEYOND A TANGLED SHORE
2496	(GUGA HUNTERS)
2572	DUNARA CRUISE 1937
2573	ROAD TO LEWIS 1936, THE
2575	UIST HOLIDAY 1937
2592	ISLES OF THE WEST

1662	(GORBALS PROCESSION)
1669	ST. ANDREWS
1697	[ARBROATH HISTORICAL PAGEANT 1947]
1699	SCOTTISH NATIONAL EXHIBITION
1708	ARBROATH HISTORICAL PAGEANT/ THE STONE RETURNS
1722	GLASGOW MAY DAY 1937
1723	PROCESSION IN COMMEMORATION OF CALTON WEAVERS/ ROBERT SMILLIE
1755-1757	BROXBURN CHILDREN'S GALA DAY
1766	[SCOTT FAMILY FILM]
1786	(FIRST COMMUNION CEREMONY)
1854	(PROVOST FLETT COLLECTION)
1871	DUMBARTON 1944-1946
1872	RURAL ROUND ABOUT
1873	THORNHILL SHOW
1876	NEW GALLOWAY GALA WEEK
1878	(TABLEAUX PARADE/ HORSE RIDING)
1879	VILLAGE VARIETIES
1925	GALA WEEK AND CROWNING CEREMONY
1929	[CUMNOCK CELEBRATION, JUNE 1951]
1957	LANARK
1969	CAER-PEN-TULACH
1975	SNAPPY SNAPS OF RUTHERGLEN
1976	(ANTI-ALCOHOL CAMPAIGN/ USSR VISIT?)
2027	DIAMOND JUBILEE BRISBANE QUEEN, LARGS
2145	(STRANRAER LOCAL EVENTS)
2184	[ISLE OF BUTE CARNIVAL]
2196	[RIDING OF THE MARCHES, ANNAN]
2228	PLAN FOR LIVING, A
2237	ONE DAY IN IRVINE
2258	LOTHIAN LANDSCAPE
2272	(WATERSIDE AND DISTRICT)
2290	JUBILEE DAY IN TAYPORT, 6TH MAY 1935
2291	CORONATION DAY, TAYPORT, 12TH MAY 1937
2294	(TAYPORT EVENTS 1946-'49)
2299	TAYPORT TOWN HALL OPENING
2304	CORONATION YEAR 1953
2335	ROTHESAY FANCY DRESS PARADE
2336	ROTHESAY PEACE CELEBRATIONS
2338	(ROTHESAY 1918)
2354-2357	EDINBURGH TEMPERANCE DAY (AND EVENTS) 1936-1939
2394	(PRESTON FAMILY FILM 1962)
2395	CHURCH ACTIVITIES, ST. MARTIN'S, EDINBURGH
2415	OLD ROTHESAY
2484	(PAUL ROBESON AT GLASGOW MAY DAY)
2495	[DUMFRIES GUID NYCHBURRIS DAY 1947]
2500	YEARS AGO IN COWDENBEATH
2532	[CORONATION PARADE WITH FLOATS, 1953?]
2583	RETURN OF THE INTERNED
2588	PARKHILL SCHOOL 1937
2589	[CORONATION DECORATIONS 1937]
2628	BORDER FESTIVALS OF 1956
2652	CROWNING OF PORTSOY GALA QUEEN
2655	PORTSOY ARMISTICE PARADE/ CULLEN GALA
2657	[FANCY DRESS PARADE, BUCKIE]
2662	ABERCHIRDER AND PORTSOY FANCY DRESS
2663	ABERCHIRDER BRITISH LEGION PARADE
2683	(DUFFTOWN SCENES)
2827-2828	(KATE KENNEDY PARADE)

2835-2837	LANARK LANIMER DAYS 1946-1949/1952
2847	[PORT ELPHINSTONE SCHOOL PICNIC]

PAINTERS and PAINTING

See ART and ARTISTS

PALACES

0037	QUEEN'S OWN HIGHLANDERS
0051	QUEEN IN SCOTLAND, THE
0054	ROYAL VISIT OF GEORGE VI
0142	ROYAL VISIT TO SCOTLAND
0182	EDINBURGH
0186	ROYAL VISIT TO SCOTLAND
0188	ROYAL OCCASIONS OF SCOTLAND
0284	CRAIGMOUNT SCHOOL FILMS
0303	FUTURE OF SCOTLAND
0364	PERTHSHIRE PANORAMA
0380	[SHOTS OF EDINBURGH]
0441	KING, GOD BLESS HIM, THE
0459	EDINBURGH FESTIVAL, THE
0472	SPIRIT OF THE GAMES, THE
0530	SCOTTISH SHALE INDUSTRY
0559	PATHE REVIEW OF THE YEAR
0665	(HOLIDAY IN LONDON)
0716	(PATHESCOPE GAZETTE/ NEW EMPIRE NEWS)
0819	ROYAL VISIT TO SCOTLAND
0829	BIRTHDAY GREETINGS TO QUEEN MARY
0968	ROYAL MILE EDINBURGH, THE
1028	HOMES IN BRITAIN
1112	STATE ENTRY INTO EDINBURGH
1113	HONOURS OF SCOTLAND
1231	EDINBURGH
1240	CAMERON HIGHLANDERS IN LONDON
1241	ROYAL MILE
1340	BRITAIN WELCOMES THE KING OF NORWAY IN EDINBURGH
1343	HISTORIC EDINBURGH
1483	EDINBURGH FESTIVAL OPENING CEREMONY
1487	EDINBURGH
1570	[RUSSELL'S LIBRARY FOOTAGE]
1653	EDINBURGH
1696	ROYAL SCOTLAND
1939	LOWLANDS OF SCOTLAND
2007	KING AND THE WHISKY, THE
2009	LIFE IN THE ORKNEYS
2024	FORTH - POWERHOUSE FOR INDUSTRY
2025	GATEWAY TO SECURITY
2123	(FFORDE COLLECTION)
2205	COUNTY ON THE MOVE
2210	GEORGE IV'S EDINBURGH
2217	LAND LIVED IN, A
2221	QUEEN IN SCOTLAND, THE
2224	SCOTLAND DANCES
2243	TAY ROAD BRIDGE
2256	SONG FOR PRINCE CHARLIE, A
2264	PRACTICAL ROMANTIC, SIR WALTER SCOTT
2605	(HOLIDAY SCOTLAND)
2735	(HERD'S CAFE AND FAMILY FARM)
2796	ZOO YEAR

359

PALAEONTOLOGY

| 0748 | SOUTH RONA EXPEDITION: THE DESCENT TO THE CAVE |
| 2069 | LIVING SEDIMENTS |

PANTOMIMES

See ENTERTAINERS and ENTERTAINMENT

PAPER TECHNOLOGY

0281	NORTH EAST CORNER
0506	ABERDEEN AND ITS INDUSTRIES
0586	DEE VALLEY
0601	(GREEN FAMILY IN INDIA, THE)
0885	FIFE
1222	PRESBYTERIAN TOUR OF CANADA
1524	HOME AND AWAY NO. 14
1738	[FIRE AT PAPER MILL, LINWOOD]
1765	LOTHIANS PART II, THE
1788	(BERTRAMS LTD.)
1956	INDUSTRIAL STIRLINGSHIRE
2040	FIBRE WEB, THE
2320	ABERDEEN
2756	HIGHLANDS, THE

PARACHUTES

0584	[SCOTTISH FLYING CLUB PAGEANT, RENFREW]
0646A	INAUGURATION OF INVERNESS AIRPORT
0781	(ARMY BOX WORK)
0856	OPENING INVERNESS MUNICIPAL AIRPORT BY HIS GRACE THE DUKE OF SUTHERLAND

PARADES

See PAGEANTS and PROCESSIONS

PARKS and PLAYGROUNDS

See also BOTANY

0008	GLASGOW UNIVERSITY CELEBRATES
0045	EMPIRE EXHIBITION
0062	GLASGOW - OUR CITY
0199	WINDSOR
0238	(ABERDEEN'S "BLACK FRIDAY")
0300	OUR PUBLIC PARKS
0317	OUR HOMES
0376D	OPENING OF DRUMPELLIER MOSS
0379	CITY SIDELIGHTS NO. 1
0385	SCOTTISH UNIVERSITIES
0393	OPENING OF SLATEFORD RECREATION GROUND
0417	MEN AND WOMEN OF TOMORROW
0429	LAND O' BURNS BAKERIES - INTRODUCTION
0455	SERVICE NOT SELF
0472	SPIRIT OF THE GAMES, THE
0518	DOLLAN AND THE DOOS
0519	(BAND CONCERT, KELVINGROVE PARK, 1928)
0531	(GUILD OF AID WORK IN THE GORBALS)
0573	GREEN OF GLASGOW, THE
0626	ROYAL ACADEMY SPORTS
0627	DEDICATION OF QUEEN'S PARK
0645	FROM TUNGSTEN ORE TO LUNA FILAMENT
0743	NEW YORK, THE WONDERFUL CITY
0760	GALASHIELS HISTORICAL PEACE PAGEANT
0769	[KILMARNOCK]
0809	(GLASGOW ACADEMY SPORTS)

0811	LOCHGELLY EQUITABLE CO-OPERATIVE SOCIETY'S SHOPPING WEEK
0819	ROYAL VISIT TO SCOTLAND
0823	(FAIR FESTIVAL)
0827	(INVERNESS COMPILATION)
0837	ENOUGH TO EAT? - THE NUTRITION FILM
0915	GLASGOW
0938	GLASGOW'S DOCKLANDS
0968	ROYAL MILE EDINBURGH, THE
0974	GLASGOW 1980
0986	GLASGOW
1049	GLASGOW, NO MEAN CITY
1062	WEALTH OF A NATION
1067	AMONG THE MANY VISITORS...
1068	SOME EVENTS IN GLASGOW 1937
1069	KIRKINTILLOCH
1070	BLIZZARD, FEBRUARY 1947
1104	(GLASGOW PARKS 1941)
1185	FAMILY RECORDS
1212	SCOTTISH HOLIDAY, A
1229	HOLIDAYS AT LARGS
1245	NEWMILNS CIVIC WEEK
1275	DEAR GREEN PLACE
1278	(EMPIRE EXHIBITION, BELLAHOUSTON PARK, GLASGOW)
1315	ST. ANDREWS 1916
1321	AYR
1324	FILM OF GLASGOW, A
1326	(MAY DAY PARADE, EDINBURGH 1937)
1332	GLASGOW 1938
1392	GREAT WESTERN ROAD 1980
1481	CLYDESCOPE
1487	EDINBURGH
1491	ROYAL JUBILEE CELEBRATIONS
1494	HOLIDAYS AT HOME 1942-'44
1497	[GLASGOW'S PROGRESS]
1499	[SCOTT CENTENARY, PERTH]
1514	[THURSO HIGH SCHOOL OPENING]
1526	HOME AND AWAY NO. 17
1548	[CROWNING OF LACE QUEEN, DARVEL, 22ND AUG 1953]
1583	BOYS' BRIGADE
1610	EDUCATION AUTHORITY OF GLASGOW SPECIAL SERVICES
1611	ROYAL HIGHLAND SHOW, DUNDEE 1957
1632	[OPENING COOPER PARK, ELGIN, AUGUST 1903]
1666	CAPITAL GARDEN
1691	GREENOCK PLANS AHEAD
1721	LET GLASGOW FLOURISH
1723	PROCESSION IN COMMEMORATION OF CALTON WEAVERS/ ROBERT SMILLIE CENTENARY
1725	[LOST TREASURES]
1726	[BOYS' BRIGADE RECRUITING MARCHES, LEITH]
1748	[ULRO KIDDIES PICNIC]
1800	PRINCESS STREET CHURCH EVENTS OF 1937
1854	(PROVOST FLETT COLLECTION)
1857	DIXINE PICTORIAL
1871	DUMBARTON 1944-1946
1966	HUNTLY GALA QUEEN
1997	FALKIRK
1999	(EDINBURGH)
2001	[NORTH OF SCOTLAND - WESTER ROSS]

2022	SCOTTISH MINERS GALA DAY
2134	GLASGOW'S SUNDAY 1963
2142	GLASGOW AND DISTRICT CO-OPERATIVE ASSOCIATION
2235	SONGS OF SCOTLAND
2301	TAYPORT PICNICS 1951/'52
2320	ABERDEEN
2395	CHURCH ACTIVITIES, ST. MARTIN'S, EDINBURGH
2415	OLD ROTHESAY
2469	MISSILE WEAPONS
2484	(PAUL ROBESON AT GLASGOW MAY DAY)
2631	HOLIDAY SCOTLAND
2673	KELVINGROVE PARK
2724	MARIAN YEAR, THE
2725	LOURDES CENTENARY CELEBRATION
2726	(CATHOLIC YOUNG MEN'S SOCIETY CENTENARY CELEBRATIONS, GLASGOW)
2727	KIRKCALDY MOTOR CYCLE ROAD RACES
2792	AYR FROM THE AULD BRIG
2793	EDINBURGH ON PARADE
2804	AS LONG AS YOU'RE YOUNG
2814	BOTANIC GARDENS AND OLD GLASGOW

PEARLS and PEARL FISHING
See MOLLUSCS

PEAT and PEAT CUTTING

0027	SKYE
0028	WESTERN ISLES
0034	FACE OF SCOTLAND
0112	CROFTER BOY
0120	CROFTERS, THE
0136	HOLIDAYING IN HARRIS
0155	WEST OF INVERNESS
0196	ROAD THROUGH THE SUNSET ISLES
0256	EILEAN AN FHRAOICH [ISLE OF LEWIS]
0281	NORTH EAST CORNER
0354	(CONTINENTAL HOLIDAYS)
0363	OVER THE SEA TO SKYE
0392	LIFE ON THE FAROE ISLANDS
0549	ISLE OF LEWIS
0622	PRIDE AND PROGRESS
0928	LIFE IN THE HIGHLANDS
0980	SCENES FROM A SHETLAND CROFT LIFE
0981	CROFTER'S LIFE IN SHETLAND, A
0991	RUGGED ISLAND
1062	WEALTH OF A NATION
1063	THEY MADE THE LAND
1096	WAY THE MONEY GOES, THE
1127	DA MAKKIN O' A KESHIE
1286	SHETLAND, PEOPLE OF MANY LANDS
1342	(ROCKET RANGE, BENBECULA)
1616	(SHETLAND - A FEW ASPECTS)
1701	ERISKAY - A POEM OF REMOTE LIVES
2202	BY LOCHABER I WILL GO
2212	HEBRIDEAN HIGHWAY
2242	IN GREAT WATERS
2259	PRIDE OF ISLANDS, A
2547	(COWAL GAMES, DUNOON 1933)
2593	MISTY ISLE
2681	HERE AND THERE/ WINTER IN WICK

2730	(J.H. JOHNSON - SEQUENCES)
2858	[OUTER HEBRIDES - HUMAN ACTIVITIES]

PEEBLES-SHIRE

0882	RIVER TWEED
0914	SOUTHERN SCOTLAND
1328	BEAUTY SPOTS IN GREAT BRITAIN
1475	[EARL HAIG UNVEILS PEEBLES WAR MEMORIAL]
1476	[PEEBLES BELTANE FESTIVALS 1920/'22]
1477	PEEBLES MARCH RIDING AND BELTANE FESTIVAL 1949
1759	BY BUS TO THE HILLS
2264	PRACTICAL ROMANTIC, SIR WALTER SCOTT
2591	FAIR RIVER, THE
2705	FISHERS ALL
2708	PEEBLES BELTANE QUEEN GAMES

PERFUMES

2641	DEESIDE INDUSTRY, A

PERTHSHIRE

0098	LIEDER DER VOLKER (SONGS OF THE PEOPLE)
0107	FREEDOM OF ABERFELDY
0255A	CAMPING WE WILL GO, A
0255B	LETTER FROM JOHNNY
0284	CRAIGMOUNT SCHOOL FILMS
0303	FUTURE OF SCOTLAND
0323	TWO SISTERS
0362	HIGHLAND HOSPITALITY
0364	PERTHSHIRE PANORAMA
0501	ROUTES AND CENTRES
0504	TAY VALLEY
0509	FICKLE FORTUNE
0512	STIRLING: GATEWAY TO THE HIGHLANDS
0531	(GUILD OF AID WORK IN THE GORBALS)
0541	[PERTH AND KINROSS BYE-ELECTION]
0631	NORTHERN SCOTLAND
0714	SCOTLAND
0752	CRIEFF - OUR TOWN
0753	[CRIEFF MASTER]
0785	HEART IS HIGHLAND, THE
0798	STRATHYRE TO BROADFORD, SKYE, BY TRAIN AND BOAT
0841	CHURCHILL RECEIVES FREEDOM OF PERTH
0935	CRIEFF HIGHLAND GATHERING
1073B	(DUKE AND DUCHESS OF YORK IN PERTH)
1350	RIVER FORTH
1375	PERTH HISTORICAL PAGEANT
1381B	FERGUSLIE THREAD WORKS OUTING TO BRAEMAR
1389	(GROSVENOR TOPICALS NO. 2)
1453	LADY OF THE LAKE
1478	SCOTS ACCLAIM ROYAL FAMILY
1485	(GUILD OF AID ANNUAL TREATS)
1488	EXCURSION TO WEMBLEY
1489	PERTH PRESENTATION
1491	ROYAL JUBILEE CELEBRATIONS
1499	[SCOTT CENTENARY, PERTH]
1535	[LOCAL EVENTS, INVERNESS AREA]
1538	LOCH LOMOND
1602	BONNETS OVER THE BORDER
1672	SCHOOL MASTER, THE
1731	SRDA CONFERENCE, GLENEAGLES
1750	[ULRO GOLF CLUB 1956]

361

1768	Job for the future, a
1783	River tay
1790	(cea conference, gleneagles c1949)
1803	Honeymoon tour
1872	Rural round about
1882	Western perthshire
1888	Touring the trossachs
1889	Loch lomond and the trossachs
1891	(hostel ski trip)
1953	Service commemorating 750th anniversary/ opening of Queen's bridge perth
1989	(simpson family film)
2021	Views of perth
2074	(stein family - school life)
2130-2131	Air canada silver broom 1969/ 1975
2135	Film-making at crieff
2143	Aberfeldy agricultural show 1952
2221	Queen in scotland, the
2243	Tay road bridge
2257	Tayside
2264	Practical romantic, sir walter scott
2368	(ncb staff bus outings)
2392	Lomond mc/ ski-ing
2396	Scotland through the lens
2450	[century of civil engineering, a]
2477	Present for the groom, a
2498	[unica, glasgow 1951]
2499	[crieff hydro weekend]
2561	(cruise and holidays)
2573	Road to lewis 1936, the
2609	Opening of the new queen's bridge, perth
2631	Holiday scotland
2638	Tales from the north
2668	Skimsters, the
2676	Old time movies
2746	Trossachs, the
2755	Circle of care
2822	[cart horse show]
2859	More than you think

PETROLEUM (oil industry, etc.)

0167	Paraffin young
0345	Busman's holiday
0487	An eye to the future
0530	Scottish shale industry
0587	Central scotland
0692	Beneath the north sea
0693	Beryl's saga: the first chapter
0694	Wells of montrose, the
0912	Heart of scotland, the
1351	County clerk
1394	Oil from iran
1395	In the land of the shah
1544	Oil blasting in scotland
1570	[russell's library footage]
1602	Bonnets over the border
1638	Wire lines
1690	[finnart ocean terminal]
1765	Lothians part ii, the

1868	Bank for scotland
1956	Industrial stirlingshire
1963	Thru' the kyles
2228	Plan for living, a
2231	Smiths in scotland, the
2236	Sea city greenock
2253	Water, water everywhere
2257	Tayside
2259	Pride of islands, a
2433	[clydeside - 1st british oil drilling ship]
2434	[ram-bow tanker]
2584	Harthill services

PHOTOGRAPHY

See also CINEMATOGRAPHY

0044	Glasgow and the clyde coast
0426	[year of destiny]
0432	Motion pictures the "kodak" way
0777	(miscellaneous scenes, renfrewshire)
0779	(more speed for less bawbees)
1114	In the shadow
1201	[god of creation]
1204	Voice of the deep
1289	Setting up the bolex s-221 (projector)
1322	(to ireland by air)
1437	Our papers
1481	Clydescope
1496	Sun pictures, the
1775	[photographic convention, glasgow 1898]
1968	Underwater story
2254	Erskine bridge, the
2327	[halfway to paradise: the cut]
2374	Annan, riding of the marches 1925
2754	Prime time: media week in stenhousemuir primary school

PHYSICALLY HANDICAPPED

See HANDICAP

PICNICS

0012	Glasgow's yesterdays
1150	[pantomime, show picnic, and variety]
1185	Family records
1231	Edinburgh
1252	Focus on bridgeton
1494	Holidays at home 1942-'44
1748	[ulro kiddies picnic]
1766	[scott family film]
1799	Princess street church [port glasgow]
1807	Fenwick events of 1934
2085	Fire at rothesay pier
2290	Jubilee day in tayport, 6th may 1935
2301	Tayport picnics 1951/'52
2394	(preston family film 1962)
2395	Church activities, st. Martin's, edinburgh
2502-2503	(Shearer family film)
2513	(macfarlane family 1938)
2520	(macfarlane family 1932)
2525	[staff picnic 1937]
2526	[picnic to ballater, no. 2]
2528	[staff picnic. Golf and willie elder]

2529	[SHOP PICNIC, CARNOUSTIE]
2533	(BENZIE'S WORKS OUTING)
2546	(DORNOCH HOLIDAY)
2547	(COWAL GAMES, DUNOON 1933)
2569-2570	(PLEASANCE TRUST BOYS' CLUB)
2576	HOLIDAYS 1933
2577A	FAMILY FILMS 1931-1938
2607	[DUNGAVEL OPEN DAY]
2625	ANNUAL PICNIC, PRINGLE'S 1950
2654	[PORTSOY SUNDAY SCHOOL PICNIC]
2656	[PORTSOY SUNDAY SCHOOL PICNIC]
2659	[PORTSOY SUNDAY SCHOOL PICNIC]
2736	(HERD FAMILY FILM)
2741	(KATE KENNEDY PROCESSION AND KIRKCALDY RIFLE RANGE)
2784	(HADDO EVENTS)
2801	(SCENES OF ORKNEY)
2805	PLEASURE ISLAND
2821	(MONTGOMERY FAMILY OUTINGS)
2847	[PORT ELPHINSTONE SCHOOL PICNIC]

PIERS

0253	TAM TRAUCHLE'S TROUBLES
0531	(GUILD OF AID WORK IN THE GORBALS)
0545	ATLANTIC TRAWLER
0568	NOBEL'S TRIP TO ROTHESAY
0670	(SCENES ON THE CLYDE AND EDINBURGH ZOO)
0703	CLYDE, THE
0749	(LOCAL FILM FROM KIRKINTILLOCH AREA)
0773	NORTHERN OUTPOST
0797	COASTS OF CLYDE, THE
0893	SUNNY DAYS
0898	(AGRICULTURAL SHOW, ISLAY?)
1061	DUNDEE
1307	(NOTRE DAME COLLEGE GRADUATES AND WEDDING)
1397	(LAUNCH OF LIFEBOAT, "SIR ARTHUR ROSE")
1398	("PS LOCHMOR" AT KYLE)
1405	(UNIDENTIFIED STEAMER ON CLYDE COAST)
1432	LOCH LOMOND
1452	(CLYDE COAST STEAMERS)
1481	CLYDESCOPE
1538	LOCH LOMOND
1539	(LOCH LOMOND PILOT FILM)
1587	[SINGER] SPORTS GALA 1961

PIGS

0440	PIGS IN CLOVER
0637	ANIMAL HUSBANDRY
0813	KIRKCALDY HOSPITAL PAGEANT
0936	CROFTERS OF WESTER ROSS
1764	LOTHIANS PART I, THE
2003	[ST. CUTHBERT'S NINETIETH BIRTHDAY]
2163	PIGS
2370	FARMER'S BOY, THE
2721	SPRING IN GALLOWAY
2734	(FAMILY WEDDING AND LIFE AT "SHANZIE")
2748	AT THE CATTLE MARKET
2753	FARM BABIES
2796	ZOO YEAR

PIPE BANDS

0034	FACE OF SCOTLAND

0044	GLASGOW AND THE CLYDE COAST
0081	HIGHLAND GAMES
0164	ABERDEEN
0180	DUMFRIES 1953 GUID NYCHBURRIS FESTIVAL
0233	GATHERING OF BRAEMAR ROYAL HIGHLAND SOCIETY
0241	CINEMA NEWS, ABERDEEN
0256	EILEAN AN FHRAOICH [ISLE OF LEWIS]
0303	FUTURE OF SCOTLAND
0310	[RAF LEUCHARS RECEIVE FREEDOM OF THE CITY OF ST. ANDREWS]
0336	BO'NESS CHILDREN'S FAIR FESTIVAL
0338-0339	BO'NESS CHILDREN'S FAIR FESTIVAL
0362	HIGHLAND HOSPITALITY
0363	OVER THE SEA TO SKYE
0364	PERTHSHIRE PANORAMA
0376A	WHERE EVERYBODY GOES
0411	BO'NESS CHILDREN'S FESTIVAL
0413	BO'NESS FAIR FESTIVAL 1952
0449	GORDON HIGHLANDERS LEAVE FOR THE BOER WAR
0482	BORDER WEAVE
0508	SCOTTISH TRADE MISSION TO CANADA
0512	STIRLING: GATEWAY TO THE HIGHLANDS
0516	(UNIVERSITY NEWS)
0522	SAY IT WITH FLOWERS
0525	(VISIT OF DUCHESS OF GLOUCESTER)
0532	CORONATION NEWSREEL
0533	CEREMONIAL PARADE AT RAF WEST FREUGH
0536	(NEIL ARMSTRONG IN LANGHOLM)
0566	ARDEER SPORTS 1929
0592	WISHAW CO-OPERATIVE SOCIETY OUTING
0595	AT INVERNESS TERRITORIAL ARMY JUBILEE
0598	[YOUTH SERVICES PARADE]
0599	HIGHLAND GATHERING
0600	[REMEMBRANCE DAY 1956]
0625	WISHAW CO-OP GALA DAY
0639A	TROOPING THE COLOUR
0639B	FERGUSLIE MILLS IN INVERNESS
0762A	GALASHIELS WAR MEMORIAL, THE
0791	[BORDERS LOCAL NEWSREELS NO. 1]
0796	DUMFRIESSHIRE JOURNEY
0797	COASTS OF CLYDE, THE
0803	(DANCE SEQUENCES)
0807	INVERNESS REMEMBRANCE SUNDAY
0808	GORDONSTOUN SCHOOL GARDEN FETE
0813	KIRKCALDY HOSPITAL PAGEANT
0825	[TAIN CARNIVAL AND ELGIN GALA WEEK]
0861	(GLASGOW 1947)
0873B	(HIGHLAND GAMES, ABERDEEN)
0875B	FLICKS ROYAL HIGHLAND GATHERING AT BRAEMAR
0878	(GUID NYCHBURRIS CELEBRATIONS)
0879	(KIRKCALDY PAGEANT WEEK 1951)
0880	GLENROTHES FESTIVAL WEEK
0883-0884	[TAIN CARNIVAL 1937/ 1949]
0896	(PRE MATCH DISPLAY, HAMPDEN STADIUM)
0899	HAMPDEN STORY, THE
0939	GLASGOW WELCOMES THE QUEEN
0943	(JOURNEY THROUGH BARRHEAD AND REVIEW OF THE FESTIVAL YEAR 1951)
0967	LOCHGELLY AT WORK AND PLAY

363

PLAYGROUNDS
See PARKS and PLAYGROUNDS

PLOUGHS and PLOUGHING

POETS and POETRY

1155	PORPHYRIA
2144	AULD TAM MCGUIRE
2185	AT THE ZOO (A.A. MILNE)
2792	AYR FROM THE AULD BRIG
2802	NORMAN MACCAIG: A MAN IN MY POSITION
2863	(SAWKINS NO. 2)

POLICE

0106	GLASGOW'S POLICE
0193	THINGS THAT HAPPEN NO. 3
0373	THINGS THAT HAPPEN NO. 1
0379	CITY SIDELIGHTS NO. 1
0494	COUNTRY POLICEMAN
0716	(PATHESCOPE GAZETTE/ NEW EMPIRE NEWS)
0720	[HIGHLAND SHOW, DUNDEE]
0813	KIRKCALDY HOSPITAL PAGEANT
0923	BENNY LYNCH SMASHES HIS WAY TO VICTORY...
0926A	WORLD FLYWEIGHT CHAMPIONSHIP, BENNY LYNCH V PETER KANE
0960A	LOCHGELLY OLD AGE PENSIONERS DRIVE TO CROOK O' DEVON
0997	OUR POLICE
1049	GLASGOW, NO MEAN CITY
1085	CROWD GATHERS, A
1107	(DRINK AND DRIVE COMMERCIALS)
2320	ABERDEEN
2537	CONSEQUENCES
2538	IT'S MORE THAN A JOB
2539	ARE YOU NEXT?
2540	IT WASN'T ME MISTER
2603	ROYAL OCCASION, A
2615	SETTLED OUT OF COURT
2658	KEITH SHOW 1948
2808	AROUND DUNDEE IN THE 1930'S
2814	BOTANIC GARDENS AND OLD GLASGOW

POLITICS (misc.)

See also ELECTIONS/ PARLIAMENT/ SOCIALISM/ SPEECHES

0032	SCOTLAND'S WATER SUPPLY
0021	LORD LOTHIAN PRESENTS HIS CREDENTIALS AT THE WHITE HOUSE
0315	HOW OUR CITY IS GOVERNED
0913	WHAT ABOUT THE WORKERS
1437	OUR PAPERS
1723	PROCESSION IN COMMEMORATION OF CALTON WEAVERS/ ROBERT SMILLIE CENTENARY
2777	SECRETARY OF STATE (FOR SCOTLAND)

POSTAL SERVICES

0155	WEST OF INVERNESS
0259	ARRIVAL OF THE MAIL STEAMER IN LERWICK
0418	ST. KILDA - BRITAIN'S LONELIEST ISLE
0605	LESSONS THROUGH THE LETTERBOX
0802	WILL YE NO' COME BACK AGAIN
0911	ST. KILDA - THE LONELY ISLANDS
0936	CROFTERS OF WESTER ROSS
0937	DUMFRIES, QUEEN OF THE SOUTH
1087	(HOLIDAY AT ARROCHAR)
1436	ORKNEY - SCENES AROUND SHAPINSAY
1617	(SHETLAND AND FAIR ISLE SCENES)
1618	FAIR ISLE, THE

2009	LIFE IN THE ORKNEYS
2032	PHYSICS FOR ALL (AN EXPERIMENTAL APPROACH)
2232	I REMEMBER, I REMEMBER
2250	LOCH LOMOND
2278	[HIGHLAND FUND IN ACTION, HIGHLAND INITIATIVE]
2478	SPRING IN SCOTLAND
2731	(GREAT NORTH OF SCOTLAND RAILWAY FILMS)

POSTERS

0334	RARE TEAR, A
0336	BO'NESS CHILDREN'S FAIR FESTIVAL
0374	HAIR
0379	CITY SIDELIGHTS NO. 1
0486	GLEN IS OURS, THE
0567	HARRY KEMP'S "SCOTCH BROTH" ENTERTAINERS
0570	GREAT WESTERN ROAD 1922
0612	YOUR SILENT SALESMAN
0647	TREASURE ISLAND
0653C	[ANNA NEAGLE]
0785	HEART IS HIGHLAND, THE
0904	(TEAZIE WEAZIE)
0974	GLASGOW 1980
1486	EDINBURGH FESTIVAL - PATHE
1491	ROYAL JUBILEE CELEBRATIONS
1493	FESTIVAL IN EDINBURGH
1607	THEATRE FIRE IN EDINBURGH
1700	[CIVIL DEFENCE SCOTTISH]
2209	FROM GLASGOW GREEN TO BENDIGO
2862	HAP DANCES, THE

POTTERY

See CERAMIC ARTS

POULTRY

0367	BANK AHEAD
0497	DUMFRIES - A MARKET TOWN
0773	NORTHERN OUTPOST
1436	OEKNEY - SCENES AROUND SHAPINSAY
1616	[SHETLAND - A FEW ASPECTS]
1655	BARRA
1784	HIGHLAND CASTLES
2003	[ST. CUTHBERT'S NINETIETH BIRTHDAY]
2009	LIFE IN THE ORKNEYS
2162	ON THE POULTRY FARM

POWER RESOURCES

0029	HARNESSING THE HILLS
0034	FACE OF SCOTLAND
0038	FRASERS' RETURN
0057	OUR TRANSPORT SERVICES
0153	KENYA TO DURBAN
0154	STEEL AND ENGINEERING
0251	INTRODUCING SCOTLAND
0274	HIGHLAND LADDIE
0279	POWER FOR THE HIGHLANDS
0296	SCOTLAND AND THE NEW WORLD
0303	FUTURE OF SCOTLAND
0345	BUSMAN'S HOLIDAY
0398	RIVER CLYDE, THE
0502	RAW MATERIALS
0507	NORTH OF THE GREAT GLEN

365

0580	RIVER CLYDE
0587	CENTRAL SCOTLAND
0622	PRIDE AND PROGRESS
0631	NORTHERN SCOTLAND
0785	HEART IS HIGHLAND, THE
0801	[CAITHNESS, ORKNEY]
0805	(KIRKWALL, WICK, DOUNREAY)
0914	SOUTHERN SCOTLAND
0986	GLASGOW
1062	WEALTH OF A NATION
1096	WAY THE MONEY GOES, THE
1132	SOUTHERN SCOTLAND
1325	CRUACHAN HYDRO-ELECTRIC, ROYAL OPENING
1342	(ROCKET RANGE, BENBECULA)
1351	COUNTY CLERK
1430	WESTER ROSS
1497	[GLASGOW'S PROGRESS]
1520-1521	HOME AND AWAY NOS 10, 11
1524-1525	HOME AND AWAY NOS 14, 16
1528	HOME AND AWAY NO. 19
1531	STEAM
1725	[LOST TREASURES]
1783	RIVER TAY
1787	[CLYDE RIVER]
1820	FORTH - POWERHOUSE FOR INDUSTRY
1854	(PROVOST FLETT COLLECTION)
1855	REVIEW OF THE YEAR 1950
1997	FALKIRK
2024	FORTH - POWERHOUSE FOR INDUSTRY
2040	FIBRE WEB, THE
2057	BEARDMORE STORY, THE
2213	HIGHLAND CAPITAL
2214	HOLLOW MOUNTAIN, THE
2221	QUEEN IN SCOTLAND, THE
2239	METAL IN HARMONY
2240	RIVERS AT WORK
2253	WATER, WATER EVERYWHERE
2254	ERSKINE BRIDGE, THE
2257	TAYSIDE
2366	FOLLOWING THE RIVER NO. 2: THE MIDDLE STRETCH
2369	LORD ROBENS INTERVIEW
2450	[CENTURY OF CIVIL ENGINEERING, A]
2585	DEMOLITION OF CHIMNEYS
2604	(REPORT ON NORTH AYRSHIRE TOWNS)
2650	HIGHLAND LINE
2756	HIGHLANDS, THE
2790	CRUACHAN

PRIME MINISTERS

0025	(HISTORY OF THE TAILOR AND GARMENT WORKERS UNION)
0128	KING'S VISIT TO CANADA,THE
0516	(UNIVERSITY NEWS)
0541	[PERTH AND KINROSS BYE-ELECTION]
0547	BURNS MEMORIAL
0553	FUNERAL OF MISS JEAN ARMOUR BURNS BROWN
0559	PATHE REVIEW OF THE YEAR
0713	REVIEW OF THE YEAR 1940
0716	(PATHESCOPE GAZETTE/ NEW EMPIRE NEWS)
0717	PRIME MINISTER AND PRESIDENT

0818	PRIME MINISTER IN SCOTLAND
0913	WHAT ABOUT THE WORKERS
1084	BOMB FELL, A
1225	NEWS PARADE, THE
1340	BRITAIN WELCOMES THE KING OF NORWAY IN EDINBURGH

PRINTING (paper)
See MACHINERY/ NEWSPAPERS and MAGAZINES

PRIORIES
See MONASTIC BUILDINGS

PRISONS
0818	PRIME MINISTER IN SCOTLAND
1705	HIGHLAND TOUR, CROOKSTON STREET SCHOOL

PROCESSIONS
See PAGEANTS and PROCESSIONS

PROPAGANDA
See also the TEMPERANCE MOVEMENT

0028	WESTERN ISLES
0030	IT BEGAN ON THE CLYDE
0033	HIGHLAND DOCTOR
0107	FREEDOM OF ABERFELDY
0113	HOSPITAL TEAM
0120	CROFTERS, THE
0194A	MINISTRY OF FOOD FLASHES
0194B	CHRISTMAS 1943
0266	CROWNING OF THE MERCHANT NAVY QUEEN, THE
0271	GOOD HEALTH TO SCOTLAND
0272	BIRTHDAY
0273	YOUR CHILDREN'S TEETH
0279	POWER FOR THE HIGHLANDS
0294	START IN LIFE, A
0490	FARM IS RECLAIMED, A
0495	SEEDS OF PROSPERITY
0545	ATLANTIC TRAWLER
0738	EATING AT WORK
0741	MACHINES AND MEN
0866	(GIVE US MORE SHIPS)
0867	(MINISTRY OF FOOD FLASHES)
0957	MINISTRY OF INFORMATION TRAILERS
1099	HELL UNLTD
1236	(GREEN'S 1917 FILM SERVICE)
1238A/B	SCOTTISH MOVING PICTURE NEWS NO. 32
1359	MINISTRY OF FOOD FLASHES

PUBLIC HEALTH
0030	IT BEGAN ON THE CLYDE
0033	HIGHLAND DOCTOR
0035	SCOTTISH WOMEN'S HOSPITALS
0113	HOSPITAL TEAM
0189	BLOOD TRANSFUSION IN BATHGATE
0231	SCOTLAND FOR FITNESS
0271	GOOD HEALTH TO SCOTLAND
0272	BIRTHDAY
0273	YOUR CHILDREN'S TEETH
0294	START IN LIFE, A
0331	OUR HEALTH SERVICES
0365	BLOOD CAN WORK MIRACLES
0484	OESOPHAGEAL SPEECH

RACE COURSES
See EQUESTRIAN SPORTS

RADAR

0390	RADAR
2046	MAGIC KEY, THE
2242	IN GREAT WATERS

RADIO

0318	RADIO SCOTLAND, PIRATE RADIO SHIP
0391	[HAPPY IN THE MORNING]
1059	CHILDREN'S STORY, THE
1269	SKYWAY AMBULANCE
1631	THIS LITTLE WORLD
2046	MAGIC KEY, THE
2126	BIRTH OF A NEW SOUND
2331	[HALFWAY TO PARADISE: NAKED RADIO]

RAILWAYS and RAIL TRANSPORT (gen.)
See also STATIONS/ STEAM TRAINS

0011	HARRY LAUDER LEAVES FOR AMERICA
0012	GLASGOW'S YESTERDAYS
0020	JAMES WATT
0042	ABERDEEN 1906
0056	TRAM ROUTES IN GLASGOW AND STEAM RAILWAYS
0057	OUR TRANSPORT SERVICES
0062	GLASGOW - OUR CITY
0108	GRAND UNION CANAL
0114	WAVERLEY STEPS
0155	WEST OF INVERNESS
0251	INTRODUCING SCOTLAND
0296	SCOTLAND AND THE NEW WORLD
0366	STEP AHEAD, A
0387	BIG MILL, THE
0388	CALLER HERRIN
0421	GLASGOW SUBWAY
0422	[BENNIE RAIL PLANE]
0433	SOLDIER COMES HOME, A
0526	OUR CITY - TODAY AND TOMORROW
0580	RIVER CLYDE
0605	LESSONS THROUGH THE LETTERBOX
0619	BEYOND THE SUNSET
0639B	FERGUSLIE MILLS IN INVERNESS
0648	DUKE AND DUCHESS OF YORK AND ROYAL ACADEMY SPORTS
0713	REVIEW OF THE YEAR 1940
0722	BILLY GRAHAM IN GLASGOW
0752	CRIEFF - OUR TOWN
0779	(MORE SPEED FOR LESS BAWBEES)
0785	HEART IS HIGHLAND, THE
0797	COASTS OF CLYDE, THE
0827	(INVERNESS COMPILATION)
0835	RAILWAY JOURNEY
0854	(SIR HENRY FOWLER)
0889	IMMORTAL MEMORY OF ROBERT BURNS
0912	HEART OF SCOTLAND, THE
0970	(EAST NEUK OF FIFE STEAM RAILWAY)
0974	GLASGOW 1980
0975	GLENROTHES
1049	GLASGOW, NO MEAN CITY
1061	DUNDEE

1108	INCIDENT AT LONGNIDDRY
1222	PRESBYTERIAN TOUR OF CANADA
1232	[GLASGOW TRAMWAYS AND CLARKSTON TROLLEY BUSES]
1252	FOCUS ON BRIDGETON
1267	(STATION FAREWELLS)
1341	GEORGE BENNIE RAIL PLANE SYSTEM OF TRANSPORT
1389	(GROSVENOR TOPICALS NO. 2)
1497	[GLASGOW'S PROGRESS]
1686	CALEDONIAN CANAL, THE
1762	RIVER IS SPANNED, THE
1766	[SCOTT FAMILY FILM]
1768	JOB FOR THE FUTURE, A
1855	REVIEW OF THE YEAR 1950
2000A	BENS, THE
2032	PHYSICS FOR ALL (AN EXPERIMENTAL APPROACH)
2066	ACTION FOR DISASTER
2099	(JOSEPH HISLOP COLLECTION)
2100	RAILWAY RIDE OVER THE TAY BRIDGE
2136	[STEAM EXCURSIONS 1959]
2189	[SCENES AROUND HALFWAY AND DISTRICT]
2204	COUNTY OF THE CLYDE
2205	COUNTY ON THE MOVE
2208	FORTH ROAD BRIDGE, THE
2232	I REMEMBER, I REMEMBER
2243	TAY ROAD BRIDGE
2257	TAYSIDE
2260	LINE TO SKYE, THE
2309	STEALING AWAY TO STORNOWAY
2340	[KILSYTH RAILWAY STATION]
2388	BONNIE SCOTLAND
2527	[KING GEORGE V AT BALLATER]
2573	ROAD TO LEWIS 1936, THE
2731	(GREAT NORTH OF SCOTLAND RAILWAY FILMS)
2732	(MARQUIS OF ABERDEEN'S RAILWAY FILMS)
2756	HIGHLANDS, THE
2818	BARS OF SILVER

REFUSE and REFUSE DISPOSAL

0420	KEEPING OUR CITY CLEAN
0605	LESSONS THROUGH THE LETTERBOX

RELIGION and RELIGIONS
See also CATHEDRALS/ CHURCHES/ MONASTIC BUILDINGS

0124	MAKING OF THE HOLY BIBLE
0142	ROYAL VISIT TO SCOTLAND
0188	ROYAL OCCASIONS OF SCOTLAND
0192	DAVID LIVINGSTONE
0196	ROAD THROUGH THE SUNSET ISLES
0236	PORTHLETHEN CHURCH
0284	CRAIGMOUNT SCHOOL FILMS
0473	SERMON IN STONE, A
0550	STORNOWAY
0643	SALTCOATS PILGRIMAGE TO LOURDES
0722	BILLY GRAHAM IN GLASGOW
0800	(CAITHNESS, ORKNEY, KIRKWALL)
0804	GREAT SCOT - MARY SLESSOR
0874	(PRIEST'S FUNERAL)
1050	(ALL SCOTLAND CRUSADE)
1096	WAY THE MONEY GOES, THE

RENTS
See PUBLIC REVENUE

REPTILES

RESIDENTIAL HOMES
See INSTITUTIONAL CARE

RESTAURANTS

RIVERS
See also CLYDE RIVER

ROADS

ROCK CLIMBING

See CLIMBING

ROSS-SHIRE

372

2737	GATHERING OF THE BRAEMAR ROYAL HIGHLAND SOCIETY, THE
2784	(HADDO EVENTS)
2785	ORDER OF ST. JOHN, THE
2786	(QUEEN MOTHER'S VISIT TO HADDO)
2800	ABERDEEN SCHOOL SPORTS
2831	[DUCHESS OF YORK IN ST. ANDREWS]
2838	(PRENTICE FAMILY EVENTS)
2872	[DUNOON OCCASIONS]

RUGBY

0182	EDINBURGH
0186	ROYAL VISIT TO SCOTLAND
0241	CINEMA NEWS, ABERDEEN
0265A	RUGBY, SCOTLAND'S TRIUMPH
0265B/C	RUGBY, SCOTLAND V IRELAND
0288	CALLY HOUSE
0291	CHILDREN OF THE CITY
0381	[ROYAL TOUR OF SCOTLAND]
0516	(UNIVERSITY NEWS)
0762B	RUGBY LEAGUE CHAMPIONSHIP
0792	[BORDERS LOCAL NEWSREELS NO. 2]
0819	ROYAL VISIT TO SCOTLAND
1112	STATE ENTRY INTO EDINBURGH
1416	RUGBY UNION FOOTBALL
1487	EDINBURGH
1494	HOLIDAYS AT HOME 1942-'44
1656	RUGBY HINTS NO. 2
1657	RUGBY HINTS NO. 5
2207	FETTES
2220	PLAYING AWAY
2223	BORDERS, THE
2237	ONE DAY IN IRVINE

RUSSIA

See EASTERN EUROPE

SAILING SHIPS

0511	SCHOONER "CAPTAIN SCOTT"
0908	INDUSTRIAL BRITAIN
1398	(PS "LOCHMOR" AT KYLE)
1470	MORAY SEA SCHOOL
1784	HIGHLAND CASTLES
2194	"MAURETANIA" AND "QUEEN MARY"
2518	(MACFARLANE FAMILY - CLYDE CRUISE 1934)
2519	(GLASGOW FLOODS 1936)
2765	ESKIMO LIFE IN GREENLAND
2850	[MOVING THE UNICORN]

SALMON and SALMON FISHING

0039	UPSTREAM
0112	CROFTER BOY
0231	SCOTLAND FOR FITNESS
0302	LAND O' CLANS
0364	PERTHSHIRE PANORAMA
0367	BANK AHEAD
0504	TAY VALLEY
0507	NORTH OF THE GREAT GLEN
0586	DEE VALLEY
0882	RIVER TWEED
0932	ARDNAMURCHAN
0934	CROFTING IN SKYE

0936	CROFTERS OF WESTER ROSS
1060	SEAFOOD
1061	DUNDEE
1078	SAGA OF THE SILVER HORDE
1338	(FAMILY HOLIDAYS 1936/'38)
1399	(SALMON FISHING AT BRORA)
1430	WESTER ROSS
1650	SALMON FISHING IN SKYE
1681	SALMON FISHING BY THE RING NET METHOD
1783	RIVER TAY
1794	NETTING SALMON
1804	IN THE LAND OF LORNE
2240	RIVERS AT WORK
2243	TAY ROAD BRIDGE
2250	LOCH LOMOND
2257	TAYSIDE
2259	PRIDE OF ISLANDS, A
2268	HOLIDAYS 1934
2631	HOLIDAY SCOTLAND
2638	TALES FROM THE NORTH

SCANDINAVIA

See NORTHERN EUROPE

SCHOOLS

See also EDUCATION

0007	SCOTS OF TOMORROW
0034	FACE OF SCOTLAND
0049B	(SCHOOL SPORTS DAY)
0090	CHARLES RENNIE MACKINTOSH
0112	CROFTER BOY
0115	LORD PROVOST P.J. DOLLAN VISITS GOVAN SCHOOLS
0245B	SCHOOL SPORTS
0271	GOOD HEALTH TO SCOTLAND
0284	CRAIGMOUNT SCHOOL FILMS
0288	CALLY HOUSE
0291	CHILDREN OF THE CITY
0294	START IN LIFE, A
0306	HAPPY WEEKEND
0307	NEW DAY
0316	OUR SCHOOLS
0416	LEARNING FOR LIVING
0417	MEN AND WOMEN OF TOMORROW
0531	(GUILD OF AID WORK IN THE GORBALS)
0594	RURAL SCHOOL
0626	ROYAL ACADEMY SPORTS
0723	[CO-OP ADVERTISEMENTS STRATHCLYDE SCHOOLWEAR]
0752	CRIEFF - OUR TOWN
0803	(DANCE SEQUENCES)
0805	(KIRKWALL, WICK, DOUNREAY)
0808	GORDONSTOUN SCHOOL GARDEN FETE
0809	(GLASGOW ACADEMY SPORTS)
0837	ENOUGH TO EAT? - THE NUTRITION FILM
0873A	ABERDEEN HIGH SCHOOL FOR GIRLS PRIMARY SPORTS
0918	DAY AT MORAY HOUSE NURSERY SCHOOL, A
0919	(AT NURSERY SCHOOL)
0922	PROGRESS REPORT NO. 2
0954	LAUREL BANK SCHOOL FILM
0957	MINISTRY OF INFORMATION TRAILERS
0960B	LOCHGELLY CHILDREN'S GALA DAY

SCIENCE FICTION

SCIENCES

SCULPTURE

See ART and ARTISTS/ ART GALLERIES

SEAWEED

See ALGAE

SELKIRKSHIRE

0763	OPENING OF OLD GALA HOUSE
0764	CROSSING THE TWEED
0765	PICTURESQUE SCENES - 4TH ANNUAL BRAW LADS GATHERING
0766	GALASHIELS AND BRAW LADS GATHERING
0767	BRAW LADS GATHERING
0791-0792	[BORDERS LOCAL NEWSREELS]
0882	RIVER TWEED
1132	SOUTHERN SCOTLAND
1478	SCOTS ACCLAIM ROYAL FAMILY
1634	(MIDSUMMER QUEEN GALA)
1884	BORDER RAID
2591	FAIR RIVER, THE
2628	BORDER FESTIVALS OF 1956
2702	WINFIELD 1950
2704	GALA 25 MILE CYCLE RACE 1951
2712	ST. RONAN'S GAMES
2804	AS LONG AS YOU'RE YOUNG

SEWING and SEWING MACHINES

See TEXTILE ARTS/ TEXTILE INDUSTRY

SHEEP

0029	HARNESSING THE HILLS
0034	FACE OF SCOTLAND
0120	CROFTERS, THE
0251	INTRODUCING SCOTLAND
0256	EILEAN AN FHRAOICH [ISLE OF LEWIS]
0274	HIGHLAND LADDIE
0280	HILL SHEEP FARM
0303	FUTURE OF SCOTLAND
0363	OVER THE SEA TO SKYE
0367	BANK AHEAD
0389	O'ER HILL AND DALE
0392	LIFE ON THE FAROE ISLANDS
0443	OVER THE HILLS AND FAR AWAY
0482	BORDER WEAVE
0490	FARM IS RECLAIMED, A
0494	COUNTRY POLICEMAN
0497	DUMFRIES - A MARKET TOWN
0504	TAY VALLEY
0507	NORTH OF THE GREAT GLEN
0548	HARRIS
0571	PURE NEW WOOL - AND SCOTTISH
0580	RIVER CLYDE
0586	DEE VALLEY
0630	SOUTHERN UPLANDS
0636	BACK TO BACK
0637	ANIMAL HUSBANDRY
0661	MUTTON
0667	(SHEEP DIPPING)
0720	[HIGHLAND SHOW, DUNDEE]
0751	(BORDER COUNTRY)
0785	HEART IS HIGHLAND, THE
0793	EVACUATION OF ST. KILDA
0800	[CAITHNESS, ORKNEY, KIRKWALL]
0882	RIVER TWEED
0911	ST. KILDA - THE LONELY ISLANDS
0914	SOUTHERN SCOTLAND
0928	LIFE IN THE HIGHLANDS

0932	ARDNAMURCHAN
0934	CROFTING IN SKYE
0936	CROFTERS OF WESTER ROSS
0978	ISLAND OF ST. KILDA, THE
0981	CROFTER'S LIFE IN SHETLAND, A
0991	RUGGED ISLAND
1061	DUNDEE
1063	THEY MADE THE LAND
1129	IN SHEEP'S CLOTHING
1132	SOUTHERN SCOTLAND
1286	SHETLAND, PEOPLE OF MANY LANDS
1338	(FAMILY HOLIDAYS 1936/'38)
1350	RIVER FORTH
1400	(SUTHERLAND)
1436	ORKNEY - SCENES AROUND SHAPINSAY
1451	LIFE IN THE HIGHLANDS
1494	HOLIDAYS AT HOME 1942-'44
1615	(SHETLAND SCENES)
1616	[SHETLAND - A FEW ASPECTS]
1617	(SHETLAND AND FAIR ISLE SCENES)
1695	MAKING TWEED
1701	ERISKAY - A POEM OF REMOTE LIVES
1764	LOTHIANS PART I, THE
1783	RIVER TAY
1792	SOLWAY COUNTIES, THE
1872	RURAL ROUND ABOUT
1874	[FILM OF MONIAIVE 1950-1955]
1876	NEW GALLOWAY GALA WEEK
1877	MONIAIVE DOG TRIALS
1879	VILLAGE VARIETIES
1913	WINTER ON THE FARM
1928	TRIP TO SKYE, ORKNEY AND SHETLAND
1943	ENCHANTED ISLES
1957	LANARK
2029	MARY'S LAMB
2036	RAIN ON THE ROOF
2050	[FARM IN SOUTHERN SCOTLAND, A]
2088	FAIR COUNTY OF AYR
2203	CHAMPIONS IN THE SUN
2215	IN GOOD HEART
2223	BORDERS, THE
2245	WEAVE ME A RAINBOW
2250	LOCH LOMOND
2256	SONG FOR PRINCE CHARLIE, A
2257	TAYSIDE
2259	PRIDE OF ISLANDS, A
2278	[HIGHLAND FUND IN ACTION, HIGHLAND INITIATIVE]
2320	ABERDEEN
2367	[ON THE ISLAND]
2478	SPRING IN SCOTLAND
2512	AYRSHIRE DAIRY FARMER
2522	(MACFARLANE FAMILY 1930)
2542	(BATTLESHIPS ON THE CLYDE)
2593	MISTY ISLE
2636	DURISDEER COTTAGE AND FARMING
2683	(DUFFTOWN SCENES)
2721	SPRING IN GALLOWAY
2735	(HERD'S CAFE AND FAMILY FARM)

SHIPS and SHIPPING (gen.)

See also LINERS/ NAVAL VESSELS/ SAILING SHIPS/ SHIPBUILDING/TANKERS

1271	DOWN TO THE SEA
1318	CLYDE RESORT: AN INTRODUCTION TO GIRVAN
1333	TRIP TO IONA AND STAFFA, OBAN DISTRICT AND GLENCOE
1517	[HOME AND AWAY NO. 2]
1521	HOME AND AWAY NO. 11
1524	HOME AND AWAY NO. 14
1597	(SCENES ON THE RIVER CLYDE)
1616	[SHETLAND - A FEW ASPECTS]
1617	(SHETLAND AND FAIR ISLE SCENES)
1638	WIRE LINES
1676	BRIDGE TOWN, THE
1680	[1938]
1694	INDUSTRIAL CLYDESDALE
1745	PORT HEALTH AUTHORITY
1766	[SCOTT FAMILY FILM]
1894	CRUISE TO SCOTTISH GARDENS, A
1983	LAND-SHIP, THE
2000A	BENS, THE
2008	[LEITH DREDGER]
2009	LIFE IN THE ORKNEYS
2110	(VIOLET ANDERSON FILM)
2122	"MAREEVE"
2194	"MAURETANIA" AND "QUEEN MARY"
2205	COUNTY ON THE MOVE
2373	[DUNDEE'S SCREEN SNAPSHOTS] SERIES
2386	["COURLAND" AT KARSHAMM]
2387	[CURRIE LINE FILMS 1 & 2]
2459	[LANGUAGE INSERTS]
2472	LONDON LINE
2497	[HIGHLAND CROFTERS' FAREWELL]
2518	(MACFARLANE FAMILY - CLYDE CRUISE 1934)
2520	(MACFARLANE FAMILY 1932)
2522	(MACFARLANE FAMILY 1930)
2562	[SPITHEAD REVIEW 1937]
2563	(CARGO LOADING AT DOCKS)
2564	(CRUISE ON SS "PERTH")
2801	(SCENES OF ORKNEY)
2808	AROUND DUNDEE IN THE 1930'S
2816	(RANGOON HOSPITAL AND SCENES FROM THE EAST)
2820	(CRICHTON COLLECTION)

SHOPS and SHOPPING

0090	CHARLES RENNIE MACKINTOSH
0114	WAVERLEY STEPS
0333	DIABOLICAL LIBERTY, A
0380	[SHOTS OF EDINBURGH]
0428	LAND O' BURNS BAKERIES
0437	SEEING IS BELIEVING
0442	BRIEF BEEF BIOGRAPHY, A
0443	OVER THE HILLS AND FAR AWAY
0571	PURE NEW WOOL - AND SCOTTISH
0592	WISHAW CO-OPERATIVE SOCIETY OUTING
0606	COUNTER COURTESY
0607	GET IT AT THE CO-OP
0608	ACHIEVEMENT
0610	HELPING HAND - SCWS BRUSH MAKING, A
0612	YOUR SILENT SALESMAN
0613	KNOW YOUR BUSINESS
0617	TOMORROW IS YOURS

0620	[BITS O' STICKS]
0622	PRIDE AND PROGRESS
0623	MEN OF ROCHDALE
0657-0658	[COME CO-OPERATIVE SHOPPING]
0659	[SAVE IN 1969]
0660	COME CO-OPERATIVE SHOPPING
0661	MUTTON
0672	OUT OF THE BOX
0675	(SCWS LEMON CURD ADVERTISEMENT)
0676	(SCWS CREAMERY BUTTER ADVERTISEMENT)
0677	(SCWS PEAR HALVES AND CREAM ADVERTISEMENT)
0678	(SCWS MARMALADE ADVERTISEMENT)
0681	(SCWS MARGARINE ADVERTISEMENT)
0683	(SCWS SPECIAL OFFERS)
0684	(SCWS MARMALADE ADVERTISEMENT)
0685	(SCWS COFFEE ESSENCE ADVERTISEMENT)
0686	(SCWS MARGARINE ADVERTISEMENT)
0690	[1968 CO-OP PRESENTATION FILM]
0698	RADIO ADDRESS BY NEIL BEATON, A
0701	(SCWS MARGARINE ADVERTISEMENT)
0712	[SAUCHIEHALL STREET ROOF TOPS]
0723	[CO-OP ADVERTISEMENTS STRATHCLYDE SCHOOLWEAR]
0724	HM THE QUEEN VISITS CENTENARY HOUSE
0735	[FACTS AND FIGURES NO. 4]
0736	(CO-OP ADVERTISEMENT)
0737	(CO-OP ADVERTS)
0811	LOCHGELLY EQUITABLE CO-OPERATIVE SOCIETY'S SHOPPING WEEK
0865	(ALLOA ADVERTS)
0891	(EAST KILBRIDE DEVELOPMENT CORPORATION TRIMS 1947/ '54)
0895	THEY FOUND A FUTURE
0914	SOUTHERN SCOTLAND
0922	PROGRESS REPORT NO. 2
0956	(DUMFRIES CINEMA ADVERTS)
0974	GLASGOW 1980
0975	GLENROTHES
0994	[SHIELDHALL COFFEE]
0995	[COME CO-OP SHOPPING]
1002	[COME CO-OP SHOPPING AT CHRISTMAS]
1003	[COPEX COOKING FAT]
1004	[MONTRIL PARTY]
1005	[GOLDEN BALL MARMALADE]
1006	[COME CO-OP SHOPPING]
1007	[CO-OP SUGAR]
1009	[PINEAPPLE AND RICE]
1010	[CWS CENTENARY EXHIBITION]
1011	[SPRING SALE]
1012	[SAUCES]
1013-1014	[COME CO-OP SHOPPING]
1017	[STAFF RECRUITMENT FILM]
1018	[LEMON CURD]
1019	[STRAWBERRY JAM]
1020	[GOLDEN BALL MARMALADE]
1021	[ORCHID BUTTER]
1022	[JELLY CRYSTALS]
1023	[CO-OP CARTOON]
1024	(SHAWLANDS CROSS)
1025	[SPOT THE LIKENESS]

1691	GREENOCK PLANS AHEAD
1910	(EDINBURGH'S HOUSING CONDITIONS)
2101	IF ONLY WE HAD THE SPACE
2102	MUNGO'S MEDALS
2471	GORBALS OLD GORBALS NEW - ONE WOMAN'S STORY
2483	(QUEEN OPENS GORBALS "HUTCHIE E")
2777	SECRETARY OF STATE (FOR SCOTLAND)

SMOKING

See TOBACCO

SNOOKER

2606	MINING REVIEW NO. 3

SNOW and SNOWSTORMS

See WINTER SCENES

SOCIAL PROBLEMS

0253	TAM TRAUCHLE'S TROUBLES
0271	GOOD HEALTH TO SCOTLAND
0291	CHILDREN OF THE CITY
0300	OUR PUBLIC PARKS
0531	(GUILD OF AID WORK IN THE GORBALS)
0888	HOMES FOR THE PEOPLE
1345	COUNTRY HOMES
2537	CONSEQUENCES
2540	IT WASN'T ME MISTER
2615	SETTLED OUT OF COURT
2755	CIRCLE OF CARE
2776	(CHILDREN'S PANEL AT WORK)

SOCIALISM

0540	[CHALLENGE TO FASCISM]
1326	(MAY DAY PARADE, EDINBURGH 1937)
1448	[MAY DAY PARADES, ETC.]
1721	GLASGOW MAY DAY 1937
1723	PROCESSION IN COMMEMORATION OF CALTON WEAVERS/ ROBERT SMILLIE CENTENARY
1976	(ANTI-ALCOHOL CAMPAIGN/ USSR VISIT?)

SONGS and SINGING

0016	ORPHEUS CHOIR
0098	LIEDER DER VOLKER (SONGS OF THE PEOPLE)
0252	GAELIC MOD
0253	TAM TRAUCHLE'S TROUBLES
0585	[BEATLES COME TO TOWN, THE]
0638	GLENFINNAN AND THE '45
0738	EATING AT WORK
0754	MUSIC FROM THE MOVIES
0799	SINGING STREET, THE
0802	WILL YE NO' COME BACK AGAIN
0806	SO MANY PARTINGS
0813	KIRKCALDY HOSPITAL PAGEANT
0815	(GAUMONT SOUND MIRROR, 1927-1931)
0819	ROYAL VISIT TO SCOTLAND
0889	IMMORTAL MEMORY OF ROBERT BURNS
0899	HAMPDEN STORY, THE
0938	GLASGOW'S DOCKLANDS
0951	STONEHOUSE NEW TOWN FESTIVAL
0955	WHY SCOTLAND, WHY EAST KILBRIDE
0976	(NATIONAL MOD TRIMS)
1188	SECOND FOLLIES, THE
1259	EMMERSON MOUNTAINEERS, THE

1474	[INVERNESS FESTIVAL YEAR 1951]
1642	GREAT WATERS MIGHTY ORGAN HARMONIES
1678	THERE'S NAE LUCK ABOUT THE HOOSE
1943	ENCHANTED ISLES
1989	(SIMPSON FAMILY FILM)
2622	ISLAND OF THE BIG CLOTH
2853	GREY METROPOLIS, THE
2872	[DUNOON OCCASIONS]

SOUTH AFRICA

0150	ROYAL SOUTH AFRICAN TOUR
1796	GB NEWS REVIEW 1948
2099	(JOSEPH HISLOP COLLECTION)
2183	(CAPE TO CAIRO - WILDLIFE AND NATIVE SCENES)
2209	FROM GLASGOW GREEN TO BENDIGO
2549	(CRUISE ON "IBERIA",I)

SOUTH AMERICA

0419	SAILING 1000 MILES UP THE AMAZON
0481	DOWN TO THE SEA
0663	PERU
1665	(MOTHERWELL FOOTBALL CLUB COLLECTION)
2553-2554	(CRUISE TO SOUTH AMERICA)

SPEECHES

0008	GLASGOW UNIVERSITY CELEBRATES
0009	FIFTH CENTENARY OF THE UNIVERSITY OF GLASGOW
0058	ONE HUNDRED YEARS OF FAMILY BUSINESS
0231	SCOTLAND FOR FITNESS
0250	NEVILE BUTLER'S TEST SPEECHES
0266	CROWNING OF THE MERCHANT NAVY QUEEN, THE
0283	MARCH
0303	FUTURE OF SCOTLAND
0311	[BOBBY JONES RECEIVES FREEDOM OF ST. ANDREWS]
0462	NEWS SPOTLIGHT
0486	GLEN IS OURS, THE
0547	BURNS MEMORIAL
0552	QUEEN MOTHER IN SCOTLAND, THE
0604	FREEDOM FOR THE RT. HON. THOMAS JOHNSTON
0638	GLENFINNAN OF THE '45
0646A	INAUGURATION OF INVERNESS AIRPORT
0756	PIONEERS THEN AND NOW
0802	WILL YE NO' COME BACK AGAIN
0814	QUEEN LAUDS SCOTTISH EXHIBITION, GLASGOW
0816	AMERICAN AMBASSADOR SPEAKS OUT
0817	AMBASSADOR KENNEDY IN EDINBURGH
0818	PRIME MINISTER IN SCOTLAND
0966	LOCHGELLY WAR MEMORIAL
1109	1959 SCOTTISH INDUSTRIES EXHIBITION, THE
1624	SCOTS HONOUR THE PRINCE
1627	PRINCESS IN STIRLING, THE
2397	(PEACE DEMONSTRATION, CLYDEBANK)

SPINNING

See TEXTILE ARTS/ TEXTILE INDUSTRY

SPORT (gen.)

See also CURLING/ FOOTBALL/ GOLF/ SCHOOLS/ SWIMMING/ WATER SPORTS

0066	DALGUISE BOYS' CAMP
0106	GLASGOW'S POLICE
0231	SCOTLAND FOR FITNESS

381

0255A	CAMPING WE WILL GO, A
0255C	CAMPING IS FUN
0328	CITY SIDELIGHTS NO. 3
0417	MEN AND WOMEN OF TOMORROW
0426	[YEAR OF DESTINY]
0471	RIGHT CHOICE, THE
0472	SPIRIT OF THE GAMES, THE
0559	PAHTE REVIEW OF THE YEAR
0562	ARDROSSAN SPORTS GALA
0566	ARDEER SPORTS 1929
0572	(INVERBERVIE PAGEANT)
0575	ARDROSSAN SHIPYARD SPORTS
0591	LOOKING BACK
0619	BEYOND THE SUNSET
0653A	[BOYS' BRIGADE]
0704	HANDBA' AT KIRKWALL, ORKNEY
0716	(PATHESCOPE GAZETTE/ NEW EMPIRE NEWS)
0761	[CHILDREN'S PROCESSION GALASHIELS]
0873C	(TABLE TENNIS)
0935	CRIEFF HIGHLAND GATHERING
0951	STONEHOUSE NEW TOWN FESTIVAL
0952	STONEHOUSE - CENTRE FOR SUCCESS (NO. 4)
0955	WHY SCOTLAND, WHY EAST KILBRIDE
0974	GLASGOW 1980
1233	GIRVAN ANNUAL ATHLETICS SPORTS MEETING
1236	(GREEN'S 1917 FILM SERVICE)
1252	FOCUS ON BRIDGETON
1283	STEWARTFIELD GALA DAY, BROXBURN
1284	UPHALL CHILDREN'S GALA ETC
1294	UPHALL STATION CHILDREN'S GALA
1301	(UNIDENTIFIED GALA AND SPORTS DAY, BROXBURN AREA NO. 1)
1302	(UNIDENTIFIED SPORTS DAY, BROXBURN AREA)
1321	AYR
1360	DUNFERMLINE CHILDREN'S GALA 1932
1362-1363	DUNFERMLINE CHILDREN'S GALA DAY 1934/1936
1366	[DUNFERMLINE CHILDREN'S GALA DAY 1952]
1368	PENICUIK CHILDREN'S GALA DAY 1953
1372	NEWMILLS, TORRYBURN AND CROMBIE GALA
1373	HUNTLY GALA DAY
1377	INVERKEITHING LAMMAS FAIR AND GAMES 1951
1380	OPENING OF BRIDGENESS MINERS INSTITUTE
1389-1390	(GROSVENOR TOPICALS NO. 1)
1422	TRAMPOLINING
1435	SAND RACING AND HILL CLIMB
1459	JEDBURGH HANDBA'
1466-1467	ELGIN CHARCITY DAY 1933/1935
1471-1472	(ELGIN GALA DAY)
1491	ROYAL JUBILEE CELEBRATIONS
1541	(CLAY PIGEON SHOOT)
1584-1587	SINGER SPORTS GALA
1594	(YMCA CAMP)
1606	(DALYELL FAMILY FILM)
1648	KIRKCALDY YOUTH PAGEANT 1952
1660	SPORTS CARNIVAL AT HAMPDEN
1667	HEALTHY HOLIDAYS
1729	[STARKS PARK]
1766C	[SCOTT FAMILY FILM]
1796	GB NEWS REVIEW 1948

382

1797	MOVIES GREATEST HEADLINES
1802	PRINCESS STREET CHURCH SNAPSHOTS OF 1939
1815	DUNBAR - THE A1 RESORT
1854	(PROVOST FLETT COLLECTION)
1856	(DIXINE MISCELLANY)
1857	DIXINE PICTORIAL
1874	[FILM OF MONIAIVE 1950-1955]
1876	NEW GALLOWAY GALA WEEK
1879	VILLAGE VARIETIES
1933	DUNDEE POLICE SPORTS
1969	CAER-PEN-TULACH
1989	(SIMPSON FAMILY FILM)
2033	[PARAPLEGIC GAMES]
2079	HECTOR VALE!
2099	(JOSEPH HISLOP COLLECTION)
2151	GLENMORE AND THE CAIRNGORMS
2205	COUNTY ON THE MOVE
2210	GEORGE IV'S EDINBURGH
2231	SMITHS IN SCOTLAND, THE
2272	(WATERSIDE AND DISTRICT)
2294	(TAYPORT EVENTS 1946-'49)
2328	[HALFWAY TO PARADISE: JOHN COLQUHOUN]
2362	(HAWICK C1913)
2395	CHURCH ACTIVITIES, ST. MARTIN'S, EDINBURGH
2397	(PEACE DEMONSTRATION, CLYDEBANK)
2398	FITNESS FOR WOMEN
2399	FITNESS FOR BOYS
2400	FITNESS FOR GIRLS
2406	[HALFWAY TO PARADISE: JOCKY WILSON]
2500	YEARS AGO IN COWDENBEATH
2538	IT'S MORE THAN A JOB
2543-2545	(ST. MORITZ 1946)
2548	(ST. MORITZ 1932)
2612	BRIGADE PARADE 1948
2613	ROYAL SALUTE
2621	(GAME OF BOWLS, A)
2653	[BB RELAY RACE]
2672	OFFICER CADET TRAINING UNIT 165
2673	KELVINGROVE PARK
2698	HIGHLAND HOLIDAY
2727	KIRKCALDY MOTOR CYCLE ROAD RACES
2729	(J.H. JOHNSON COLLECTION)
2735	(HERD'S CAFE AND FAMILY FARM)
2738	ORIENTEERING
2756	HIGHLANDS, THE
2808	AROUND DUNDEE IN THE 1930'S
2829	[CLAY PIGEON SHOOTING]
2841	FAMILY SCRAPBOOK NO. 3
2843	FAMILY SCRAPBOOK NO. 5

STANDING STONES, CELTIC CROSSES etc.

See RELIGIOUS MONUMENTS

STATIONS

0011	HARRY LAUDER LEAVES FOR AMERICA
0012	GLASGOW'S YESTERDAYS
0042	ABERDEEN 1906
0044	GLASGOW AND THE CLYDE COAST
0051	QUEEN IN SCOTLAND, THE
0056	TRAM ROUTES IN GLASGOW AND STEAM RAILWAYS

STATUES

STEAM ENGINEERING

STEAM TRAINS

STEAMERS

See also PADDLE STEAMERS

2756	HIGHLANDS, THE

STIRLING and STIRLINGSHIRE

0034	FACE OF SCOTLAND
0167	PARAFFIN YOUNG
0201	HIGHLAND HORSE SHOW, ALLOA
0251	INTRODUCING SCOTLAND
0302	LAND O' CLANS
0345	BUSMAN'S HOLIDAY
0416	LEARNING FOR LIVING
0501	ROUTES AND CENTRES
0512	STIRLING: GATEWAY TO THE HIGHLANDS
0521	STIRLING CHARITIES DAY
0587	CENTRAL SCOTLAND
0877	(MAKING SOAP)
0912	HEART OF SCOTLAND, THE
0916	PADDY'S MILESTONE
1062	WEALTH OF A NATION
1212	SCOTTISH HOLIDAY, A
1227	CRUISING ON LOCH LOMOND
1305	[SCOTTISH NATIONALISTS' BANNOCKBURN CELEBRATIONS]
1350	RIVER FORTH
1351	COUNTY CLERK
1432	LOCH LOMOND
1453	LADY OF THE LAKE
1538	LOCH LOMOND
1539	(LOCH LOMOND PILOT FILM)
1570	[RUSSELL'S LIBRARY FOOTAGE]
1581	(HOLIDAY SCOTLAND)
1627	PRINCESS IN STIRLING, THE
1687	FORTH AND CLYDE CANAL, THE
1696	ROYAL SCOTLAND
1858	HOSPITALS FOR ALL
1888	TOURING THE TROSSACHS
1939	LOWLANDS OF SCOTLAND
1956	INDUSTRIAL STIRLINGSHIRE
1997	FALKIRK
2024	FORTH - POWERHOUSE FOR INDUSTRY
2070	(CASTLECARY EVENTS)
2071	(BRICKMAKING)
2073-2075	(STEIN FAMILY FILMS)
2123	(FFORDE COLLECTION)
2133	(SCOTTISH SCENES 1931-'35)
2217	LAND LIVED IN, A
2224	SCOTLAND DANCES
2227	CUMBERNAULD, TOWN FOR TOMORROW
2253	WATER, WATER EVERYWHERE
2256	SONG FOR PRINCE CHARLIE, A
2340	[KILSYTH RAILWAY STATION]
2355	(TEMPERANCE DAYS AND ORGANISATIONS 1936)
2368	(NCB STAFF BUS OUTINGS)
2387	[CURRIE LINE FILMS 1 & 2]
2498	[UNICA, GLASGOW 1951]
2601	DIVIDED WE STAND
2605	(HOLIDAY SCOTLAND)
2610	RESTORATION OF THE CHURCH OF THE HOLY RUDE
2631	HOLIDAY SCOTLAND
2746	TROSSACHS, THE
2768	(GEORGE MAY FAMILY FILM)

STREETS and STREETSCENES

0044	GLASGOW AND THE CLYDE COAST
0048	PORT OF GLASGOW
0062	GLASGOW - OUR CITY
0075	GROWTH OF AN INDUSTRY
0114	WAVERLEY STEPS
0123	CITY SIDELIGHTS NO. 2
0239	ABERDEEN CELEBRATES THE CORONATION
0251	INTRODUCING SCOTLAND
0281	NORTH EAST CORNER
0296	SCOTLAND AND THE NEW WORLD
0305	[GASKIN REPORT, THE]
0330	CITY SIDELIGHTS NO. 4
0360	HOMEWARD BOUND 1939
0364	PERTHSHIRE PANORAMA
0367	BANK AHEAD
0379	CITY SIDELIGHTS NO. 1
0418	ST. KILDA - BRITAIN'S LONELIEST ISLE
0420	KEEPING OUR CITY CLEAN
0473	SERMON IN STONE, A
0497	DUMFRIES - A MARKET TOWN
0501	ROUTES AND CENTRES
0504	TAY VALLEY
0546	GLASGOW
0570	GREAT WESTERN ROAD 1922
0590	(CHRISTMAS STREET DECORATIONS IN GLASGOW)
0610	HELPING HAND - SCWS BRUSH MAKING, A
0619	BEYOND THE SUNSET
0631	NORTHERN SCOTLAND
0637	ANIMAL HUSBANDRY
0639B	FERGUSLIE MILLS IN INVERNESS
0694	WELLS OF MONTROSE, THE
0712	[SAUCHIEHALL STREET ROOF TOPS]
0769	[KILMARNOCK]
0792	[BORDERS LOCAL NEWSREELS NO. 2]
0794	(GLASGOW TRAMS c1902)
0795	(ARRIVAL AT WHITEHART HOTEL, CAMPBELTOWN)
0800	[CAITHNESS, ORKNEY, KIRKWALL]
0802	WILL YE NO' COME BACK AGAIN
0819	ROYAL VISIT TO SCOTLAND
0911	ST. KILDA - THE LONELY ISLANDS
0913	WHAT ABOUT THE WORKERS
0917	GLASGOW - MASS ASSAULT ON TB
0920	(BUS TOUR, THE)
0922	PROGRESS REPORT NO. 2
0938	GLASGOW'S DOCKLANDS
0967	LOCHGELLY AT WORK AND PLAY
0968	ROYAL MILE EDINBURGH, THE
0969	HOLIDAY IN THE HIGHLANDS
1049	GLASGOW, NO MEAN CITY
1061	DUNDEE
1062	WEALTH OF A NATION
1080A	ABERDEEN AWA' AUGUST 1949
1083	(WARTIME DUMBARTON)
1091	(TRAMS IN EDINBURGH AND BRUSSELS)
1104	(GLASGOW PARKS 1941)
1252	FOCUS ON BRIDGETON
1275	DEAR GREEN PLACE

388

STRIKES and LOCK-OUTS

SUBMARINE BASES and SUBMARINES

See NAVY and NAVAL VESSELS

SURGERY and RELATED TOPICS

SUTHERLAND

SWEETS

See CONFECTIONERY

SWIMMING and DIVING

0472	SPIRIT OF THE GAMES, THE
0528	ALL ON A SUMMER'S DAY
0529D	(OPENING OF NEW BATHS, ABERDEEN)
0802	WILL YE NO' COME BACK AGAIN
0955	WHY SCOTLAND, WHY EAST KILBRIDE
1243	(LEISURE TIME)
1412	SWIMMING THE CRAWL WITH IAN BLACK
1418	LIFESAVING LAND DRILLS
1419	SWIMMING LAND DRILLS
1424	FEET OFF THE BOTTOM
1469	INVERNESSS SWIMMING CLUB
1497	[GLASGOW'S PROGRESS]
1667	HEALTHY HOLIDAYS
1698	[ARBROATH HIGH SCHOOL SPORTS AND OPENING OF BATHING POOL]
1764	LOTHIANS PART I, THE
1772	[BOAT OF GARTEN 1932]
1855	REVIEW OF THE YEAR 1950
1857	DIXINE PICTORIAL
1969	CAER-PEN-TULACH
1989	(SIMPSON FAMILY FILM)
2026	QUEST, THE (GIRLS' GUILDRY)
2033	[PARAPLEGIC GAMES]
2084	SALUTE THE SOLDIER WEEK
2228	PLAN FOR LIVING, A
2231	SMITHS IN SCOTLAND, THE
2258	LOTHIAN LANDSCAPE
2293	(WARTIME IN TAYPORT)
2304	CORONATION YEAR 1953
2307	IN SEARCH OF TAYPORT
2320	ABERDEEN
2328	[HALFWAY TO PARADISE: JOHN COLQUHOUN]
2372	ARBROATH'S NEW SWIMMING POOL
2373	[DUNDEE'S SCREEN SNAPSHOTS] SERIES
2399	FITNESS FOR BOYS
2400	FITNESS FOR GIRLS
2531	[SHOP PICNIC, FARLAIR SWIMMING POOL]
2538	IT'S MORE THAN A JOB
2550	(CRUISE ON "IBERIA", II)
2553	(CRUISE TO SOUTH AMERICA, I)
· 2672	OFFICER CADET TRAINING UNIT 165
2729	(J.H. JOHNSON COLLECTION)
2756	HIGHLANDS, THE
2768	(GEORGE MAY FAMILY FILM)
2805	PLEASURE ISLAND
2808	AROUND DUNDEE IN THE 1930'S
2832	[TOWN COUNCIL ELECTION DAY]

SYNAGOGUES

2586	(JEWISH WEDDING, A)

TANKERS

0345	BUSMAN'S HOLIDAY
0377	RIVER CLYDE - A SURVEY OF SCOTLAND'S GREATEST RIVER
0481	DOWN TO THE SEA
0487	AN EYE TO THE FUTURE
0587	CENTRAL SCOTLAND
0690	[1968 CO-OP PRESENTATION FILM]
0692	BENEATH THE NORTH SEA
0694	WELLS OF MONTROSE, THE

1787	[CLYDE RIVER]
2254	ERSKINE BRIDGE, THE
2448	(CONSTRUCTION OF TANKER "NORDIC CLANSMAN")

TARTAN

See CLANS/ COSTUME/ TEXTILE CRAFTS/ TEXTILE INDUSTRY

TAXATION

See also PUBLIC REVENUE

1103	CINEMA ADVERTS
1288C	YOU AND YOUR MONEY
2201	DRAM LIKE THIS, A
2404	[HALFWAY TO PARADISE: POLL TAX]

TEA CULTIVATION and TEA DRINKING

0134	HIMALAYAN HOLIDAY
0140	IDLING IN INDIA
0146	CEYLON CALLING
0153	KENYA TO DURBAN
0614	EASTERN ROSE
0624	ROSE OF THE ORIENT
0821	(BOY SCOUTS PARADE, SCOTLAND)
1921	WEST PILTON GALA DAY 1952
2503	(SHEARER FAMILY FILM TWO)
2736	(HERD FAMILY FILM)

TELEPHONE, The

0301	LAND OF INVENTION
0373	THINGS THAT HAPPEN NO. 1
0826B	AT YOUR SERVICE
1204	VOICE OF THE DEEP
1249	IT COMES FROM COAL
1351	COUNTY CLERK
2046	MAGIC KEY, THE

TELEVISION

0800	[CAITHNESS, ORKNEY, KIRKWALL]
0801	[CAITHNESS, ORKNEY]
0805	(KIRKWALL, WICK, DOUNREAY)
1840	LOOK AROUND NORTH LANARK, SEVENTH DISTRICT
2472	LONDON LINE
2473	DISCOVERY OF TELEVISION
2783	[HADDO ESTATE OPERATIONS 1966-'67]

TEMPERANCE MOVEMENT, The

1191	FAR FROM ALONE
1193	LIQUID LORE
1194	BENEFICENT REPROBATE, THE
1195	IT'S THE BRAIN THAT COUNTS
1196	ALCOHOL AND THE HUMAN BODY
1198	WHICH IS BEST?
1199	WHAT'S IN A GLASS?
1202	ETHYL ALCOHOL. ITS NATURE AND ITS PROPERTIES
1203	TO YOUR HEALTH
1205	NEMESIS
2353	RISE IN WAGES, A
2354	EDINBURGH TEMPERANCE DAY
2355	(TEMPERANCE DAYS AND ORGANISATIONS 1936)
2356	(TEMPERANCE DAY, EDINBURGH 1936-'37)
2358	MARGARET BAKER IN LECTURES AND STORIES

TENEMENTS

See also HOUSING CONDITIONS/ SLUMS

0253	TAM TRAUCHLE'S TROUBLES
0268	PROGRESS REPORT
0291	CHILDREN OF THE CITY
0300	OUR PUBLIC PARKS
0316	OUR SCHOOLS
0473	SERMON IN STONE, A
0480	DUNDEE
0705	SADNESS AND GLADNESS
0891	(EAST KILBRIDE DEVELOPMENT CORPORATION TRIMS 1947/ '54)
0893	SUNNY DAYS
0915	GLASGOW
0922	PROGRESS REPORT NO. 2
0938	GLASGOW'S DOCKLANDS
0939	GLASGOW WELCOMES THE QUEEN
0968	ROYAL MILE EDINBURGH, THE
0974	GLASGOW 1980
1061	DUNDEE
1062	WEALTH OF A NATION
1275	DEAR GREEN PLACE
1324	FILM OF GLASGOW, A
1497	[GLASGOW'S PROGRESS]
1676	BRIDGE TOWN, THE
1687	FORTH AND CLYDE CANAL, THE
1761	FAIR RENT
1979	VITAL STATISTICS
2102	MUNGO'S MEDALS
2219	LIVINGSTON - A TOWN FOR THE LOTHIANS
2235	SONGS OF SCOTLAND
2236	SEA CITY GREENOCK

TENNIS

0417	MEN AND WOMEN OF TOMORROW
0426	[YEAR OF DESTINY]
0441	KING, GOD BLESS HIM, THE
0716	(PATHESCOPE GAZETTE/ NEW EMPIRE NEWS)
0829	BIRTHDAY GREETINGS TO QUEEN MARY
1243	(LEISURE TIME)
1772	[BOAT OF GARTEN 1932]
2842	FAMILY SCRAPBOOK NO. 4
2870	DUNOON - THE GEM OF THE CLYDE

TEXTILE CRAFTS (eg. Spinning)

0136	HOLIDAYING IN HARRIS
0363	OVER THE SEA TO SKYE
0392	LIFE ON THE FAROE ISLANDS
0418	ST. KILDA - BRITAIN'S LONELIEST ISLE
0431	CRUISE TO ST. KILDA AND THE WESTERN ISLES
0531	(GUILD OF AID WORK IN THE GORBALS)
0662	TEXTILES
0672	OUT OF THE BOX
0763	OPENING OF OLD GALA HOUSE
0793	EVACUATION OF ST. KILDA
0908	INDUSTRIAL BRITAIN
0928	LIFE IN THE HIGHLANDS
0936	CROFTERS OF WESTER ROSS
0940	ST. KILDA 1929
0978	ISLAND OF ST. KILDA, THE
0981	CROFTER'S LIFE IN SHETLAND, A
1096	WAY THE MONEY GOES, THE
1129	IN SHEEP'S CLOTHING
1451	LIFE IN THE HIGHLANDS
1616	[SHETLAND - A FEW ASPECTS]
1695	MAKING TWEED
1701	ERISKAY - A POEM OF REMOTE LIVES
1943	ENCHANTED ISLES
2127	HOMESPUN
2202	BY LOCHABER I WILL GO
2367	[ON THE ISLAND]
2592	ISLES OF THE WEST
2593	MISTY ISLE
2646	LINEN WEAVING
2703	MAN AND HIS KILT, A
2720	[BRAEMAR GAMES, TWEED MAKING AND EDINBURGH]
2757	SPINNING
2766	DOMESTIC SCIENCE AS A CAREER
2768	(GEORGE MAY FAMILY FILM)

TEXTILE INDUSTRY

0028	WESTERN ISLES
0071	HESSIAN LOOM AND COP LOADER
0136	HOLIDAYING IN HARRIS
0160	JUTE MANUFACTURE
0185	DUNDEE JUTE
0197	GLENHAR FACTORY, HILLINGTON
0251	INTRODUCING SCOTLAND
0274	HIGHLAND LADDIE
0303	OVER THE SEA TO SKYE
0367	BANK AHEAD
0460	SONG OF THE CLYDE
0482	BORDER WEAVE
0505	COUNTY OF DUNBARTON
0506	ABERDEEN AND ITS INDUSTRIES
0510	BEAUTIFUL DRIMA
0544	[FROM WOOL TO WEARER]
0571	PURE NEW WOOL - AND SCOTTISH
0578	CASHMERE IS SCOTTISH
0579	WORLD OF CASHMERE
0580	RIVER CLYDE
0587	CENTRAL SCOTLAND
0630	SOUTHERN UPLANDS
0636	BACK TO BACK
0814	QUEEN LAUDS SCOTTISH EXHIBITION, GLASGOW
0836	CONSIDER THE CARPET
0857	(SHIELDHALL PART TWO)
0914	SOUTHERN SCOTLAND
1030	KNITWEAR WITHOUT TEARS
1061	DUNDEE
1087	(HOLIDAY AT ARROCHAR)
1096	WAY THE MONEY GOES, THE
1129	IN SHEEP'S CLOTHING
1132	SOUTHERN SCOTLAND
1249	IT COMES FROM COAL
1342	(ROCKET RANGE, BENBECULA)
1350	RIVER FORTH
1429	J. & P. COATS - THREAD SPLICER
1501	BEYOND THE GRAMPIANS

UNITED STATES of AMERICA

See NORTH AMERICA

VETERINARY SURGERY

VISUALLY HANDICAPPED

See HANDICAP

VIVISECTION

WALES

WAR (misc.)

See also WEAPONRY/ WORLD WARS I and II

WAR MEMORIALS

WATER (e.g. dams, reservoirs)

0301	LAND OF INVENTION
0460	SONG OF THE CLYDE
0481	DOWN TO THE SEA
0487	AN EYE TO THE FUTURE
0526	OUR CITY - TODAY AND TOMORROW
0587	CENTRAL SCOTLAND
1248	STEEL GOES TO SEA
1270	VISIT TO A SHIPBUILDING YARD
1530	WELDING IN BOILER MANUFACTURE
1531	STEAM
1570	[RUSSELL'S LIBRARY FOOTAGE]
1783	RIVER TAY
2019	CLYDE FITTINGS
2208	FORTH ROAD BRIDGE, THE

WEST LOTHIAN

0335A	BO'NESS UNITED VERSUS FORTH RANGERS
0335B	SCOTTISH JUNIOR CUP FINAL
0336-0344	BO'NESS CHILDREN'S FAIR FESTIVAL
0400	BO'NESS PUBLIC SCHOOL: QUEEN MARY SMITH
0401A	BORROWSTOUN SCHOOL: QUEEN JOAN CAMPBELL
0401B	KINNEIL SCHOOL: QUEEN ELIZABETH SNEDDON
0402A	GRANGE SCHOOL: QUEEN ANNE CURRIE
0402B	BO'NESS PUBLIC SCHOOL: QUEEN ANNE PETRIE
0402C	ST. MARY'S RC SCHOOL: QUEEN HELEN SHAW
0403	KINNEIL SCHOOL: QUEEN JOAN PATERSON
0404A	BO'NESS PUBLIC SCHOOL: QUEEN KATHLEEN JAMIESON
0404B	ST. MARY'S RC SCHOOL: QUEEN MARY MARKIE
0404C	BO'NESS ACADEMY 1932: QUEEN HELEN BURNETT
0404D	BORROWSTOUN SCHOOL 1933: QUEEN MARGARET MCMAHON
0404E	KINNEIL PUBLIC SCHOOL: QUEEN HELEN YOUNG
0405	BORROWSTOUN SCHOOL 1927: QUEEN RUBY HYSLOP
0406	BO'NESS ACADEMY 1925: QUEEN CATHERINE SNEDDON
0407A	KINNEIL SCHOOL 1928: QUEEN ELIZABETH KAY
0407B	GRANGE SCHOOL 1929: QUEEN MARION KILPATRICK
0408	ST. MARY'S SCHOOL 1937: QUEEN ANNE
0409	JUBILEE YEAR 1947: QUEEN MARY SNEDDON
0410	QUEEN JEANETTE MCGUIRE. ST. MARY'S SCHOOL 1948
0411	BO'NESS CHILDREN'S FESTIVAL
0412A/B	[BO'NESS FAIR]
0412C	GRANGE PUBLIC SCHOOL: QUEEN ANDREA WALKER
0413	BO'NESS FAIR FESTIVAL 1952
0414	[BO'NESS FAIR C1911-1913]
0527	JOHN NEWLAND'S DAY, 1950, BATHGATE
1280	(CORONATION? PARADE, BROXBURN C1910)
1281	[FERRY FAIR]
1282	WINCHBURGH CHILDREN'S GALA DAY
1283	STEWARTFIELD GALA DAY, BROXBURN
1284	UPHALL CHILDREN'S GALA ETC
1291	BROXBURN GALA DAY AND CROWNING OF QUEEN
1293	BROXBURN HIGH SCHOOL SPORTS
1294	UPHALL STATON SCHOOL SPORTS
1295	FERRY FAIR 1955
1296	KIRKLISTON CHILDREN'S GALA AND CROWNING OF QUEEN
1297	FERRY FAIR OF 1954
1298	GALA DAY AND CROWNING CEREMONY AT BROXBURN
1299A	BROXBURN HIGH SCHOOL SPORTS

1299B	HM QUEEN ELIZABETH AND HRH DUKE OF EDINBURGH PASSING THROUGH BROXBURN
1300	BROXBURN AND DISTRICT CHILDREN'S GALA DAY AND CROWNING CEREMONY
1301	(UNIDENTIFIED GALA AND SPORTS DAY, BROXBURN AREA
1302	(UNIDENTIFIED SPORTS DAY, BROXBURN AREA)
1303	(BROXBURN GALA DAY 1953)
1316	[BO'NESS FAIR 1912]
1350	RIVER FORTH
1370	[BO'NESS V FORTH RANGERS AND GRANGE ROVERS]
1376	(MAY DAY PARADE, BO'NESS)
1379	LAYING FOUNDATION STONE, FREE GARDENERS' HALL
1380	OPENING OF BRIDGENESS MINERS INSTITUTE
1387	UNVEILING BO'NESS AND CARRIDAN WAR MEMORIAL
1546	(HIPPODROME CINEMA, BO'NESS)
1647	BO'NESS CHILDREN'S FAIR FESTIVAL 1957
1696	ROYAL SCOTLAND
1755-1757	BROXBURN CHILDREN'S GALA DAY
1764-1765	LOTHIANS PART I/II
1939	LOWLANDS OF SCOTLAND
1948	JOHN NEWLAND'S DAY, BATHGATE
1952	BATHGATE FESTIVAL WEEK 1951
2024	FORTH - POWERHOUSE FOR INDUSTRY
2072	[WALLHOUSE - MINING CLAY]
2205	COUNTY ON THE MOVE
2388	BONNIE SCOTLAND
2451	ETNA BRICKWORKS

WESTERN ISLES

See INNER HEBRIDES/ OUTER HEBRIDES

WHALING

0632	ANTARCTIC WHALE HUNT
1061	DUNDEE
1310	WHALING
2834	PRIDE OF PENGUINS, A

WHISKY

See DISTILLED LIQUORS

WIGTOWNSHIRE

0345	BUSMAN'S HOLIDAY
0483	GOOD NEIGHBOURS
0532	CORONATION NEWSREEL
0533	CEREMONIAL PARADE AT RAF WEST FREUGH
0534	KOSB FREEDOM OF ENTRY INTO THE BURGH
0551	FUNERAL OF PROVOST YOUNG, STRANRAER
0615	BLADNOCH CREAMERY
0876	(HOW BLUEBELL MARGARINE IS MADE)
0914	SOUTHERN SCOTLAND
1132	SOUTHERN SCOTLAND
1792	SOLWAY COUNTIES, THE
1872	RURAL ROUND ABOUT
2002	COUNTRY OF THE BLIND
2132	STRANRAER ROYAL VISIT 1955
2145	(STRANRAER LOCAL EVENTS)
2630	(CARAVAN HOLIDAYS)
2721	SPRING IN GALLOWAY

WINE

0190	YOUR GLASS OF SHERRY

YACHTS and YACHTING

YOUTH ORGANISATIONS (BB's, Girl Guides etc.)

X-RAYS

ZOOS and WILDLIFE PARKS